# Quantitative Methods for Business

Custom Edition for Southern Methodist University

Looseleaf Edition

David R. Anderson | Dennis J. Sweeney |
Thomas A. Williams | Jeffrey D. Camm |
James J. Cochran | Michael J. Fry | Jeffrey W. Ohlmann

CENGAGE
Learning

Australia • Brazil • Japan • Korea • Mexico • Singapore • Spain • United Kingdom • United States

**CENGAGE**
Learning·

Quantitative Methods for Business: Custom Edition for Southern Methodist University, Looseleaf Edition

Quantitative Methods for Business, 12th Edition
David R. Anderson | Dennis J. Sweeney | Thomas A. Williams | Jeffrey D. Camm | James J. Cochran | Michael J. Fry | Jeffrey W. Ohlmann

© 2013, 2010 South-Western, Cengage Learning. All rights reserved.

Executive Editors:
Maureen Staudt
Michael Stranz

Senior Project Development Manager:
Linda deStefano

Marketing Specialist:
Courtney Sheldon

Senior Production/Manufacturing Manager:
Donna M. Brown

Production Editorial Manager:
Kim Fry

Sr. Rights Acquisition Account Manager:
Todd Osborne

For product information and technology assistance, contact us at
Cengage Learning Customer & Sales Support, 1-800-354-9706
For permission to use material from this text or product,
submit all requests online at cengage.com/permissions
Further permissions questions can be emailed to
permissionrequest@cengage.com

This book contains select works from existing Cengage Learning resources and was produced by Cengage Learning Custom Solutions for collegiate use. As such, those adopting and/or contributing to this work are responsible for editorial content accuracy, continuity and completeness.

Compilation © 2012 Cengage Learning
ISBN-13: 978-1-285-02735-7

ISBN-10: 1-285-02735-3

Cengage Learning
5191 Natorp Boulevard
Mason, Ohio 45040
USA

Cengage Learning is a leading provider of customized learning solutions with office locations around the globe, including Singapore, the United Kingdom, Australia, Mexico, Brazil, and Japan. Locate your local office at:
international.cengage.com/region.

Cengage Learning products are represented in Canada by Nelson Education, Ltd.
For your lifelong learning solutions, visit www.cengage.com/custom.
Visit our corporate website at www.cengage.com.

Printed in the United States of America

# Brief Contents

# CHAPTER 1

# Introduction

This book is concerned with the use of quantitative methods to assist in decision making. It emphasizes not the methods themselves, but rather how they can contribute to better decisions. A variety of names exists for the body of knowledge involving quantitative approaches to decision making. Today, the terms most commonly used—*management science* (MS), *operations research* (OR), *decision science* and *business analytics*—are often used interchangeably.

The scientific management revolution of the early 1900s, initiated by Frederic W. Taylor, provided the foundation for the use of quantitative methods in management. However, modern research in the use of quantitative methods in decision making, for the most part, originated during the World War II period. At that time, teams of people with diverse specialties (e.g., mathematicians, engineers, and behavioral scientists) were formed to deal with strategic and tactical problems faced by the military. After the war, many of these team members continued their research into quantitative approaches to decision making.

Two developments that occurred during the post–World War II period led to the growth and use of quantitative methods in nonmilitary applications. First, continued research resulted in numerous methodological developments. Arguably the most notable of these developments was the discovery by George Dantzig, in 1947, of the simplex method for solving linear programming problems. At the same time these methodological developments were taking place, digital computers prompted a virtual explosion in computing power. Computers enabled practitioners to use the methodological advances to solve a large variety of problems. The computer technology explosion continues, and personal computers can now be used to solve problems larger than those solved on mainframe computers in the 1990s.

## Q.M. *in* ACTION

### REVENUE MANAGEMENT AT AT&T PARK*

Imagine the difficult position Russ Stanley, Vice President of Ticket Services for the San Francisco Giants, found himself facing late in the 2010 baseball season. Prior to the season, his organization had adopted a dynamic approach to pricing its tickets similar to the model successfully pioneered by Thomas M. Cook and his operations research group at American Airlines. Stanley desparately wanted the Giants to clinch a playoff birth, but he didn't want the team to do so *too quickly*.

When dynamically pricing a good or service, an organization regularly reviews supply and demand of the product and uses operations research to determine if the price should be changed to reflect these conditions. As the scheduled takeoff date for a flight nears, the cost of a ticket increases if seats for the flight are relatively scarce. On the other hand, the airline discounts tickets for an approaching flight with relatively few ticketed passengers. Through the use of optimization to dynamically set ticket prices, American Airlines generates nearly $1 billion annually in incremental revenue.

The management team of the San Francisco Giants recognized similarities between their primary product (tickets to home games) and the primary product sold by airlines (tickets for flights) and adopted a similar revenue management system. If a particular Giants' game is appealing to fans, tickets sell quickly and demand far exceeds supply as the date of the game approaches; under these conditions fans will be willing to pay more and the Giants charge a premium for the ticket. Similarly, tickets for less attractive games are discounted to reflect relatively low demand by fans. This is why Stanley found himself in a quandary at the end of the 2010 baseball season. The Giants were in the middle of a tight pennant race with the San Diego Padres that effectively increased demand for tickets to Giants' games, and the team was actually scheduled to play the Padres in San Fransisco for the last three

*Based on Peter Horner, "The Sabre Story," *OR/MS Today* (June 2000); Ken Belson, "Baseball Tickets Too Much? Check Back Tomorrow," *New York Times.com* (May 18, 2009); and Rob Gloster, "Giants Quadruple Price of Cheap Seats as Playoffs Drive Demand," *Bloomberg Businessweek* (September 30, 2010).

*(continued)*

games of the season. While Stanley certainly wanted his club to win its division and reach the Major League Baseball playoffs, he also recognized that his team's revenues would be greatly enhanced if it didn't qualify for the playoffs until the last day of the season. "I guess financially it is better to go all the way down to the last game," Stanley said in a late season interview. "Our hearts are in our stomachs; we're pacing watching these games."

Does revenue management and operations research work? Today, virtually every airline uses some sort of revenue-management system, and the cruise, hotel, and car rental industries also now apply revenue-management methods. As for the Giants, Stanley said dynamic pricing provided a 7 to 8% increase in revenue per seat for Giants' home games during the 2010 season. Coincidentally, the Giants did win the National League West division on the last day of the season and ultimately won the World Series. Several professional sports franchises are now looking to the Giants' example and considering implementation of similar dynamic ticket-pricing systems.

To reinforce the applied nature of the text and to provide a better understanding of the variety of applications in which *quantitative methods* (Q.M.) have been used successfully, Q.M. in Action articles are presented throughout the text. Each Q.M. in Action article summarizes an application of quantitative methods in practice. The first Q.M. in Action, Revenue Management at AT&T Park, describes one of the most important applications of quantitative methods in the sports and entertainment industry.

# Problem Solving and Decision Making

**Problem solving** can be defined as the process of identifying a difference between the actual and the desired state of affairs and then taking action to resolve this difference. For problems important enough to justify the time and effort of careful analysis, the problem-solving process involves the following seven steps:

1. Identify and define the problem.
2. Determine the set of alternative solutions.
3. Determine the criterion or criteria that will be used to evaluate the alternatives.
4. Evaluate the alternatives.
5. Choose an alternative.
6. Implement the selected alternative.
7. Evaluate the results to determine whether a satisfactory solution has been obtained.

**Decision making** is the term generally associated with the first five steps of the problem-solving process. Thus, the first step of decision making is to identify and define the problem. Decision making ends with the choosing of an alternative, which is the act of making the decision.

Let us consider the following example of the decision-making process. For the moment, assume you are currently unemployed and that you would like a position that will lead to a satisfying career. Suppose your job search results in offers from companies in Rochester, New York; Dallas, Texas; Greensboro, North Carolina; and Pittsburgh, Pennsylvania. Further suppose that it is unrealistic for you to decline all of these offers. Thus, the alternatives for your decision problem can be stated as follows:

1. Accept the position in Rochester.
2. Accept the position in Dallas.
3. Accept the position in Greensboro.
4. Accept the position in Pittsburgh.

The next step of the problem-solving process involves determining the criteria that will be used to evaluate the four alternatives. Obviously, the starting salary is a factor of some importance. If salary were the only criterion important to you, the alternative selected as "best" would be the one with the highest starting salary. Problems in which the objective is to find the best solution with respect to one criterion are referred to as **single-criterion decision problems**.

Suppose that you also conclude that the potential for advancement and the location of the job are two other criteria of major importance. Thus, the three criteria in your decision problem are starting salary, potential for advancement, and location. Problems that involve more than one criterion are referred to as **multicriteria decision problems**.

The next step of the decision-making process is to evaluate each of the alternatives with respect to each criterion. For example, evaluating each alternative relative to the starting salary criterion is done simply by recording the starting salary for each job alternative. However, evaluating each alternative with respect to the potential for advancement and the location of the job is more difficult because these evaluations are based primarily on subjective factors that are often difficult to quantify. Suppose for now that you decide to measure potential for advancement and job location by rating each of these criteria as poor, fair, average, good, or excellent. The data you compile are shown in Table 1.1.

You are now ready to make a choice from the available alternatives. What makes this choice phase so difficult is that the criteria are probably not all equally important, and no one alternative is "best" with regard to all criteria. When faced with a multicriteria decision problem, the third step in the decision-making process often includes an assessment of the relative importance of the criteria. Although we will present a method for dealing with situations like this one later in the text, for now let us suppose that after a careful evaluation of the data in Table 1.1, you decide to select alternative 3. Alternative 3 is thus referred to as the **decision**.

At this point in time, the decision-making process is complete. In summary, we see that this process involves five steps:

1. Define the problem.
2. Identify the alternatives.
3. Determine the criteria.
4. Evaluate the alternatives.
5. Choose an alternative.

Note that missing from this list are the last two steps in the problem-solving process: implementing the selected alternative and evaluating the results to determine whether a satisfactory solution has been obtained. This omission is not meant to diminish the importance

**TABLE 1.1**    DATA FOR THE JOB EVALUATION DECISION-MAKING PROBLEM

| Alternative | Starting Salary | Potential for Advancement | Job Location |
|---|---|---|---|
| 1. Rochester | $48,500 | Average | Average |
| 2. Dallas | $46,000 | Excellent | Good |
| 3. Greensboro | $46,000 | Good | Excellent |
| 4. Pittsburgh | $47,000 | Average | Good |

**FIGURE 1.1**   THE RELATIONSHIP BETWEEN PROBLEM SOLVING AND DECISION
MAKING

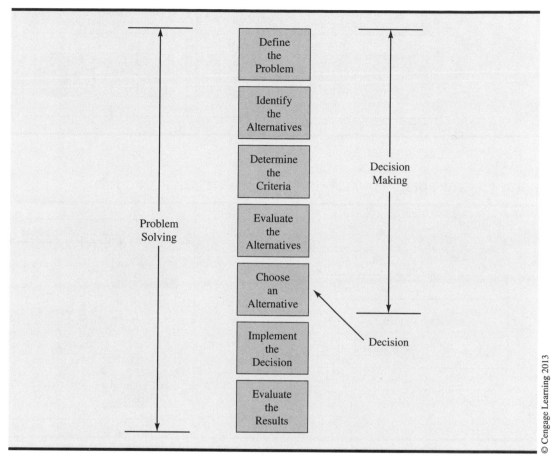

of each of these activities, but to emphasize the more limited scope of the term *decision making* as compared to the term *problem solving*. Figure 1.1 summarizes the relationship between these two concepts.

## 1.2   Quantitative Analysis and Decision Making

Consider the flowchart presented in Figure 1.2. Note that we combined the first three steps of the decision-making process under the heading of "Structuring the Problem" and the latter two steps under the heading "Analyzing the Problem." Let us now consider in greater detail how to carry out the activities that make up the decision-making process.

Figure 1.3 shows that the analysis phase of the decision-making process may take two basic forms: qualitative and quantitative. Qualitative analysis is based primarily on the manager's judgment and experience; it includes the manager's intuitive "feel" for the problem and is more an art than a science. If the manager has had experience with similar problems, or if the problem is relatively simple, heavy emphasis may be placed upon a qualitative analysis. However, if the manager has had little experience with similar problems, or if the problem

**FIGURE 1.2**     A SUBCLASSIFICATION OF THE DECISION-MAKING PROCESS

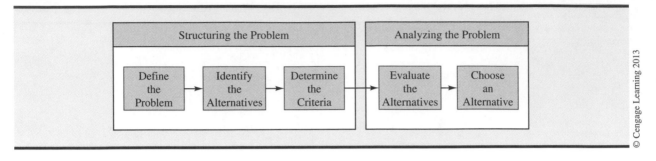

**FIGURE 1.3**     THE ROLE OF QUALITATIVE AND QUANTITATIVE ANALYSIS

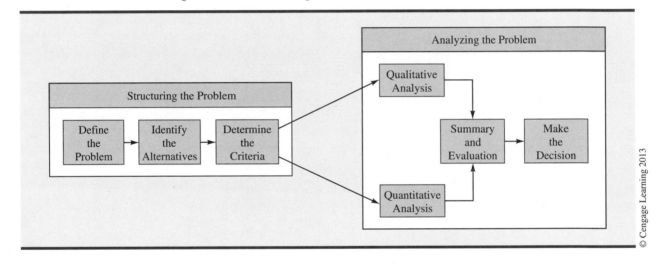

*Quantitative methods are especially helpful with large, complex problems. For example, in the coordination of the thousands of tasks associated with landing the Apollo 11 safely on the moon, quantitative techniques helped to ensure that more than 300,000 pieces of work performed by more than 400,000 people were integrated smoothly.*

is sufficiently complex, then a quantitative analysis of the problem can be an especially important consideration in the manager's final decision.

When using a quantitative approach, an analyst will concentrate on the quantitative facts or data associated with the problem and develop mathematical expressions that describe the objectives, constraints, and other relationships that exist in the problem. Then, by using one or more mathematical methods, the analyst will make a recommendation based on the quantitative aspects of the problem.

Although skills in the qualitative approach are inherent in the manager and usually increase with experience, the skills of the quantitative approach can be learned only by studying the assumptions and methods of management science. A manager can increase decision-making effectiveness by learning more about quantitative methodology and by better understanding its contribution to the decision-making process. A manager who is knowledgeable in quantitative decision-making procedures is in a much better position to compare and evaluate the qualitative and quantitative sources of recommendations and ultimately to combine the two sources to make the best possible decision.

The box in Figure 1.3 entitled "Quantitative Analysis" encompasses most of the subject matter of this text. We will consider a managerial problem, introduce the appropriate quantitative methodology, and then develop the recommended decision.

*Try Problem 4 to test your understanding of why quantitative approaches might be needed in a particular problem.*

Some of the reasons why a quantitative approach might be used in the decision-making process include the following:

1. The problem is complex, and the manager cannot develop a good solution without the aid of quantitative analysis.
2. The problem is critical (e.g., a great deal of money is involved), and the manager desires a thorough analysis before making a decision.
3. The problem is new, and the manager has no previous experience from which to draw.
4. The problem is repetitive, and the manager saves time and effort by relying on quantitative procedures to automate routine decision recommendations.

## ( 1.3 )  Quantitative Analysis

From Figure 1.3 we see that quantitative analysis begins once the problem has been structured. It usually takes imagination, teamwork, and considerable effort to transform a rather general problem description into a well-defined problem that can be approached via quantitative analysis. It is important to involve the stakeholders (the decision maker, users of results, etc.) in the process of structuring the problem to improve the likelihood that the ensuing quantitative analysis will make an important contribution to the decision-making process. When those familiar with the problem agree that it has been adequately structured, work can begin on developing a model to represent the problem mathematically. Solution procedures can then be employed to find the best solution for the model. This best solution for the model then becomes a recommendation to the decision maker. The process of developing and solving models is the essence of the quantitative analysis process.

### Model Development

**Models** are representations of real objects or situations and can be presented in various forms. For example, a scale model of an airplane is a representation of a real airplane. Similarly, a child's toy truck is a model of a real truck. The model airplane and toy truck are examples of models that are physical replicas of real objects. In modeling terminology, physical replicas are referred to as **iconic models**.

A second classification includes models that are physical in form but do not have the same physical appearance as the object being modeled. Such models are referred to as **analog models**. The speedometer of an automobile is an analog model; the position of the needle on the dial represents the speed of the automobile. A thermometer is another analog model representing temperature.

A third classification of models—the type we will primarily be studying—includes representations of a problem by a system of symbols and mathematical relationships or expressions. Such models are referred to as **mathematical models** and are a critical part of any quantitative approach to decision making. For example, the total profit from the sale of a product can be determined by multiplying the profit per unit by the quantity sold. Let $x$ represent the number of units produced and sold, and let $P$ represent the total profit. With a profit of $10 per unit, the following mathematical model defines the total profit earned by producing and selling $x$ units:

$$P = 10x \qquad \textbf{(1.1)}$$

The purpose, or value, of any model is that it enables us to make inferences about the real situation by studying and analyzing the model. For example, an airplane designer might test an iconic model of a new airplane in a wind tunnel to learn about the potential flying characteristics of the full-size airplane. Similarly, a mathematical model may be used to make inferences about how much profit will be earned if a specified quantity of a particular product is sold. According to the mathematical model of equation (1.1), we would expect that selling three units of the product ($x = 3$) would provide a profit of $P = 10(3) = \$30$.

In general, experimenting with models requires less time and is less expensive than experimenting with the real object or situation. One can certainly build and study a model airplane in less time and for less money than it would take to build and study the full-size airplane. Similarly, the mathematical model in equation (1.1) allows a quick identification of profit expectations without requiring the manager to actually produce and sell $x$ units. Models also reduce the risks associated with experimenting with the real situation. In particular, bad designs or bad decisions that cause the model airplane to crash or the mathematical model to project a \$10,000 loss can be avoided in the real situation.

*Herbert A. Simon, a Nobel Prize winner in economics and an expert in decision making, said that a mathematical model does not have to be exact; it just has to be close enough to provide better results than can be obtained by common sense.*

The value of model-based conclusions and decisions depends on how well the model represents the real situation. The more closely the model airplane represents the real airplane, the more accurate will be the conclusions and predictions. Similarly, the more closely the mathematical model represents the company's true profit–volume relationship, the more accurate will be the profit projections.

Because this text deals with quantitative analysis based on mathematical models, let us look more closely at the mathematical modeling process. When initially considering a managerial problem, we usually find that the problem definition phase leads to a specific objective, such as maximization of profit or minimization of cost, and possibly a set of restrictions or **constraints**, which express limitations on resources. The success of the mathematical model and quantitative approach will depend heavily on how accurately the objective and constraints can be expressed in mathematical equations or relationships.

The mathematical expression that defines the quantity to be maximized or minimized is referred to as the **objective function**. For example, suppose $x$ denotes the number of units produced and sold each week, and the firm's objective is to maximize total weekly profit. With a profit of \$10 per unit, the objective function is $10x$. A production capacity constraint would be necessary if, for instance, 5 hours are required to produce each unit and only 40 hours are available per week. The production capacity constraint is given by

$$5x \leq 40 \qquad\qquad \textbf{(1.2)}$$

The value of $5x$ is the total time required to produce $x$ units; the symbol $\leq$ indicates that the production time required must be less than or equal to the 40 hours available.

The decision problem or question is the following: How many units of the product should be produced each week to maximize profit? A complete mathematical model for this simple production problem is

$$
\begin{aligned}
\text{Maximize} \quad & 10x \quad \text{objective function} \\
\text{subject to (s.t.)} \quad & \\
& \left.\begin{array}{r} 5x \leq 40 \\ x \geq 0 \end{array}\right\} \text{constraints}
\end{aligned}
$$

The $x \geq 0$ constraint requires the production quantity $x$ to be greater than or equal to zero, which simply recognizes the fact that it is not possible to manufacture a negative number

**FIGURE 1.4** FLOWCHART OF THE PROCESS OF TRANSFORMING MODEL INPUTS INTO OUTPUT

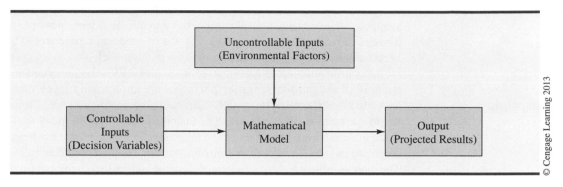

of units. The optimal solution to this simple model can be easily calculated and is given by $x = 8$, with an associated profit of $80. This model is an example of a linear programming model. In subsequent chapters we will discuss more complicated mathematical models and learn how to solve them in situations for which the answers are not nearly so obvious.

In the preceding mathematical model, the profit per unit ($10), the production time per unit (5 hours), and the production capacity (40 hours) are factors not under the control of the manager or decision maker. Such factors, which can affect both the objective function and the constraints, are referred to as **uncontrollable inputs** to the model. Inputs that are controlled or determined by the decision maker are referred to as **controllable inputs** to the model. In the example given, the production quantity $x$ is the controllable input to the model. Controllable inputs are the decision alternatives specified by the manager and thus are also referred to as the **decision variables** of the model.

Once all controllable and uncontrollable inputs are specified, the objective function and constraints can be evaluated and the output of the model determined. In this sense, the output of the model is simply the projection of what would happen if those particular factors and decisions occurred in the real situation. A flowchart of how controllable and uncontrollable inputs are transformed by the mathematical model into output is shown in Figure 1.4. A similar flowchart showing the specific details for the production model is shown in Figure 1.5. Note that we have used "Max" as an abbreviation for maximize.

**FIGURE 1.5** FLOWCHART FOR THE PRODUCTION MODEL

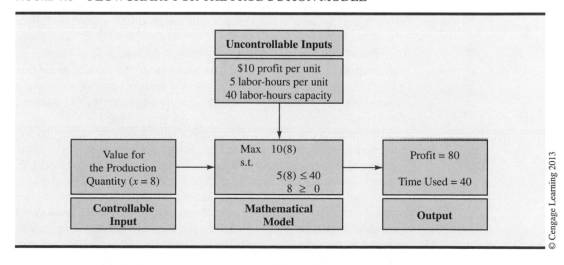

As stated earlier, the uncontrollable inputs are those the decision maker cannot influence. The specific controllable and uncontrollable inputs of a model depend on the particular problem or decision-making situation. In the production problem, the production time available (40) is an uncontrollable input. However, if it were possible to hire more employees or use overtime, the number of hours of production time would become a controllable input and therefore a decision variable in the model.

Uncontrollable inputs can either be known exactly or be uncertain and subject to variation. If all uncontrollable inputs to a model are known and cannot vary, the model is referred to as a **deterministic model**. Corporate income tax rates are not under the influence of the manager and thus constitute an uncontrollable input in many decision models. Because these rates are known and fixed (at least in the short run), a mathematical model with corporate income tax rates as the only uncontrollable input would be a deterministic model. The distinguishing feature of a deterministic model is that the uncontrollable input values are known in advance.

If any of the uncontrollable inputs are uncertain and subject to variation, the model is referred to as a **stochastic** or **probabilistic model**. An uncontrollable input in many production planning models is demand for the product. Because future demand may be any of a range of values, a mathematical model that treats demand with uncertainty would be considered a stochastic model. In the production model, the number of hours of production time required per unit, the total hours available, and the unit profit were all uncontrollable inputs. Because the uncontrollable inputs were all known to take on fixed values, the model was deterministic. If, however, the number of hours of production time per unit could vary from 3 to 6 hours depending on the quality of the raw material, the model would be stochastic. The distinguishing feature of a stochastic model is that the value of the output cannot be determined even if the value of the controllable input is known because the specific values of the uncontrollable inputs are unknown. In this respect, stochastic models are often more difficult to analyze.

## Data Preparation

Another step in the quantitative analysis of a problem is the preparation of the data required by the model. Data in this sense refer to the values of the uncontrollable inputs to the model. All uncontrollable inputs or data must be specified before we can analyze the model and recommend a decision or solution for the problem.

In the production model, the values of the uncontrollable inputs or data were $10 per unit for profit, 5 hours per unit for production time, and 40 hours for production capacity. In the development of the model, these data values were known and incorporated into the model as it was being developed. If the model is relatively small with respect to the number of the uncontrollable input values, the quantitative analyst will probably combine model development and data preparation into one step. In these situations the data values are inserted as the equations of the mathematical model are developed.

However, in many mathematical modeling situations the data or uncontrollable input values are not readily available. In these situations the analyst may know that the model will require profit per unit, production time, and production capacity data, but the values will not be known until the accounting, production, and engineering departments can be consulted. Rather than attempting to collect the required data as the model is being developed, the analyst will usually adopt a general notation for the model development step, and a separate data preparation step will then be performed to obtain the uncontrollable input values required by the model.

Using the general notation

$$c = \text{profit per unit}$$
$$a = \text{production time in hours per unit}$$
$$b = \text{production capacity in hours}$$

the model development step for the production problem would result in the following general model (recall $x$ = the number of units to produce and sell):

$$\text{Max } cx$$
$$\text{s.t.}$$
$$ax \le b$$
$$x \ge 0$$

A separate data preparation step to identify the values for $c$, $a$, and $b$ would then be necessary to complete the model.

Many inexperienced quantitative analysts assume that once the problem is defined and a general model developed, the problem is essentially solved. These individuals tend to believe that data preparation is a trivial step in the process and can be easily handled by clerical staff. Actually, this is a potentially dangerous assumption that could not be further from the truth, especially with large-scale models that have numerous data input values. For example, a moderate-sized linear programming model with 50 decision variables and 25 constraints could have more than 1300 data elements that must be identified in the data preparation step. The time required to collect and prepare these data and the possibility of data collection errors will make the data preparation step a critical part of the quantitative analysis process. Often, a fairly large database is needed to support a mathematical model, and information systems specialists also become involved in the data preparation step.

## Model Solution

Once the model development and data preparation steps are completed, we proceed to the model solution step. In this step, the analyst attempts to identify the values of the decision variables that provide the "best" output for the model. The specific decision-variable value or values providing the "best" output are referred to as the **optimal solution** for the model. For the production problem, the model solution step involves finding the value of the production quantity decision variable $x$ that maximizes profit while not causing a violation of the production capacity constraint.

One procedure that might be used in the model solution step involves a trial-and-error approach in which the model is used to test and evaluate various decision alternatives. In the production model, this procedure would mean testing and evaluating the model using various production quantities or values of $x$. As noted in Figure 1.5, we could input trial values for $x$ and check the corresponding output for projected profit and satisfaction of the production capacity constraint. If a particular decision alternative does not satisfy one or more of the model constraints, the decision alternative is rejected as being **infeasible**, regardless of the corresponding objective function value. If all constraints are satisfied, the decision alternative is **feasible** and is a candidate for the "best" solution or recommended decision. Through this trial-and-error process of evaluating selected decision alternatives, a decision maker can identify a good—and possibly the best—feasible solution to the problem. This solution would then be the recommended decision for the problem.

**TABLE 1.2** TRIAL-AND-ERROR SOLUTION FOR THE PRODUCTION MODEL OF FIGURE 1.5

| Decision Alternative (Production Quantity) $x$ | Projected Profit | Total Hours of Production | Feasible Solution? (Hours Used ≤ 40) |
|:---:|:---:|:---:|:---:|
| 0 | 0 | 0 | Yes |
| 2 | 20 | 10 | Yes |
| 4 | 40 | 20 | Yes |
| 6 | 60 | 30 | Yes |
| 8 | 80 | 40 | Yes |
| 10 | 100 | 50 | No |
| 12 | 120 | 60 | No |

Table 1.2 shows the results of a trial-and-error approach to solving the production model of Figure 1.5. The recommended decision is a production quantity of 8 because the feasible solution with the highest projected profit occurs at $x = 8$.

Although the trial-and-error solution process is often acceptable and can provide valuable information for the manager, it has the drawbacks of not necessarily providing the best solution and of being inefficient in terms of requiring numerous calculations if many decision alternatives are considered. Thus, quantitative analysts have developed special solution procedures for many models that are much more efficient than the trial-and-error approach. Throughout this text, you will be introduced to solution procedures that are applicable to the specific mathematical models. Some relatively small models or problems can be solved by hand computations, but most practical applications require the use of a computer.

The model development and model solution steps are not completely separable. An analyst will want both to develop an accurate model or representation of the actual problem situation and to be able to find a solution to the model. If we approach the model development step by attempting to find the most accurate and realistic mathematical model, we may find the model so large and complex that it is impossible to obtain a solution. In this case, a simpler and perhaps more easily understood model with a readily available solution procedure is preferred even though the recommended solution may be only a rough approximation of the best decision. As you learn more about quantitative solution procedures, you will form a better understanding of the types of mathematical models that can be developed and solved.

*Try Problem 8 to test your understanding of the concept of a mathematical model and what is referred to as the optimal solution to the model.*

After obtaining a model solution, the quantitative analyst will be interested in determining the quality of the solution. Even though the analyst has undoubtedly taken many precautions to develop a realistic model, often the usefulness or accuracy of the model cannot be assessed until model solutions are generated. Model testing and validation are frequently conducted with relatively small "test" problems with known or at least expected solutions. If the model generates the expected solutions, and if other output information appears correct or reasonable, the go-ahead may be given to use the model on the full-scale problem. However, if the model test and validation identify potential problems or inaccuracies inherent in the model, corrective action, such as model modification or collection of more accurate input data, may be taken. Whatever the corrective action, the model solution will not be used in practice until the model satisfactorily passes testing and validation.

## Report Generation

An important part of the quantitative analysis process is the preparation of managerial reports based on the model's solution. As indicated in Figure 1.3, the solution based on the quantitative analysis of a problem is one of the inputs the manager considers before making a final decision. Thus, the results of the model must appear in a managerial report that can be easily understood by the decision maker. The report includes the recommended decision and other pertinent information about the results that may be useful to the decision maker.

## A Note Regarding Implementation

As discussed in Section 1.2, the manager is responsible for integrating the quantitative solution with qualitative considerations to determine the best possible decision. After completing the decision-making process, the manager must oversee the implementation and follow-up evaluation of the decision. During the implementation and follow-up, the manager should continue to monitor the performance of the model. At times, this process may lead to requests for model expansion or refinement that will require the quantitative analyst to return to an earlier step of the process.

Successful implementation of results is critical to any application of quantitative analysis. If the results of the quantitative analysis are not correctly implemented, the entire effort may be of no value. Because implementation often requires people to change the way they do things, it often meets with resistance. People may want to know, "What's wrong with the way we've been doing it?" One of the most effective ways to ensure successful implementation is to include users throughout the modeling process. A user who feels a part of identifying the problem and developing the solution is much more likely to enthusiastically implement the results, and the input the quantitative analyst receives from these users can substantially enhance the models being developed. The success rate for implementing the results of a quantitative analysis project is much greater for those projects characterized by extensive user involvement. The Q.M. in Action, Quantitative Analysis at Merrill Lynch, discusses some of the reasons for the success of quantitative analysis at Merrill Lynch.

---

**Q.M. *in* ACTION**

*QUANTITATIVE ANALYSIS AT MERRILL LYNCH\**

For over 25 years, the Management Science Group at Merrill Lynch has successfully implemented quantitative models for a wide variety of decision problems. The group has applied quantitative methods for portfolio optimization, asset allocation, financial planning, marketing analysis, credit and liquidity assessment, as well as developing pricing and compensation structures. Although technical expertise and objectivity are clearly important factors in any analytical group, the management science group attributes much of its success to commu-

nications skills, teamwork, professional development for its members, and consulting skills.

From the earliest discussion of a potential project, the group focuses on fully understanding the problem and its business impact. Each client is asked, "Whose life will this change?" and "By how much?" The answers to these questions help the group understand who really has responsibility for the project, the processes involved, and how recommendations will be implemented. Analysts assigned to a project are fully engaged from start to finish. They are involved in project scope definition, data collection, analysis, development of recommendations, and

*\*Based on R. Nigam, "Structuring and Sustaining Excellence in Management Science at Merrill Lynch," Interfaces 38, no. 3 (May/June 2008): 202–209.*

*(continued)*

marketing those recommendations to the client. The group prides itself on technology transfer; that is, it gives any models it develops to the clients with assistance and training on the use of the models. This leads to longer-term impact through ongoing use of the model. Finally, like any good organization focused on improvement, the Management Science Group seeks feedback from clients after every project it completes.

This approach to problem solving and the implementation of quantitative analysis has been a hallmark of the Management Science Group. The impact and success of the group translates into hard dollars, repeat business, and recognition through a number of prestigious professional awards. The group received the annual Edelman Award given by the Institute for Operations Research and the Management Sciences (INFORMS) for effective use of management science for organizational success as well as the INFORMS Prize, given for long-term and high-impact use of quantitative methods within an organization.

## NOTES AND COMMENTS

1. Developments in computer technology have increased the availability of quantitative methods to decision makers. A variety of software packages is now available for personal computers. Versions of Microsoft Excel and LINGO are widely used to apply quantitative methods to business problems. Various chapter appendixes provide step-by-step instructions for using Excel and LINGO to solve problems in the text.

## 1.4 Models of Cost, Revenue, and Profit

Some of the most basic quantitative models arising in business and economic applications involve the relationships among a volume variable—such as production volume or sales volume—and cost, revenue, and profit. Through the use of these models, a manager can determine the projected cost, revenue, or profit associated with a planned production quantity or a forecasted sales volume. Financial planning, production planning, sales quotas, and other areas of decision making can benefit from such cost, revenue, and profit models.

### Cost and Volume Models

The cost of manufacturing or producing a product is a function of the volume produced. This cost can usually be defined as a sum of two costs: fixed cost and variable cost. **Fixed cost** is the portion of the total cost that does not depend on the production volume; this cost remains the same no matter how much is produced. **Variable cost**, on the other hand, is the portion of the total cost that depends on and varies with the production volume. To illustrate how cost and volume models can be developed, we will consider a manufacturing problem faced by Nowlin Plastics.

Nowlin Plastics produces a variety of compact disc (CD) storage cases. Nowlin's best-selling product is the CD-50, a slim plastic CD holder with a specially designed lining that protects the optical surface of each CD. Several products are produced on the same manufacturing line, and a setup cost is incurred each time a changeover is made for a new product. Suppose the setup cost for the CD-50 is $3000; this setup cost is a fixed cost and is incurred regardless of the number of units eventually produced. In addition, suppose that variable labor and material costs are $2 for each unit produced. The cost–volume model for producing $x$ units of the CD-50 can be written as

$$C(x) = 3000 + 2x \qquad \textbf{(1.3)}$$

where

$x$ = production volume in units

$C(x)$ = total cost of producing $x$ units

Once a production volume is established, the model in equation (1.3) can be used to compute the total production cost. For example, the decision to produce $x = 1200$ units would result in a total cost of $C(1200) = 3000 + 2(1200) = \$5400$.

**Marginal cost** is defined as the rate of change of the total cost with respect to production volume; that is, the cost increase associated with a one-unit increase in the production volume. In the cost model of equation (1.3), we see that the total cost $C(x)$ will increase by \$2 for each unit increase in the production volume. Thus, the marginal cost is \$2. With more complex total cost models, marginal cost may depend on the production volume. In such cases, we could have marginal cost increasing or decreasing with the production volume $x$.

## Revenue and Volume Models

Management of Nowlin Plastics will also want information about projected revenue associated with selling a specified number of units. Thus, a model of the relationship between revenue and volume is also needed. Suppose that each CD-50 storage unit sells for \$5. The model for total revenue can be written as

$$R(x) = 5x \qquad\qquad \textbf{(1.4)}$$

where

$x$ = sales volume in units

$R(x)$ = total revenue associated with selling $x$ units

**Marginal revenue** is defined as the rate of change of total revenue with respect to sales volume, that is, the increase in total revenue resulting from a one-unit increase in sales volume. In the model of equation (1.4), we see that the marginal revenue is \$5. In this case, marginal revenue is constant and does not vary with the sales volume. With more complex models, we may find that marginal revenue increases or decreases as the sales volume $x$ increases.

## Profit and Volume Models

One of the most important criteria for management decision making is profit. Managers need to know the profit implications of their decisions. If we assume that we will only produce what can be sold, the production volume and sales volume will be equal. We can then combine equations (1.3) and (1.4) to develop a profit–volume model that determines profit associated with a specified production-sales volume. Total profit is total revenue minus total cost; therefore, the following model provides the profit associated with producing and selling $x$ units:

$$\begin{aligned} P(x) &= R(x) - C(x) \\ &= 5x - (3000 + 2x) = -3000 + 3x \end{aligned} \qquad\qquad \textbf{(1.5)}$$

Thus, the model for profit $P(x)$ can be derived from the models of the revenue–volume and cost–volume relationships.

## Breakeven Analysis

Using equation (1.5), we can now determine the profit associated with any production volume $x$. For example, suppose that a demand forecast indicates that 500 units of the product can be sold. The decision to produce and sell the 500 units results in a projected profit of

$$P(500) = -3000 + 3(500) = -1500$$

In other words, a loss of $1500 is predicted. If sales are expected to be 500 units, the manager may decide against producing the product. However, a demand forecast of 1800 units would show a projected profit of

$$P(1800) = -3000 + 3(1800) = 2400$$

This profit may be sufficient to justify proceeding with the production and sale of the product.

We see that a volume of 500 units will yield a loss, whereas a volume of 1800 provides a profit. The volume that results in total revenue equaling total cost (providing $0 profit) is called the **breakeven point**. If the breakeven point is known, a manager can quickly infer that a volume above the breakeven point will generate a profit, whereas a volume below the breakeven point will result in a loss. Thus, the breakeven point for a product provides valuable information for a manager who must make a yes/no decision concerning production of the product.

Let us now return to the Nowlin Plastics example and show how the profit model in equation (1.5) can be used to compute the breakeven point. The breakeven point can be found by setting the profit expression equal to zero and solving for the production volume. Using equation (1.5), we have

$$P(x) = -3000 + 3x = 0$$
$$3x = 3000$$
$$x = 1000$$

*Try Problem 12 to test your ability to determine the breakeven point for a quantitative model.*

With this information, we know that production and sales of the product must exceed 1000 units before a profit can be expected. The graphs of the total cost model, the total revenue model, and the location of the breakeven point are shown in Figure 1.6. In Appendix 1.1 we also show how Excel can be used to perform a breakeven analysis for the Nowlin Plastics production example.

**FIGURE 1.6**    GRAPH OF THE BREAKEVEN ANALYSIS FOR NOWLIN PLASTICS

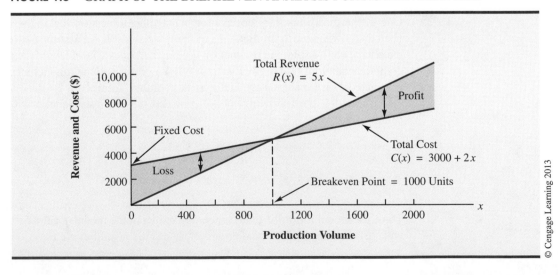

# Quantitative Methods in Practice

In this section we present a brief overview of the quantitative methods covered in this text. There are numerous applications for each of the following methods.

**Linear Programming** Linear programming is a problem-solving approach developed for situations involving maximizing or minimizing a linear function subject to linear constraints that limit the degree to which the objective can be pursued. The production model developed in Section 1.3 (see Figure 1.5) is an example of a simple linear programming model.

**Integer Linear Programming** Integer linear programming is an approach used for problems that can be set up as linear programs with the additional requirement that some or all of the decision recommendations be integer values.

**Project Scheduling: PERT/CPM** In many situations managers are responsible for planning, scheduling, and controlling projects that consist of numerous separate jobs or tasks performed by a variety of departments, individuals, and so forth. PERT (Program Evaluation and Review Technique) and CPM (Critical Path Method) help managers carry out their project scheduling and tracking responsibilities.

**Inventory Models** Inventory models are used by managers faced with the problem of maintaining sufficient inventories to meet demand for goods while incurring the lowest possible inventory holding costs.

**Waiting Line or Queueing Models** Waiting line or queueing models help managers understand and make better decisions concerning the operation of systems involving waiting lines.

**Simulation** Simulation is a technique used to model the operation of a complex system. This technique employs a computer program to model the operation and perform simulation computations.

**Decision Analysis** Decision analysis can be used to determine optimal strategies in situations involving several decision alternatives and an uncertain or risk-filled pattern of future events.

**Forecasting** Forecasting methods are techniques that can be used to predict future aspects of a business operation.

**Markov-Process Models** Markov-process models are useful in studying the evolution of certain systems over repeated trials. For example, Markov processes have been used to describe the probability that a machine, functioning in one period, will function or break down in some future period.

## Methods Used Most Frequently

We believe barriers to the use of quantitative methods can best be removed by increasing the manager's understanding of how quantitative analysis can be applied. The text will help you develop an understanding of which quantitative methods are most useful, how they are used, and, most importantly, how they can assist managers in making better decisions.

The Q.M. in Action, Impact of Operations Research on Everyday Living, describes some of the many ways quantitative analysis affects our everyday lives.

---

**Q.M. *in* ACTION**

*IMPACT OF OPERATIONS RESEARCH ON EVERYDAY LIVING\**

Mark Eisner, Communications Associate of the School of Operations Research and Information Engineering at Cornell University, once said that operations research "is probably the most important field nobody has ever heard of." The impact of operations research on everyday living over the past 20 years is substantial.

Suppose you schedule a vacation to Florida and use the Orbitz website to book your flights. An algorithm developed by operations researchers will search among millions of options to find the cheapest fare. Another algorithm will schedule the flight crews and aircraft used by the airline. If you rent a car in Florida, the price you pay for the car is determined by a mathematical model that seeks to maximize revenue for the car rental firm. If you do some shopping on your trip and decide to ship your purchases home using UPS, another algorithm

determines the truck on which your packages are loaded, which route the truck should follow, and where your packages should be placed on the truck to minimize loading and unloading time.

If you enjoy watching college basketball, operations research plays a role in what games you see. Michael Trick, a professor at the Tepper School of Business at Carnegie Mellon, designed a system for scheduling each year's Atlantic Coast Conference men's and women's basketball games. Even though it might initially appear that scheduling 16 games among the nine men's teams would be easy, it requires sorting through hundreds of millions of possible combinations of possible schedules. Each of those possibilities entails some desirable and some undesirable characteristics. For example, you do not want to schedule too many consecutive home games for any team, and you want to ensure that each team plays the same number of weekend games.

*\*Based on Virginia Postrel, "Operations Everything," The Boston Globe, June 27, 2004.*

---

**NOTES AND COMMENTS**

1. In the United States, the Institute for Operations Research and the Management Sciences (INFORMS) and the Decision Sciences Institute (DSI) are two flagship professional societies that publish journals and newsletters dealing with current research and applications of operations research and management science techniques. In Canada, the Canadian Operational Research Society (CORS) provides similar services.

2. Several European countries, including (but not limited to) Great Britain, France, Italy, Germany, Austria, and the Czech Republic, have their own professional operations research and management science societies, and these societies belong to the Association of European Operational Research Societies (EURO). Professional operations research and management science societies from Latin American and Iberian peninsula countries, including (but not limited to) Chile, Brazil, Argentina, Colombia, Spain, Uruguay, Portugal, and Mexico, all belong to the Asociación Latino-Iberoamericana de Investigación Operativa (ALIO). Professional operations research and management science societies from Australia, Japan, China, India, Malaysia, Thailand, New Zealand, and other countries from Asia and the Pacific Rim belong to the Association of Asian Pacific Operational Research Societies (APORS). African operations research societies include the Operations Research Society of South Africa (ORSSA) and the Operations Research Society of Eastern Africa (ORSEA). The International Federation of Operational Research Societies (IFORS) is the global organization to which most of these (and other) professional operations research and management science societies belong.

## Summary

This text focuses on the use of quantitative methods to help managers make better decisions. The discussion in this chapter centered on the problem orientation of the decision-making process and an overview of how mathematical models can be used in this type of analysis.

The difference between the model and the situation or managerial problem it represents is an important consideration. Mathematical models are abstractions of real-world situations and, as such, cannot capture all the aspects of the real situation. However, if a model can capture the major relevant aspects of the problem and can then provide a meaningful solution recommendation, it can be a valuable aid to decision making.

One of the characteristics of quantitative analysis that will become increasingly apparent as we proceed through the text is the search for a best solution to the problem. In carrying out the quantitative analysis, we attempt to develop procedures for finding the "best" or optimal solution.

## Glossary

**Problem solving**  The process of identifying a difference between the actual and the desired state of affairs and then taking action to resolve the difference.

**Decision making**  The process of defining the problem, identifying the alternatives, determining the criteria, evaluating the alternatives, and choosing an alternative.

**Single-criterion decision problem**  A problem in which the objective is to find the "best" solution with respect to just one criterion.

**Multicriteria decision problem**  A problem that involves more than one criterion; the objective is to find the "best" solution, taking into account all the criteria.

**Decision**  The alternative selected.

**Model**  A representation of a real object or situation.

**Iconic model**  A physical replica, or representation, of a real object.

**Analog model**  Although physical in form, an analog model does not have a physical appearance similar to the real object or situation it represents.

**Mathematical model**  Mathematical symbols and expressions used to represent a real situation.

**Constraint**  A restriction or limitation imposed on a problem.

**Objective function**  The mathematical expression that defines the quantity to be maximized or minimized.

**Uncontrollable input**  The factors that cannot be controlled by the decision maker.

**Controllable input**  The decision alternatives that can be specified by the decision maker.

**Decision variable**  Another term for controllable input.

**Deterministic model**  A model in which all uncontrollable inputs are known and cannot vary.

**Stochastic model**  A model in which at least one uncontrollable input is uncertain and subject to variation; stochastic models are also referred to as probabilistic models.

**Optimal solution**  The specific decision variable value or values that provide the "best" output for the model.

**Infeasible solution**  A decision alternative or solution that violates one or more constraints.

**Feasible solution**  A decision alternative or solution that satisfies all constraints.

**Fixed cost**  The portion of the total cost that does not depend on the volume; this cost remains the same no matter how much is produced.

**Variable cost**  The portion of the total cost that is dependent on and varies with the volume.

**Marginal cost**  The rate of change of the total cost with respect to volume.

**Marginal revenue** The rate of change of total revenue with respect to volume.

**Breakeven point** The volume at which total revenue equals total cost.

## Problems

1. Define the terms *management science* and *operations research.*

2. List and discuss the steps of the decision-making process.

3. Discuss the different roles played by the qualitative and quantitative approaches to managerial decision making. Why is it important for a manager or decision maker to have a good understanding of both of these approaches to decision making?

4. A firm recently built a new plant that will use more than 50 production lines and machines to produce over 500 different products. The production scheduling decisions are critical because sales will be lost if customer demand is not met on time. If no individual in the firm has had experience with this production operation, and if new production schedules must be generated each week, why should the firm consider a quantitative approach to the production scheduling problem?

5. What are the advantages of analyzing and experimenting with a model as opposed to a real object or situation?

6. Suppose a manager must choose between the following two mathematical models of a given situation: (a) a relatively simple model that is a reasonable approximation of the real situation and (b) a thorough and complex model that is the most accurate mathematical representation of the real situation possible. Why might the model described in part (a) be preferred by the manager?

7. Suppose you are going on a weekend trip to a city that is $d$ miles away. Develop a model that determines your round-trip gasoline costs. What assumptions or approximations are necessary to treat this model as a deterministic model? Are these assumptions or approximations acceptable to you?

8. Recall the production model from Section 1.3:

$$\text{Max} \quad 10x$$
$$\text{s.t.}$$
$$5x \le 40$$
$$x \ge 0$$

Suppose the firm in this example considers a second product that has a unit profit of $5 and requires 2 hours for each unit produced. Assume total production capacity remains 40 units. Use $y$ as the number of units of product 2 produced.

a. Show the mathematical model when both products are considered simultaneously.

b. Identify the controllable and uncontrollable inputs for this model.

c. Draw the flowchart of the input–output process for this model (see Figure 1.5).

d. What are the optimal solution values of $x$ and $y$?

e. Is this model a deterministic or a stochastic model? Explain.

9. Suppose we modify the production model from Section 1.3 to obtain the following mathematical model:

$$\text{Max} \quad 10x$$
$$\text{s.t.}$$
$$ax \le 40$$
$$x \ge 0$$

where $a$ is the number of hours required for each unit produced. With $a = 5$, the optimal solution is $x = 8$. If we have a stochastic model in which the value of $a$ varies between 3 and 6 (i.e., $a = 3$, $a = 4$, $a = 5$, or $a = 6$) as the possible values for the number of hours required per unit, what is the optimal value for $x$? What problems does this stochastic model cause?

10. A retail store in Des Moines, Iowa, receives shipments of a particular product from Kansas City and Minneapolis. Let

$$x = \text{units of product received from Kansas City}$$
$$y = \text{units of product received from Minneapolis}$$

   a. Write an expression for the total units of product received by the retail store in Des Moines.

   b. Shipments from Kansas City cost $0.20 per unit, and shipments from Minneapolis cost $0.25 per unit. Develop an objective function representing the total cost of shipments to Des Moines.

   c. Assuming the monthly demand at the retail store is 5000 units, develop a constraint that requires 5000 units to be shipped to Des Moines.

   d. No more than 4000 units can be shipped from Kansas City and no more than 3000 units can be shipped from Minneapolis in a month. Develop constraints to model this situation.

   e. Of course, negative amounts cannot be shipped. Combine the objective function and constraints developed to state a mathematical model for satisfying the demand at the Des Moines retail store at minimum cost.

11. For most products, higher prices result in a decreased demand, whereas lower prices result in an increased demand (economists refer to such products as *normal goods*). Let

$$d = \text{annual demand for a product in units}$$
$$p = \text{price per unit}$$

Assume that a firm accepts the following price–demand relationship as being a realistic representation of its market:

$$d = 800 - 10p$$

where $p$ must be between $20 and $70.

   a. How many units can the firm sell at the $20 per-unit price? At the $70 per-unit price?

   b. What happens to annual units demanded for the product if the firm increases the per-unit price from $26 to $27? From $42 to $43? From $68 to $69? What is the suggested relationship between per-unit price and annual demand for the product in units?

   c. Show the mathematical model for the total revenue (TR), which is the annual demand multiplied by the unit price.

   d. Based on other considerations, the firm's management will only consider price alternatives of $30, $40, and $50. Use your model from part (b) to determine the price alternative that will maximize the total revenue.

   e. What are the expected annual demand and the total revenue according to your recommended price?

12. The O'Neill Shoe Manufacturing Company will produce a special-style shoe if the order size is large enough to provide a reasonable profit. For each special-style order, the company incurs a fixed cost of $2000 for the production setup. The variable cost is $60 per pair, and each pair sells for $80.

   a. Let $x$ indicate the number of pairs of shoes produced. Develop a mathematical model for the total cost of producing $x$ pairs of shoes.

b.   Let $P$ indicate the total profit. Develop a mathematical model for the total profit realized from an order for $x$ pairs of shoes.

c.   What is the breakeven point?

13.  Micromedia offers computer training seminars on a variety of topics. In the seminars each student works at a personal computer, practicing the particular activity that the instructor is presenting. Micromedia is currently planning a two-day seminar on the use of Microsoft Excel in statistical analysis. The projected fee for the seminar is $600 per student. The cost for the conference room, instructor compensation, lab assistants, and promotion is $9600. Micromedia rents computers for its seminars at a cost of $60 per computer per day.

a.   Develop a model for the total cost to put on the seminar. Let $x$ represent the number of students who enroll in the seminar.

b.   Develop a model for the total profit if $x$ students enroll in the seminar.

c.   Micromedia has forecasted an enrollment of 30 students for the seminar. How much profit will be earned if its forecast is accurate?

d.   Compute the breakeven point.

14.  Eastman Publishing Company is considering publishing a paperback textbook on spreadsheet applications for business. The fixed cost of manuscript preparation, textbook design, and production setup is estimated to be $160,000. Variable production and material costs are estimated to be $6 per book. Demand over the life of the book is estimated to be 4000 copies. The publisher plans to sell the text to college and university bookstores for $46 each.

a.   What is the breakeven point?

b.   What profit or loss can be anticipated with a demand of 3500 copies?

c.   With a demand of 3500 copies, what is the minimum price per copy that the publisher must charge to break even?

d.   If the publisher believes that the price per copy could be increased to $50.95 and not affect the anticipated demand of 4000 copies, what action would you recommend? What profit or loss can be anticipated?

15.  Preliminary plans are underway for construction of a new stadium for a major league baseball team. City officials question the number and profitability of the luxury corporate boxes planned for the upper deck of the stadium. Corporations and selected individuals may purchase a box for $300,000. The fixed construction cost for the upper-deck area is estimated to be $4,500,000, with a variable cost of $150,000 for each box constructed.

a.   What is the breakeven point for the number of luxury boxes in the new stadium?

b.   Preliminary drawings for the stadium show that space is available for the construction of up to 50 luxury boxes. Promoters indicate that buyers are available and that all 50 could be sold if constructed. What is your recommendation concerning the construction of luxury boxes? What profit is anticipated?

16.  Financial Analysts, Inc., is an investment firm that manages stock portfolios for a number of clients. A new client has requested that the firm handle an $800,000 portfolio. As an initial investment strategy, the client would like to restrict the portfolio to a mix of the following two stocks:

| Stock | Price/ Share | Estimated Annual Return/Share |
|-------|--------------|-------------------------------|
| Oil Alaska | $50 | $6 |
| Southwest Petroleum | $30 | $4 |

Let

$x$ = number of shares of Oil Alaska
$y$ = number of shares of Southwest Petroleum

    a.   Develop the objective function, assuming that the client desires to maximize the total annual return.

    b.   Show the mathematical expression for each of the following three constraints:

        (1) Total investment funds available are $800,000.

        (2) Maximum Oil Alaska investment is $500,000.

        (3) Maximum Southwest Petroleum investment is $450,000.

*Note:* Adding the $x \geq 0$ and $y \geq 0$ constraints provides a linear programming model for the investment problem. A solution procedure for this model will be discussed in Chapter 7.

17.   Models of inventory systems frequently consider the relationships among a beginning inventory, a production quantity, a demand or sales, and an ending inventory. For a given production period $j$, let

$s_{j-1}$ = beginning inventory for period $j$ (ending inventory from period $j-1$, the previous period)

$x_j$ = production quantity in period $j$

$d_j$ = demand in period $j$

$s_j$ = ending inventory for period $j$

    a.   Write the mathematical relationship or model that shows ending inventory as a function of beginning inventory, production, and demand.

    b.   What constraint should be added if production capacity for period $j$ is given by $C_j$?

    c.   What constraint should be added if inventory requirements for period $j$ mandate an ending inventory of at least $I_j$?

**Case Problem**  # Scheduling a Golf League

Chris Lane, the head professional at Royal Oak Country Club, must develop a schedule of matches for the couples' golf league that begins its season at 4:00 P.M. tomorrow. Eighteen couples signed up for the league, and each couple must play every other couple over the course of the 17-week season. Chris thought it would be fairly easy to develop a schedule, but after working on it for a couple of hours, he has been unable to come up with a schedule. Because Chris must have a schedule ready by tomorrow afternoon, he has asked you to help him. A possible complication is that one of the couples told Chris that they may have to cancel for the season. They told Chris they would let him know by 1:00 P.M. tomorrow whether they will be able to play this season.

## Managerial Report

Prepare a report for Chris Lane. Your report should include, at a minimum, the following items:

1.  A schedule that will enable each of the 18 couples to play every other couple over the 17-week season.

2.  A contingency schedule that can be used if the couple that contacted Chris decides to cancel for the season.

**Appendix 1.1**  # Using Excel for Breakeven Analysis

In Section 1.4 we introduced the Nowlin Plastics production example to illustrate how quantitative models can be used to help a manager determine the projected cost, revenue, and profit associated with an established production quantity or a forecasted sales volume. In this appendix we introduce spreadsheet applications by showing how to use Excel to perform a quantitative analysis of the Nowlin Plastics example.

**FIGURE 1.7    FORMULA WORKSHEET FOR THE NOWLIN PLASTICS PRODUCTION EXAMPLE**

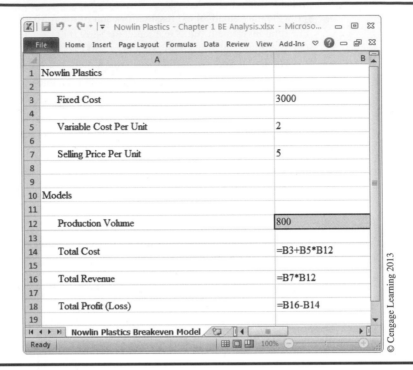

Refer to the worksheet shown in Figure 1.7. We begin by entering the problem data into the top portion of the worksheet. The value of 3000 in cell B3 is the setup cost, the value of 2 in cell B5 is the variable labor and material costs per unit, and the value of 5 in cell B7 is the selling price per unit. In general, whenever we perform a quantitative analysis using Excel, we will enter the problem data in the top portion of the worksheet and reserve the bottom portion for model development. The label "Models" in cell B10 helps to provide a visual reminder of this convention.

Cell B12 in the models portion of the worksheet contains the proposed production volume in units. Because the values for total cost, total revenue, and total profit depend upon the value of this decision variable, we placed a border around cell B12 and screened the cell for emphasis. Based upon the value in cell B12, the cell formulas in cells B14, B16, and B18 are used to compute values for total cost, total revenue, and total profit (loss), respectively. First, recall that the value of total cost is the sum of the fixed cost (cell B3) and the total variable cost. Because the total variable cost is the product of the variable cost per unit (cell B5) and the production volume (cell B12), it is given by B5*B12. Thus, to compute total cost we entered the formula =B3+B5*B12 into cell B14. Next, total revenue is the product of the selling price per unit (cell B7) and the number of units produced (cell B12); therefore in cell B16 we have entered the formula =B7*B12. Finally, the total profit (or loss) is the difference between the total revenue (cell B16) and the total cost (cell B14). Thus, in cell B18 we have entered the formula =B16-B14. The worksheet in Figure 1.7 shows the formulas used to make these computations; we refer to it as a formula worksheet.

To examine the effect of selecting a particular value for the production volume, we have entered a value of 800 in cell B12. The worksheet shown in Figure 1.8 shows the values obtained by the formulas; a production volume of 800 units results in a total cost of $4600, a

**FIGURE 1.8**    SOLUTION FOR THE NOWLIN PLASTICS PRODUCTION EXAMPLE USING A PRODUCTION VOLUME OF 800 UNITS

**Nowlin**

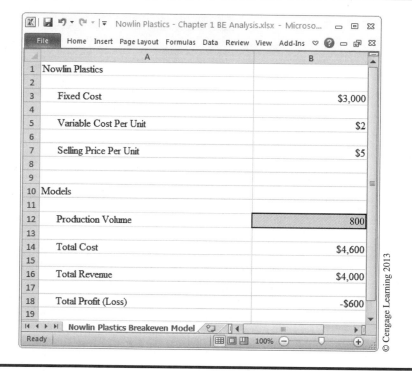

total revenue of $4000, and a loss of $600. To examine the effect of other production volumes, we only need to enter the other values into cell B12. To examine the effect of different costs and selling prices, we simply enter the appropriate values in the data portion of the worksheet; the results will be displayed in the model section of the worksheet.

In Section 1.4 we illustrated breakeven analysis. Let us now see how a spreadsheet can be used to compute the breakeven point for the Nowlin Plastics production example.

## Determining the Breakeven Point Using Excel's Goal Seek Tool

The breakeven point is the production volume that results in total revenue equal to total cost and hence a profit of $0. One way to determine the breakeven point is to use a trial-and-error approach. For example, in Figure 1.8 we saw that a trial production volume of 800 units resulted in a loss of $600. Because this trial solution resulted in a loss, a production volume of 800 units cannot be the breakeven point. We could continue to experiment with other production volumes by simply entering different values into cell B12 and observing the resulting profit or loss in cell B18. A better approach is to use Excel's Goal Seek tool to determine the breakeven point.

Excel's Goal Seek tool allows the user to determine the value for an input cell that will cause the value of a related output cell to equal some specified value (called the *goal*). In the case of breakeven analysis, the "goal" is to set total profit to zero by "seeking" an appropriate value for production volume. Goal Seek will allow us to find the value of production volume

**FIGURE 1.9**    GOAL SEEK DIALOG BOX FOR THE NOWLIN PLASTICS PRODUCTION EXAMPLE

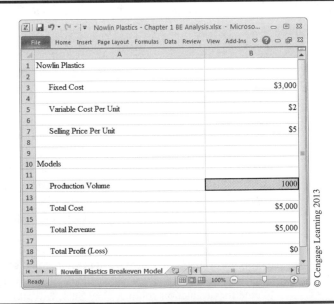

that will set Nowlin Plastics' total profit to zero. The following steps describe how to use Goal Seek to find the breakeven point for Nowlin Plastics:

**Step 1.** Select the **Data** tab at the top of the Ribbon
**Step 2.** Select **What-If Analysis** in the **Data Tools** group
**Step 3.** Select **Goal Seek** in **What-If-Analysis**
**Step 4.** When the **Goal Seek** dialog box appears (see Figure 1.9):
   Enter B18 in the **Set cell** box
   Enter 0 in the **To value** box
   Enter B12 in the **By changing cell** box
   Click **OK**

The completed Goal Seek dialog box is shown in Figure 1.9, and the worksheet obtained is shown in Figure 1.10. The total profit in cell B18 is zero, and the production volume in cell B12 has been set to the breakeven point of 1000.

**FIGURE 1.10**    BREAKEVEN POINT FOUND USING GOAL SEEK TOOL FOR THE NOWLIN PLASTICS PRODUCTION EXAMPLE

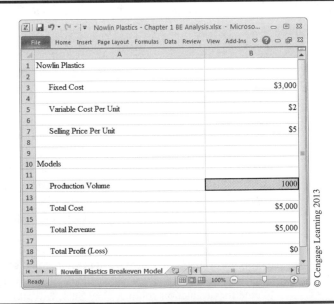

# CHAPTER 4

# Decision Analysis

**CONTENTS**

Decision analysis can be used to develop an optimal strategy when a decision maker is faced with several decision alternatives and an uncertain or risk-filled pattern of future events. For example, Ohio Edison used decision analysis to choose the best type of particulate control equipment for coal-fired generating units when it faced future uncertainties concerning sulfur content restrictions, construction costs, and so on. The State of North Carolina used decision analysis in evaluating whether to implement a medical screening test to detect metabolic disorders in newborns. The Q.M. in Action, Phytopharm's New Product Research and Development, discusses the use of decision analysis to manage Phytopharm's pipeline of pharmaceutical products, which have long development times and relatively high levels of uncertainty.

Even when a careful decision analysis has been conducted, the uncertain future events make the final consequence uncertain. In some cases, the selected decision alternative may provide good or excellent results. In other cases, a relatively unlikely future event may occur, causing the selected decision alternative to provide only fair or even poor results. The risk associated with any decision alternative is a direct result of the uncertainty associated with the final consequence. A good decision analysis includes careful consideration of risk. Through risk analysis the decision maker is provided with probability information about the favorable as well as the unfavorable consequences that may occur.

We begin the study of decision analysis by considering problems that involve reasonably few decision alternatives and reasonably few possible future events. Influence diagrams and payoff tables are introduced to provide a structure for the decision problem and

**Q.M.** *in* ACTION

*PHYTOPHARM'S NEW PRODUCT RESEARCH AND DEVELOPMENT\**

As a pharmaceutical development and functional food company, Phytopharm's primary revenue streams come from licensing agreements with larger companies. After Phytopharm establishes proof of principle for a new product by successfully completing early clinical trials, it seeks to reduce its risk by licensing the product to a large pharmaceutical or nutrition company that will further develop and market the product.

There is substantial uncertainty regarding the future sales potential of early stage products, as only one in ten of such products makes it to market and only 30% of these yield a healthy return. Phytopharm and its licensing partners would often initially propose very different terms of the licensing agreement. Therefore, Phytopharm employed a team of researchers to develop a flexible methodology for appraising a product's

potential and subsequently supporting the negotiation of the lump-sum payments for development milestones and royalties on eventual sales that comprise the licensing agreement.

Using computer simulation, the resulting decision analysis model allows Phytopharm to perform sensitivity analysis on estimates of development cost, the probability of successful Food & Drug Administration clearance, launch date, market size, market share, and patent expiry. In particular, a decision tree model allows Phytopharm and its licensing partner to mutually agree upon the number of development milestones. Depending on the status of the project at a milestone, the licensing partner can opt to abandon the project or continue development. Laying out these sequential decisions in a decision tree allows Phytopharm to negotiate milestone payments and royalties that equitably split the project's value between Phytopharm and its potential licensee.

*Pascale Crama, Bert De Ryck, Zeger Degraeve, and Wang Chong, "Research and Development Project Valuation and Licensing Negotiations at Phytopharm plc," Interfaces, 37 no. 5: 472–487.*

to illustrate the fundamentals of decision analysis. We then introduce decision trees to show the sequential nature of decision problems. Decision trees are used to analyze more complex problems and to identify an optimal sequence of decisions, referred to as an optimal decision strategy. Sensitivity analysis shows how changes in various aspects of the problem affect the recommended decision alternative.

## ( 4.1 )  Problem Formulation

The first step in the decision analysis process is problem formulation. We begin with a verbal statement of the problem. We then identify the **decision alternatives**; the uncertain future events, referred to as **chance events**; and the **consequences** associated with each combination of decision alternative and chance event outcome. Let us begin by considering a construction project of the Pittsburgh Development Corporation.

Pittsburgh Development Corporation (PDC) purchased land that will be the site of a new luxury condominium complex. The location provides a spectacular view of downtown Pittsburgh and the Golden Triangle, where the Allegheny and Monongahela Rivers meet to form the Ohio River. PDC plans to price the individual condominium units between $300,000 and $1,400,000.

PDC commissioned preliminary architectural drawings for three different projects: one with 30 condominiums, one with 60 condominiums, and one with 90 condominiums. The financial success of the project depends upon the size of the condominium complex and the chance event concerning the demand for the condominiums. The statement of the PDC decision problem is to select the size of the new luxury condominium project that will lead to the largest profit given the uncertainty concerning the demand for the condominiums.

Given the statement of the problem, it is clear that the decision is to select the best size for the condominium complex. PDC has the following three decision alternatives:

$$d_1 = \text{a small complex with 30 condominiums}$$
$$d_2 = \text{a medium complex with 60 condominiums}$$
$$d_3 = \text{a large complex with 90 condominiums}$$

A factor in selecting the best decision alternative is the uncertainty associated with the chance event concerning the demand for the condominiums. When asked about the possible demand for the condominiums, PDC's president acknowledged a wide range of possibilities but decided that it would be adequate to consider two possible chance event outcomes: a strong demand and a weak demand.

In decision analysis, the possible outcomes for a chance event are referred to as the **states of nature**. The states of nature are defined so they are mutually exclusive (no more than one can occur) and collectively exhaustive (at least one must occur); thus one and only one of the possible states of nature will occur. For the PDC problem, the chance event concerning the demand for the condominiums has two states of nature:

$$s_1 = \text{strong demand for the condominiums}$$
$$s_2 = \text{weak demand for the condominiums}$$

Management must first select a decision alternative (complex size); then a state of nature follows (demand for the condominiums) and finally a consequence will occur. In this case, the consequence is PDC's profit.

## Influence Diagrams

An **influence diagram** is a graphical device that shows the relationships among the decisions, the chance events, and the consequences for a decision problem. The **nodes** in an influence diagram represent the decisions, chance events, and consequences. Rectangles or squares depict **decision nodes**, circles or ovals depict **chance nodes**, and diamonds depict **consequence nodes**. The lines connecting the nodes, referred to as *arcs,* show the direction of influence that the nodes have on one another. Figure 4.1 shows the influence diagram for the PDC problem. The complex size is the decision node, demand is the chance node, and profit is the consequence node. The arcs connecting the nodes show that both the complex size and the demand influence PDC's profit.

## Payoff Tables

Given the three decision alternatives and the two states of nature, which complex size should PDC choose? To answer this question, PDC will need to know the consequence associated with each decision alternative and each state of nature. In decision analysis, we refer to the consequence resulting from a specific combination of a decision alternative and a state of nature as a **payoff**. A table showing payoffs for all combinations of decision alternatives and states of nature is a **payoff table**.

*Payoffs can be expressed in terms of profit, cost, time, distance, or any other measure appropriate for the decision problem being analyzed.*

Because PDC wants to select the complex size that provides the largest profit, profit is used as the consequence. The payoff table with profits expressed in millions of dollars is shown in Table 4.1. Note, for example, that if a medium complex is built and demand turns out to be strong, a profit of $14 million will be realized. We will use the notation $V_{ij}$ to denote the payoff associated with decision alternative $i$ and state of nature $j$. Using Table 4.1, $V_{31} = 20$ indicates a payoff of $20 million occurs if the decision is to build a large complex ($d_3$) and the strong demand state of nature ($s_1$) occurs. Similarly, $V_{32} = -9$ indicates a loss of $9 million if the decision is to build a large complex ($d_3$) and the weak demand state of nature ($s_2$) occurs.

**FIGURE 4.1**    INFLUENCE DIAGRAM FOR THE PDC PROJECT

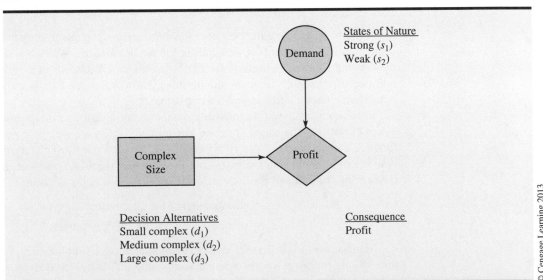

States of Nature
Strong ($s_1$)
Weak ($s_2$)

Decision Alternatives
Small complex ($d_1$)
Medium complex ($d_2$)
Large complex ($d_3$)

Consequence
Profit

© Cengage Learning 2013

**TABLE 4.1** PAYOFF TABLE FOR THE PDC CONDOMINIUM PROJECT
(PAYOFFS IN $ MILLIONS)

| | State of Nature | |
|---|---|---|
| **Decision Alternative** | **Strong Demand $s_1$** | **Weak Demand $s_2$** |
| Small complex, $d_1$ | 8 | 7 |
| Medium complex, $d_2$ | 14 | 5 |
| Large complex, $d_3$ | 20 | −9 |

© Cengage Learning 2013

## Decision Trees

A **decision tree** provides a graphical representation of the decision-making process. Figure 4.2 presents a decision tree for the PDC problem. Note that the decision tree shows the natural or logical progression that will occur over time. First, PDC must make a decision regarding the size of the condominium complex ($d_1$, $d_2$, or $d_3$). Then, after the decision is implemented, either state of nature $s_1$ or $s_2$ will occur. The number at each endpoint of the tree indicates the payoff associated with a particular sequence. For example, the topmost payoff of 8 indicates that an $8 million profit is anticipated if PDC constructs a small condominium complex ($d_1$) and demand turns out to be strong ($s_1$). The next payoff of 7 indicates an anticipated profit of $7 million if PDC constructs a small condominium complex ($d_1$) and demand turns out to be weak ($s_2$). Thus, the decision tree provides a graphical depiction of the sequences of decision alternatives and states of nature that provide the six possible payoffs for PDC.

*If you have a payoff table, you can develop a decision tree. Try Problem 1, part (a).*

The decision tree in Figure 4.2 shows four nodes, numbered 1−4. Squares are used to depict decision nodes and circles are used to depict chance nodes. Thus, node 1 is a decision node, and nodes 2, 3, and 4 are chance nodes. The **branches** connect the nodes; those

**FIGURE 4.2** DECISION TREE FOR THE PDC CONDOMINIUM PROJECT
(PAYOFFS IN $ MILLIONS)

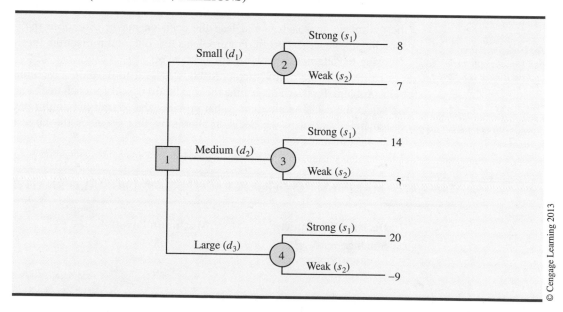

© Cengage Learning 2013

leaving the decision node correspond to the decision alternatives. The branches leaving each chance node correspond to the states of nature. The payoffs are shown at the end of the states-of-nature branches. We now turn to the question: How can the decision maker use the information in the payoff table or the decision tree to select the best decision alternative? Several approaches may be used.

---

**NOTES AND COMMENTS**

1. The first step in solving a complex problem is to decompose the problem into a series of smaller subproblems. Decision trees provide a useful way to decompose a problem and illustrate the sequential nature of the decision process.

2. People often view the same problem from different perspectives. Thus, the discussion regarding the development of a decision tree may provide additional insight about the problem.

---

## Decision Making Without Probabilities

In this section we consider approaches to decision making that do not require knowledge of the probabilities of the states of nature. These approaches are appropriate in situations in which the decision maker has little confidence in his or her ability to assess the probabilities, or in which a simple best-case and worst-case analysis is desirable. Because different approaches sometimes lead to different decision recommendations, the decision maker must understand the approaches available and then select the specific approach that, according to the judgment of the decision maker, is the most appropriate.

*Many people think of a good decision as one in which the consequence is good. However, in some instances, a good, well-thought-out decision may still lead to a bad or undesirable consequence while a poor, ill-conceived decision may still lead to a good or desirable consequence.*

### Optimistic Approach

The **optimistic approach** evaluates each decision alternative in terms of the *best* payoff that can occur. The decision alternative that is recommended is the one that provides the best possible payoff. For a problem in which maximum profit is desired, as in the PDC problem, the optimistic approach would lead the decision maker to choose the alternative corresponding to the largest profit. For problems involving minimization, this approach leads to choosing the alternative with the smallest payoff.

*For a maximization problem, the optimistic approach often is referred to as the maximax approach; for a minimization problem, the corresponding terminology is minimin.*

To illustrate the optimistic approach, we use it to develop a recommendation for the PDC problem. First, we determine the maximum payoff for each decision alternative; then we select the decision alternative that provides the overall maximum payoff. These steps systematically identify the decision alternative that provides the largest possible profit. Table 4.2 illustrates these steps.

**TABLE 4.2**   MAXIMUM PAYOFF FOR EACH PDC DECISION ALTERNATIVE

| Decision Alternative | Maximum Payoff | |
|---|---|---|
| Small complex, $d_1$ | 8 | |
| Medium complex, $d_2$ | 14 | |
| Large complex, $d_3$ | 20 | ← Maximum of the maximum payoff values |

Because 20, corresponding to $d_3$, is the largest payoff, the decision to construct the large condominium complex is the recommended decision alternative using the optimistic approach.

## Conservative Approach

*For a maximization problem, the conservative approach is often referred to as the maximin approach; for a minimization problem, the corresponding terminology is minimax.*

The **conservative approach** evaluates each decision alternative in terms of the *worst* payoff that can occur. The decision alternative recommended is the one that provides the best of the worst possible payoffs. For a problem in which the output measure is profit, as in the PDC problem, the conservative approach would lead the decision maker to choose the alternative that maximizes the minimum possible profit that could be obtained. For problems involving minimization, this approach identifies the alternative that will minimize the maximum payoff.

To illustrate the conservative approach, we use it to develop a recommendation for the PDC problem. First, we identify the minimum payoff for each of the decision alternatives; then we select the decision alternative that maximizes the minimum payoff. Table 4.3 illustrates these steps for the PDC problem.

Because 7, corresponding to $d_1$, yields the maximum of the minimum payoffs, the decision alternative of a small condominium complex is recommended. This decision approach is considered conservative because it identifies the worst possible payoffs and then recommends the decision alternative that avoids the possibility of extremely "bad" payoffs. In the conservative approach, PDC is guaranteed a profit of at least $7 million. Although PDC may make more, it *cannot* make less than $7 million.

## Minimax Regret Approach

In decision analysis, **regret** is the difference between the payoff associated with a particular decision alternative and the payoff associated with the decision that would yield the most desirable payoff for a given state of nature. Thus, regret represents how much potential payoff one would forgo by selecting a particular decision alternative given that a specific state of nature will occur. This is why regret is often referred to as **opportunity loss**.

As its name implies, under the **minimax regret approach** to decision making one would choose the decision alternative that minimizes the maximum state of regret that could occur over all possible states of nature. This approach is neither purely optimistic nor purely conservative. Let us illustrate the minimax regret approach by showing how it can be used to select a decision alternative for the PDC problem.

Suppose that PDC constructs a small condominium complex ($d_1$) and demand turns out to be strong ($s_1$). Table 4.1 showed that the resulting profit for PDC would be $8 million. However, given that the strong demand state of nature ($s_1$) has occurred, we realize

**TABLE 4.3**   MINIMUM PAYOFF FOR EACH PDC DECISION ALTERNATIVE

| Decision Alternative | Minimum Payoff | |
|---|---|---|
| Small complex, $d_1$ | 7 | ← Maximum of the minimum payoff values |
| Medium complex, $d_2$ | 5 | |
| Large complex, $d_3$ | −9 | |

**TABLE 4.4**   OPPORTUNITY LOSS, OR REGRET, TABLE FOR THE PDC CONDOMINIUM
PROJECT ($ MILLIONS)

| | State of Nature | |
|---|---|---|
| **Decision Alternative** | **Strong Demand $s_1$** | **Weak Demand $s_2$** |
| Small complex, $d_1$ | 12 | 0 |
| Medium complex, $d_2$ | 6 | 2 |
| Large complex, $d_3$ | 0 | 16 |

that the decision to construct a large condominium complex ($d_3$), yielding a profit of
$20 million, would have been the best decision. The difference between the payoff for the
best decision alternative ($20 million) and the payoff for the decision to construct a small
condominium complex ($8 million) is the regret or opportunity loss associated with deci-
sion alternative $d_1$ when state of nature $s_1$ occurs; thus, for this case, the opportunity loss
or regret is $20 million − $8 million = $12 million. Similarly, if PDC makes the decision
to construct a medium condominium complex ($d_2$) and the strong demand state of nature
($s_1$) occurs, the opportunity loss, or regret, associated with $d_2$ would be $20 million −
$14 million = $6 million.

In general, the following expression represents the opportunity loss, or regret:

$$R_{ij} = |V_j^* - V_{ij}| \tag{4.1}$$

where

$R_{ij}$ = the regret associated with decision alternative $d_i$ and state of nature $s_j$

$V_j^*$ = the payoff value[1] corresponding to the best decision for the state of nature $s_j$

$V_{ij}$ = the payoff corresponding to decision alternative $d_i$ and state of nature $s_j$

Note the role of the absolute value in equation (4.1). For minimization problems, the best
payoff, $V_j^*$, is the smallest entry in column $j$. Because this value always is less than or equal
to $V_{ij}$, the absolute value of the difference between $V_j^*$ and $V_{ij}$ ensures that the regret is
always the magnitude of the difference.

Using equation (4.1) and the payoffs in Table 4.1, we can compute the regret associated
with each combination of decision alternative $d_i$ and state of nature $s_j$. Because the PDC
problem is a maximization problem, $V_j^*$ will be the largest entry in column $j$ of the payoff
table. Thus, to compute the regret, we simply subtract each entry in a column from the
largest entry in the column. Table 4.4 shows the opportunity loss, or regret, table for the
PDC problem.

The next step in applying the minimax regret approach is to list the maximum regret
for each decision alternative; Table 4.5 shows the results for the PDC problem. Selecting
the decision alternative with the *minimum* of the *maximum* regret values—hence, the name
*minimax regret*—yields the minimax regret decision. For the PDC problem, the alternative
to construct the medium condominium complex, with a corresponding maximum regret of
$6 million, is the recommended minimax regret decision.

---

[1]In maximization problems, $V_j^*$ will be the largest entry in column $j$ of the payoff table. In minimization problems, $V_j^*$ will be
the smallest entry in column $j$ of the payoff table.

**TABLE 4.5**   MAXIMUM REGRET FOR EACH PDC DECISION ALTERNATIVE

| Decision Alternative | Maximum Regret | |
|---|---|---|
| Small complex, $d_1$ | 12 | |
| Medium complex, $d_2$ | 6 | ← Minimum of the maximum regret |
| Large complex, $d_3$ | 16 | |

*For practice in developing a decision recommendation using the optimistic, conservative, and minimax regret approaches, try Problem 1, part (b).*

Note that the three approaches discussed in this section provide different recommendations, which in itself isn't bad. It simply reflects the difference in decision-making philosophies that underlie the various approaches. Ultimately, the decision maker will have to choose the most appropriate approach and then make the final decision accordingly. The main criticism of the approaches discussed in this section is that they do not consider any information about the probabilities of the various states of nature. In the next section we discuss an approach that utilizes probability information in selecting a decision alternative.

## 4.3   Decision Making With Probabilities

In many decision-making situations, we can obtain probability assessments for the states of nature. When such probabilities are available, we can use the **expected value approach** to identify the best decision alternative. Let us first define the expected value of a decision alternative and then apply it to the PDC problem.

Let

$$N = \text{the number of states of nature}$$

$$P(s_j) = \text{the probability of state of nature } s_j$$

Because one and only one of the $N$ states of nature can occur, the probabilities must satisfy two conditions:

$$P(s_j) \geq 0 \qquad \text{for all states of nature} \tag{4.2}$$

$$\sum_{j=1}^{N} P(s_j) = P(s_1) + P(s_2) + \cdots + P(s_N) = 1 \tag{4.3}$$

The **expected value (EV)** of decision alternative $d_i$ is defined as follows:

$$\text{EV}(d_i) = \sum_{j=1}^{N} P(s_j)V_{ij} \tag{4.4}$$

In words, the expected value of a decision alternative is the sum of weighted payoffs for the decision alternative. The weight for a payoff is the probability of the associated state of nature and therefore the probability that the payoff will occur. Let us return to the PDC problem to see how the expected value approach can be applied.

PDC is optimistic about the potential for the luxury high-rise condominium complex. Suppose that this optimism leads to an initial subjective probability assessment of 0.8 that demand will be strong ($s_1$) and a corresponding probability of 0.2 that demand will be weak ($s_2$).

*Can you now use the expected value approach to develop a decision recommendation? Try Problem 5.*

Thus, $P(s_1) = 0.8$ and $P(s_2) = 0.2$. Using the payoff values in Table 4.1 and equation (4.4), we compute the expected value for each of the three decision alternatives as follows:

$$EV(d_1) = 0.8(8) + 0.2(7) \quad = 7.8$$
$$EV(d_2) = 0.8(14) + 0.2(5) \quad = 12.2$$
$$EV(d_3) = 0.8(20) + 0.2(-9) = 14.2$$

Thus, using the expected value approach, we find that the large condominium complex, with an expected value of $14.2 million, is the recommended decision.

The calculations required to identify the decision alternative with the best expected value can be conveniently carried out on a decision tree. Figure 4.3 shows the decision tree for the PDC problem with state-of-nature branch probabilities. Working backward through the decision tree, we first compute the expected value at each chance node. That is, at each chance node, we weight each possible payoff by its probability of occurrence. By doing so, we obtain the expected values for nodes 2, 3, and 4, as shown in Figure 4.4.

*Computer packages are available to help in constructing more complex decision trees. See Appendix 4.1.*

Because the decision maker controls the branch leaving decision node 1 and because we are trying to maximize the expected profit, the best decision alternative at node 1 is $d_3$. Thus, the decision tree analysis leads to a recommendation of $d_3$, with an expected value of $14.2 million. Note that this recommendation is also obtained with the expected value approach in conjunction with the payoff table.

Other decision problems may be substantially more complex than the PDC problem, but if a reasonable number of decision alternatives and states of nature are present, you can use the decision tree approach outlined here. First, draw a decision tree consisting of decision nodes, chance nodes, and branches that describe the sequential nature of the problem. If you use the expected value approach, the next step is to determine the probabilities for each of the states of nature and compute the expected value at each chance node. Then select the decision branch leading to the chance node with the best expected value. The decision alternative associated with this branch is the recommended decision.

The Q.M. in Action, Early Detection of High-Risk Worker Disability Claims, describes how the Workers' Compensation Board of British Columbia used a decision tree and expected cost to help determine whether a short-term disability claim should be considered a high-risk or a low-risk claim.

**FIGURE 4.3**   PDC DECISION TREE WITH STATE-OF-NATURE BRANCH PROBABILITIES

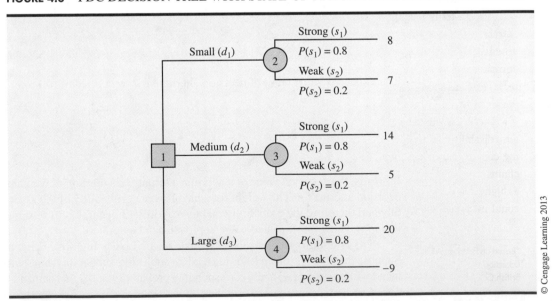

**FIGURE 4.4**    APPLYING THE EXPECTED VALUE APPROACH USING A DECISION TREE

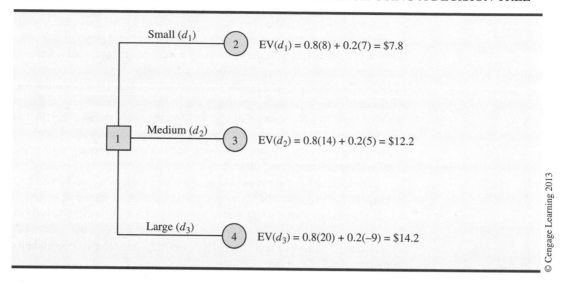

**Q.M.** *in* ACTION

*EARLY DETECTION OF HIGH-RISK WORKER DISABILITY CLAIMS\**

The Workers' Compensation Board of British Columbia (WCB) helps workers and employers maintain safe workplaces and helps injured workers obtain disability income and return to work safely. The funds used to make the disability compensation payments are obtained from assessments levied on employers. In return, employers receive protection from lawsuits arising from work-related injuries. In recent years, the WCB spent more than $1 billion on worker compensation and rehabilitation.

A short-term disability claim occurs when a worker suffers an injury or illness that results in temporary absence from work. Whenever a worker fails to recover completely from a short-term disability, the claim is reclassified as a long-term disability claim, and more expensive long-term benefits are paid.

The WCB wanted a systematic way to identify short-term disability claims that posed a high financial risk of being converted to the more expensive long-term disability claims. If a short-term disability claim could be classified as high risk early in the process, a WCB management team could intervene and monitor the claim and the recovery

process more closely. As a result, WCB could improve the management of the high-risk claims and reduce the cost of any subsequent long-term disability claims.

The WCB used a decision analysis approach to classify each new short-term disability claim as being either a high-risk claim or a low-risk claim. A decision tree consisting of two decision nodes and two states-of-nature nodes was developed. The two decision alternatives were: (1) Classify the new short-term claim as high-risk and intervene; (2) classify the new short-term claim as low-risk and do not intervene. The two states of nature were: (1) The short-term claim converts to a long-term claim; (2) the short-term claim does not convert to a long-term claim. The characteristics of each new short-term claim were used to determine the probabilities for the states of nature. The payoffs were the disability claim costs associated with each decision alternative and each state-of-nature outcome. The objective of minimizing the expected cost determined whether a new short-term claim should be classified as high risk.

Implementation of the decision analysis model improved the practice of claim management for the Workers' Compensation Board. Early intervention on the high-risk claims saved an estimated $4.7 million per year.

\*Based on E. Urbanovich, E. Young, M. Puterman, and S. Fattedad, "Early Detection of High-Risk Claims at the Workers' Compensation Board of British Columbia," *Interfaces* (July/August 2003): 15–26.

## Expected Value of Perfect Information

Suppose that PDC has the opportunity to conduct a market research study that would help evaluate buyer interest in the condominium project and provide information that management could use to improve the probability assessments for the states of nature. To determine the potential value of this information, we begin by supposing that the study could provide *perfect information* regarding the states of nature; that is, we assume for the moment that PDC could determine with certainty, prior to making a decision, which state of nature is going to occur. To make use of this perfect information, we will develop a decision strategy that PDC should follow once it knows which state of nature will occur. A decision strategy is simply a decision rule that specifies the decision alternative to be selected after new information becomes available.

To help determine the decision strategy for PDC, we reproduced PDC's payoff table as Table 4.6. Note that, if PDC knew for sure that state of nature $s_1$ would occur, the best decision alternative would be $d_3$, with a payoff of $20 million. Similarly, if PDC knew for sure that state of nature $s_2$ would occur, the best decision alternative would be $d_1$, with a payoff of $7 million. Thus, we can state PDC's optimal decision strategy when the perfect information becomes available as follows:

If $s_1$, select $d_3$ and receive a payoff of $20 million.

If $s_2$, select $d_1$ and receive a payoff of $7 million.

What is the expected value for this decision strategy? To compute the expected value with perfect information, we return to the original probabilities for the states of nature: $P(s_1) = 0.8$ and $P(s_2) = 0.2$. Thus, there is a 0.8 probability that the perfect information will indicate state of nature $s_1$, and the resulting decision alternative $d_3$ will provide a $20 million profit. Similarly, with a 0.2 probability for state of nature $s_2$, the optimal decision alternative $d_1$ will provide a $7 million profit. Thus, from equation (4.4) the expected value of the decision strategy that uses perfect information is $0.8(20) + 0.2(7) = 17.4$.

We refer to the expected value of $17.4 million as the *expected value with perfect information* (EVwPI).

Earlier in this section we showed that the recommended decision using the expected value approach is decision alternative $d_3$, with an expected value of $14.2 million. Because this decision recommendation and expected value computation were made without the benefit of perfect information, $14.2 million is referred to as the *expected value without perfect information* (EVwoPI).

The expected value with perfect information is $17.4 million, and the expected value without perfect information is $14.2; therefore, the expected value of the perfect information (EVPI) is $17.4 − $14.2 = $3.2 million. In other words, $3.2 million represents the additional expected value that can be obtained if perfect information were available about the states of nature.

**TABLE 4.6**    PAYOFF TABLE FOR THE PDC CONDOMINIUM PROJECT ($ MILLIONS)

| Decision Alternative | State of Nature | |
| --- | --- | --- |
|  | Strong Demand $s_1$ | Weak Demand $s_2$ |
| Small complex, $d_1$ | 8 | 7 |
| Medium complex, $d_2$ | 14 | 5 |
| Large complex, $d_3$ | 20 | −9 |

*It would be worth $3.2 million for PDC to learn the level of market acceptance before selecting a decision alternative.*

Generally speaking, a market research study will not provide "perfect" information; however, if the market research study is a good one, the information gathered might be worth a sizable portion of the $3.2 million. Given the EVPI of $3.2 million, PDC might seriously consider a market survey as a way to obtain more information about the states of nature.

In general, the **expected value of perfect information (EVPI)** is computed as follows:

$$\text{EVPI} = |\text{EVwPI} - \text{EVwoPI}| \qquad\qquad \textbf{(4.5)}$$

where

> $\text{EVPI}$ = expected value of perfect information
> $\text{EVwPI}$ = expected value *with* perfect information about the states of nature
> $\text{EVwoPI}$ = expected value *without* perfect information about the states of nature

*For practice in determining the expected value of perfect information, try Problem 14.*

Note the role of the absolute value in equation (4.5). For minimization problems, the expected value with perfect information is always less than or equal to the expected value without perfect information. In this case, EVPI is the magnitude of the difference between EVwPI and EVwoPI, or the absolute value of the difference as shown in equation (4.5).

## NOTES AND COMMENTS

**1.** We restate the *opportunity loss,* or *regret,* table for the PDC problem (see Table 4.4) as follows:

| | State of Nature | |
|---|---|---|
| | **Strong Demand** | **Weak Demand** |
| **Decision** | $s_1$ | $s_2$ |
| Small complex, $d_1$ | 12 | 0 |
| Medium complex, $d_2$ | 6 | 2 |
| Large complex, $d_3$ | 0 | 16 |

Using $P(s_1)$, $P(s_2)$, and the opportunity loss values, we can compute the *expected opportunity loss* (EOL) for each decision alternative. With $P(s_1) = 0.8$ and $P(s_2) = 0.2$, the expected opportunity loss for each of the three decision alternatives is

$$\text{EOL}(d_1) = 0.8(12) + 0.2(0) \ = 9.6$$
$$\text{EOL}(d_2) = 0.8(6) \ + 0.2(2) \ = 5.2$$
$$\text{EOL}(d_3) = 0.8(0) \ + 0.2(16) = 3.2$$

Regardless of whether the decision analysis involves maximization or minimization, the *minimum* expected opportunity loss always provides the best decision alternative. Thus, with $\text{EOL}(d_3) = 3.2$, $d_3$ is the recommended decision. In addition, the minimum expected opportunity loss always is *equal to the expected value of perfect information.* That is, EOL(best decision) = EVPI; for the PDC problem, this value is $3.2 million.

# Risk Analysis and Sensitivity Analysis

**Risk analysis** helps the decision maker recognize the difference between the expected value of a decision alternative and the payoff that may actually occur. **Sensitivity analysis** also helps the decision maker by describing how changes in the state-of-nature probabilities and/or changes in the payoffs affect the recommended decision alternative.

## Risk Analysis

A decision alternative and a state of nature combine to generate the payoff associated with a decision. The **risk profile** for a decision alternative shows the possible payoffs along with their associated probabilities.

**FIGURE 4.5**    RISK PROFILE FOR THE LARGE COMPLEX DECISION ALTERNATIVE FOR
THE PDC CONDOMINIUM PROJECT

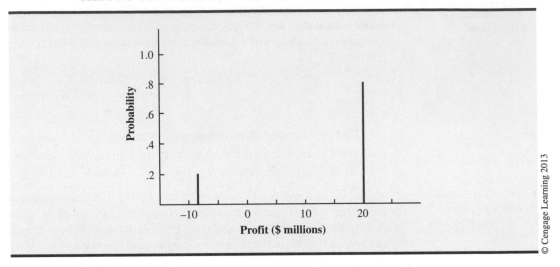

Let us demonstrate risk analysis and the construction of a risk profile by returning to the PDC condominium construction project. Using the expected value approach, we identified the large condominium complex ($d_3$) as the best decision alternative. The expected value of $14.2 million for $d_3$ is based on a 0.8 probability of obtaining a $20 million profit and a 0.2 probability of obtaining a $9 million loss. The 0.8 probability for the $20 million payoff and the 0.2 probability for the $-$9 million payoff provide the risk profile for the large complex decision alternative. This risk profile is shown graphically in Figure 4.5.

Sometimes a review of the risk profile associated with an optimal decision alternative may cause the decision maker to choose another decision alternative even though the expected value of the other decision alternative is not as good. For example, the risk profile for the medium complex decision alternative ($d_2$) shows a 0.8 probability for a $14 million payoff and a 0.2 probability for a $5 million payoff. Because no probability of a loss is associated with decision alternative $d_2$, the medium complex decision alternative would be judged less risky than the large complex decision alternative. As a result, a decision maker might prefer the less risky medium complex decision alternative even though it has an expected value of $2 million less than the large complex decision alternative.

## Sensitivity Analysis

Sensitivity analysis can be used to determine how changes in the probabilities for the states of nature or changes in the payoffs affect the recommended decision alternative. In many cases, the probabilities for the states of nature and the payoffs are based on subjective assessments. Sensitivity analysis helps the decision maker understand which of these inputs are critical to the choice of the best decision alternative. If a small change in the value of one of the inputs causes a change in the recommended decision alternative, the solution to the decision analysis problem is sensitive to that particular input. Extra effort and care should be taken to make sure the input value is as accurate as possible. On the other hand, if a modest-to-large change in the value of one of the inputs does not cause a change in the recommended decision alternative, the solution to the decision analysis problem is not sensitive to that particular input. No extra time or effort would be needed to refine the estimated input value.

One approach to sensitivity analysis is to select different values for the probabilities of the states of nature and the payoffs and then resolve the decision analysis problem. If the recommended decision alternative changes, we know that the solution is sensitive to the changes made. For example, suppose that in the PDC problem the probability for a strong demand is revised to 0.2 and the probability for a weak demand is revised to 0.8. Would the recommended decision alternative change? Using $P(s_1) = 0.2$, $P(s_2) = 0.8$, and equation (4.4), the revised expected values for the three decision alternatives are

$$EV(d_1) = 0.2(8)\ \ + 0.8(7)\ \ =\ \ 7.2$$
$$EV(d_2) = 0.2(14) + 0.8(5)\ \ =\ \ 6.8$$
$$EV(d_3) = 0.2(20) + 0.8(-9) = -3.2$$

With these probability assessments, the recommended decision alternative is to construct a small condominium complex ($d_1$), with an expected value of $7.2 million. The probability of strong demand is only 0.2, so constructing the large condominium complex ($d_3$) is the least preferred alternative, with an expected value of $-$3.2 million (a loss).

Thus, when the probability of strong demand is large, PDC should build the large complex; when the probability of strong demand is small, PDC should build the small complex. Obviously, we could continue to modify the probabilities of the states of nature and learn even more about how changes in the probabilities affect the recommended decision alternative. The drawback to this approach is the numerous calculations required to evaluate the effect of several possible changes in the state-of-nature probabilities.

*Computer software packages for decision analysis make it easy to calculate these revised scenarios.*

For the special case of two states of nature, a graphical procedure can be used to determine how changes for the probabilities of the states of nature affect the recommended decision alternative. To demonstrate this procedure, we let $p$ denote the probability of state of nature $s_1$; that is, $P(s_1) = p$. With only two states of nature in the PDC problem, the probability of state of nature $s_2$ is

$$P(s_2) = 1 - P(s_1) = 1 - p$$

Using equation (4.4) and the payoff values in Table 4.1, we determine the expected value for decision alternative $d_1$ as follows:

$$EV(d_1) = P(s_1)(8) + P(s_2)(7)$$
$$= p(8) + (1 - p)(7) \qquad \textbf{(4.6)}$$
$$= 8p + 7 - 7p = p + 7$$

Repeating the expected value computations for decision alternatives $d_2$ and $d_3$, we obtain expressions for the expected value of each decision alternative as a function of $p$:

$$EV(d_2) = 9p + 5 \qquad\qquad \textbf{(4.7)}$$

$$EV(d_3) = 29p - 9 \qquad\qquad \textbf{(4.8)}$$

Thus, we have developed three equations that show the expected value of the three decision alternatives as a function of the probability of state of nature $s_1$.

We continue by developing a graph with values of $p$ on the horizontal axis and the associated EVs on the vertical axis. Because equations (4.6), (4.7), and (4.8) are linear equations, the graph of each equation is a straight line. For each equation, we can obtain the line

**FIGURE 4.6**   EXPECTED VALUE FOR THE PDC DECISION ALTERNATIVES
AS A FUNCTION OF $p$

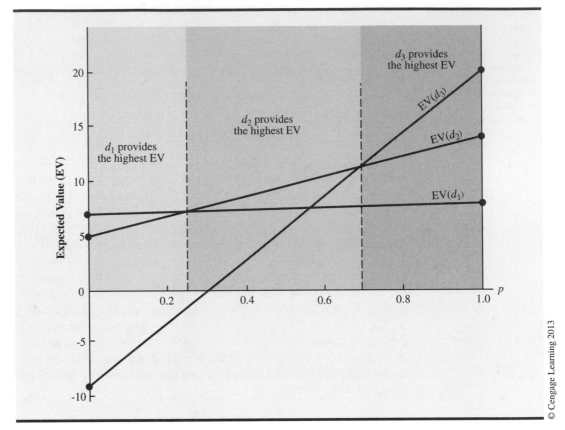

by identifying two points that satisfy the equation and drawing a line through the points. For instance, if we let $p = 0$ in equation (4.6), $EV(d_1) = 7$. Then, letting $p = 1$, $EV(d_1) = 8$. Connecting these two points, $(0,7)$ and $(1,8)$, provides the line labeled $EV(d_1)$ in Figure 4.6. Similarly, we obtain the lines labeled $EV(d_2)$ and $EV(d_3)$; these lines are the graphs of equations (4.7) and (4.8), respectively.

Figure 4.6 shows how the recommended decision changes as $p$, the probability of the strong demand state of nature ($s_1$), changes. Note that for small values of $p$, decision alternative $d_1$ (small complex) provides the largest expected value and is thus the recommended decision. When the value of $p$ increases to a certain point, decision alternative $d_2$ (medium complex) provides the largest expected value and is the recommended decision. Finally, for large values of $p$, decision alternative $d_3$ (large complex) becomes the recommended decision.

The value of $p$ for which the expected values of $d_1$ and $d_2$ are equal is the value of $p$ corresponding to the intersection of the $EV(d_1)$ and the $EV(d_2)$ lines. To determine this value, we set $EV(d_1) = EV(d_2)$ and solve for the value of $p$:

$$p + 7 = 9p + 5$$
$$8p = 2$$
$$p = \frac{2}{8} = 0.25$$

Hence, when $p = 0.25$, decision alternatives $d_1$ and $d_2$ provide the same expected value. Repeating this calculation for the value of $p$ corresponding to the intersection of the EV($d_2$) and EV($d_3$) lines, we obtain $p = 0.70$.

*Graphical sensitivity analysis shows how changes in the probabilities for the states of nature affect the recommended decision alternative. Try Problem 8.*

Using Figure 4.6, we can conclude that decision alternative $d_1$ provides the largest expected value for $p \leq 0.25$, decision alternative $d_2$ provides the largest expected value for $0.25 \leq p \leq 0.70$, and decision alternative $d_3$ provides the largest expected value for $p \geq 0.70$. Because $p$ is the probability of state of nature $s_1$ and $(1 - p)$ is the probability of state of nature $s_2$, we now have the sensitivity analysis information that tells us how changes in the state-of-nature probabilities affect the recommended decision alternative.

Sensitivity analysis calculations can also be made for the values of the payoffs. In the original PDC problem, the expected values for the three decision alternatives were as follows: EV($d_1$) = 7.8, EV($d_2$) = 12.2, and EV($d_3$) = 14.2. Decision alternative $d_3$ (large complex) was recommended. Note that decision alternative $d_2$ with EV($d_2$) = 12.2 was the second best decision alternative. Decision alternative $d_3$ will remain the optimal decision alternative as long as EV($d_3$) is greater than or equal to the expected value of the second best decision alternative. Thus, decision alternative $d_3$ will remain the optimal decision alternative as long as

$$\text{EV}(d_3) \geq 12.2 \tag{4.9}$$

Let

$$S = \text{the payoff of decision alternative } d_3 \text{ when demand is strong}$$
$$W = \text{the payoff of decision alternative } d_3 \text{ when demand is weak}$$

Using $P(s_1) = 0.8$ and $P(s_2) = 0.2$, the general expression for EV($d_3$) is

$$\text{EV}(d_3) = 0.8S + 0.2W \tag{4.10}$$

Assuming that the payoff for $d_3$ stays at its original value of $-\$9$ million when demand is weak, the large complex decision alternative will remain optimal as long as

$$\text{EV}(d_3) = 0.8S + 0.2(-9) \geq 12.2 \tag{4.11}$$

Solving for $S$, we have

$$0.8S - 1.8 \geq 12.2$$
$$0.8S \geq 14$$
$$S \geq 17.5$$

Recall that when demand is strong, decision alternative $d_3$ has an estimated payoff of $20 million. The preceding calculation shows that decision alternative $d_3$ will remain optimal as long as the payoff for $d_3$ when demand is strong is at least $17.5 million.

Assuming that the payoff for $d_3$ when demand is strong stays at its original value of $20 million, we can make a similar calculation to learn how sensitive the optimal solution is with regard to the payoff for $d_3$ when demand is weak. Returning to the expected value calculation of equation (4.10), we know that the large complex decision alternative will remain optimal as long as

$$\text{EV}(d_3) = 0.8(20) + 0.2W \geq 12.2 \tag{4.12}$$

Solving for $W$, we have

$$16 + 0.2 \geq 12.2$$
$$0.2W \geq -3.8$$
$$W \geq -19$$

Recall that when demand is weak, decision alternative $d_3$ has an estimated payoff of $-\$9$ million. The preceding calculation shows that decision alternative $d_3$ will remain optimal as long as the payoff for $d_3$ when demand is weak is at least $-\$19$ million.

Based on this sensitivity analysis, we conclude that the payoffs for the large complex decision alternative ($d_3$) could vary considerably, and $d_3$ would remain the recommended decision alternative. Thus, we conclude that the optimal solution for the PDC decision problem is not particularly sensitive to the payoffs for the large complex decision alternative. We note, however, that this sensitivity analysis has been conducted based on only one change at a time. That is, only one payoff was changed and the probabilities for the states of nature remained $P(s_1) = 0.8$ and $P(s_2) = 0.2$. Note that similar sensitivity analysis calculations can be made for the payoffs associated with the small complex decision alternative $d_1$ and the medium complex decision alternative $d_2$. However, in these cases, decision alternative $d_3$ remains optimal only if the changes in the payoffs for decision alternatives $d_1$ and $d_2$ meet the requirements that $EV(d_1) \leq 14.2$ and $EV(d_2) \leq 14.2$.

*Sensitivity analysis can assist management in deciding whether more time and effort should be spent obtaining better estimates of payoffs and probabilities.*

## NOTES AND COMMENTS

1. Some decision analysis software automatically provides the risk profiles for the optimal decision alternative. These packages also allow the user to obtain the risk profiles for other decision alternatives. After comparing the risk profiles, a decision maker may decide to select a decision alternative with a good risk profile even though the expected value of the decision alternative is not as good as the optimal decision alternative.

2. A *tornado diagram,* a graphical display, is particularly helpful when several inputs combine to determine the value of the optimal solution. By varying each input over its range of values, we obtain information about how each input affects the value of the optimal solution. To display this information, a bar is constructed for the input, with the width of the bar showing how the input affects the value of the optimal solution. The widest bar corresponds to the input that is most sensitive. The bars are arranged in a graph with the widest bar at the top, resulting in a graph that has the appearance of a tornado.

 **4.5** # Decision Analysis with Sample Information

In applying the expected value approach, we showed how probability information about the states of nature affects the expected value calculations and thus the decision recommendation. Frequently, decision makers have preliminary or **prior probability** assessments for the states of nature that are the best probability values available at that time. However, to make the best possible decision, the decision maker may want to seek additional information about the states of nature. This new information can be used to revise or update the prior probabilities so that the final decision is based on more accurate probabilities for the states of nature. Most often, additional information is obtained through experiments designed to provide **sample information** about the states of nature. Raw material sampling, product testing, and market research studies are examples of experiments (or studies) that may enable management to revise or update the state-of-nature probabilities. These revised probabilities are called **posterior probabilities**.

Let us return to the PDC problem and assume that management is considering a 6-month market research study designed to learn more about potential market acceptance of the PDC condominium project. Management anticipates that the market research study will provide one of the following two results:

1.  Favorable report: A substantial number of the individuals contacted express interest in purchasing a PDC condominium.
2.  Unfavorable report: Very few of the individuals contacted express interest in purchasing a PDC condominium.

## Influence Diagram

By introducing the possibility of conducting a market research study, the PDC problem becomes more complex. The influence diagram for the expanded PDC problem is shown in Figure 4.7. Note that the two decision nodes correspond to the research study and the complex-size decisions. The two chance nodes correspond to the research study results and demand for the condominiums. Finally, the consequence node is the profit. From the arcs of the influence diagram, we see that demand influences both the research study results and profit. Although demand is currently unknown to PDC, some level of demand for the condominiums already exists in the Pittsburgh area. If existing demand is strong, the research study is likely to find a substantial number of individuals who express an interest in purchasing a condominium. However, if the existing demand is weak, the research study is more likely to find a substantial number of individuals who express little interest in purchasing a condominium. In this sense, existing demand for the condominiums will influence the research study results, and clearly, demand will have an influence upon PDC's profit.

The arc from the research study decision node to the complex-size decision node indicates that the research study decision precedes the complex-size decision. No arc spans from the research study decision node to the research study results node because the decision to conduct the research study does not actually influence the research study results. The decision to conduct the research study makes the research study results available, but it does not influence the results of the research study. Finally, the complex-size node and

**FIGURE 4.7**   INFLUENCE DIAGRAM FOR THE PDC PROBLEM WITH SAMPLE INFORMATION

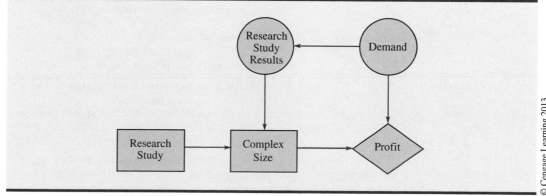

the demand node both influence profit. Note that if a stated cost to conduct the research study were given, the decision to conduct the research study would also influence profit. In such a case, we would need to add an arc from the research study decision node to the profit node to show the influence that the research study cost would have on profit.

## Decision Tree

The decision tree for the PDC problem with sample information shows the logical sequence for the decisions and the chance events in Figure 4.8.

First, PDC's management must decide whether the market research should be conducted. If it is conducted, PDC's management must be prepared to make a decision about the size of the condominium project if the market research report is favorable and, possibly, a different decision about the size of the condominium project if the market research report is unfavorable. In Figure 4.8, the squares are decision nodes and the circles are chance nodes. At each decision node, the branch of the tree that is taken is based on the decision made. At each chance node, the branch of the tree that is taken is based on probability or chance. For example, decision node 1 shows that PDC must first make the decision of whether to conduct the market research study. If the market research study is undertaken, chance node 2 indicates that both the favorable report branch and the unfavorable report branch are not under PDC's control and will be determined by chance. Node 3 is a decision node, indicating that PDC must make the decision to construct the small, medium, or large complex if the market research report is favorable. Node 4 is a decision node showing that PDC must make the decision to construct the small, medium, or large complex if the market research report is unfavorable. Node 5 is a decision node indicating that PDC must make the decision to construct the small, medium, or large complex if the market research is not undertaken. Nodes 6 to 14 are chance nodes indicating that the strong demand or weak demand state-of-nature branches will be determined by chance.

Analysis of the decision tree and the choice of an optimal strategy require that we know the branch probabilities corresponding to all chance nodes. PDC has developed the following branch probabilities:

If the market research study is undertaken

*We explain in Section 4.6 how the branch probabilities for P(Favorable report) and P(Unfavorable report) can be developed.*

$$P(\text{Favorable report}) = 0.77$$
$$P(\text{Unfavorable report}) = 0.23$$

If the market research report is favorable

$$P(\text{Strong demand given a favorable report}) = 0.94$$
$$P(\text{Weak demand given a favorable report}) = 0.06$$

If the market research report is unfavorable

$$P(\text{Strong demand given a favorable report}) = 0.35$$
$$P(\text{Weak demand given a favorable report}) = 0.65$$

If the market research report is not undertaken, the prior probabilities are applicable.

$$P(\text{Strong demand}) = 0.80$$
$$P(\text{Weak demand}) = 0.20$$

The branch probabilities are shown on the decision tree in Figure 4.9.

**FIGURE 4.8** THE PDC DECISION TREE INCLUDING THE MARKET RESEARCH STUDY

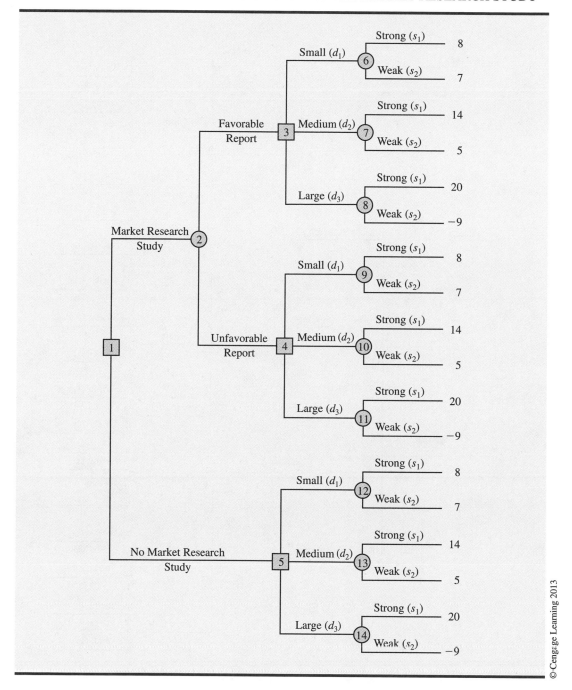

**FIGURE 4.9**    THE PDC DECISION TREE WITH BRANCH PROBABILITIES

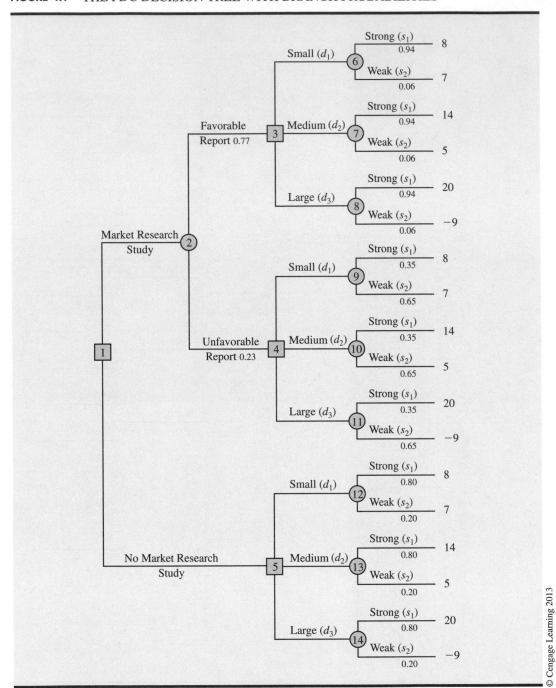

## Decision Strategy

A **decision strategy** is a sequence of decisions and chance outcomes where the decisions chosen depend on the yet-to-be-determined outcomes of chance events.

The approach used to determine the optimal decision strategy is based on a backward pass through the decision tree using the following steps:

**1.** At chance nodes, compute the expected value by multiplying the payoff at the end of each branch by the corresponding branch probabilities.
**2.** At decision nodes, select the decision branch that leads to the best expected value. This expected value becomes the expected value at the decision node.

Starting the backward pass calculations by computing the expected values at chance nodes 6 to 14 provides the following results:

$$EV(\text{Node } 6) = 0.94(8) + 0.06(7) \quad = 7.94$$
$$EV(\text{Node } 7) = 0.94(14) + 0.06(5) \quad = 13.46$$
$$EV(\text{Node } 8) = 0.94(20) + 0.06(-9) = 18.26$$
$$EV(\text{Node } 9) = 0.35(8) + 0.65(7) \quad = 7.35$$
$$EV(\text{Node } 10) = 0.35(14) + 0.65(5) \quad = 8.15$$
$$EV(\text{Node } 11) = 0.35(20) + 0.65(-9) = 1.15$$
$$EV(\text{Node } 12) = 0.80(8) + 0.20(7) \quad = 7.80$$
$$EV(\text{Node } 13) = 0.80(14) + 0.20(5) \quad = 12.20$$
$$EV(\text{Node } 14) = 0.80(20) + 0.20(-9) = 14.20$$

Figure 4.10 shows the reduced decision tree after computing expected values at these chance nodes.

Next, move to decision nodes 3, 4, and 5. For each of these nodes, we select the decision alternative branch that leads to the best expected value. For example, at node 3 we have the choice of the small complex branch with EV(Node 6) = 7.94, the medium complex branch with EV(Node 7) = 13.46, and the large complex branch with EV(Node 8) = 18.26. Thus, we select the large complex decision alternative branch and the expected value at node 3 becomes EV(Node 3) = 18.26.

For node 4, we select the best expected value from nodes 9, 10, and 11. The best decision alternative is the medium complex branch that provides EV(Node 4) = 8.15. For node 5, we select the best expected value from nodes 12, 13, and 14. The best decision alternative is the large complex branch that provides EV(Node 5) = 14.20. Figure 4.11 shows the reduced decision tree after choosing the best decisions at nodes 3, 4, and 5.

The expected value at chance node 2 can now be computed as follows:

$$EV(\text{Node } 2) = 0.77EV(\text{Node } 3) + 0.23EV(\text{Node } 4)$$
$$= 0.77(18.26) + 0.23(8.15) = 15.93$$

This calculation reduces the decision tree to one involving only the two decision branches from node 1 (see Figure 4.12).

Finally, the decision can be made at decision node 1 by selecting the best expected values from nodes 2 and 5. This action leads to the decision alternative to conduct the market research study, which provides an overall expected value of 15.93.

**FIGURE 4.10    PDC DECISION TREE AFTER COMPUTING EXPECTED VALUES AT CHANCE NODES 6 TO 14**

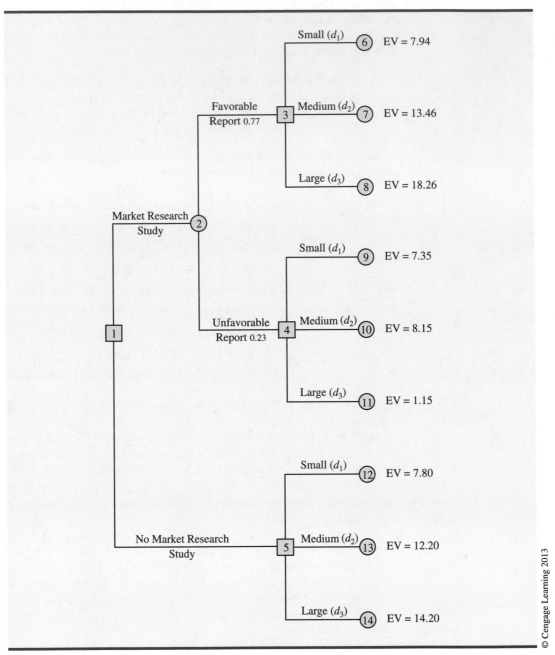

*Problem 16 will test your ability to develop an optimal decision strategy.*

The optimal decision for PDC is to conduct the market research study and then carry out the following decision strategy:

If the market research is favorable, construct the large condominium complex.

If the market research is unfavorable, construct the medium condominium complex.

**FIGURE 4.11**   PDC DECISION TREE AFTER CHOOSING BEST DECISIONS AT NODES 3, 4, AND 5

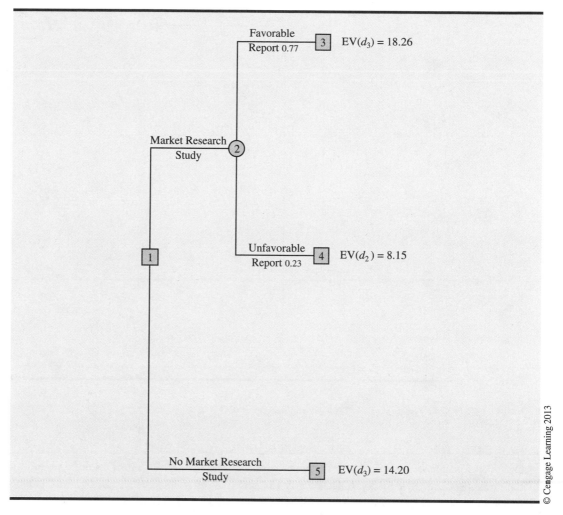

The analysis of the PDC decision tree describes the methods that can be used to analyze more complex sequential decision problems. First, draw a decision tree consisting of decision and chance nodes and branches that describe the sequential nature of the problem. Determine the probabilities for all chance outcomes. Then, by working backward through the tree, compute expected values at all chance nodes and select the best decision branch at all decision nodes. The sequence of optimal decision branches determines the optimal decision strategy for the problem.

The Q.M. in Action, New Drug Decision Analysis at Bayer Pharmaceuticals, describes how an extension of the decision analysis principles presented in this section enabled Bayer to make decisions about the development and marketing of a new drug.

## Risk Profile

Figure 4.13 provides a reduced decision tree showing only the sequence of decision alternatives and chance events for the PDC optimal decision strategy. By implementing the

**FIGURE 4.12**    PDC DECISION TREE REDUCED TO TWO DECISION BRANCHES

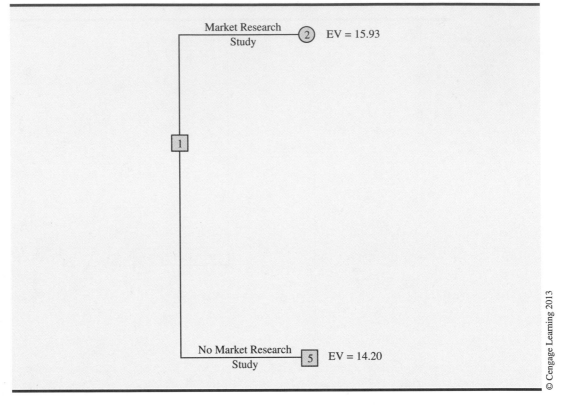

© Cengage Learning 2013

## NEW DRUG DECISION ANALYSIS AT BAYER PHARMACEUTICALS*

Drug development in the United States requires substantial investment and is very risky. It takes nearly 15 years to research and develop a new drug. The Bayer Biological Products (BP) group used decision analysis to evaluate the potential for a new blood-clot busting drug. An influence diagram was used to describe the complex structure of the decision analysis process. Six key yes-or-no decision nodes were identified: (1) begin preclinical development; (2) begin testing in humans; (3) continue development into phase 3; (4) continue development into phase 4; (5) file a license application with the FDA; and (6) launch the new drug into the marketplace. More than 50 chance nodes appeared in the influence diagram. The chance nodes showed how uncertainties—related to

factors such as direct labor costs, process development costs, market share, tax rate, and pricing—affected the outcome. Net present value provided the consequence and the decision-making criterion.

Probability assessments were made concerning both the technical risk and market risk at each stage of the process. The resulting sequential decision tree had 1955 possible paths that led to different net present value outcomes. Cost inputs, judgments of potential outcomes, and the assignment of probabilities helped evaluate the project's potential contribution. Sensitivity analysis was used to identify key variables that would require special attention by the project team and management during the drug development process. Application of decision analysis principles allowed Bayer to make good decisions about how to develop and market the new drug.

*Based on Jeffrey S. Stonebraker, "How Bayer Makes Decisions to Develop New Drugs," *Interfaces* no. 6 (November/December 2002): 77–90.

**FIGURE 4.13**   PDC DECISION TREE SHOWING ONLY BRANCHES ASSOCIATED WITH OPTIMAL DECISION STRATEGY

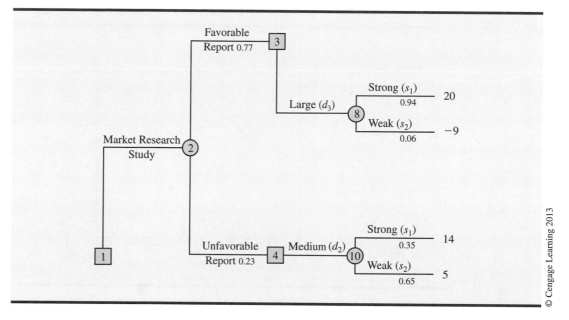

optimal decision strategy, PDC will obtain one of the four payoffs shown at the terminal branches of the decision tree. Recall that a risk profile shows the possible payoffs with their associated probabilities. Thus, in order to construct a risk profile for the optimal decision strategy, we will need to compute the probability for each of the four payoffs.

Note that each payoff results from a sequence of branches leading from node 1 to the payoff. For instance, the payoff of $20 million is obtained by following the upper branch from node 1, the upper branch from node 2, the lower branch from node 3, and the upper branch from node 8. The probability of following that sequence of branches can be found by multiplying the probabilities for the branches from the chance nodes in the sequence. Thus, the probability of the $20 million payoff is $(0.77)(0.94) = 0.72$. Similarly, the probabilities for each of the other payoffs are obtained by multiplying the probabilities for the branches from the chance nodes leading to the payoffs. By doing so, we find the probability of the $-$9 million payoff is $(0.77)(0.06) = 0.05$; the probability of the $14 million payoff is $(0.23)(0.35) = 0.08$; and the probability of the $5 million payoff is $(0.23)(0.65) = 0.15$. The following table showing the probability distribution for the payoffs for the PDC optimal decision strategy is the tabular representation of the risk profile for the optimal decision strategy.

| Payoff ($ millions) | Probability |
|---|---|
| −9 | 0.05 |
| 5 | 0.15 |
| 14 | 0.08 |
| 20 | 0.72 |
| | 1.00 |

Figure 4.14 provides a graphical representation of the risk profile. Comparing Figures 4.5 and 4.14, we see that the PDC risk profile is changed by the strategy to conduct the

**FIGURE 4.14**    RISK PROFILE FOR PDC CONDOMINIUM PROJECT WITH SAMPLE
INFORMATION SHOWING PAYOFFS ASSOCIATED WITH OPTIMAL
DECISION STRATEGY

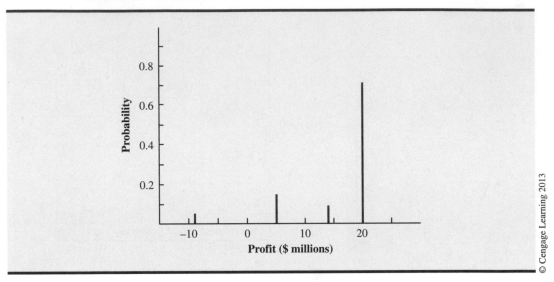

market research study. In fact, the use of the market research study lowered the probability
of the $9 million loss from 0.20 to 0.05. PDC's management would most likely view that
change as a considerable reduction in the risk associated with the condominium project.

## Expected Value of Sample Information

In the PDC problem, the market research study is the sample information used to determine
the optimal decision strategy. The expected value associated with the market research study
is $15.93. In Section 4.3 we showed that the best expected value if the market research study
is *not* undertaken is $14.20. Thus, we can conclude that the difference, $15.93 − $14.20 =
$1.73, is the **expected value of sample information (EVSI)**. In other words, conducting the
market research study adds $1.73 million to the PDC expected value. In general, the ex-
pected value of sample information is as follows:

$$EVSI = |EVwSI - EVwoSI| \qquad \textbf{(4.13)}$$

where

EVSI = expected value of sample information

EVwSI = expected value *with* sample information about the states of nature

EVwoSI = expected value *without* sample information about the states of nature

*The EVSI = $1.73 million
suggests PDC should be
willing to pay up to $1.73
million to conduct the
market research study.*

Note the role of the absolute value in equation (4.13). For minimization problems, the expected value with sample information is always less than or equal to the expected value without sample information. In this case, EVSI is the magnitude of the difference between EVwSI
and EVwoSI; thus, by taking the absolute value of the difference as shown in equation (4.13),
we can handle both the maximization and minimization cases with one equation.

## Efficiency of Sample Information

In Section 4.3 we showed that the expected value of perfect information (EVPI) for the PDC problem is $3.2 million. We never anticipated that the market research report would obtain perfect information, but we can use an **efficiency** measure to express the value of the market research information. With perfect information having an efficiency rating of 100%, the efficiency rating E for sample information is computed as follows:

$$E = \frac{EVSI}{EVPI} \times 100 \qquad\qquad \textbf{(4.14)}$$

For the PDC problem,

$$E = \frac{1.73}{3.2} \times 100 = 54.1\%$$

In other words, the information from the market research study is 54.1% as efficient as perfect information.

Low efficiency ratings for sample information might lead the decision maker to look for other types of information. However, high efficiency ratings indicate that the sample information is almost as good as perfect information and that additional sources of information would not yield substantially better results.

# Computing Branch Probabilities

In Section 4.5 the branch probabilities for the PDC decision tree chance nodes were specified in the problem description. No computations were required to determine these probabilities. In this section we show how **Bayes' theorem** can be used to compute branch probabilities for decision trees.

The PDC decision tree is shown again in Figure 4.15. Let

$$F = \text{Favorable market research report}$$
$$U = \text{Unfavorable market research report}$$
$$s_1 = \text{Strong demand (state of nature 1)}$$
$$s_2 = \text{Weak demand (state of nature 2)}$$

At chance node 2, we need to know the branch probabilities $P(F)$ and $P(U)$. At chance nodes 6, 7, and 8, we need to know the branch probabilities $P(s_1 \mid F)$, the probability of state of nature 1 given a favorable market research report, and $P(s_2 \mid F)$, the probability of state of nature 2 given a favorable market research report. $P(s_1 \mid F)$ and $P(s_2 \mid F)$ are referred to as *posterior probabilities* because they are conditional probabilities based on the outcome of the sample information. At chance nodes 9, 10, and 11, we need to know the branch probabilities $P(s_1 \mid U)$ and $P(s_2 \mid U)$; note that these are also posterior probabilities, denoting the probabilities of the two states of nature *given* that the market research report is unfavorable. Finally, at chance nodes 12, 13, and 14, we need the probabilities for the states of nature, $P(s_1)$ and $P(s_2)$, if the market research study is not undertaken.

In performing the probability computations, we need to know PDC's assessment of the probabilities for the two states of nature, $P(s_1)$ and $P(s_2)$, which are the prior probabilities as discussed earlier. In addition, we must know the **conditional probability** of the market

**FIGURE 4.15   THE PDC DECISION TREE**

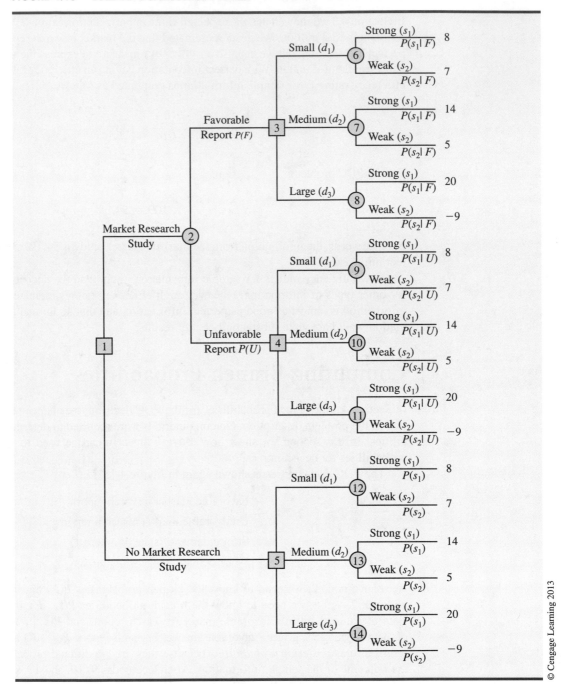

research outcomes (the sample information) *given* each state of nature. For example, we need to know the conditional probability of a favorable market research report given that the state of nature is strong demand for the PDC project; note that this conditional probability of $F$ given state of nature $s_1$ is written $P(F \mid s_1)$. To carry out the probability calculations, we will need conditional probabilities for all sample outcomes given all states of nature, that is, $P(F \mid s_1)$, $P(F \mid s_2)$, $P(U \mid s_1)$, and $P(U \mid s_2)$. In the PDC problem we assume that the following assessments are available for these conditional probabilities:

| State of Nature | Market Research | |
|---|---|---|
| | Favorable, $F$ | Unfavorable, $U$ |
| Strong demand, $s_1$ | $P(F \mid s_1) = 0.90$ | $P(U \mid s_1) = 0.10$ |
| Weak demand, $s_2$ | $P(F \mid s_2) = 0.25$ | $P(U \mid s_2) = 0.75$ |

*A favorable market research report given that the state of nature is weak demand is often referred to as a "false positive," while the converse (an unfavorable market research report given that the state of nature is strong demand) is referred to as a "false negative."*

Note that the preceding probability assessments provide a reasonable degree of confidence in the market research study. If the true state of nature is $s_1$, the probability of a favorable market research report is 0.90, and the probability of an unfavorable market research report is 0.10. If the true state of nature is $s_2$, the probability of a favorable market research report is 0.25, and the probability of an unfavorable market research report is 0.75. The reason for a 0.25 probability of a potentially misleading favorable market research report for state of nature $s_2$ is that when some potential buyers first hear about the new condominium project, their enthusiasm may lead them to overstate their real interest in it. A potential buyer's initial favorable response can change quickly to a "no thank you" when later faced with the reality of signing a purchase contract and making a down payment.

In the following discussion we present a tabular approach as a convenient method for carrying out the probability computations. The computations for the PDC problem based on a favorable market research report ($F$) are summarized in Table 4.7. The steps used to develop this table are as follows:

**Step 1.** In column 1 enter the states of nature. In column 2 enter the *prior probabilities* for the states of nature. In column 3 enter the *conditional probabilities* of a favorable market research report ($F$) given each state of nature.

**Step 2.** In column 4 compute the **joint probabilities** by multiplying the prior probability values in column 2 by the corresponding conditional probability values in column 3.

**Step 3.** Sum the joint probabilities in column 4 to obtain the probability of a favorable market research report, $P(F)$.

**Step 4.** Divide each joint probability in column 4 by $P(F) = 0.77$ to obtain the revised or *posterior probabilities,* $P(s_1 \mid F)$ and $P(s_2 \mid F)$.

Table 4.7 shows that the probability of obtaining a favorable market research report is $P(F) = 0.77$. In addition, $P(s_1 \mid F) = 0.94$ and $P(s_2 \mid F) = 0.06$. In particular, note that a

**TABLE 4.7** BRANCH PROBABILITIES FOR THE PDC CONDOMINIUM PROJECT BASED ON A FAVORABLE MARKET RESEARCH REPORT

| States of Nature $s_j$ | Prior Probabilities $P(s_j)$ | Conditional Probabilities $P(F \mid s_j)$ | Joint Probabilities $P(F \cap s_j)$ | Posterior Probabilities $P(s_j \mid F)$ |
|---|---|---|---|---|
| $s_1$ | 0.8 | 0.90 | 0.72 | 0.94 |
| $s_2$ | 0.2 | 0.25 | 0.05 | 0.06 |
| | 1.0 | | $P(F) = 0.77$ | 1.00 |

**TABLE 4.8**    BRANCH PROBABILITIES FOR THE PDC CONDOMINIUM PROJECT BASED ON AN UNFAVORABLE MARKET RESEARCH REPORT

| States of Nature $s_j$ | Prior Probabilities $P(s_j)$ | Conditional Probabilities $P(U \mid s_j)$ | Joint Probabilities $P(U \cup s_j)$ | Posterior Probabilities $P(s_j \mid U)$ |
|---|---|---|---|---|
| $s_1$ | 0.8 | 0.10 | 0.08 | 0.35 |
| $s_2$ | 0.2 | 0.75 | 0.15 | 0.65 |
|  | 1.0 |  | $P(U) = 0.23$ | 1.00 |

© Cengage Learning 2013

*Problem 23 asks you to compute the posterior probabilities.*

favorable market research report will prompt a revised or posterior probability of 0.94 that the market demand of the condominium will be strong, $s_1$.

The tabular probability computation procedure must be repeated for each possible sample information outcome. Table 4.8 shows the computations of the branch probabilities of the PDC problem based on an unfavorable market research report. Note that the probability of obtaining an unfavorable market research report is $P(U) = 0.23$. If an unfavorable report is obtained, the posterior probability of a strong market demand, $s_1$, is 0.35 and of a weak market demand, $s_2$, is 0.65. The branch probabilities from Tables 4.7 and 4.8 were shown on the PDC decision tree in Figure 4.9.

The discussion in this section shows an underlying relationship between the probabilities on the various branches in a decision tree. To assume different prior probabilities, $P(s_1)$ and $P(s_2)$, without determining how these changes would alter $P(F)$ and $P(U)$, as well as the posterior probabilities $P(s_1 \mid F)$, $P(s_2 \mid F)$, $P(s_1 \mid U)$, and $P(s_2 \mid U)$, would be inappropriate.

The Q.M. in Action, Decision Analysis Helps Treat and Prevent Hepatitis B, discusses how medical researchers use posterior probability information and decision analysis to understand the risks and costs associated with treatment and screening procedures.

## Q.M. *in* ACTION

### DECISION ANALYSIS HELPS TREAT AND PREVENT HEPATITIS B*

Hepatitis B is a viral disease that left untreated can lead to fatal liver conditions such as cirrhosis and cancer. The hepatitis B virus can be treated, and there exists a vaccine to prevent it. However, in order to make economically prudent allocations of their limited health care budgets, public health officials require analysis on the cost effectiveness (health benefit per dollar investment) of any potential health program. Unfortunately, since hepatitis B is a slow-progressing condition whose victims are often

unaware of their potentially fatal infection, gathering data on the benefits of any public health policy addressing hepatitis B would take decades.

A multidisciplinary team consisting of management science researchers and a liver transplant surgeon from Stanford University applied decision analysis techniques to determine which combination of hepatitis B screening, treatment, and vaccination would be appropriate in the United States. Their decision tree contained the sequential decisions of: (1) whether or not to perform a blood test to screen an individual for a hepatitis B

*David W. Hutton, Margaret L. Brandeau, and Samuel K. So, "Doing Good With Good OR: Supporting Cost-Effective Hepatitis B Interventions," *Interfaces* May/June 2011 41:289–300.

*(continued)*

infection, (2) whether or not to treat infected individuals, and (3) whether or not to vaccinate a noninfected (or nonscreened) individual.

For each policy, composed of a sequence of screening, treatment, and vaccination decisions, the researchers utilized existing infection and treatment knowledge to model future disease progression. Implementing their decision model in an Excel spreadsheet, the researchers concluded that it is cost effective to screen adult Asian and Pacific Islanders so that infected individuals can be treated (these individuals are genetically at a high risk for hepatitis B infection). Although it is not cost effective to universally vaccinate all U.S. adult Asian and Pacific Islanders, it proves to be cost effective to vaccinate people in close contact with infected individuals. Influenced by these findings, the Centers for Disease Control updated its official policy in 2008 to recommend screening all adult Asian and Pacific Islanders and all adults in areas of intermediate (2 to 7%) hepatitis B prevalence.

## Summary

Decision analysis can be used to determine a recommended decision alternative or an optimal decision strategy when a decision maker is faced with an uncertain and risk-filled pattern of future events. The goal of decision analysis is to identify the best decision alternative or the optimal decision strategy given information about the uncertain events and the possible consequences or payoffs. The uncertain future events are called chance events, and the outcomes of the chance events are called states of nature.

We showed how influence diagrams, payoff tables, and decision trees could be used to structure a decision problem and describe the relationships among the decisions, the chance events, and the consequences. We presented three approaches to decision making without probabilities: the optimistic approach, the conservative approach, and the minimax regret approach. When probability assessments are provided for the states of nature, the expected value approach can be used to identify the recommended decision alternative or decision strategy.

In cases where sample information about the chance events is available, a sequence of decisions has to be made. First we must decide whether to obtain the sample information. If the answer to this decision is yes, an optimal decision strategy based on the specific sample information must be developed. In this situation, decision trees and the expected value approach can be used to determine the optimal decision strategy.

Even though the expected value approach can be used to obtain a recommended decision alternative or optimal decision strategy, the payoff that actually occurs will usually have a value different from the expected value. A risk profile provides a probability distribution for the possible payoffs and can assist the decision maker in assessing the risks associated with different decision alternatives. Finally, sensitivity analysis can be conducted to determine the effect changes in the probabilities for the states of nature and changes in the values of the payoffs have on the recommended decision alternative.

## Glossary

**Decision alternatives**  Options available to the decision maker.

**Chance event**  An uncertain future event affecting the consequence, or payoff, associated with a decision.

**Consequence**  The result obtained when a decision alternative is chosen and a chance event occurs. A measure of the consequence is often called a payoff.

**States of nature**  The possible outcomes for chance events that affect the payoff associated with a decision alternative.

**Influence diagram**  A graphical device that shows the relationship among decisions, chance events, and consequences for a decision problem.

**Node**  An intersection or junction point of an influence diagram or a decision tree.

**Decision nodes**  Nodes indicating points where a decision is made.

**Chance nodes**  Nodes indicating points where an uncertain event will occur.

**Consequence nodes**  Nodes of an influence diagram indicating points where a payoff will occur.

**Payoff**  A measure of the consequence of a decision such as profit, cost, or time. Each combination of a decision alternative and a state of nature has an associated payoff (consequence).

**Payoff table**  A tabular representation of the payoffs for a decision problem.

**Decision tree**  A graphical representation of the decision problem that shows the sequential nature of the decision-making process.

**Branch**  Lines showing the alternatives from decision nodes and the outcomes from chance nodes.

**Optimistic approach**  An approach to choosing a decision alternative without using probabilities. For a maximization problem, it leads to choosing the decision alternative corresponding to the largest payoff; for a minimization problem, it leads to choosing the decision alternative corresponding to the smallest payoff.

**Conservative approach**  An approach to choosing a decision alternative without using probabilities. For a maximization problem, it leads to choosing the decision alternative that maximizes the minimum payoff; for a minimization problem, it leads to choosing the decision alternative that minimizes the maximum payoff.

**Opportunity loss, or regret**  The amount of loss (lower profit or higher cost) from not making the best decision for each state of nature.

**Minimax regret approach**  An approach to choosing a decision alternative without using probabilities. For each alternative, the maximum regret is computed, which leads to choosing the decision alternative that minimizes the maximum regret.

**Expected value approach**  An approach to choosing a decision alternative based on the expected value of each decision alternative. The recommended decision alternative is the one that provides the best expected value.

**Expected value (EV)**  For a chance node, it is the weighted average of the payoffs. The weights are the state-of-nature probabilities.

**Expected value of perfect information (EVPI)**  The expected value of information that would tell the decision maker exactly which state of nature is going to occur (i.e., perfect information).

**Risk analysis**  The study of the possible payoffs and probabilities associated with a decision alternative or a decision strategy.

**Sensitivity analysis**  The study of how changes in the probability assessments for the states of nature or changes in the payoffs affect the recommended decision alternative.

**Risk profile**  The probability distribution of the possible payoffs associated with a decision alternative or decision strategy.

**Prior probabilities**  The probabilities of the states of nature prior to obtaining sample information.

**Sample information**  New information obtained through research or experimentation that enables an updating or revision of the state-of-nature probabilities.

**Posterior (revised) probabilities**  The probabilities of the states of nature after revising the prior probabilities based on sample information.

Decision strategy A strategy involving a sequence of decisions and chance outcomes to provide the optimal solution to a decision problem.

Expected value of sample information (EVSI) The difference between the expected value of an optimal strategy based on sample information and the "best" expected value without any sample information.

Efficiency The ratio of EVSI to EVPI as a percentage; perfect information is 100% efficient.

Bayes' theorem A theorem that enables the use of sample information to revise prior probabilities.

Conditional probabilities The probability of one event given the known outcome of a (possibly) related event.

Joint probabilities The probabilities of both sample information and a particular state of nature occurring simultaneously.

## Problems

1. The following payoff table shows profit for a decision analysis problem with two decision alternatives and three states of nature:

|  | State of Nature | | |
| --- | --- | --- | --- |
| Decision Alternative | $s_1$ | $s_2$ | $s_3$ |
| $d_1$ | 250 | 100 | 25 |
| $d_2$ | 100 | 100 | 75 |

   a. Construct a decision tree for this problem.
   b. If the decision maker knows nothing about the probabilities of the three states of nature, what is the recommended decision using the optimistic, conservative, and minimax regret approaches?

2. Suppose that a decision maker faced with four decision alternatives and four states of nature develops the following profit payoff table:

|  | State of Nature | | | |
| --- | --- | --- | --- | --- |
| Decision Alternative | $s_1$ | $s_2$ | $s_3$ | $s_4$ |
| $d_1$ | 14 | 9 | 10 | 5 |
| $d_2$ | 11 | 10 | 8 | 7 |
| $d_3$ | 9 | 10 | 10 | 11 |
| $d_4$ | 8 | 10 | 11 | 13 |

   a. If the decision maker knows nothing about the probabilities of the four states of nature, what is the recommended decision using the optimistic, conservative, and minimax regret approaches?
   b. Which approach do you prefer? Explain. Is establishing the most appropriate approach before analyzing the problem important for the decision maker? Explain.
   c. Assume that the payoff table provides *cost* rather than profit payoffs. What is the recommended decision using the optimistic, conservative, and minimax regret approaches?

3. Southland Corporation's decision to produce a new line of recreational products resulted in the need to construct either a small plant or a large plant. The best selection of plant size depends on how the marketplace reacts to the new product line. To conduct an analysis, marketing management has decided to view the possible long-run demand as low, medium, or high. The following payoff table shows the projected profit in millions of dollars:

|            | Long-Run Demand | | |
| Plant Size | Low | Medium | High |
|---|---|---|---|
| Small | 150 | 200 | 200 |
| Large | 50 | 200 | 500 |

a. What is the decision to be made, and what is the chance event for Southland's problem?
b. Construct an influence diagram.
c. Construct a decision tree.
d. Recommend a decision based on the use of the optimistic, conservative, and minimax regret approaches.

4. Amy Lloyd is interested in leasing a new Honda and has contacted three automobile dealers for pricing information. Each dealer offered Amy a closed-end 36-month lease with no down payment due at the time of signing. Each lease includes a monthly charge and a mileage allowance. Additional miles receive a surcharge on a per-mile basis. The monthly lease cost, the mileage allowance, and the cost for additional miles follow:

| Dealer | Monthly Cost | Mileage Allowance | Cost per Additional Mile |
|---|---|---|---|
| Hepburn Honda | $299 | 36,000 | $0.15 |
| Midtown Motors | $310 | 45,000 | $0.20 |
| Hopkins Automotive | $325 | 54,000 | $0.15 |

Amy decided to choose the lease option that will minimize her total 36-month cost. The difficulty is that Amy is not sure how many miles she will drive over the next three years. For purposes of this decision, she believes it is reasonable to assume that she will drive 12,000 miles per year, 15,000 miles per year, or 18,000 miles per year. With this assumption Amy estimated her total costs for the three lease options. For example, she figures that the Hepburn Honda lease will cost her $10,764 if she drives 12,000 miles per year, $12,114 if she drives 15,000 miles per year, or $13,464 if she drives 18,000 miles per year.

a. What is the decision, and what is the chance event?
b. Construct a payoff table for Amy's problem.
c. If Amy has no idea which of the three mileage assumptions is most appropriate, what is the recommended decision (leasing option) using the optimistic, conservative, and minimax regret approaches?
d. Suppose that the probabilities that Amy drives 12,000, 15,000, and 18,000 miles per year are 0.5, 0.4, and 0.1, respectively. What option should Amy choose using the expected value approach?
e. Develop a risk profile for the decision selected in part (d). What is the most likely cost, and what is its probability?
f. Suppose that after further consideration Amy concludes that the probabilities that she will drive 12,000, 15,000, and 18,000 miles per year are 0.3, 0.4, and 0.3, respectively. What decision should Amy make using the expected value approach?

5. The following profit payoff table was presented in Problem 1. Suppose that the decision maker obtained the probability assessments $P(s_1) = 0.65$, $P(s_2) = 0.15$, and $P(s_3) = 0.20$. Use the expected value approach to determine the optimal decision.

| Decision Alternative | State of Nature | | |
| --- | --- | --- | --- |
| | $s_1$ | $s_2$ | $s_3$ |
| $d_1$ | 250 | 100 | 25 |
| $d_2$ | 100 | 100 | 75 |

6. Investment advisors estimated the stock market returns for four market segments: computers, financial, manufacturing, and pharmaceuticals. Annual return projections vary depending on whether the general economic conditions are improving, stable, or declining. The anticipated annual return percentages for each market segment under each economic condition are as follows:

| Market Segment | Economic Condition | | |
| --- | --- | --- | --- |
| | Improving | Stable | Declining |
| Computers | 10 | 2 | −4 |
| Financial | 8 | 5 | −3 |
| Manufacturing | 6 | 4 | −2 |
| Pharmaceuticals | 6 | 5 | −1 |

a. Assume that an individual investor wants to select one market segment for a new investment. A forecast shows stable to declining economic conditions with the following probabilities: improving (0.2), stable (0.5), and declining (0.3). What is the preferred market segment for the investor, and what is the expected return percentage?

b. At a later date, a revised forecast shows a potential for an improvement in economic conditions. New probabilities are as follows: improving (0.4), stable (0.4), and declining (0.2). What is the preferred market segment for the investor based on these new probabilities? What is the expected return percentage?

7. Hudson Corporation is considering three options for managing its data processing operation: continuing with its own staff, hiring an outside vendor to do the managing (referred to as *outsourcing*), or using a combination of its own staff and an outside vendor. The cost of the operation depends on future demand. The annual cost of each option (in thousands of dollars) depends on demand as follows:

| Staffing Options | Demand | | |
| --- | --- | --- | --- |
| | High | Medium | Low |
| Own staff | 650 | 650 | 600 |
| Outside vendor | 900 | 600 | 300 |
| Combination | 800 | 650 | 500 |

a. If the demand probabilities are 0.2, 0.5, and 0.3, which decision alternative will minimize the expected cost of the data processing operation? What is the expected annual cost associated with that recommendation?

b. Construct a risk profile for the optimal decision in part (a). What is the probability of the cost exceeding $700,000?

8.  The following payoff table shows the profit for a decision problem with two states of nature and two decision alternatives:

| | State of Nature | |
|---|---|---|
| Decision Alternative | $s_1$ | $s_2$ |
| $d_1$ | 10 | 1 |
| $d_2$ | 4 | 3 |

a.  Use graphical sensitivity analysis to determine the range of probabilities of state of nature $s_1$ for which each of the decision alternatives has the largest expected value.
b.  Suppose $P(s_1) = 0.2$ and $P(s_2) = 0.8$. What is the best decision using the expected value approach?
c.  Perform sensitivity analysis on the payoffs for decision alternative $d_1$. Assume the probabilities are as given in part (b), and find the range of payoffs under states of nature $s_1$ and $s_2$ that will keep the solution found in part (b) optimal. Is the solution more sensitive to the payoff under state of nature $s_1$ or $s_2$?

9.  Myrtle Air Express decided to offer direct service from Cleveland to Myrtle Beach. Management must decide between a full-price service using the company's new fleet of jet aircraft and a discount service using smaller capacity commuter planes. It is clear that the best choice depends on the market reaction to the service Myrtle Air offers. Management developed estimates of the contribution to profit for each type of service based upon two possible levels of demand for service to Myrtle Beach: strong and weak. The following table shows the estimated quarterly profits (in thousands of dollars):

| | Demand for Service | |
|---|---|---|
| Service | Strong | Weak |
| Full price | $960 | −$490 |
| Discount | $670 | $320 |

a.  What is the decision to be made, what is the chance event, and what is the consequence for this problem? How many decision alternatives are there? How many outcomes are there for the chance event?
b.  If nothing is known about the probabilities of the chance outcomes, what is the recommended decision using the optimistic, conservative, and minimax regret approaches?
c.  Suppose that management of Myrtle Air Express believes that the probability of strong demand is 0.7 and the probability of weak demand is 0.3. Use the expected value approach to determine an optimal decision.
d.  Suppose that the probability of strong demand is 0.8 and the probability of weak demand is 0.2. What is the optimal decision using the expected value approach?
e.  Use graphical sensitivity analysis to determine the range of demand probabilities for which each of the decision alternatives has the largest expected value.

10. Video Tech is considering marketing one of two new video games for the coming holiday season: Battle Pacific or Space Pirates. Battle Pacific is a unique game and appears to have no competition. Estimated profits (in thousands of dollars) under high, medium, and low demand are as follows:

| | Demand | | |
|---|---|---|---|
| Battle Pacific | High | Medium | Low |
| Profit | $1000 | $700 | $300 |
| Probability | 0.2 | 0.5 | 0.3 |

Video Tech is optimistic about its Space Pirates game. However, the concern is that profitability will be affected by a competitor's introduction of a video game viewed as similar to Space Pirates. Estimated profits (in thousands of dollars) with and without competition are as follows:

| Space Pirates with Competition | Demand | | |
|---|---|---|---|
| | **High** | **Medium** | **Low** |
| Profit | $800 | $400 | $200 |
| Probability | 0.3 | 0.4 | 0.3 |

| Space Pirates without Competition | Demand | | |
|---|---|---|---|
| | **High** | **Medium** | **Low** |
| Profit | $1600 | $800 | $400 |
| Probability | 0.5 | 0.3 | 0.2 |

a. Develop a decision tree for the Video Tech problem.
b. For planning purposes, Video Tech believes there is a 0.6 probability that its competitor will produce a new game similar to Space Pirates. Given this probability of competition, the director of planning recommends marketing the Battle Pacific video game. Using expected value, what is your recommended decision?
c. Show a risk profile for your recommended decision.
d. Use sensitivity analysis to determine what the probability of competition for Space Pirates would have to be for you to change your recommended decision alternative.

11. For the Pittsburgh Development Corporation problem in Section 4.3, the decision alternative to build the large condominium complex was found to be optimal using the expected value approach. In Section 4.4 we conducted a sensitivity analysis for the payoffs associated with this decision alternative. We found that the large complex remained optimal as long as the payoff for the strong demand was greater than or equal to $17.5 million and as long as the payoff for the weak demand was greater than or equal to −$19 million.
   a. Consider the medium complex decision. How much could the payoff under strong demand increase and still keep decision alternative $d_3$ the optimal solution?
   b. Consider the small complex decision. How much could the payoff under strong demand increase and still keep decision alternative $d_3$ the optimal solution?

12. The distance from Potsdam to larger markets and limited air service have hindered the town in attracting new industry. Air Express, a major overnight delivery service, is considering establishing a regional distribution center in Potsdam. However, Air Express will not establish the center unless the length of the runway at the local airport is increased. Another candidate for new development is Diagnostic Research, Inc. (DRI), a leading producer of medical testing equipment. DRI is considering building a new manufacturing plant. Increasing the length of the runway is not a requirement for DRI, but the planning commission feels that doing so will help convince DRI to locate its new plant in Potsdam. Assuming that the town lengthens the runway, the Potsdam planning commission believes that the probabilities shown in the following table are applicable.

| | **DRI Plant** | **No DRI Plant** |
|---|---|---|
| Air Express Center | 0.30 | 0.10 |
| No Air Express Center | 0.40 | 0.20 |

For instance, the probability that Air Express will establish a distribution center and DRI will build a plant is 0.30.

The estimated annual revenue to the town, after deducting the cost of lengthening the runway, is as follows:

|  | DRI Plant | No DRI Plant |
|---|---|---|
| Air Express Center | $600,000 | $150,000 |
| No Air Express Center | $250,000 | −$200,000 |

If the runway expansion project is not conducted, the planning commission assesses the probability that DRI will locate its new plant in Potsdam at 0.6; in this case, the estimated annual revenue to the town will be $450,000. If the runway expansion project is not conducted and DRI does not locate in Potsdam, the annual revenue will be $0 because no cost will have been incurred and no revenues will be forthcoming.

a. What is the decision to be made, what is the chance event, and what is the consequence?

b. Compute the expected annual revenue associated with the decision alternative to lengthen the runway.

c. Compute the expected annual revenue associated with the decision alternative not to lengthen the runway.

d. Should the town elect to lengthen the runway? Explain.

e. Suppose that the probabilities associated with lengthening the runway were as follows:

|  | DRI Plant | No DRI Plant |
|---|---|---|
| Air Express Center | 0.40 | 0.10 |
| No Air Express Center | 0.30 | 0.20 |

What effect, if any, would this change in the probabilities have on the recommended decision?

13. Seneca Hill Winery recently purchased land for the purpose of establishing a new vineyard. Management is considering two varieties of white grapes for the new vineyard: Chardonnay and Riesling. The Chardonnay grapes would be used to produce a dry Chardonnay wine, and the Riesling grapes would be used to produce a semidry Riesling wine. It takes approximately four years from the time of planting before new grapes can be harvested. This length of time creates a great deal of uncertainty concerning future demand and makes the decision about the type of grapes to plant difficult. Three possibilities are being considered: Chardonnay grapes only; Riesling grapes only; and both Chardonnay and Riesling grapes. Seneca management decided that for planning purposes it would be adequate to consider only two demand possibilities for each type of wine: strong or weak. With two possibilities for each type of wine, it was necessary to assess four probabilities. With the help of some forecasts in industry publications, management made the following probability assessments:

|  | Riesling Demand | |
|---|---|---|
| Chardonnay Demand | Weak | Strong |
| Weak | 0.05 | 0.50 |
| Strong | 0.25 | 0.20 |

Revenue projections show an annual contribution to profit of $20,000 if Seneca Hill only plants Chardonnay grapes and demand is weak for Chardonnay wine, and $70,000 if Seneca only plants Chardonnay grapes and demand is strong for Chardonnay wine. If Seneca only plants Riesling grapes, the annual profit projection is $25,000 if demand is weak for Riesling grapes and $45,000 if demand is strong for Riesling grapes. If Seneca plants both types of grapes, the annual profit projections are shown in the following table:

| Chardonnay Demand | Riesling Demand | |
|---|---|---|
| | **Weak** | **Strong** |
| Weak | $22,000 | $40,000 |
| Strong | $26,000 | $60,000 |

a.  What is the decision to be made, what is the chance event, and what is the consequence? Identify the alternatives for the decisions and the possible outcomes for the chance events.
b.  Develop a decision tree.
c.  Use the expected value approach to recommend which alternative Seneca Hill Winery should follow in order to maximize expected annual profit.
d.  Suppose management is concerned about the probability assessments when demand for Chardonnay wine is strong. Some believe it is likely for Riesling demand to also be strong in this case. Suppose the probability of strong demand for Chardonnay and weak demand for Riesling is 0.05 and that the probability of strong demand for Chardonnay and strong demand for Riesling is 0.40. How does this change the recommended decision? Assume that the probabilities when Chardonnay demand is weak are still 0.05 and 0.50.
e.  Other members of the management team expect the Chardonnay market to become saturated at some point in the future, causing a fall in prices. Suppose that the annual profit projections fall to $50,000 when demand for Chardonnay is strong and Chardonnay grapes only are planted. Using the original probability assessments, determine how this change would affect the optimal decision.

14. The following profit payoff table was presented in Problem 1:

| Decision Alternative | State of Nature | | |
|---|---|---|---|
| | $s_1$ | $s_2$ | $s_3$ |
| $d_1$ | 250 | 100 | 25 |
| $d_2$ | 100 | 100 | 75 |

The probabilities for the states of nature are $P(s_1) = 0.65$, $P(s_2) = 0.15$, and $P(s_3) = 0.20$.
a.  What is the optimal decision strategy if perfect information were available?
b.  What is the expected value for the decision strategy developed in part (a)?
c.  Using the expected value approach, what is the recommended decision without perfect information? What is its expected value?
d.  What is the expected value of perfect information?

15. The Lake Placid Town Council decided to build a new community center to be used for conventions, concerts, and other public events, but considerable controversy surrounds the appropriate size. Many influential citizens want a large center that would be a showcase for the area. But the mayor feels that if demand does not support such a center, the community will lose a large amount of money. To provide structure for the decision process, the council narrowed the building alternatives to three sizes: small, medium, and large. Everybody agreed that the critical factor in choosing the best size is the number of people who will want to use the new facility. A regional planning consultant provided demand estimates under three scenarios: worst case, base case, and best case. The worst-case scenario

corresponds to a situation in which tourism drops substantially; the base-case scenario cor-responds to a situation in which Lake Placid continues to attract visitors at current levels; and the best-case scenario corresponds to a substantial increase in tourism. The consultant has provided probability assessments of 0.10, 0.60, and 0.30 for the worst-case, base-case, and best-case scenarios, respectively.

The town council suggested using net cash flow over a 5-year planning horizon as the criterion for deciding on the best size. The following projections of net cash flow (in thousands of dollars) for a 5-year planning horizon have been developed. All costs, including the consultant's fee, have been included.

|  | Demand Scenario | | |
|---|---|---|---|
| Center Size | Worst Case | Base Case | Best Case |
| Small | 400 | 500 | 660 |
| Medium | −250 | 650 | 800 |
| Large | −400 | 580 | 990 |

a.  What decision should Lake Placid make using the expected value approach?
b.  Construct risk profiles for the medium and large alternatives. Given the mayor's concern over the possibility of losing money and the result of part (a), which alternative would you recommend?
c.  Compute the expected value of perfect information. Do you think it would be worth trying to obtain additional information concerning which scenario is likely to occur?
d.  Suppose the probability of the worst-case scenario increases to 0.2, the probability of the base-case scenario decreases to 0.5, and the probability of the best-case scenario remains at 0.3. What effect, if any, would these changes have on the decision recommendation?
e.  The consultant has suggested that an expenditure of $150,000 on a promotional campaign over the planning horizon will effectively reduce the probability of the worst-case scenario to zero. If the campaign can be expected to also increase the probability of the best-case scenario to 0.4, is it a good investment?

16.  Consider a variation of the PDC decision tree shown in Figure 4.9. The company must first decide whether to undertake the market research study. If the market research study is conducted, the outcome will either be favorable ($F$) or unfavorable ($U$). Assume there are only two decision alternatives, $d_1$ and $d_2$, and two states of nature, $s_1$ and $s_2$. The payoff table showing profit is as follows:

|  | State of Nature | |
|---|---|---|
| Decision Alternative | $s_1$ | $s_2$ |
| $d_1$ | 100 | 300 |
| $d_2$ | 400 | 200 |

a.  Show the decision tree.
b.  Using the following probabilities, what is the optimal decision strategy?

| | | | |
|---|---|---|---|
| $P(F) = 0.56$ | $P(s_1 \mid F) = 0.57$ | $P(s_1 \mid U) = 0.18$ | $P(s_1) = 0.40$ |
| $P(U) = 0.44$ | $P(s_2 \mid F) = 0.43$ | $P(s_2 \mid U) = 0.82$ | $P(s_2) = 0.60$ |

17.  Hemmingway, Inc., is considering a $5 million research and development (R&D) project. Profit projections appear promising, but Hemmingway's president is concerned because the probability that the R&D project will be successful is only 0.50. Furthermore, the president knows that even if the project is successful, it will require that the company build

**FIGURE 4.16**   DECISION TREE FOR HEMMINGWAY, INC.

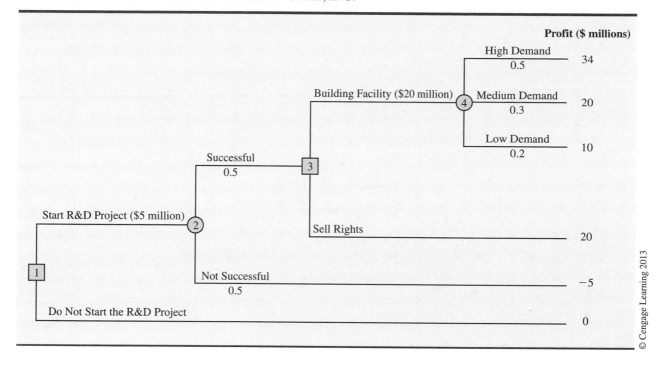

a new production facility at a cost of $20 million in order to manufacture the product. If the facility is built, uncertainty remains about the demand and thus uncertainty about the profit that will be realized. Another option is that if the R&D project is successful, the company could sell the rights to the product for an estimated $25 million. Under this option, the company would not build the $20 million production facility.

The decision tree is shown in Figure 4.16. The profit projection for each outcome is shown at the end of the branches. For example, the revenue projection for the high demand outcome is $59 million. However, the cost of the R&D project ($5 million) and the cost of the production facility ($20 million) show the profit of this outcome to be $59 − $5 − $20 = $34 million. Branch probabilities are also shown for the chance events.

a. Analyze the decision tree to determine whether the company should undertake the R&D project. If it does, and if the R&D project is successful, what should the company do? What is the expected value of your strategy?

b. What must the selling price be for the company to consider selling the rights to the product?

c. Develop a risk profile for the optimal strategy.

18. Dante Development Corporation is considering bidding on a contract for a new office building complex. Figure 4.17 shows the decision tree prepared by one of Dante's analysts. At node 1, the company must decide whether to bid on the contract. The cost of preparing the bid is $200,000. The upper branch from node 2 shows that the company has a 0.8 probability of winning the contract if it submits a bid. If the company wins the bid, it will have to pay $2,000,000 to become a partner in the project. Node 3 shows that the company will then consider doing a market research study to forecast demand for the office units prior to beginning construction. The cost of this study is $150,000. Node 4 is a chance node showing the possible outcomes of the market research study.

Nodes 5, 6, and 7 are similar in that they are the decision nodes for Dante to either build the office complex or sell the rights in the project to another developer. The decision to build the complex will result in an income of $5,000,000 if demand is high and $3,000,000 if

**FIGURE 4.17**   DECISION TREE FOR THE DANTE DEVELOPMENT CORPORATION

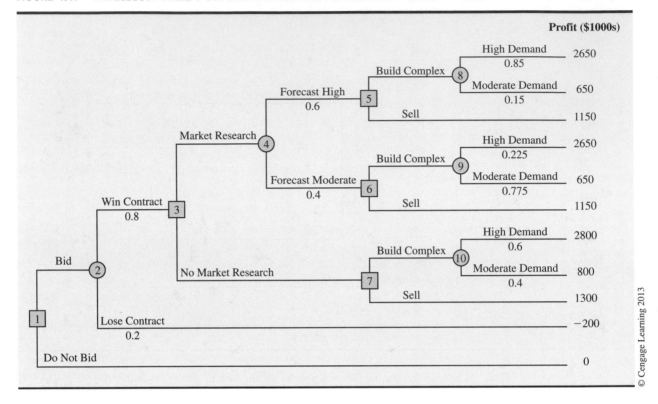

demand is moderate. If Dante chooses to sell its rights in the project to another developer, income from the sale is estimated to be $3,500,000. The probabilities shown at nodes 4, 8, and 9 are based on the projected outcomes of the market research study.

a.   Verify Dante's profit projections shown at the ending branches of the decision tree by calculating the payoffs of $2,650,000 and $650,000 for first two outcomes.

b.   What is the optimal decision strategy for Dante, and what is the expected profit for this project?

c.   What would the cost of the market research study have to be before Dante would change its decision about the market research study?

d.   Develop a risk profile for Dante.

19.  Hale's TV Productions is considering producing a pilot for a comedy series in the hope of selling it to a major television network. The network may decide to reject the series, but it may also decide to purchase the rights to the series for either one or two years. At this point in time, Hale may either produce the pilot and wait for the network's decision or transfer the rights for the pilot and series to a competitor for $100,000. Hale's decision alternatives and profits (in thousands of dollars) are as follows:

| Decision Alternative | State of Nature | | |
|---|---|---|---|
| | Reject, $s_1$ | 1 Year, $s_2$ | 2 Years, $s_3$ |
| Produce pilot, $d_1$ | −100 | 50 | 150 |
| Sell to competitor, $d_2$ | 100 | 100 | 100 |

The probabilities for the states of nature are $P(s_1) = 0.20$, $P(s_2) = 0.30$, and $P(s_3) = 0.50$. For a consulting fee of $5000, an agency will review the plans for the comedy series and indicate the overall chances of a favorable network reaction to the series. Assume that the agency review will result in a favorable ($F$) or an unfavorable ($U$) review and that the following probabilities are relevant:

$$P(F) = 0.69 \qquad P(s_1 \mid F) = 0.09 \qquad P(s_1 \mid U) = 0.45$$
$$P(U) = 0.31 \qquad P(s_2 \mid F) = 0.26 \qquad P(s_2 \mid U) = 0.39$$
$$\qquad\qquad\qquad P(s_3 \mid F) = 0.65 \qquad P(s_3 \mid U) = 0.16$$

a. Construct a decision tree for this problem.
b. What is the recommended decision if the agency opinion is not used? What is the expected value?
c. What is the expected value of perfect information?
d. What is Hale's optimal decision strategy assuming the agency's information is used?
e. What is the expected value of the agency's information?
f. Is the agency's information worth the $5000 fee? What is the maximum that Hale should be willing to pay for the information?
g. What is the recommended decision?

20. Embassy Publishing Company received a six-chapter manuscript for a new college textbook. The editor of the college division is familiar with the manuscript and estimated a 0.65 probability that the textbook will be successful. If successful, a profit of $750,000 will be realized. If the company decides to publish the textbook and it is unsuccessful, a loss of $250,000 will occur.

Before making the decision to accept or reject the manuscript, the editor is considering sending the manuscript out for review. A review process provides either a favorable ($F$) or unfavorable ($U$) evaluation of the manuscript. Past experience with the review process suggests that probabilities $P(F) = 0.7$ and $P(U) = 0.3$ apply. Let $s_1 =$ the textbook is successful, and $s_2 =$ the textbook is unsuccessful. The editor's initial probabilities of $s_1$ and $s_2$ will be revised based on whether the review is favorable or unfavorable. The revised probabilities are as follows:

$$P(s_1 \mid F) = 0.75 \qquad P(s_1 \mid U) = 0.417$$
$$P(s_2 \mid F) = 0.25 \qquad P(s_2 \mid U) = 0.583$$

a. Construct a decision tree assuming that the company will first make the decision of whether to send the manuscript out for review and then make the decision to accept or reject the manuscript.
b. Analyze the decision tree to determine the optimal decision strategy for the publishing company.
c. If the manuscript review costs $5000, what is your recommendation?
d. What is the expected value of perfect information? What does this EVPI suggest for the company?

21. A real estate investor has the opportunity to purchase land currently zoned residential. If the county board approves a request to rezone the property as commercial within the next year, the investor will be able to lease the land to a large discount firm that wants to open a new store on the property. However, if the zoning change is not approved, the investor will have to sell the property at a loss. Profits (in thousands of dollars) are shown in the following payoff table:

| | State of Nature | |
| --- | --- | --- |
| | Rezoning Approved | Rezoning Not Approved |
| **Decision Alternative** | $s_1$ | $s_2$ |
| Purchase, $d_1$ | 600 | −200 |
| Do not purchase, $d_2$ | 0 | 0 |

a.  If the probability that the rezoning will be approved is 0.5, what decision is recommended? What is the expected profit?

b.  The investor can purchase an option to buy the land. Under the option, the investor maintains the rights to purchase the land anytime during the next three months while learning more about possible resistance to the rezoning proposal from area residents. Probabilities are as follows:

$$Let\ H = \text{High resistance to rezoning}$$
$$L = \text{Low resistance to rezoning}$$

| $P(H) = 0.55$ | $P(s_1\,|\,H) = 0.18$ | $P(s_2\,|\,H) = 0.82$ |
| $P(L) = 0.45$ | $P(s_1\,|\,L) = 0.89$ | $P(s_2\,|\,L) = 0.11$ |

What is the optimal decision strategy if the investor uses the option period to learn more about the resistance from area residents before making the purchase decision?

c.  If the option will cost the investor an additional $10,000, should the investor purchase the option? Why or why not? What is the maximum that the investor should be willing to pay for the option?

22. Lawson's Department Store faces a buying decision for a seasonal product for which demand can be high, medium, or low. The purchaser for Lawson's can order one, two, or three lots of the product before the season begins but cannot reorder later. Profit projections (in thousands of dollars) are shown.

| | **State of Nature** | | |
| | **High Demand** | **Medium Demand** | **Low Demand** |
| **Decision Alternative** | $s_1$ | $s_2$ | $s_3$ |
| Order 1 lot, $d_1$ | 60 | 60 | 50 |
| Order 2 lots, $d_2$ | 80 | 80 | 30 |
| Order 3 lots, $d_3$ | 100 | 70 | 10 |

a.  If the prior probabilities for the three states of nature are 0.3, 0.3, and 0.4, respectively, what is the recommended order quantity?

b.  At each preseason sales meeting, the vice president of sales provides a personal opinion regarding potential demand for this product. Because of the vice president's enthusiasm and optimistic nature, the predictions of market conditions have always been either "excellent" ($E$) or "very good" ($V$). Probabilities are as follows:

| $P(E) = 0.70$ | $P(s_1\,|\,E) = 0.34$ | $P(s_1\,|\,V) = 0.20$ |
| $P(V) = 0.30$ | $P(s_2\,|\,E) = 0.32$ | $P(s_2\,|\,V) = 0.26$ |
| | $P(s_3\,|\,E) = 0.34$ | $P(s_3\,|\,V) = 0.54$ |

What is the optimal decision strategy?

c.  Use the efficiency of sample information and discuss whether the firm should consider a consulting expert who could provide independent forecasts of market conditions for the product.

23. Suppose that you are given a decision situation with three possible states of nature: $s_1$, $s_2$, and $s_3$. The prior probabilities are $P(s_1) = 0.2$, $P(s_2) = 0.5$, and $P(s_3) = 0.3$. With sample information $I$, $P(I\,|\,s_1) = 0.1$, $P(I\,|\,s_2) = 0.05$, and $P(I\,|\,s_3) = 0.2$. Compute the revised or posterior probabilities: $P(s_1\,|\,I)$, $P(s_2\,|\,I)$, and $P(s_3\,|\,I)$.

24. To save on expenses, Rona and Jerry agreed to form a carpool for traveling to and from work. Rona preferred to use the somewhat longer but more consistent Queen City Avenue. Although Jerry preferred the quicker expressway, he agreed with Rona that they should take Queen City Avenue if the expressway had a traffic jam. The following payoff table provides the one-way time estimate in minutes for traveling to or from work:

|  | State of Nature | |
|---|---|---|
| **Decision Alternative** | **Expressway Open** $s_1$ | **Expressway Jammed** $s_2$ |
| Queen City Avenue, $d_1$ | 30 | 30 |
| Expressway, $d_2$ | 25 | 45 |

Based on their experience with traffic problems, Rona and Jerry agreed on a 0.15 probability that the expressway would be jammed.

In addition, they agreed that weather seemed to affect the traffic conditions on the expressway. Let

$$C = \text{clear}$$
$$O = \text{overcast}$$
$$R = \text{rain}$$

The following conditional probabilities apply:

| | | |
|---|---|---|
| $P(C\,|\,s_1) = 0.8$ | $P(O\,|\,s_1) = 0.2$ | $P(R\,|\,s_1) = 0.0$ |
| $P(C\,|\,s_2) = 0.1$ | $P(O\,|\,s_2) = 0.3$ | $P(R\,|\,s_2) = 0.6$ |

a. Use Bayes' theorem for probability revision to compute the probability of each weather condition and the conditional probability of the expressway open, $s_1$, or jammed, $s_2$, given each weather condition.
b. Show the decision tree for this problem.
c. What is the optimal decision strategy, and what is the expected travel time?

25. The Gorman Manufacturing Company must decide whether to manufacture a component part at its Milan, Michigan, plant or purchase the component part from a supplier. The resulting profit is dependent upon the demand for the product. The following payoff table shows the projected profit (in thousands of dollars):

|  | State of Nature | | |
|---|---|---|---|
| **Decision Alternative** | **Low Demand** $s_1$ | **Medium Demand** $s_2$ | **High Demand** $s_3$ |
| Manufacture, $d_1$ | −20 | 40 | 100 |
| Purchase, $d_2$ | 10 | 45 | 70 |

The state-of-nature probabilities are $P(s_1) = 0.35$, $P(s_2) = 0.35$, and $P(s_3) = 0.30$.
a. Use a decision tree to recommend a decision.
b. Use EVPI to determine whether Gorman should attempt to obtain a better estimate of demand.

c.  A test market study of the potential demand for the product is expected to report either a favorable $(F)$ or unfavorable $(U)$ condition. The relevant conditional probabilities are as follows:

$$P(F \mid s_1) = 0.10 \qquad P(U \mid s_1) = 0.90$$
$$P(F \mid s_2) = 0.40 \qquad P(U \mid s_2) = 0.60$$
$$P(F \mid s_3) = 0.60 \qquad P(U \mid s_3) = 0.40$$

What is the probability that the market research report will be favorable?
d.  What is Gorman's optimal decision strategy?
e.  What is the expected value of the market research information?
f.  What is the efficiency of the information?

# Case Problem 1   Property Purchase Strategy

Glenn Foreman, president of Oceanview Development Corporation, is considering submitting a bid to purchase property that will be sold by sealed bid at a county tax foreclosure. Glenn's initial judgment is to submit a bid of $5 million. Based on his experience, Glenn estimates that a bid of $5 million will have a 0.2 probability of being the highest bid and securing the property for Oceanview. The current date is June 1. Sealed bids for the property must be submitted by August 15. The winning bid will be announced on September 1.

If Oceanview submits the highest bid and obtains the property, the firm plans to build and sell a complex of luxury condominiums. However, a complicating factor is that the property is currently zoned for single-family residences only. Glenn believes that a referendum could be placed on the voting ballot in time for the November election. Passage of the referendum would change the zoning of the property and permit construction of the condominiums.

The sealed-bid procedure requires the bid to be submitted with a certified check for 10% of the amount bid. If the bid is rejected, the deposit is refunded. If the bid is accepted, the deposit is the down payment for the property. However, if the bid is accepted and the bidder does not follow through with the purchase and meet the remainder of the financial obligation within six months, the deposit will be forfeited. In this case, the county will offer the property to the next highest bidder.

To determine whether Oceanview should submit the $5 million bid, Glenn conducted some preliminary analysis. This preliminary work provided an assessment of 0.3 for the probability that the referendum for a zoning change will be approved and resulted in the following estimates of the costs and revenues that will be incurred if the condominiums are built:

| Cost and Revenue Estimates | |
| --- | --- |
| Revenue from condominium sales | $15,000,000 |
| Cost | |
|     Property | $5,000,000 |
|     Construction expenses | $8,000,000 |

If Oceanview obtains the property and the zoning change is rejected in November, Glenn believes that the best option would be for the firm not to complete the purchase of the property. In this case, Oceanview would forfeit the 10% deposit that accompanied the bid.

Because the likelihood that the zoning referendum will be approved is such an important factor in the decision process, Glenn suggested that the firm hire a market research service to conduct a survey of voters. The survey would provide a better estimate of the likelihood that the referendum for a zoning change would be approved. The market research firm that Oceanview Development has worked with in the past has agreed to do the study for $15,000. The results of the study will be available August 1, so that Oceanview will have this information before the August 15 bid deadline. The results of the survey will be either a prediction that the zoning change will be approved or a prediction that the zoning change will be rejected. After considering the record of the market research service in previous studies conducted for Oceanview, Glenn developed the following probability estimates concerning the accuracy of the market research information:

$$P(A \mid s_1) = 0.9 \qquad P(N \mid s_1) = 0.1$$
$$P(A \mid s_2) = 0.2 \qquad P(N \mid s_2) = 0.8$$

where

$A$ = prediction of zoning change approval

$N$ = prediction that zoning change will not be approved

$s_1$ = the zoning change is approved by the voters

$s_2$ = the zoning change is rejected by the voters

## Managerial Report

Perform an analysis of the problem facing the Oceanview Development Corporation, and prepare a report that summarizes your findings and recommendations. Include the following items in your report:

1. A decision tree that shows the logical sequence of the decision problem
2. A recommendation regarding what Oceanview should do if the market research information is not available
3. A decision strategy that Oceanview should follow if the market research is conducted
4. A recommendation as to whether Oceanview should employ the market research firm, along with the value of the information provided by the market research firm

Include the details of your analysis as an appendix to your report.

# Case Problem 2    Lawsuit Defense Strategy

John Campbell, an employee of Manhattan Construction Company, claims to have injured his back as a result of a fall while repairing the roof at one of the Eastview apartment buildings. He filed a lawsuit against Doug Reynolds, the owner of Eastview Apartments, asking for damages of $1,500,000. John claims that the roof had rotten sections and that his fall could have been prevented if Mr. Reynolds had told Manhattan Construction about the problem. Mr. Reynolds notified his insurance company, Allied Insurance, of the lawsuit. Allied must defend Mr. Reynolds and decide what action to take regarding the lawsuit.

Some depositions and a series of discussions took place between both sides. As a result, John Campbell offered to accept a settlement of $750,000. Thus, one option is for Allied to pay John $750,000 to settle the claim. Allied is also considering making John a counteroffer of $400,000 in the hope that he will accept a lesser amount to avoid the time and cost of going to trial. Allied's preliminary investigation shows that John's case is strong; Allied is concerned that John may reject its counteroffer and request a jury trial. Allied's lawyers spent some time exploring John's likely reaction if they make a counteroffer of $400,000.

The lawyers concluded that it is adequate to consider three possible outcomes to represent John's possible reaction to a counteroffer of $400,000: (1) John will accept the counteroffer and the case will be closed; (2) John will reject the counteroffer and elect to have a jury decide the settlement amount; or (3) John will make a counteroffer to Allied of $600,000. If John does make a counteroffer, Allied decided that it will not make additional counteroffers. It will either accept John's counteroffer of $600,000 or go to trial.

If the case goes to a jury trial, Allied considers three outcomes possible: (1) the jury may reject John's claim and Allied will not be required to pay any damages; (2) the jury will find in favor of John and award him $750,000 in damages; or (3) the jury will conclude that John has a strong case and award him the full amount of $1,500,000.

Key considerations as Allied develops its strategy for disposing of the case are the probabilities associated with John's response to an Allied counteroffer of $400,000 and the probabilities associated with the three possible trial outcomes. Allied's lawyers believe that the probability that John will accept a counteroffer of $400,000 is 0.10, the probability that John will reject a counteroffer of $400,000 is 0.40, and the probability that John will, himself, make a counteroffer to Allied of $600,000 is 0.50. If the case goes to court, they believe that the probability that the jury will award John damages of $1,500,000 is 0.30, the probability that the jury will award John damages of $750,000 is 0.50, and the probability that the jury will award John nothing is 0.20.

## Managerial Report

Perform an analysis of the problem facing Allied Insurance and prepare a report that summarizes your findings and recommendations. Be sure to include the following items:

1. A decision tree
2. A recommendation regarding whether Allied should accept John's initial offer to settle the claim for $750,000
3. A decision strategy that Allied should follow if they decide to make John a counteroffer of $400,000
4. A risk profile for your recommended strategy

## Appendix 4.1    Decision Analysis with TreePlan

TreePlan[2] is an Excel add-in that can be used to develop decision trees for decision analysis problems. The software package is provided at the website that accompanies this text. Instructions for installation and a manual containing additional information are also available at the website. In this appendix we show how to use TreePlan to build a decision tree and solve the PDC problem presented in Section 4.3. The decision tree for the PDC problem is shown in Figure 4.18.

---

[2]TreePlan was developed by Professor Michael R. Middleton at the University of San Francisco and modified for use by Professor James E. Smith at Duke University. The TreePlan website is *http://www.treeplan.com.*

**FIGURE 4.18**   PDC DECISION TREE

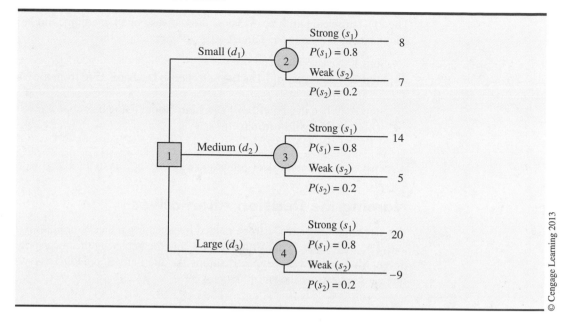

## Getting Started: An Initial Decision Tree

We begin by assuming that TreePlan has been installed and an Excel workbook is open. To build a TreePlan version of the PDC decision tree, proceed as follows:

**Step 1.** Select cell A1

**Step 2.** Select the **Add-Ins tab** and choose **Decision Tree** from the **Menu Commands** group

**Step 3.** When the **TreePlan - New Tree** dialog box appears:
Click **New Tree**

A decision tree with one decision node and two branches (initially labeled as *Alternatives*) is provided in Figure 4.19.

**FIGURE 4.19**   A DECISION TREE WITH ONE DECISION NODE AND TWO BRANCHES
DEVELOPED BY TREEPLAN

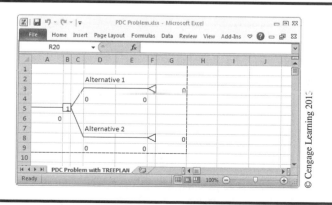

## Adding a Branch

The PDC problem has three decision alternatives (small, medium, and large condominium complexes), so we must add another decision branch to the tree.

**Step 1.** Select cell B5
**Step 2.** Select the **Add-Ins tab** and choose **Decision Tree** from the **Menu Commands** group
**Step 3.** When the **TreePlan - Decision Node** dialog box appears:
Select **Add branch**
Click **OK**

A revised tree with three decision branches now appears in the Excel worksheet.

## Naming the Decision Alternatives

The decision alternatives can be named by selecting the cells containing the labels Alternative 1, Alternative 2, and Alternative 3, and then entering the corresponding PDC names Small, Medium, and Large. After naming the alternatives, the PDC tree with three decision branches appears as shown in Figure 4.20.

**FIGURE 4.20**    TREEPLAN DECISION TREE WITH AN ADDITIONAL DECISION NODE AND LABELS ON THE BRANCHES

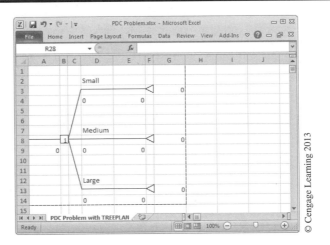

## Adding Chance Nodes

The chance event for the PDC problem is the demand for the condominiums, which may be either strong or weak. Thus, a chance node with two branches must be added at the end of each decision alternative branch. To add a chance node with two branches to the top decision alternative branch:

**Step 1.** Select cell F3
**Step 2.** Select the **Add-Ins tab** and choose **Decision Tree** from the **Menu Commands** group

**Step 3.** When the **TreePlan - Terminal Node** dialog box appears:
  Select **Change to event node**
  Select **Two** in the **Branches** section
  Click **OK**

The tree now appears as shown in Figure 4.21.

**FIGURE 4.21**   TREEPLAN DECISION TREE WITH A CHANCE NODE ADDED TO THE
                 END OF THE FIRST DECISION BRANCH

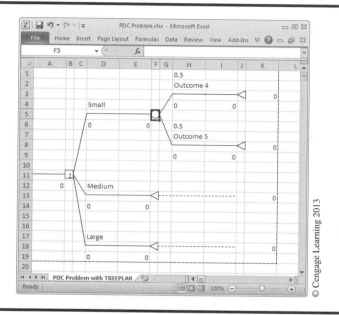

We next select the cells containing Outcome 4 and Outcome 5 and rename them Strong
and Weak to provide the proper names for the PDC states of nature. After doing so we can
copy the subtree for the chance node in cell F5 to the other two decision branches to complete the structure of the PDC decision tree as follows:

**Step 1.** Select cell F5
**Step 2.** Select the **Add-Ins tab** and choose **Decision Tree** from the **Menu Commands**
  group
**Step 3.** When the **TreePlan Event** dialog box appears:
  Select **Copy subtree**
  Click **OK**
**Step 4.** Select cell F13
**Step 5.** Select the **Add-Ins tab** and choose **Decision Tree** from the **Menu Commands**
  group
**Step 6.** When the **TreePlan - Terminal Node** dialog box appears:
  Select **Paste subtree**
  Click **OK**

**FIGURE 4.22**    THE PDC DECISION TREE DEVELOPED BY TREEPLAN

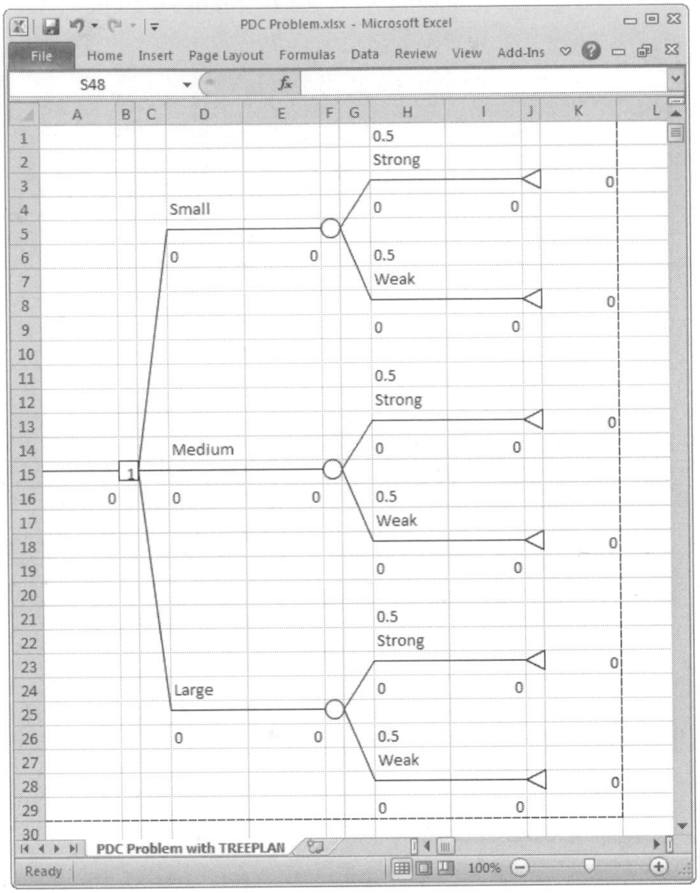

© Cengage Learning 2013

This copy/paste procedure places a chance node at the end of the Medium decision branch. Repeating the same copy/paste procedure for the Large decision branch completes the structure of the PDC decision tree as shown in Figure 4.22.

## Inserting Probabilities and Payoffs

TreePlan provides the capability of inserting probabilities and payoffs into the decision tree. In Figure 4.19 we see that TreePlan automatically assigned an equal probability 0.5 to each of the chance outcomes. For PDC, the probability of strong demand is 0.8 and the probability of weak demand is 0.2. We can select cells H1, H6, H11, H16, H21, and H26 and insert the appropriate probabilities. The payoffs for the chance outcomes are inserted in cells H4, H9, H14, H19, H24, and H29. After inserting the PDC probabilities and payoffs, the PDC decision tree appears as shown in Figure 4.23.

Note that the payoffs also appear in the right-hand margin of the decision tree (column K in this problem). The payoffs in the right margin are computed by a formula that adds the payoffs on all of the branches leading to the associated terminal node. For the PDC problem,

**FIGURE 4.23**   THE PDC DECISION TREE WITH BRANCH PROBABILITIES AND PAYOFFS

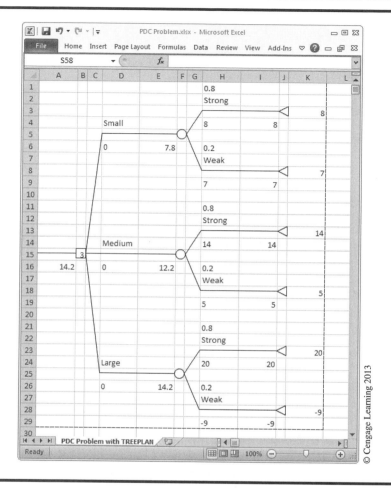

no payoffs are associated with the decision alternatives branches so we leave the default values of zero in cells D6, D16, and D26. The PDC decision tree is now complete.

## Interpreting the Result

When probabilities and payoffs are inserted, TreePlan automatically makes the backward pass computations necessary to determine the optimal solution. Optimal decisions are identified by the number in the corresponding decision node. In the PDC decision tree in Figure 4.20, cell D15 contains the decision node. Note that a 3 appears in this node, which tells us that decision alternative branch 3 provides the optimal decision. Thus, decision analysis recommends PDC construct the Large condominium complex. The expected value of this decision appears at the beginning of the tree in cell A16. Thus, we see the optimal expected value is $14.2 million. The expected values of the other decision alternatives are displayed at the end of the corresponding decision branch. Thus, referring to cells E6 and E16, we see that the expected value of the Small complex is $7.8 million and the expected value of the Medium complex is $12.2 million.

## Other Options

TreePlan defaults to a maximization objective. If you would like a minimization objective, follow these steps:

**Step 1.** Select **Decision Tree** from the **Menu Commands** group
**Step 2.** Select **Options**
**Step 3.** Choose **Minimize (costs)**
           Click **OK**

In using a TreePlan decision tree, we can modify probabilities and payoffs and quickly observe the impact of the changes on the optimal solution. Using this "what if" type of sensitivity analysis, we can identify changes in probabilities and payoffs that would change the optimal decision. Also, because TreePlan is an Excel add-in, most of Excel's capabilities are available. For instance, we could use boldface to highlight the name of the optimal decision alternative on the final decision tree solution. A variety of other options TreePlan provides is contained in the TreePlan manual on the website that accompanies this text. Computer software packages such as TreePlan make it easier to do a thorough analysis of a decision problem.

# CHAPTER 7

# Introduction to Linear Programming

## CONTENTS

Linear programming is a problem-solving approach developed to help managers make decisions. Numerous applications of linear programming can be found in today's competitive business environment. For instance, IBM uses linear programming to perform capacity planning and to make capacity investment decisions for its semiconductor manufacturing operations. GE Capital uses linear programming to help determine optimal lease structuring. Marathon Oil Company uses linear programming for gasoline blending and to evaluate the economics of a new terminal or pipeline. The Q.M. in Action, Timber Harvesting Model at MeadWestvaco Corporation, provides another example of the use of linear programming. Later in the chapter another Q.M. in Action illustrates how the United States Navy uses linear programming to reduce fuel consumption for its ships.

To illustrate some of the properties that all linear programming problems have in common, consider the following typical applications:

1. A manufacturer wants to develop a production schedule and an inventory policy that will satisfy sales demand in future periods. Ideally, the schedule and policy will enable the company to satisfy demand and at the same time *minimize* the total production and inventory costs.

2. A financial analyst must select an investment portfolio from a variety of stock and bond investment alternatives. The analyst would like to establish the portfolio that *maximizes* the return on investment.

3. A marketing manager wants to determine how best to allocate a fixed advertising budget among alternative advertising media such as radio, television, newspaper, and magazine. The manager would like to determine the media mix that *maximizes* advertising effectiveness.

4. A company has warehouses in a number of locations. Given specific customer demands, the company would like to determine how much each warehouse should ship to each customer so that total transportation costs are *minimized.*

These examples are only a few of the situations in which linear programming has been used successfully, but they illustrate the diversity of linear programming applications. A close scrutiny reveals one basic property they all have in common. In each example, we were concerned with *maximizing* or *minimizing* some quantity. In example 1, the manufacturer wanted to minimize costs; in example 2, the financial analyst wanted to maximize return on investment; in example 3, the marketing manager wanted to maximize advertising effectiveness; and in example 4, the company wanted to minimize total transportation costs. In all linear programming problems, the maximization or minimization of some quantity is the objective.

## Q.M. *in* ACTION

### TIMBER HARVESTING MODEL AT MEADWESTVACO CORPORATION*

MeadWestvaco Corporation is a major producer of premium papers for periodicals, books, commercial printing, and business forms. The company also produces pulp and lumber, designs and manufactures packaging systems for beverage and other consumables markets, and is a world leader in the production of coated board and shipping containers. Quantitative analyses at MeadWestvaco are developed and implemented by the company's Decision Analysis Department. The department assists decision makers by providing them with analytical tools of quantitative methods as well as personal analysis and recommendations.

*Based on information provided by Dr. Edward P. Winkofsky of MeadWestvaco Corporation.

*(continued)*

MeadWestvaco uses quantitative models to assist with the long-range management of the company's timberland. Through the use of large-scale linear programs, timber harvesting plans are developed to cover a substantial time horizon. These models consider wood market conditions, mill pulpwood requirements, harvesting capacities, and general forest management principles. Within these constraints, the model arrives at an optimal harvesting and purchasing schedule based on discounted cash flow. Alternative schedules reflect changes in the various assumptions concerning forest growth, wood availability, and general economic conditions.

Quantitative methods are also used in the development of the inputs for the linear programming models. Timber prices and supplies as well as mill requirements must be forecast over the time horizon, and advanced sampling techniques are used to evaluate land holdings and to project forest growth. The harvest schedule is then developed using quantitative methods.

*Linear programming was initially referred to as "programming in a linear structure." In 1948 Tjalling Koopmans suggested to George Dantzig that the name was much too long: Koopman's suggestion was to shorten it to linear programming. George Dantzig agreed and the field we now know as linear programming was named.*

All linear programming problems also have a second property: restrictions or **constraints** that limit the degree to which the objective can be pursued. In the first example, the manufacturer is restricted by constraints requiring product demand to be satisfied and by the constraints limiting production capacity. The financial analyst's portfolio problem is constrained by the total amount of investment funds available and the maximum amounts that can be invested in each stock or bond. The marketing manager's media selection decision is constrained by a fixed advertising budget and the availability of the various media. In the transportation problem, the minimum-cost shipping schedule is constrained by the supply of product available at each warehouse. Thus, constraints are another general feature of every linear programming problem.

## 7.1  A Simple Maximization Problem

RMC, Inc., is a small firm that produces a variety of chemical-based products. In a particular production process, three raw materials are used to produce two products: a fuel additive and a solvent base. The fuel additive is sold to oil companies and is used in the production of gasoline and related fuels. The solvent base is sold to a variety of chemical firms and is used in both home and industrial cleaning products. The three raw materials are blended to form the fuel additive and solvent base as indicated in Table 7.1, which shows that a ton of fuel additive is a mixture of 0.4 tons of material 1 and 0.6 tons of material 3. A ton of solvent base is a mixture of 0.5 tons of material 1, 0.2 tons of material 2, and 0.3 tons of material 3.

**TABLE 7.1**   MATERIAL REQUIREMENTS PER TON FOR THE RMC PROBLEM

| | Product | |
| --- | --- | --- |
| | **Fuel Additive** | **Solvent Base** |
| Material 1 | 0.4 | 0.5 |
| Material 2 | | 0.2 |
| Material 3 | 0.6 | 0.3 |

0.6 tons of material 3 is used
in each ton of fuel additive

© Cengage Learning 2013

RMC's production is constrained by a limited availability of the three raw materials. For the current production period, RMC has available the following quantities of each raw material:

| Material | Amount Available for Production |
|---|---|
| Material 1 | 20 tons |
| Material 2 | 5 tons |
| Material 3 | 21 tons |

*It is important to understand that we are maximizing profit contribution, not profit. Overhead and other shared costs must be deducted before arriving at a profit figure.*

Because of spoilage and the nature of the production process, any materials not used for current production are useless and must be discarded.

The accounting department analyzed the production figures, assigned all relevant costs, and arrived at prices for both products that will result in a profit contribution[1] of $40 for every ton of fuel additive produced and $30 for every ton of solvent base produced. Let us now use linear programming to determine the number of tons of fuel additive and the number of tons of solvent base to produce in order to maximize total profit contribution.

## Problem Formulation

**Problem formulation** is the process of translating a verbal statement of a problem into a mathematical statement. The mathematical statement of the problem is referred to as a **mathematical model**. Developing an appropriate mathematical model is an art that can only be mastered with practice and experience. Even though every problem has at least some unique features, most problems also have many common or similar features. As a result, some general guidelines for developing a mathematical model can be helpful. We will illustrate these guidelines by developing a mathematical model for the RMC problem.

**Understand the Problem Thoroughly** The RMC problem is relatively easy to understand. RMC wants to determine how much of each product to produce in order to maximize the total contribution to profit. The number of tons available for the three materials that are required to produce the two products will limit the number of tons of each product that can be produced. More complex problems will require more work in order to understand the problem. However, understanding the problem thoroughly is the first step in developing any mathematical model.

**Describe the Objective** RMC's objective is to maximize the total contribution to profit.

**Describe Each Constraint** Three constraints limit the number of tons of fuel additive and the number of tons of solvent base that can be produced.

**Constraint 1:** The number of tons of material 1 used must be less than or equal to the 20 tons available.

**Constraint 2:** The number of tons of material 2 used must be less than or equal to the 5 tons available.

**Constraint 3:** The number of tons of material 3 used must be less than or equal to the 21 tons available.

---

[1]From an accounting perspective, profit contribution is more correctly described as the contribution margin per ton; overhead and other shared costs have not been allocated to the fuel additive and solvent base costs.

**Define the Decision Variables**   The **decision variables** are the controllable inputs in the problem. For the RMC problem the two decision variables are (1) the number of tons of fuel additive produced, and (2) the number of tons of solvent base produced. In developing the mathematical model for the RMC problem, we will use the following notation for the decision variables:

$$F = \text{number of tons of fuel additive}$$
$$S = \text{number of tons of solvent base}$$

**Write the Objective in Terms of the Decision Variables**   RMC's profit contribution comes from the production of $F$ tons of fuel additive and $S$ tons of solvent base. Because RMC makes \$40 for every ton of fuel additive produced and \$30 for every ton of solvent base produced, the company will make \$40$F$ from the production of the fuel additive and \$30$S$ from the production of the solvent base. Thus,

$$\text{Total profit contribution} = 40F + 30S$$

Because the objective—maximize total profit contribution—is a function of the decision variables $F$ and $S$, we refer to $40F + 30S$ as the **objective function**. Using "Max" as an abbreviation for maximize, we can write RMC's objective as follows:

$$\text{Max } 40F + 30S \tag{7.1}$$

**Write the Constraints in Terms of the Decision Variables**
**Constraint 1:**

$$\text{Tons of material 1 used} \leq \text{Tons of material 1 available}$$

Every ton of fuel additive that RMC produces will use 0.4 tons of material 1. Thus, $0.4F$ tons of material 1 is used to produce $F$ tons of fuel additive. Similarly, every ton of solvent base that RMC produces will use 0.5 tons of material 1. Thus, $0.5S$ tons of material 1 is used to produce $S$ tons of solvent base. Therefore, the number of tons of material 1 used to produce $F$ tons of fuel additive and $S$ tons of solvent base is

$$\text{Tons of material 1 used} = 0.4F + 0.5S$$

Because 20 tons of material 1 are available for use in production, the mathematical statement of constraint 1 is

$$0.4F + 0.5S \leq 20 \tag{7.2}$$

**Constraint 2:**

$$\text{Tons of material 2 used} \leq \text{Tons of material 2 available}$$

Fuel additive does not use material 2. However, every ton of solvent base that RMC produces will use 0.2 tons of material 2. Thus, $0.2S$ tons of material 2 is used to produce $S$ tons of solvent base. Therefore, the number of tons of material 2 used to produce $F$ tons of fuel additive and $S$ tons of solvent base is

$$\text{Tons of material 2 used} = 0.2S$$

Because 5 tons of material 2 are available for production, the mathematical statement of constraint 2 is

$$0.2S \leq 5 \qquad \textbf{(7.3)}$$

**Constraint 3:**

Tons of material 3 used $\leq$ Tons of material 3 available

Every ton of fuel additive RMC produces will use 0.6 tons of material 3. Thus, $0.6F$ tons of material 1 is used to produce $F$ tons of fuel additive. Similarly, every ton of solvent base RMC produces will use 0.3 tons of material 3. Thus, $0.3S$ tons of material 1 is used to produce $S$ tons of solvent base. Therefore, the number of tons of material 3 used to produce $F$ tons of fuel additive and $S$ tons of solvent base is

Tons of material 3 used $= 0.6F + 0.3S$

Because 21 tons of material 3 are available for production, the mathematical statement of constraint 3 is

$$0.6F + 0.3S \leq 21 \qquad \textbf{(7.4)}$$

**Add the Nonnegativity Constraints**  RMC cannot produce a negative number of tons of fuel additive or a negative number of tons of solvent base. Therefore, **nonnegativity constraints** must be added to prevent the decision variables $F$ and $S$ from having negative values. These nonnegativity constraints are

$F \geq 0$ and $S \geq 0$

Nonnegativity constraints are a general feature of many linear programming problems and may be written in the abbreviated form:

$$F, S \geq 0 \qquad \textbf{(7.5)}$$

## Mathematical Model for the RMC Problem

Problem formulation is now complete. We have succeeded in translating the verbal statement of the RMC problem into the following mathematical model:

$$\text{Max } 40F + 30S$$

Subject to (s.t.)

$$
\begin{aligned}
0.4F + 0.5S &\leq 20 \qquad \text{Material 1} \\
0.2S &\leq 5 \qquad \text{Material 2} \\
0.6F + 0.3S &\leq 21 \qquad \text{Material 3} \\
F, S &\geq 0
\end{aligned}
$$

Our job now is to find the product mix (i.e., the combination of $F$ and $S$) that satisfies all the constraints and, at the same time, yields a maximum value for the objective function. Once these values of $F$ and $S$ are calculated, we will have found the optimal solution to the problem.

This mathematical model of the RMC problem is a **linear program**. The RMC problem has an objective and constraints that, as we said earlier, are common properties of all *linear* programs. But what is the special feature of this mathematical model that makes it a linear program? The special feature that makes it a linear program is that the objective function and all constraint functions (the left-hand sides of the constraint inequalities) are linear functions of the decision variables.

Mathematical functions in which each variable appears in a separate term and is raised to the first power are called **linear functions**. The objective function ($40F + 30S$) is linear because each decision variable appears in a separate term and has an exponent of 1. The amount of material 1 used ($0.4F + 0.5S$) is also a linear function of the decision variables for the same reason. Similarly, the functions on the left-hand side of the material 2 and material 3 constraint inequalities (the constraint functions) are also linear functions. Thus, the mathematical formulation is referred to as a linear program.

*Try Problem 1 to test your ability to recognize the types of mathematical relationships that can be found in a linear program.*

Linear *programming* has nothing to do with computer programming. The use of the word *programming* here means "choosing a course of action." Linear programming involves choosing a course of action when the mathematical model of the problem contains only linear functions.

## NOTES AND COMMENTS

1. The three assumptions necessary for a linear programming model to be appropriate are proportionality, additivity, and divisibility. *Proportionality* means that the contribution to the objective function and the amount of resources used in each constraint are proportional to the value of each decision variable. *Additivity* means that the value of the objective function and the total resources used can be found by summing the objective function contribution and the resources used for all decision variables. *Divisibility* means that the decision variables are continuous. The divisibility assumption plus the nonnegativity constraints mean that decision variables can take on any value greater than or equal to zero.

2. Quantitative analysts formulate and solve a variety of mathematical models that contain an objective function and a set of constraints. Models of this type are referred to as *mathematical programming models*. Linear programming models are a special type of mathematical programming model in that the objective function and all constraint functions are linear.

# 7.2 Graphical Solution Procedure

A linear programming problem involving only two decision variables can be solved using a graphical solution procedure. Let us begin the graphical solution procedure by developing a graph that displays the possible solutions ($F$ and $S$ values) for the RMC problem. The graph in Figure 7.1 has values of $F$ on the horizontal axis and values of $S$ on the vertical axis. Any point on the graph can be identified by its $F$ and $S$ values, which indicate the position of the point along the horizontal and vertical axes, respectively. Thus, every point on the graph corresponds to a possible solution. The solution of $F = 0$ and $S = 0$ is referred to as the origin. Because both $F$ and $S$ must be nonnegative, the graph in Figure 7.1 only displays solutions where $F \geq 0$ and $S \geq 0$.

Earlier we determined that the inequality representing the material 1 constraint was

$$0.4F + 0.5S \leq 20$$

To show all solutions that satisfy this relationship, we start by graphing the line corresponding to the equation

$$0.4F + 0.5S = 20$$

**FIGURE 7.1**    GRAPH SHOWING TWO SOLUTIONS FOR THE TWO-VARIABLE
RMC PROBLEM

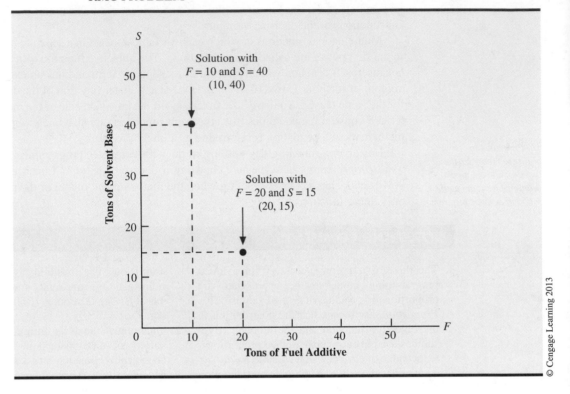

We graph this equation by identifying two points that satisfy this equation and then drawing a line through the points. Setting $F = 0$ and solving for $S$ gives $0.5S = 20$, or $S = 40$; hence the solution ($F = 0$, $S = 40$) satisfies the preceding equation. To find a second solution satisfying this equation, we set $S = 0$ and solve for $F$. Doing so, we obtain $0.4F = 20$, or $F = 50$. Thus, a second solution satisfying the equation is ($F = 50$, $S = 0$). With these two points, we can now graph the line. This line, called the *material 1 constraint line,* is shown in Figure 7.2.

Recall that the inequality representing the material 1 constraint is

$$0.4F + 0.5S \leq 20$$

Can you identify all the solutions that satisfy this constraint? First, note that any point on the line $0.4F + 0.5S = 20$ must satisfy the constraint. But where are the solutions satisfying $0.4F + 0.5S < 20$? Consider two solutions ($F = 10$, $S = 10$) and ($F = 40$, $S = 30$). Figure 7.2 shows that the first solution is on the same side of the constraint line as the origin while the second solution is on the side of the constraint line opposite of the origin. Which of these solutions satisfies the material 1 constraint? For ($F = 10$, $S = 10$) we have

$$0.4F + 0.5S = 0.4(10) + 0.5(10) = 9$$

Because 9 tons is less than the 20 tons of material 1 available, the $F = 10$, $S = 10$ solution satisfies the constraint. For $F = 40$ and $S = 30$ we have

$$0.4F + 0.5S = 0.4(40) + 0.5(30) = 31$$

**FIGURE 7.2** MATERIAL 1 CONSTRAINT LINE

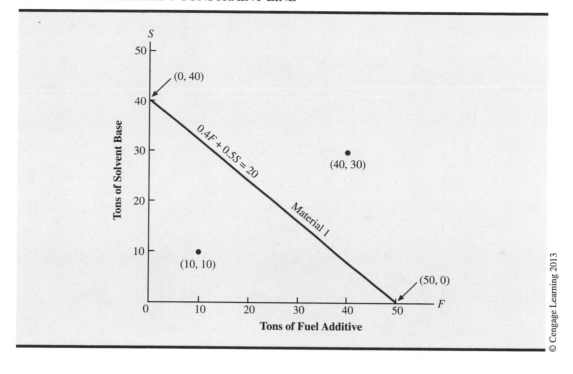

The 31 tons is greater than the 20 tons available, so the $F = 40$, $S = 30$ solution does not satisfy the constraint.

*You should now be able to graph a constraint line and find the solution points that satisfy the constraint. Try Problem 2.*

If a particular solution satisfies the constraint, all other solutions on the same side of the constraint line will also satisfy the constraint. If a particular solution does not satisfy the constraint, all other solutions on the same side of the constraint line will not satisfy the constraint. Thus, you need to evaluate only one solution to determine which side of a constraint line provides solutions that will satisfy the constraint. The shaded area in Figure 7.3 shows all the solutions that satisfy the material 1 constraint.

Next let us identify all solutions that satisfy the material 2 constraint:

$$0.2S \leq 5$$

We start by drawing the constraint line corresponding to the equation $0.2S = 5$. Because this equation is equivalent to the equation $S = 25$, we simply draw a line whose $S$ value is 25 for every value of $F$; this line is parallel to and 25 units above the horizontal axis. Figure 7.4 shows the line corresponding to the material 2 constraint. Following the approach we used for the material 1 constraint, we realize that only solutions on or below the line will satisfy the material 2 constraint. Thus, in Figure 7.4 the shaded area corresponds to the solutions that satisfy the material 2 constraint.

Similarly, we can determine the solutions that satisfy the material 3 constraint. Figure 7.5 shows the result. For practice, try to graph the feasible solutions that satisfy the material 3 constraint and determine whether your result agrees with that shown in Figure 7.5.

We now have three separate graphs showing the solutions that satisfy each of the three constraints. In a linear programming problem, we need to identify the solutions that satisfy

**FIGURE 7.3**    SOLUTIONS THAT SATISFY THE MATERIAL 1 CONSTRAINT

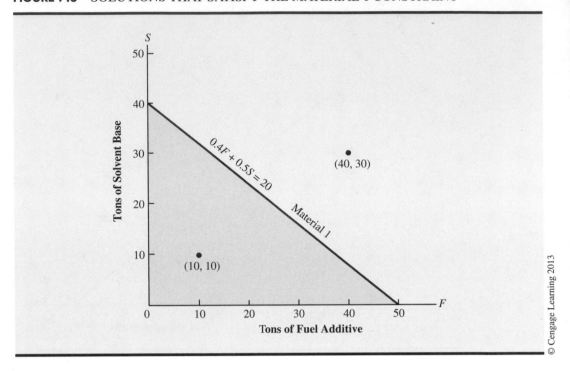

**FIGURE 7.4**    SOLUTIONS THAT SATISFY THE MATERIAL 2 CONSTRAINT

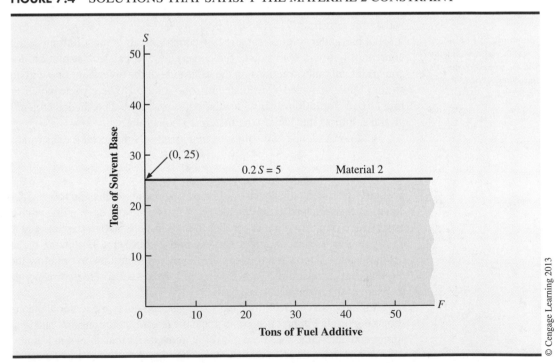

**FIGURE 7.5**    SOLUTIONS THAT SATISFY THE MATERIAL 3 CONSTRAINT

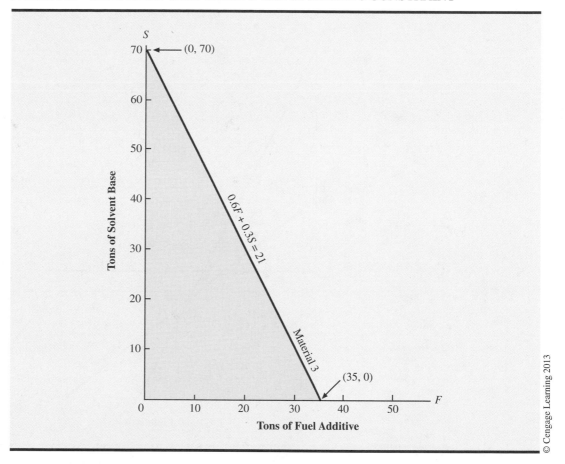

*all* the constraints *simultaneously.* To find these solutions, we can draw the three constraints on one graph and observe the region containing the points that do in fact satisfy all the constraints simultaneously.

The graphs in Figures 7.3, 7.4, and 7.5 can be superimposed to obtain one graph with all three constraints. Figure 7.6 shows this combined constraint graph. The shaded region in this figure includes every solution point that satisfies all the constraints simultaneously. Because solutions that satisfy all the constraints simultaneously are termed **feasible solutions**, the shaded region is called the *feasible solution region,* or simply the **feasible region**. Any point on the boundary of the feasible region, or within the feasible region, is a *feasible solution point* for the linear programming problem.

*Can you now find the feasible region given several constraints? Try Problem 7.*

Now that we have identified the feasible region, we are ready to proceed with the graphical solution method and find the optimal solution to the RMC problem. Recall that the optimal solution for a linear programming problem is the feasible solution that provides the best possible value of the objective function. Let us start the optimizing step of the graphical solution procedure by redrawing the feasible region on a separate graph. Figure 7.7 shows the graph.

One approach to finding the optimal solution would be to evaluate the objective function for each feasible solution; the optimal solution would then be the one yielding the

**FIGURE 7.6**    FEASIBLE REGION FOR THE RMC PROBLEM

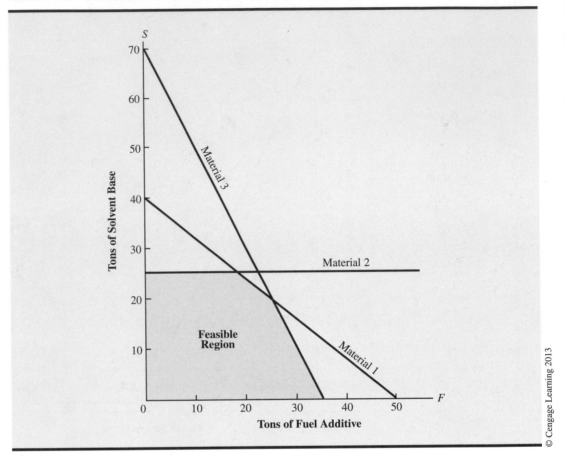

largest value. The difficulty with this approach is that the infinite number of feasible solutions makes evaluating all feasible solutions impossible. Hence, this trial-and-error procedure cannot be used to identify the optimal solution.

Rather than trying to compute the profit contribution for each feasible solution, we select an arbitrary value for profit contribution and identify all the feasible solutions that yield the selected value. For example, what feasible solutions provide a profit contribution of $240? These solutions are given by the values of $F$ and $S$ in the feasible region that will make the objective function

$$40F + 30S = 240$$

This expression is simply the equation of a line. Thus all feasible solutions $(F, S)$ yielding a profit contribution of $240 must be on the line. We learned earlier in this section how to graph a constraint line. The procedure for graphing the profit or objective function line is the same. Letting $F = 0$, we see that $S$ must be 8; thus the solution point $(F = 0, S = 8)$ is on the line. Similarly, by letting $S = 0$ we see that the solution point $(F = 6, S = 0)$ is also on the line. Drawing the line through these two points identifies all the solutions that have a profit contribution of $240. A graph of this profit line is presented in Figure 7.8. The graph shows that an infinite number of feasible production combinations will provide a $240 profit contribution.

**FIGURE 7.7**   FEASIBLE REGION FOR THE RMC PROBLEM

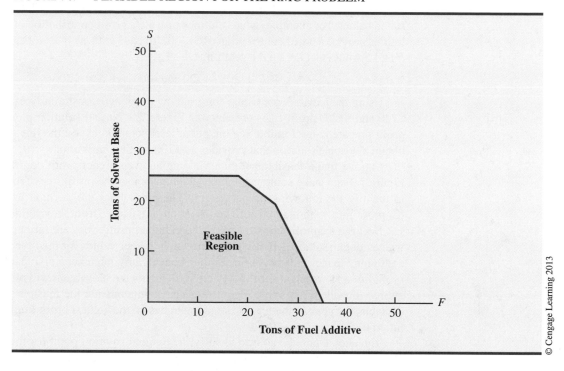

**FIGURE 7.8**   $240 PROFIT LINE FOR THE RMC PROBLEM

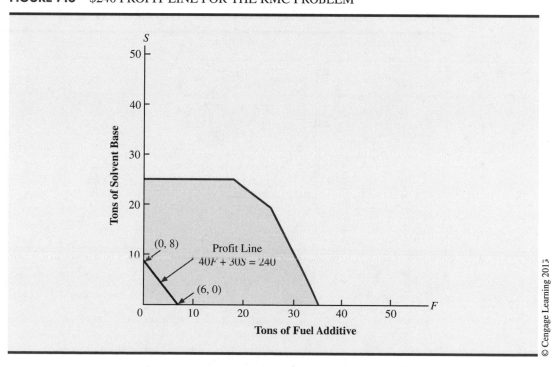

The objective is to find the feasible solution yielding the highest profit contribution, so we proceed by selecting higher profit contributions and finding the solutions that yield the stated values. For example, what solutions provide a profit contribution of $720? What solutions provide a profit contribution of $1200? To answer these questions, we must find the $F$ and $S$ values that are on the profit lines:

$$40F + 30S = 720 \text{ and } 40F + 30S = 1200$$

Using the previous procedure for graphing profit and constraint lines, we graphed the $720 and $1200 profit lines presented in Figure 7.9. Not all solution points on the $1200 profit line are in the feasible region, but at least some points on the line are; thus, we can obtain a feasible solution that provides a $1200 profit contribution.

Can we find a feasible solution yielding an even higher profit contribution? Look at Figure 7.9 and make some general observations about the profit lines. You should be able to identify the following properties: (1) The profit lines are *parallel* to each other, and (2) profit lines with higher profit contributions are farther from the origin.

Because the profit lines are parallel and higher profit lines are farther from the origin, we can obtain solutions that yield increasingly higher values for the objective function by continuing to move the profit line farther from the origin but keeping it parallel to the other profit lines. However, at some point any further outward movement will place the profit line entirely outside the feasible region. Because points outside the feasible region are unacceptable, the point in the feasible region that lies on the highest profit line is an optimal solution to the linear program.

You should now be able to identify the optimal solution point for the RMC problem. Use a ruler and move the profit line as far from the origin as you can. What is the last point in the feasible region? This point, which is the optimal solution, is shown graphically in Figure 7.10. The optimal values for the decision variables are the $F$ and $S$ values at this point.

**FIGURE 7.9**   SELECTED PROFIT LINES FOR THE RMC PROBLEM

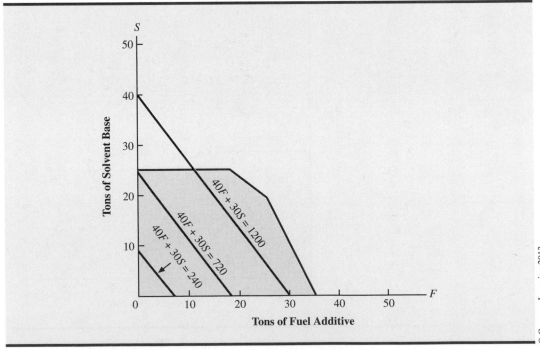

**FIGURE 7.10**    OPTIMAL SOLUTION FOR THE RMC PROBLEM

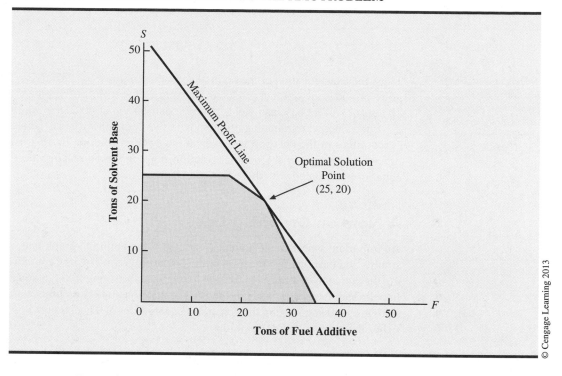

Depending on the accuracy of your graph, you may or may not be able to determine the exact optimal values of $F$ and $S$ directly from the graph. However, refer to Figure 7.6 and note that the optimal solution point for the RMC example is at the *intersection* of the material 1 and material 3 constraint lines. That is, the optimal solution is on both the material 1 constraint line,

$$0.4F + 0.5S = 20 \qquad\qquad \textbf{(7.6)}$$

and the material 3 constraint line,

$$0.6F + 0.3S = 21 \qquad\qquad \textbf{(7.7)}$$

Thus, the values of the decision variables $F$ and $S$ must satisfy both equations (7.6) and (7.7) simultaneously. Using (7.6) and solving for $F$ gives

$$0.4F = 20 - 0.5S$$

or

$$F = 50 \quad 1.25S \qquad\qquad \textbf{(7.8)}$$

Substituting this expression for $F$ into equation (7.7) and solving for $S$ yields

$$0.6(50 - 1.25S) + 0.3S = 21$$
$$30 - 0.75S + 0.3S = 21$$
$$-0.45S = -9$$
$$S = 20$$

Substituting $S = 20$ in equation (7.8) and solving for $F$ provides

$$F = 50 - 1.25(20)$$
$$= 50 - 25 = 25$$

*Although the optimal solution to the RMC problem consists of integer values for the decision variables, this result will not always be the case.*

Thus, the exact location of the optimal solution point is $F = 25$ and $S = 20$. This solution point provides the optimal production quantities for RMC at 25 tons of fuel additive and 20 tons of solvent base and yields a profit contribution of $40(25) + 30(20) = \$1600$.

For a linear programming problem with two decision variables, you can determine the exact values of the decision variables at the optimal solution by first using the graphical procedure to identify the optimal solution point and then solving the two simultaneous equations associated with this point.

## A Note on Graphing Lines

An important aspect of the graphical method is the ability to graph lines showing the constraints and the objective function of the linear program. The procedure we used for graphing the equation of a line is to find any two points satisfying the equation and then draw the line through the two points. For the RMC constraints, the two points were easily found by setting $F = 0$ and solving the constraint equation for $S$. Then we set $S = 0$ and solved for $F$. For the material 1 constraint line

$$0.4F + 0.5S = 20$$

this procedure identified the two points $(F = 0, S = 40)$ and $(F = 50, S = 0)$. The material 1 constraint line was then graphed by drawing a line through these two points.

*Try Problem 10 to test your ability to use the graphical solution procedure to identify the optimal solution and find the exact values of the decision variables at the optimal solution.*

All constraints and objective function lines in two-variable linear programs can be graphed if two points on the line can be identified. However, finding the two points on the line is not always as easy as shown in the RMC problem. For example, suppose a company manufactures two models of a small hand-held computer: the Professional $(P)$ and the Assistant $(A)$. Management needs 50 units of the Professional model for its own sales force and expects sales of the remaining Professionals to be less than or equal to 50% of the sales of the Assistant. A constraint enforcing this requirement is

$$P - 50 \leq 0.5A$$

or

$$P - 0.5A \leq 50$$

Using the equality form of the constraint and setting $P = 0$, we find that the point $(P = 0, A = -100)$ is on the constraint line. Setting $A = 0$, we find a second point $(P = 50, A = 0)$ on the constraint line. If we have drawn only the nonnegative $(P \geq 0, A \geq 0)$ portion of the graph, the first point $(P = 0, A = -100)$ cannot be plotted because $A = -100$ is not on the graph. Whenever we have two points on the line, but one or both of the points cannot be plotted in the nonnegative portion of the graph, the simplest approach is to enlarge the graph. In this example, the point $(P = 0, A = -100)$ can be plotted by extending the graph to include the negative $A$ axis. Once both points satisfying the constraint equation have been located, the line can be drawn. The constraint line and the solutions that satisfy the constraint $P - 0.5A \leq 50$ are shown in Figure 7.11.

**FIGURE 7.11** SOLUTIONS THAT SATISFY THE CONSTRAINT $P - 0.5A \leq 50$

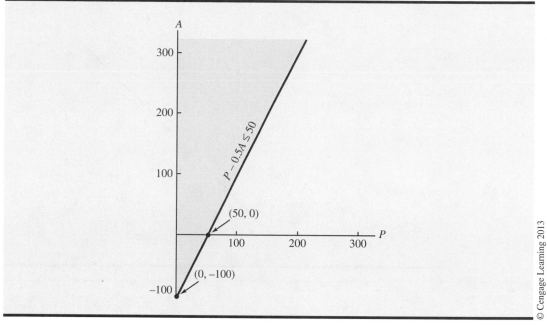

As another example, consider a problem involving two decision variables, $R$ and $T$. Suppose that the number of units of $R$ produced has to at least equal to the number of units of $T$ produced. A constraint enforcing this requirement is

$$R \geq T$$

or

$$R - T \geq 0$$

*Can you graph a constraint line when the origin is on the constraint line? Try Problem 5.*

To find all solutions satisfying the constraint as an equality, we first set $R = 0$ and solve for $T$. This result shows that the origin ($T = 0$, $R = 0$) is on the constraint line. Setting $T = 0$ and solving for $R$ provides the same point. However, we can obtain a second point on the line by setting $T$ equal to any value other than zero and then solving for $R$. For instance, setting $T = 100$ and solving for $R$, we find that the point ($T = 100$, $R = 100$) is on the line. With the two points ($R = 0$, $T = 0$) and ($R = 100$, $T = 100$), the constraint line $R - T = 0$ and the solutions that satisfy the constraint $R - T \geq 0$ can be plotted as shown in Figure 7.12.

## Summary of the Graphical Solution Procedure for Maximization Problems

*For additional practice in using the graphical solution procedure, try Problem 24.*

As we have seen, the graphical solution procedure is a method for solving two-variable linear programming problems such as the RMC problem. The steps of the graphical solution procedure for a maximization problem are summarized here:

1. Prepare a graph for each constraint that shows the solutions that satisfy the constraint.
2. Determine the feasible region by identifying the solutions that satisfy all the constraints simultaneously.

**FIGURE 7.12**   FEASIBLE SOLUTIONS FOR THE CONSTRAINT $R - T \geq 0$

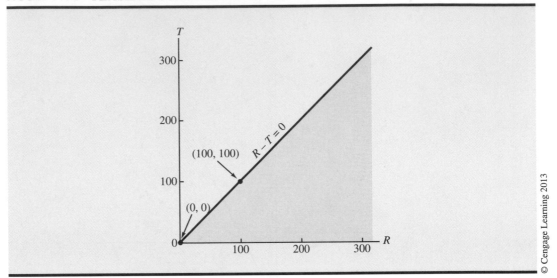

3. Draw an objective function line showing the values of the decision variables that yield a specified value of the objective function.
4. Move parallel objective function lines toward larger objective function values until further movement would take the line completely outside the feasible region.
5. Any feasible solution on the objective function line with the largest value is an optimal solution.

## Slack Variables

In addition to the optimal solution and its associated profit contribution, the RMC managers will want information about the production requirements for the three materials. We can determine this information by substituting the optimal solution values ($F = 25$, $S = 20$) into the constraints of the linear program.

| Constraint | Tons Required for $F = 25$, $S = 20$ Tons | Tons Available | Unused Tons |
|---|---|---|---|
| Material 1 | $0.4(25) + 0.5(20) = 20$ | 20 | 0 |
| Material 2 | $0.2(20) = 4$ | 5 | 1 |
| Material 3 | $0.6(25) + 0.3(20) = 21$ | 21 | 0 |

Thus, the optimal solution tells management that the production of 25 tons of fuel additive and 20 tons of solvent base will require all available material 1 and material 3 but only 4 of the 5 tons of material 2. The 1 ton of unused material 2 is referred to as *slack*. In linear programming terminology, any unused or idle capacity for a $\leq$ constraint is referred to as the *slack associated with the constraint*. Thus, the material 2 constraint has a slack of 1 ton.

*Can you identify the slack associated with a constraint? Try Problem 24, part (e).*

Often variables, called **slack variables**, are added to the formulation of a linear programming problem to represent the slack, or unused capacity, associated with a constraint. Unused capacity makes no contribution to profit, so slack variables have coefficients of zero in the objective function. More generally, slack variables represent the difference between

*Can you write a linear program in standard form? Try Problem 18.*

the right-hand side and the left-hand side of a $\leq$ constraint. After the addition of three slack variables, denoted $S_1$, $S_2$, and $S_3$, the mathematical model of the RMC problem becomes

$$\text{Max} \quad 40F + 30S + 0S_1 + 0S_2 + 0S_3$$

s.t.

$$
\begin{aligned}
0.4F + 0.5S + 1S_1 \qquad\qquad &= 20 \\
0.2S \qquad + 1S_2 \quad\;\; &= 5 \\
0.6F + 0.3S \qquad\qquad + 1S_3 &= 21 \\
F, S, S_1, S_2, S_3 &\geq 0
\end{aligned}
$$

Whenever a linear program is written in a form with all the constraints expressed as equalities, it is said to be written in **standard form**.

Referring to the standard form of the RMC problem, we see that at the optimal solution ($F = 25$, $S = 20$) the values for the slack variables are

| Constraint | Value of Slack Variable |
|---|---|
| Material 1 | $S_1 = 0$ |
| Material 2 | $S_2 = 1$ |
| Material 3 | $S_3 = 0$ |

Could we have used the graphical analysis to provide some of the previous information? The answer is yes. By finding the optimal solution in Figure 7.6, we see that the material 1 constraint and the material 3 constraint restrict, or *bind*, the feasible region at this point. Thus, the optimal solution requires the use of all of these two resources. In other words, the graph shows that at the optimal solution material 1 and material 3 will have zero slack. But, because the material 2 constraint is not binding the feasible region at the optimal solution, we can expect some slack for this resource.

*Recognizing redundant constraints is easy with the graphical solution method. In problems with more than two decision variables, however, redundant constraints usually will not be apparent.*

Finally, some linear programs may have one or more constraints that do not affect the feasible region; that is, the feasible region remains the same whether or not the constraint is included in the problem. Because such a constraint does not affect the feasible region and thus cannot affect the optimal solution, it is called a **redundant constraint**. Redundant constraints can be dropped from the problem without having any effect on the optimal solution. However, in most linear programming problems redundant constraints are not discarded because they are not immediately recognizable as being redundant. The RMC problem had no redundant constraints because each constraint had an effect on the feasible region.

## NOTES AND COMMENTS

1. In the standard form representation of a linear program, the objective function coefficients for the slack variables are zero. This condition implies that slack variables, which represent unused resources, do not affect the value of the objective function. However, in some applications, some or all of the unused resources can be sold and contribute to profit. In such cases the corresponding slack variables become decision variables representing the amount of resources to be sold. For each of these variables, a nonzero coefficient in the objective function would reflect the profit associated with selling a unit of the corresponding resource.

2. Redundant constraints do not affect the feasible region; as a result they can be removed from a linear programming model without affecting the optimal solution. However, if the linear programming model is to be resolved later, changes in some of the data might change a previously redundant constraint into a binding constraint. Thus, we recommend keeping all constraints in the linear programming model even though one or more of the constraints may be redundant.

## 7.3   Extreme Points and the Optimal Solution

Suppose that the profit contribution for 1 ton of solvent base increases from \$30 to \$60 while the profit contribution for 1 ton of fuel additive and all the constraints remain unchanged. The complete linear programming model of this new problem is identical to the mathematical model in Section 7.2, except for the revised objective function:

$$\text{Max } 40F + 60S$$

How does this change in the objective function affect the optimal solution to the RMC problem? Figure 7.13 shows the graphical solution of the RMC problem with the revised objective function. Note that because the constraints do not change, the feasible region remains unchanged. However, the profit lines must be altered to reflect the new objective function.

By moving the profit line in a parallel manner away from the origin, we find the optimal solution as shown in Figure 7.13. The values of the decision variables at this point are $F = 18.75$ and $S = 25$. The increased profit for the solvent base caused a change in the optimal solution. In fact, as you might suspect, we cut back the production of the lower profit fuel additive and increase the production of the higher profit solvent base.

What do you notice about the location of the optimal solutions in the linear programming problems that we solved thus far? Look closely at the graphical solutions in Figures 7.10 and 7.13. An important observation that you should be able to make is that the optimal solutions occur at one of the vertices, or "corners," of the feasible region. In linear programming terminology these vertices are referred to as the **extreme points** of the feasible region. Thus,

**FIGURE 7.13**   OPTIMAL SOLUTION FOR THE RMC PROBLEM WITH AN OBJECTIVE FUNCTION OF $40F + 60S$

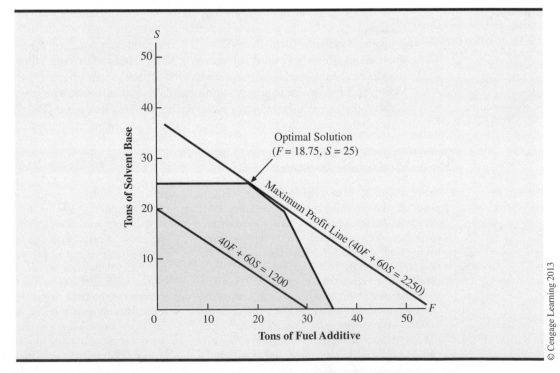

**FIGURE 7.14** THE FIVE EXTREME POINTS OF THE FEASIBLE REGION FOR THE RMC PROBLEM

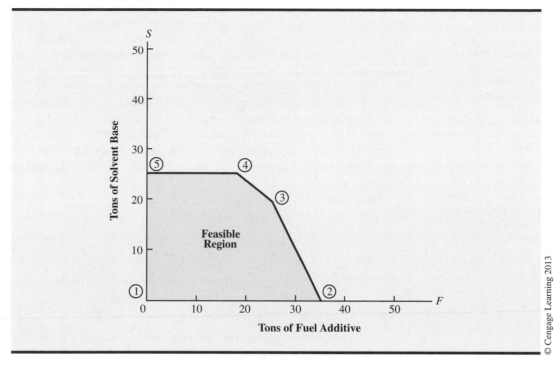

the RMC has five vertices or five extreme points (Figure 7.14). We can now state our observation about the location of optimal solutions:[2]

> The optimal solution to a linear programming problem can be found at an extreme point of the feasible region for the problem.

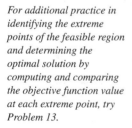

*For additional practice in identifying the extreme points of the feasible region and determining the optimal solution by computing and comparing the objective function value at each extreme point, try Problem 13.*

This property means that, if you are looking for the optimal solution to a linear programming problem, you do not have to evaluate all feasible solution points. In fact, you have to consider *only* the feasible solutions that occur at the extreme points of the feasible region. Thus, for the RMC problem, instead of computing and comparing the profit for all feasible solutions, we can find the optimal solution by evaluating the five extreme-point solutions and selecting the one that provides the highest profit. Actually, the graphical solution procedure is nothing more than a convenient way of identifying an optimal extreme point for two-variable problems.

## 7.4 Computer Solution of the RMC Problem

Computer programs designed to solve linear programming problems are widely available. After a short period of familiarization with the specific features of the program, most users can solve linear programming problems with few difficulties. Problems involving thousands of variables and thousands of constraints are now routinely solved with computer packages. Some of the leading commercial packages include CPLEX, LINGO, MOSEK, Gurobi, and Xpress-MP.

---

[2]In Section 7.6 we show that two special cases (infeasibility and unboundedness) in linear programming have no optimal solution. The observation stated does not apply to these cases.

*In January 1952 the first successful computer solution of a linear programming problem was performed on the SEAC (Standards Eastern Automatic Computer). The SEAC, the first digital computer built by the National Bureau of Standards under U.S. Air Force sponsorship, had a 512-word memory and magnetic tape for external storage.*

*Instructions on how to solve linear programs using Excel and LINGO are provided in appendixes at the end of the chapter.*

Packages are also available for free download. A good example is Clp (COIN-OR linear programming) available from the COIN-OR organization at *http://www.coin-or.org*.

A large number of user-friendly computer programs that can solve linear programs are now available. These programs, developed by academicians and small software companies, are almost all easy to use. Most of these programs are designed to solve smaller linear programs (a few hundred variables), but some can be used to solve problems involving thousands of variables and constraints. Linear programming solvers are also available in the spreadsheet environment. In Appendix 7.1 we show how to use the solver available with Excel. Appendix 7.2 demonstrates the use of LINGO, a stand-alone software package for solving optimization problems.

Probably the most widely used tool is Solver, which is built into Microsoft Excel. Therefore, the computer output we discuss is based on the output provided by Excel Solver. The complete details for how to formulate the RMC problem in Excel and use Solver are contained in Appendix 7.1.

Recall the RMC linear program:

$$\text{Max} \quad 40F + 30S$$

s.t.

$$
\begin{array}{rll}
0.4F + 0.5S &\leq 20 & \text{Material 1} \\
0.2S &\leq 5 & \text{Material 2} \\
0.6F + 0.3S &\leq 21 & \text{Material 3} \\
F, S &\geq 0 &
\end{array}
$$

Figure 7.15 shows the optimal solution to the RMC problem. This output is based on the Answer Report from Excel Solver, but includes the variable names we have used in our linear programming model. This allows you to easily link the answer report to the model under discussion. We will use this style to show the solutions to optimization problems throughout Chapters 7–12.

## Interpretation of Answer Report

Let us look more closely at the answer report in Figure 7.15 and interpret the computer solution provided for the RMC problem. First, note the number 1600.000 in the Objective Cells

**FIGURE 7.15**    ANSWER REPORT FOR THE RMC PROBLEM

WEB file

RMC

**Objective Cells (Max)**

| Name | Original Value | Final Value |
|---|---|---|
| Maximize Total Profit | 0.000 | 1600.000 |

**Variable Cells**

| Model Variable | Name | Original Value | Final Value | Integer |
|---|---|---|---|---|
| F | Tons Produced Fuel Additive | 0.000 | 25.000 | Contin |
| S | Tons Produced Solvent Base | 0.000 | 20.000 | Contin |

**Constraints**

| Constraint Number | Name | Cell Value | Status | Slack |
|---|---|---|---|---|
| 1 | Material 1 Amount Used | 20.000 | Binding | 0.000 |
| 2 | Material 2 Amount Used | 4.000 | Not Binding | 1.000 |
| 3 | Material 3 Amount Used | 21.000 | Binding | 0.000 |

(Max) section, which appears in the Final Value column to the right of objective function value, Maximize Total Profit. This number indicates that the optimal solution to this problem will provide a profit of $1600. Directly below the objective function value are the values of the decision variables at the optimal solution. These are shown as the Final Value column of the Variable Cells section in the answer report. Thus, we have $F = 25$ tons of fuel additive and $S = 20$ tons of solvent base as the optimal production quantities. We will discuss the meaning of the Integer column in the Variable Cells section in Chapter 11.

The Constraints section of the answer report provides information about the status of the constraints. Recall that the RMC problem had three less-than-or-equal-to constraints corresponding to the tons available for each of the three raw materials. The information shown in the Slack column provides the value of the slack variable for each of the three constraints. This information is summarized as follows:

| Constraint Number | Constraint Name | Value of Slack Variable |
|:---:|:---:|:---:|
| 1 | Material 1 Amount Used | 0 |
| 2 | Material 2 Amount Used | 1 |
| 3 | Material 3 Amount Used | 0 |

Thus, we see that the binding constraints (the Material 1 Amount Used and Material 3 Amount Used constraints) have zero slack at the optimal solution. The Material 2 Amount Used constraint has 1 ton of slack, or unused capacity.

## (7.5) A Simple Minimization Problem

M&D Chemicals produces two products that are sold as raw materials to companies manufacturing bath soaps and laundry detergents. Based on an analysis of current inventory levels and potential demand for the coming month, M&D's management has specified that the combined production for products A and B must total at least 350 gallons. Separately, a major customer's order for 125 gallons of product A must also be satisfied. Product A requires 2 hours of processing time per gallon while product B requires 1 hour of processing time per gallon, and for the coming month, 600 hours of processing time are available. M&D's objective is to satisfy these requirements at a minimum total production cost. Production costs are $2 per gallon for product A and $3 per gallon for product B.

To find the minimum-cost production schedule, we will formulate the M&D Chemicals problem as a linear program. Following a procedure similar to the one used for the RMC problem, we first define the decision variables and the objective function for the problem. Let

$$A = \text{number of gallons of product A}$$
$$B = \text{number of gallons of product B}$$

Because the production costs are $2 per gallon for product A and $3 per gallon for product B, the objective function that corresponds to the minimization of the total production cost can be written as

$$\text{Min } 2A + 3B$$

Next, consider the constraints placed on the M&D Chemicals problem. To satisfy the major customer's demand for 125 gallons of product A, we know $A$ must be at least 125. Thus, we write the constraint

$$1A \geq 125$$

Because the combined production for both products must total at least 350 gallons, we can write the constraint

$$1A + 1B \geq 350$$

Finally, the limitation on available processing time of 600 hours means that we need to add the constraint

$$2A + 1B \leq 600$$

After adding the nonnegativity constraints ($A, B \geq 0$), we have the following linear program for the M&D Chemicals problem:

$$\text{Max} \quad 2A + 3B$$

s.t.

| | | |
|---|---|---|
| $1A$ | $\geq 125$ | Demand for product A |
| $1A + 1B$ | $\geq 350$ | Total production |
| $2A + 1B$ | $\leq 600$ | Processing time |
| $A, B \geq 0$ | | |

Because the linear programming model has only two decision variables, the graphical solution procedure can be used to find the optimal production quantities. The graphical method for this problem, just as in the RMC problem, requires us to first graph the constraint lines to find the feasible region. By graphing each constraint line separately and then checking points on either side of the constraint line, the solutions that satisfy each constraint can be identified. By combining the solutions that satisfy each constraint on the same graph, we obtain the feasible region shown in Figure 7.16.

**FIGURE 7.16**    FEASIBLE REGION FOR THE M&D CHEMICALS PROBLEM

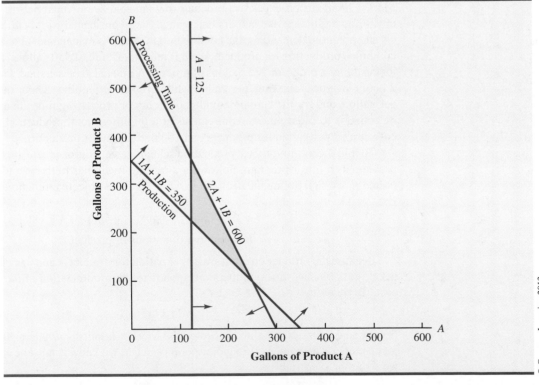

**FIGURE 7.17**   GRAPHICAL SOLUTION FOR THE M&D CHEMICALS PROBLEM

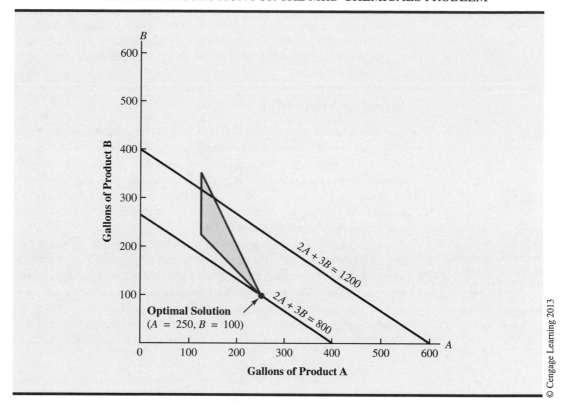

To find the minimum-cost solution, we now draw the objective function line corresponding to a particular total cost value. For example, we might start by drawing the line $2A + 3B = 1200$. This line is shown in Figure 7.17. Clearly some points in the feasible region would provide a total cost of $1200. To find the values of $A$ and $B$ that provide smaller total cost values, we move the objective function line in a lower left direction until, if we moved it any farther, it would be entirely outside the feasible region. Note that the objective function line $2A + 3B = 800$ intersects the feasible region at the extreme point $A = 250$ and $B = 100$. This extreme point provides the minimum-cost solution with an objective function value of 800. From Figures 7.16 and 7.17, we can see that the total production constraint and the processing time constraint are binding. Just as in every linear programming problem, the optimal solution occurs at an extreme point of the feasible region.

## Summary of the Graphical Solution Procedure for Minimization Problems

*Can you use the graphical solution procedure to determine the optimal solution for a minimization problem? Try Problem 31.*

The steps of the graphical solution procedure for a minimization problem are summarized here:

1. Prepare a graph for each constraint that shows the solutions that satisfy the constraint.
2. Determine the feasible region by identifying the solutions that satisfy all the constraints simultaneously.

3. Draw an objective function line showing the values of the decision variables that yield a specified value of the objective function.
4. Move parallel objective function lines toward smaller objective function values until further movement would take the line completely outside the feasible region.
5. Any feasible solution on the objective function line with the smallest value is an optimal solution.

## Surplus Variables

The optimal solution to the M&D Chemicals problem shows that the desired total production of $A + B = 350$ gallons is achieved by using all available processing time of $2A + 1B = 2(250) + 1(100) = 600$ hours. In addition, note that the constraint requiring that product A demand be met is satisfied with $A = 250$ gallons. In fact, the production of product A exceeds its minimum level by $250 - 125 = 125$ gallons. This excess production for product A is referred to as *surplus*. In linear programming terminology, any excess quantity corresponding to a $\geq$ constraint is referred to as surplus.

*Excel Solver refers to all nonbinding constraints as having positive slack values regardless of whether they are $\geq$ or $\leq$ constraints. However, we will use "surplus" when referring to a nonbinding $\geq$ constraint.*

Recall that with a $\leq$ constraint, a slack variable can be added to the left-hand side of the inequality to convert the constraint to equality form. With a $\geq$ constraint, a **surplus variable** can be subtracted from the left-hand side of the inequality to convert the constraint to equality form. Just as with slack variables, surplus variables are given a coefficient of zero in the objective function because they have no effect on its value. After including two surplus variables, $S_1$ and $S_2$, for the $\geq$ constraints and one slack variable, $S_3$, for the $\leq$ constraint, the linear programming model of the M&D Chemicals problem becomes

$$\text{Min} \quad 2A + 3B + 0S_1 + 0S_2 + 0S_3$$
$$\text{s.t.}$$
$$1A \quad\quad\quad - 1S_1 \quad\quad\quad\quad\quad = 125$$
$$1A + 1B \quad\quad\quad - 1S_2 \quad\quad\quad = 350$$
$$2A + 1B \quad\quad\quad\quad\quad\quad + 1S_3 = 600$$
$$A, B, S_1, S_2, S_3 \geq 0$$

*Try Problem 35 to test your ability to use slack and surplus variables to write a linear program in standard form.*

All the constraints are now equalities. Hence, the preceding formulation is the standard form representation of the M&D Chemicals problem. At the optimal solution of $A = 250$ and $B = 100$, the values of the surplus and slack variables are as follows:

| Constraint | Value of Surplus or Slack Variable |
|---|---|
| Demand for product A | $S_1 = 125$ |
| Total production | $S_2 = 0$ |
| Processing time | $S_3 = 0$ |

Refer to Figures 7.16 and 7.17. Note that the zero surplus and slack variables are associated with the constraints that are binding at the optimal solution—that is, the total production and processing time constraints. The surplus of 125 units is associated with the nonbinding constraint on the demand for product A.

In the RMC problem all the constraints were of the $\leq$ type, and in the M&D Chemicals problem the constraints were a mixture of $\geq$ and $\leq$ types. The number and types of constraints encountered in a particular linear programming problem depend on the specific conditions existing in the problem. Linear programming problems may have some $\leq$ constraints, some $\geq$ constraints, and some $=$ constraints. For an equality constraint, feasible solutions must lie directly on the constraint line.

*Try Problem 34 to practice solving a linear program with all three constraint forms.*

An example of a linear program with two decision variables, $G$ and $H$, and all three constraint forms is given here:

$$\text{Min} \quad 2G + 2H$$

s.t.

$$1G + 3H \leq 12$$
$$3G + 1H \geq 13$$
$$1G - 1H = 3$$
$$G, H \geq 0$$

The standard-form representation of this problem is

$$\text{Min} \quad 2G + 2H + 0S_1 + 0S_2$$

s.t.

$$1G + 3H + 1S_1 \quad\quad = 12$$
$$3G + 1H \quad\quad - 1S_2 = 13$$
$$1G - 1H \quad\quad\quad = 3$$
$$G, H, S_1, S_2 \geq 0$$

The standard form requires a slack variable for the $\leq$ constraint and a surplus variable for the $\geq$ constraint. However, neither a slack nor a surplus variable is required for the third constraint because it is already in equality form.

When solving linear programs graphically, it is not necessary to write the problem in its standard form. Nevertheless, it is helpful to be able to compute the values of the slack and surplus variables and understand what they mean. A final point: The standard form of the linear programming problem is equivalent to the original formulation of the problem. That is, the optimal solution to any linear programming problem is the same as the optimal solution to the standard form of the problem. The standard form does not change the basic problem; it only changes how we write the constraints for the problem.

## Computer Solution of the M&D Chemicals Problem

The answer report for the M&D Chemicals Problem is presented in Figure 7.18. The answer report shows that the minimum-cost solution yields an objective function value of $800. The

**FIGURE 7.18**   ANSWER REPORT FOR THE M&D CHEMICALS PROBLEM

Objective Cells (Min)

| Name | Original Value | Final Value |
|---|---|---|
| Minimize Total Cost Product A | 0.000 | 800.000 |

**M&D**   Variable Cells

| Model Variable | Name | Original Value | Final Value | Integer |
|---|---|---|---|---|
| A | Gallons Produced Product A | 0.000 | 250.000 | Contin |
| B | Gallons Produced Product B | 0.000 | 100.000 | Contin |

Constraints

| Constraint Number | Name | Cell Value | Status | Slack |
|---|---|---|---|---|
| 1 | Demand for Product A | 250.000 | Not Binding | 125.000 |
| 2 | Total Production | 350.000 | Binding | 0.000 |
| 3 | Processing Time | 600.000 | Binding | 0.000 |

values of the decision variables show that 250 gallons of product A and 100 gallons of product B provide the minimum-cost solution.

The Slack column in the Constraints section of the answer report shows that the $\geq$ constraint corresponding to the demand for product A (see constraint 1) has a value of 125 units. Excel uses "slack" when referring to nonbinding $\geq$ or $\leq$ constraints. However, since this is a $\geq$ constraint, it tells us that production of product A in the optimal solution exceeds demand by 125 gallons. In other words, the demand for product A (constraint 1) has a surplus value of 125 units. The slack values are zero for the total production requirement (constraint 2) and the processing time limitation (constraint 3), which indicates that these constraints are binding at the optimal solution.

 **7.6    Special Cases**

In this section we discuss three special situations that can arise when we attempt to solve linear programming problems.

### Alternative Optimal Solutions

From our discussion of the graphical solution procedure, we know that optimal solutions can be found at the extreme points of the feasible region. Now let us consider the special case where the optimal objective function line coincides with one of the binding constraint lines. It can lead to **alternative optimal solutions**, whereby more than one solution provides the optimal value for the objective function.

To illustrate the case of alternative optimal solutions, we return to the RMC problem. However, let us assume that the profit contribution for the solvent base ($S$) has increased to $50. The revised objective function is $40F + 50S$. Figure 7.19 shows the graphical solution to this problem. Note that the optimal solution still occurs at an extreme point. In fact, it occurs at two extreme points: extreme point ③ ($F = 25, S = 20$) and extreme point ④ ($F = 18.75, S = 25$).

The objective function values at these two extreme points are identical; that is,

$$40F + 50S = 40(25) + 50(20) = 2000$$

and

$$40F + 50S = 40(18.75) + 50(25) = 2000$$

Furthermore, any point on the line connecting the two optimal extreme points also provides an optimal solution. For example, the solution point ($F = 21.875, S = 22.5$), which is halfway between the two extreme points, also provides the optimal objective function value of

$$40F + 50S = 40(21.875) + 50(22.5) = 2000$$

A linear programming problem with alternative optimal solutions is generally a good situation for the manager or decision maker. It means that several combinations of the decision variables are optimal and that the manager can select the most desirable optimal solution. Unfortunately, determining whether a problem has alternative optimal solutions is not a simple matter.

### Infeasibility

**Infeasibility** means that no solution to the linear programming problem satisfies all constraints, including the nonnegativity constraints. Graphically, infeasibility means that a feasible region does not exist; that is, no points satisfy all constraint equations and

**FIGURE 7.19**   OPTIMAL SOLUTIONS FOR THE RMC PROBLEM WITH AN OBJECTIVE
FUNCTION OF $40F + 50S$

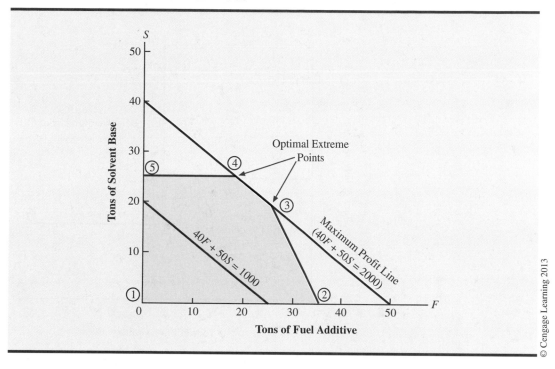

nonnegativity conditions simultaneously. To illustrate this situation, let us return to the problem facing RMC.

*Problems with no feasible solution do arise in practice, most often because management's expectations are too high or because too many restrictions have been placed on the problem.*

Suppose that management specified that at least 30 tons of fuel additive and at least 15 tons of solvent base must be produced. Figure 7.20 shows the graph of the solution region that reflects these requirements. The shaded area in the lower left-hand portion of the graph depicts those points satisfying the less-than-or-equal-to constraints on the amount of materials available. The shaded area in the upper right-hand portion depicts those points satisfying the minimum production requirements of 30 tons of fuel additive and 15 tons of solvent base. But none of the points satisfy both sets of constraints. Thus, if management imposes these minimum production requirements, no feasible solution to the linear programming problem is possible.

How should we interpret this infeasibility in terms of the current problem? First, we should tell management that, for the available amounts of the three materials, producing 30 tons of fuel additive and 15 tons of solvent base isn't possible. Moreover, we can tell management exactly how much more of each material is needed.

| Material | Minimum Tons Required for $F = 30, S = 15$ | Tons Available | Additional Tons Required |
|---|---|---|---|
| Material 1 | $0.4(30) + 0.5(15) = 19.5$ | 20 | — |
| Material 2 | $0.2(15) = 3$ | 5 | — |
| Material 3 | $0.6(30) + 0.3(15) = 22.5$ | 21 | 1.5 |

**FIGURE 7.20**    NO FEASIBLE REGION FOR THE RMC PROBLEM WITH MINIMUM
PRODUCTION REQUIREMENTS

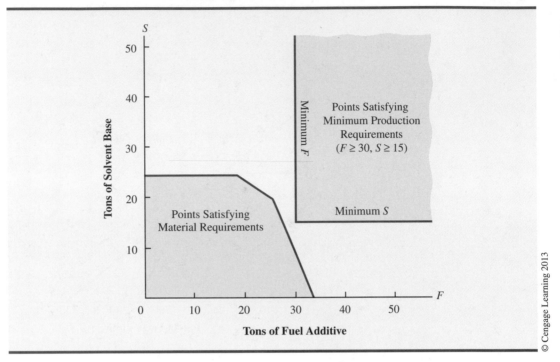

Thus, RMC has a sufficient supply of materials 1 and 2 but will need 1.5 additional tons of material 3 to meet management's production requirements of 30 tons of fuel additive and 15 tons of solvent base. If, after reviewing the preceding analysis, management still wants this level of production for the two products, RMC will have to obtain the additional 1.5 tons of material 3.

Often, many possibilities are available for corrective management action, once we discover the lack of a feasible solution. The important thing to realize is that linear programming analysis can help determine whether management's plans are feasible. By analyzing the problem using linear programming, we are often able to point out infeasible conditions and initiate corrective action.

Whenever you attempt to solve a problem that is infeasible using Excel Solver, you will obtain a message that says "Solver could not find a feasible solution." In this case, you know that no solution to the linear programming problem will satisfy all constraints. Careful inspection of your formulation is necessary to identify why the problem is infeasible. In some situations the only reasonable approach is to drop one or more constraints and resolve the problem. If you are able to find an optimal solution for this revised problem, you will know that the constraint(s) that were omitted are causing the problem to be infeasible.

## Unbounded

The solution to a maximization linear programming problem is **unbounded** if the value of the solution may be made infinitely large without violating any of the constraints; for a minimization problem, the solution is unbounded if the value may be made infinitely small. This condition might be termed *managerial utopia*; for example, if this condition were to occur in a profit maximization problem, the manager could achieve an unlimited profit.

However, in linear programming models of real problems, the occurrence of an un-bounded solution means that the problem has been improperly formulated. We know it is not possible to increase profits indefinitely. Therefore, we must conclude that if a profit maximization problem results in an unbounded solution, the mathematical model doesn't represent the real-world problem sufficiently. Usually, an unbounded problem results from the inadvertent omission of a constraint during problem formulation.

As an illustration, consider the following linear program with two decision variables, $X$ and $Y$:

$$\text{Max} \quad 20X + 10Y$$
$$\text{s.t.}$$
$$1X \quad\quad \geq 2$$
$$1Y \leq 5$$
$$X, Y \geq 0$$

In Figure 7.21 we graphed the feasible region associated with this problem. Note that we can only indicate part of the feasible region because the feasible region extends indefinitely in the direction of the $X$-axis. Looking at the objective function lines in Figure 7.21, we see that the solution to this problem may be made as large as we desire. No matter what solution we pick, we will always be able to reach some feasible solution with a larger value. Thus, we say that the solution to this linear program is *unbounded*.

**FIGURE 7.21**   EXAMPLE OF AN UNBOUNDED PROBLEM

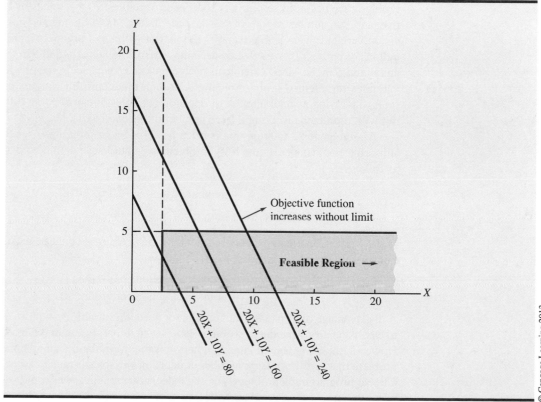

*Can you recognize whether a linear program involves alternative optimal solutions, infeasibility, or is unbounded? Try Problems 42 and 43.*

Whenever you attempt to solve a problem that is unbounded using Excel Solver, you will obtain a message that says, "The Objective Cell values do not converge." Because unbounded solutions cannot occur in real problems, the first thing you should do is to review your model to determine whether you have incorrectly formulated the problem.

## NOTES AND COMMENTS

1. Infeasibility is independent of the objective function. It exists because the constraints are so restrictive that they allow no feasible region for the linear programming model. Thus, when you encounter infeasibility, making changes in the coefficients of the objective function will not help; the problem will remain infeasible.
2. The occurrence of an unbounded solution is often the result of a missing constraint. However, a change in the objective function may cause a previously unbounded problem to become bounded with an optimal solution. For example, the graph in Figure 7.21 shows an unbounded solution for the objective function Max $20X + 10Y$. However, changing the objective function to Max $-20X - 10Y$ will provide the optimal solution $X = 2$ and $Y = 0$ even though no changes have been made in the constraints.

 **7.7**  # General Linear Programming Notation

In this chapter we showed how to formulate mathematical models for the RMC and M&D Chemicals linear programming problems. To formulate a mathematical model of the RMC problem, we began by defining two decision variables: $F$ = number of tons of fuel additive, and $S$ = number of tons of solvent base. In the M&D Chemicals problem, the two decision variables were defined as $A$ = number of gallons of product A, and $B$ = number of gallons of product B. We selected decision variable names of $F$ and $S$ in the RMC problem and $A$ and $B$ in the M&D Chemicals problem to make it easier to recall what these decision variables represented in the problem. Although this approach works well for linear programs involving a small number of decision variables, it can become difficult when dealing with problems involving a large number of decision variables.

A more general notation that is often used for linear programs uses the letter $x$ with a subscript. For instance, in the RMC problem, we could have defined the decision variables as follows:

$$x_1 = \text{number of tons of fuel additive}$$

$$x_2 = \text{number of tons of solvent base}$$

In the M&D Chemicals problem, the same variable names would be used, but their definitions would change:

$$x_1 = \text{number of gallons of product A}$$

$$x_2 = \text{number of gallons of product B}$$

A disadvantage of using general notation for decision variables is that we are no longer able to easily identify what the decision variables actually represent in the mathematical model. However, the advantage of general notation is that formulating a mathematical model for a problem that involves a large number of decision variables is much easier. For instance, for a linear programming problem with three decision variables, we would use variable names of $x_1$, $x_2$, and $x_3$; for a problem with four decision variables, we would use variable names of $x_1, x_2, x_3,$ and $x_4$; and so on. Clearly, if a problem involved 1000 decision variables, trying to identify 1000 unique names would be difficult. However, using the general linear programming notation, the decision variables would be defined as $x_1, x_2, x_3, \ldots, x_{1000}$.

To illustrate the graphical solution procedure for a linear program written using general linear programming notation, consider the following mathematical model for a maximization problem involving two decision variables:

$$\text{Max} \quad 3x_1 + 2x_2$$
$$\text{s.t.}$$
$$2x_1 + 2x_2 \leq 8$$
$$1x_1 + 0.5x_2 \leq 3$$
$$x_1, x_2 \geq 0$$

We must first develop a graph that displays the possible solutions ($x_1$ and $x_2$ values) for the problem. The usual convention is to plot values of $x_1$ along the horizontal axis and values of $x_2$ along the vertical axis. Figure 7.22 shows the graphical solution for this two-variable

**FIGURE 7.22**    GRAPHICAL SOLUTION OF A TWO-VARIABLE LINEAR PROGRAM WITH GENERAL NOTATION

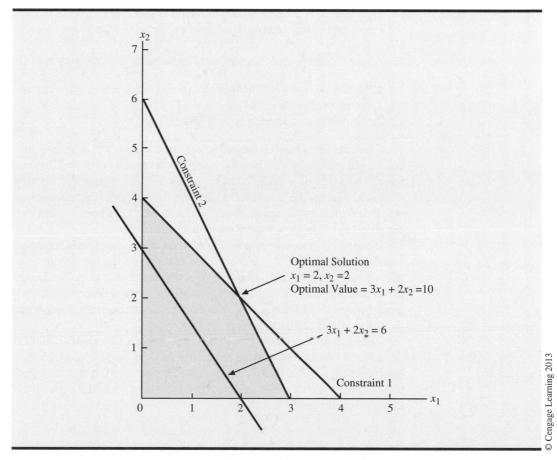

problem. Note that for this problem the optimal solution is $x_1 = 2$ and $x_2 = 2$, with an objective function value of 10.

Using general linear programming notation, we can write the standard form of the preceding problem as follows:

$$\text{Max} \quad 3x_1 + \quad 2x_2 + 0s_1 + 0s_2$$
$$\text{s.t.}$$
$$2x_1 + \quad 2x_2 + 1s_1 \qquad\quad = 8$$
$$1x_1 + 0.5x_2 + \qquad\quad 1s_2 = 3$$
$$x_1, x_2, s_1, s_2 \geq 0$$

Thus, at the optimal solution $x_1 = 2$ and $x_2 = 2$, the values of the slack variables are $s_1 = s_2 = 0$.

## Summary

We formulated linear programming models for the RMC maximization problem and the M&D Chemicals minimization problem. For both problems we showed how a graphical solution procedure and Excel Solver can be used to identify an optimal solution. In formulating a linear programming model of these problems, we developed a general definition of a linear program.

A linear program is a mathematical model with the following qualities:

1. A linear objective function that is to be maximized or minimized
2. A set of linear constraints
3. Variables restricted to nonnegative values

Slack variables may be used to write less-than-or-equal-to constraints in equality form, and surplus variables may be used to write greater-than-or-equal-to constraints in equality form. The value of a slack variable can usually be interpreted as the amount of unused resource, whereas the value of a surplus variable indicates the amount over and above some stated minimum requirement. When all constraints have been written as equalities, the linear program has been written in its standard form.

If the solution to a linear program is infeasible or unbounded, no optimal solution to the problem can be found. In the case of infeasibility, no feasible solutions are possible. In the case of an unbounded solution, the objective function can be made infinitely large for a maximization problem and infinitely small for a minimization problem. In the case of alternative optimal solutions, two or more optimal extreme points exist, and all the points on the line segment connecting them are also optimal.

The chapter concluded with a section showing how to write a mathematical model using general linear programming notation. The Q.M. in Action, The U.S. Navy Uses Linear Programming for Fuel Conservation, provides just one of many examples of the widespread use of linear programming. In the next two chapters we will see many more applications of linear programming.

## Q.M. *in* ACTION

### THE U.S. NAVY USES LINEAR PROGRAMMING FOR FUEL CONSERVATION*

The U.S. Navy spends approximately one billion dollars per year on fuel for its ships. The major determinant of fuel consumption for a ship is speed. A ship can be operated in a number of different modes. For example, a naval destroyer ship, with four engines available to run two shafts for propelling the ship, may operate in three different modes: trail-shaft, split-plant, and full-power. In trail-shaft mode, one of the four engines runs a single shaft. In split-plant mode, two engines run, each driving its own shaft. Full-power mode has all four engines running, two on each shaft. Full-power has the highest full consumption rate as measured in gallons per hour. Depending on the mode, a ship may consume between 600 to 7000 gallons of fuel per hour.

The captain of a ship which needs to get from point A to point B in a certain amount of time has mode options, each of which consumes different amounts of fuel. The ship can run at a steady speed or at variable speeds. For example, a ship can operate in a faster mode during first portion of the trip and in a slower mode during the remaining portion of the trip and still arrive at the same time as a vessel running at the required constant speed. The U.S. Navy uses a spreadsheet-based linear programming model to determine the most fuel efficient way to make a trip in a required amount of time.

The decision variables of the linear program are the amount of time (in hours) to run at a given speed. The objective is to minimize fuel consumption subject to constraints that the required distance must be covered within a specified amount of time. The solution to the linear program specifies the amount of time to run at each speed, but the order in which the speeds are implemented is flexible. Compared to the fuel consumption when operating in a single mode, fuel savings ranging from 2% to 54% have been realized by implementing the variable modes recommended by the linear programming model.

*Based on G. Brown, J. Kline, R. Rosenthal, and A. Washburn, "Steaming on Convex Hulls," *Interfaces* 37, no. 4 (July–August 2007): 342–352.

## Glossary

**Constraint** An equation or inequality that rules out certain combinations of decision variables as feasible solutions.

**Problem formulation** The process of translating a verbal statement of a problem into a mathematical statement called the *mathematical model*.

**Mathematical model** A representation of a problem where the objective and all constraint conditions are described by mathematical expressions.

**Decision variable** A controllable input for a linear programming model.

**Objective function** The expression that defines the quantity to be maximized or minimized in a linear programming model.

**Nonnegativity constraints** A set of constraints that requires all variables to be nonnegative.

**Linear program** A mathematical model with a linear objective function, a set of linear constraints, and nonnegative variables.

**Linear functions** Mathematical expressions in which the variables appear in separate terms and are raised to the first power.

**Feasible solution** A solution that satisfies all the constraints simultaneously.

**Feasible region** The set of all feasible solutions.

**Slack variable** A variable added to the left-hand side of a less-than-or-equal-to constraint to convert the constraint into an equality. The value of this variable can usually be interpreted as the amount of unused resource.

**Standard form** A linear program in which all the constraints are written as equalities. The optimal solution of the standard form of a linear program is the same as the optimal solution of the original formulation of the linear program.

**Redundant constraint** A constraint that does not affect the feasible region. If a constraint is redundant, it can be removed from the problem without affecting the feasible region.

**Extreme point** Graphically speaking, extreme points are the feasible solution points occurring at the vertices, or "corners," of the feasible region. With two-variable problems, extreme points are determined by the intersection of the constraint lines.

**Surplus variable** A variable subtracted from the left-hand side of a greater-than-or-equal-to constraint to convert the constraint into an equality. The value of this variable can usually be interpreted as the amount over and above some required minimum level.

**Alternative optimal solutions** The case in which more than one solution provides the optimal value for the objective function.

**Infeasibility** The situation in which no solution to the linear programming problem satisfies all the constraints.

**Unbounded** The situation in which the value of the solution may be made infinitely large in a maximization linear programming problem or infinitely small in a minimization problem without violating any of the constraints.

## Problems

1.  Which of the following mathematical relationships could be found in a linear programming model, and which could not? For the relationships that are unacceptable for linear programs, state why.
    a.  $-1A + 2B \leq 70$
    b.  $2A - 2B = 50$
    c.  $1A - 2B^2 \leq 10$
    d.  $3\sqrt{A} + 2B \geq 15$
    e.  $1A + 1B = 6$
    f.  $2A + 5B + 1AB \leq 25$

2.  Find the solutions that satisfy the following constraints:
    a.  $4A + 2B \leq 16$
    b.  $4A + 2B \geq 16$
    c.  $4A + 2B = 16$

3.  Show a separate graph of the constraint lines and the solutions that satisfy each of the following constraints:
    a.  $3A + 2B \leq 18$
    b.  $12A + 8B \geq 480$
    c.  $5A + 10B = 200$

4.  Show a separate graph of the constraint lines and the solutions that satisfy each of the following constraints:
    a.  $3A - 4B \geq 60$
    b.  $-6A + 5B \leq 60$
    c.  $5A - 2B \leq 0$

5. Show a separate graph of the constraint lines and the solutions that satisfy each of the following constraints:
   a.  $A \geq 0.25 (A + B)$
   b.  $B \leq 0.10 (A + B)$
   c.  $A \leq 0.50 (A + B)$

6. Three objective functions for linear programming problems are $7A + 10B$, $6A + 4B$, and $-4A + 7B$. Show the graph of each for objective function values equal to 420.

7. Identify the feasible region for the following set of constraints:

$$0.5A + 0.25B \geq 30$$
$$1A + 5B \geq 250$$
$$0.25A + 0.5B \leq 50$$
$$A, B \geq 0$$

8. Identify the feasible region for the following set of constraints:

$$2A - 1B \leq 0$$
$$-1A + 1.5B \leq 200$$
$$A, B \geq 0$$

9. Identify the feasible region for the following set of constraints:

$$3A - 2B \geq 0$$
$$2A - 1B \leq 200$$
$$1A \leq 150$$
$$A, B \geq 0$$

10. For the linear program

$$\text{Max} \quad 2A + 3B$$
$$\text{s.t.}$$
$$1A + 2B \leq 6$$
$$5A + 3B \leq 15$$
$$A, B \geq 0$$

   find the optimal solution using the graphical solution procedure. What is the value of the objective function at the optimal solution?

11. Solve the following linear program using the graphical solution procedure:

$$\text{Max} \quad 5A + 5B$$
$$\text{s.t.}$$
$$1A \leq 100$$
$$1B \leq 80$$
$$2A + 4B \leq 400$$
$$A, B \geq 0$$

12. Consider the following linear programming problem:

$$\text{Max} \quad 3A + 3B$$
$$\text{s.t.}$$
$$2A + 4B \leq 12$$
$$6A + 4B \leq 24$$
$$A, B \geq 0$$

a.  Find the optimal solution using the graphical solution procedure.
b.  If the objective function is changed to $2A + 6B$, what will the optimal solution be?
c.  How many extreme points are there? What are the values of $A$ and $B$ at each extreme point?

13. Consider the following linear program:

$$\text{Max} \quad 1A + 2B$$
$$\text{s.t.}$$
$$1A \qquad\quad \leq 5$$
$$\quad 1B \leq 4$$
$$2A + 2B = 12$$
$$A, B \geq 0$$

a.  Show the feasible region.
b.  What are the extreme points of the feasible region?
c.  Find the optimal solution using the graphical procedure.

14. Par, Inc., is a small manufacturer of golf equipment and supplies. Par's distributor believes a market exists for both a medium-priced golf bag, referred to as a standard model, and a high-priced golf bag, referred to as a deluxe model. The distributor is so confident of the market that, if Par can make the bags at a competitive price, the distributor will purchase all the bags that Par can manufacture over the next three months. A careful analysis of the manufacturing requirements resulted in the following table, which shows the production time requirements for the four required manufacturing operations and the accounting department's estimate of the profit contribution per bag:

| | **Production Time (hours)** | | | | |
| --- | --- | --- | --- | --- | --- |
| **Product** | **Cutting and Dyeing** | **Sewing** | **Finishing** | **Inspection and Packaging** | **Profit per Bag** |
| Standard | $7/10$ | $1/2$ | $1$ | $1/10$ | $\$10$ |
| Deluxe | $1$ | $5/6$ | $2/3$ | $1/4$ | $\$\,9$ |

The director of manufacturing estimates that 630 hours of cutting and dyeing time, 600 hours of sewing time, 708 hours of finishing time, and 135 hours of inspection and packaging time will be available for the production of golf bags during the next three months.
a.  If the company wants to maximize total profit contribution, how many bags of each model should it manufacture?
b.  What profit contribution can Par earn on those production quantities?
c.  How many hours of production time will be scheduled for each operation?
d.  What is the slack time in each operation?

15. Suppose that Par's management (Problem 14) encounters the following situations:
a.  The accounting department revises its estimate of the profit contribution for the deluxe bag to $18 per bag.
b.  A new low-cost material is available for the standard bag, and the profit contribution per standard bag can be increased to $20 per bag. (Assume that the profit contribution of the deluxe bag is the original $9 value.)
c.  New sewing equipment is available that would increase the sewing operation capacity to 750 hours. (Assume that $10A + 9B$ is the appropriate objective function.)
If each of these situations is encountered separately, what is the optimal solution and the total profit contribution?

16. Refer to the feasible region for Par, Inc., in Problem 14.
    a. Develop an objective function that will make extreme point (0, 540) the optimal extreme point.
    b. What is the optimal solution for the objective function you selected in part (a)?
    c. What are the values of the slack variables associated with this solution?

17. Write the following linear program in standard form:

$$\text{Max} \quad 5A + 2B$$
$$\text{s.t.}$$
$$1A - 2B \leq 420$$
$$2A + 3B \leq 610$$
$$6A - 1B \leq 125$$
$$A, B \geq 0$$

18. For the linear program

$$\text{Max} \quad 4A + 1B$$
$$\text{s.t.}$$
$$10A + 2B \leq 30$$
$$3A + 2B \leq 12$$
$$2A + 2B \leq 10$$
$$A, B \geq 0$$

    a. Write this problem in standard form.
    b. Solve the problem using the graphical solution procedure.
    c. What are the values of the three slack variables at the optimal solution?

19. Given the linear program

$$\text{Max} \quad 3A + 4B$$
$$\text{s.t.}$$
$$-1A + 2B \leq 8$$
$$1A + 2B \leq 12$$
$$2A + 1B \leq 16$$
$$A, B \geq 0$$

    a. Write the problem in standard form.
    b. Solve the problem using the graphical solution procedure.
    c. What are the values of the three slack variables at the optimal solution?

20. For the linear program

$$\text{Max} \quad 3A + 2B$$
$$\text{s.t.}$$
$$A + B \geq 4$$
$$3A + 4B \leq 24$$
$$A \quad\quad \geq 2$$
$$A - B \leq 0$$
$$A, B \geq 0$$

    a.   Write the problem in standard form.

    b.   Solve the problem.

    c.   What are the values of the slack and surplus variables at the optimal solution?

21.   Consider the following linear program:

$$\text{Max} \quad 2A + 3B$$
$$\text{s.t.}$$
$$5A + 5B \leq 400 \quad \text{Constraint 1}$$
$$-1A + 1B \leq 10 \quad \text{Constraint 2}$$
$$1A + 3B \geq 90 \quad \text{Constraint 3}$$
$$A, B \geq 0$$

Figure 7.23 shows a graph of the constraint lines.

    a.   Place a number (1, 2, or 3) next to each constraint line to identify which constraint it represents.

    b.   Shade in the feasible region on the graph.

    c.   Identify the optimal extreme point. What is the optimal solution?

    d.   Which constraints are binding? Explain.

    e.   How much slack or surplus is associated with the nonbinding constraint?

22.   Reiser Sports Products wants to determine the number of All-Pro ($A$) and College ($C$) footballs to produce in order to maximize profit over the next four-week planning horizon. Constraints affecting the production quantities are the production capacities in three departments: cutting and dyeing; sewing; and inspection and packaging. For the four-week planning period, 340 hours of cutting and dyeing time, 420 hours of sewing time, and 200 hours of inspection and packaging time are available. All-Pro footballs provide a profit

**FIGURE 7.23**   GRAPH OF THE CONSTRAINT LINES FOR EXERCISE 21

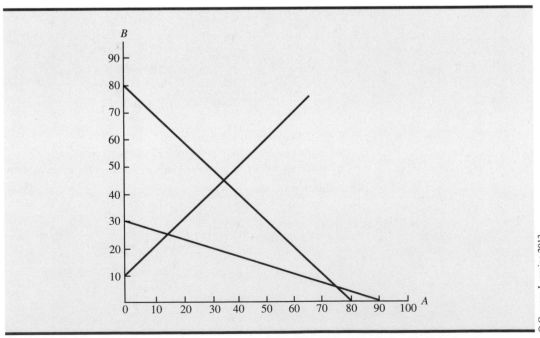

of $5 per unit and College footballs provide a profit of $4 per unit. The linear programming model with production times expressed in minutes is as follows:

$$\text{Max} \quad 5A + 4C$$
s.t.
$$
\begin{aligned}
12A + 6C &\leq 20{,}400 \quad \text{Cutting and dyeing} \\
9A + 15C &\leq 25{,}200 \quad \text{Sewing} \\
6A + 6C &\leq 12{,}000 \quad \text{Inspection and packaging} \\
A, C &\geq 0
\end{aligned}
$$

A portion of the graphical solution to the Reiser problem is shown in Figure 7.24.
a.  Shade the feasible region for this problem.
b.  Determine the coordinates of each extreme point and the corresponding profit. Which extreme point generates the highest profit?
c.  Draw the profit line corresponding to a profit of $4000. Move the profit line as far from the origin as you can in order to determine which extreme point will provide the optimal solution. Compare your answer with the approach you used in part (b).
d.  Which constraints are binding? Explain.
e.  Suppose that the values of the objective function coefficients are $4 for each All-Pro model produced and $5 for each College model. Use the graphical solution procedure to determine the new optimal solution and the corresponding value of profit.

**FIGURE 7.24**  PORTION OF THE GRAPHICAL SOLUTION FOR EXERCISE 22

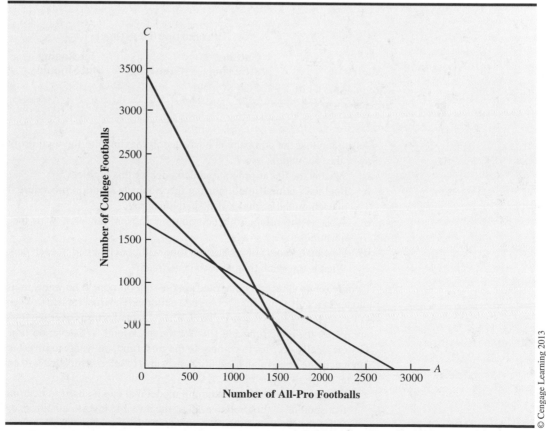

23. Embassy Motorcycles (EM) manufacturers two lightweight motorcycles designed for easy handling and safety. The EZ-Rider model has a new engine and a low profile that make it easy to balance. The Lady-Sport model is slightly larger, uses a more traditional engine, and is specifically designed to appeal to women riders. Embassy produces the engines for both models at its Des Moines, Iowa, plant. Each EZ-Rider engine requires 6 hours of manufacturing time and each Lady-Sport engine requires 3 hours of manufacturing time. The Des Moines plant has 2100 hours of engine manufacturing time available for the next production period. Embassy's motorcycle frame supplier can supply as many EZ-Rider frames as needed. However, the Lady-Sport frame is more complex and the supplier can only provide up to 280 Lady-Sport frames for the next production period. Final assembly and testing requires 2 hours for each EZ-Rider model and 2.5 hours for each Lady-Sport model. A maximum of 1000 hours of assembly and testing time are available for the next production period. The company's accounting department projects a profit contribution of $2400 for each EZ-Rider produced and $1800 for each Lady-Sport produced.

   a. Formulate a linear programming model that can be used to determine the number of units of each model that should be produced in order to maximize the total contribution to profit.
   b. Solve the problem graphically. What is the optimal solution?
   c. Which constraints are binding?

24. Kelson Sporting Equipment, Inc., makes two different types of baseball gloves: a regular model and a catcher's model. The firm has 900 hours of production time available in its cutting and sewing department, 300 hours available in its finishing department, and 100 hours available in its packaging and shipping department. The production time requirements and the profit contribution per glove are given in the following table:

| | **Production Time (hours)** | | | |
| | | | | |
| Model | Cutting and Sewing | Finishing | Packaging and Shipping | Profit/Glove |
| --- | --- | --- | --- | --- |
| Regular model | 1 | $1/2$ | $1/8$ | $5 |
| Catcher's model | $3/2$ | $1/3$ | $1/4$ | $8 |

Assuming that the company is interested in maximizing the total profit contribution, answer the following:

   a. What is the linear programming model for this problem?
   b. Find the optimal solution using the graphical solution procedure. How many gloves of each model should Kelson manufacture?
   c. What is the total profit contribution Kelson can earn with the given production quantities?
   d. How many hours of production time will be scheduled in each department?
   e. What is the slack time in each department?

25. George Johnson recently inherited a large sum of money; he wants to use a portion of this money to set up a trust fund for his two children. The trust fund has two investment options: (1) a bond fund and (2) a stock fund. The projected returns over the life of the investments are 6% for the bond fund and 10% for the stock fund. Whatever portion of the inheritance George finally decides to commit to the trust fund, he wants to invest at least 30% of that amount in the bond fund. In addition, he wants to select a mix that will enable him to obtain a total return of at least 7.5%.

   a. Formulate a linear programming model that can be used to determine the percentage that should be allocated to each of the possible investment alternatives.
   b. Solve the problem using the graphical solution procedure.

26. The Sea Wharf Restaurant would like to determine the best way to allocate a monthly advertising budget of $1000 between newspaper advertising and radio advertising. Management decided that at least 25% of the budget must be spent on each type of media, and that the amount of money spent on local newspaper advertising must be at least twice the amount spent on radio advertising. A marketing consultant developed an index that measures audience exposure per dollar of advertising on a scale from 0 to 100, with higher values implying greater audience exposure. If the value of the index for local newspaper advertising is 50 and the value of the index for spot radio advertising is 80, how should the restaurant allocate its advertising budget in order to maximize the value of total audience exposure?

    a.  Formulate a linear programming model that can be used to determine how the restaurant should allocate its advertising budget in order to maximize the value of total audience exposure.

    b.  Solve the problem using the graphical solution procedure.

27. Blair & Rosen, Inc. (B&R) is a brokerage firm that specializes in investment portfolios designed to meet the specific risk tolerances of its clients. A client who contacted B&R this past week has a maximum of $50,000 to invest. B&R's investment advisor decides to recommend a portfolio consisting of two investment funds: an Internet fund and a Blue Chip fund. The Internet fund has a projected annual return of 12%, while the Blue Chip fund has a projected annual return of 9%. The investment advisor requires that at most $35,000 of the client's funds should be invested in the Internet fund. B&R services include a risk rating for each investment alternative. The Internet fund, which is the more risky of the two investment alternatives, has a risk rating of 6 per thousand dollars invested. The Blue Chip fund has a risk rating of 4 per thousand dollars invested. For example, if $10,000 is invested in each of the two investment funds, B&R's risk rating for the portfolio would be 6(10) + 4(10) = 100. Finally, B&R developed a questionnaire to measure each client's risk tolerance. Based on the responses, each client is classified as a conservative, moderate, or aggressive investor. Suppose that the questionnaire results classified the current client as a moderate investor. B&R recommends that a client who is a moderate investor limit his or her portfolio to a maximum risk rating of 240.

    a.  What is the recommended investment portfolio for this client? What is the annual return for the portfolio?

    b.  Suppose that a second client with $50,000 to invest has been classified as an aggressive investor. B&R recommends that the maximum portfolio risk rating for an aggressive investor is 320. What is the recommended investment portfolio for this aggressive investor? Discuss what happens to the portfolio under the aggressive investor strategy.

    c.  Suppose that a third client with $50,000 to invest has been classified as a conservative investor. B&R recommends that the maximum portfolio risk rating for a conservative investor is 160. Develop the recommended investment portfolio for the conservative investor. Discuss the interpretation of the slack variable for the total investment fund constraint.

28. Tom's, Inc., produces various Mexican food products and sells them to Western Foods, a chain of grocery stores located in Texas and New Mexico. Tom's, Inc., makes two salsa products: Western Foods Salsa and Mexico City Salsa. Essentially, the two products have different blends of whole tomatoes, tomato sauce, and tomato paste. The Western Foods Salsa is a blend of 50% whole tomatoes, 30% tomato sauce, and 20% tomato paste. The Mexico City Salsa, which has a thicker and chunkier consistency, consists of 70% whole tomatoes, 10% tomato sauce, and 20% tomato paste. Each jar of salsa produced weighs 10 ounces. For the current production period, Tom's, Inc., can purchase up to 280 pounds of whole tomatoes, 130 pounds of tomato sauce, and 100 pounds of tomato paste; the price

per pound for these ingredients is $0.96, $0.64, and $0.56, respectively. The cost of the spices and the other ingredients is approximately $0.10 per jar. Tom's, Inc., buys empty glass jars for $0.02 each, and labeling and filling costs are estimated to be $0.03 for each jar of salsa produced. Tom's contract with Western Foods results in sales revenue of $1.64 for each jar of Western Foods Salsa and $1.93 for each jar of Mexico City Salsa.

    a.   Develop a linear programming model that will enable Tom's to determine the mix of salsa products that will maximize the total profit contribution.

    b.   Find the optimal solution.

29.   AutoIgnite produces electronic ignition systems for automobiles at a plant in Cleveland, Ohio. Each ignition system is assembled from two components produced at AutoIgnite's plants in Buffalo, New York, and Dayton, Ohio. The Buffalo plant can produce 2000 units of component 1, 1000 units of component 2, or any combination of the two components each day. For instance, 60% of Buffalo's production time could be used to produce component 1 and 40% of Buffalo's production time could be used to produce component 2; in this case, the Buffalo plant would be able to produce 0.6(2000) = 1200 units of component 1 each day and 0.4(1000) = 400 units of component 2 each day. The Dayton plant can produce 600 units of component 1, 1400 units of component 2, or any combination of the two components each day. At the end of each day, the component production at Buffalo and Dayton is sent to Cleveland for assembly of the ignition systems on the following workday.

    a.   Formulate a linear programming model that can be used to develop a daily production schedule for the Buffalo and Dayton plants that will maximize daily production of ignition systems at Cleveland.

    b.   Find the optimal solution.

30.   A financial advisor at Diehl Investments identified two companies that are likely candidates for a takeover in the near future. Eastern Cable is a leading manufacturer of flexible cable systems used in the construction industry, and ComSwitch is a new firm specializing in digital switching systems. Eastern Cable is currently trading for $40 per share, and ComSwitch is currently trading for $25 per share. If the takeovers occur, the financial advisor estimates that the price of Eastern Cable will go to $55 per share and ComSwitch will go to $43 per share. At this point in time, the financial advisor has identified ComSwitch as the higher-risk alternative. Assume that a client indicated a willingness to invest a maximum of $50,000 in the two companies. The client wants to invest at least $15,000 in Eastern Cable and at least $10,000 in ComSwitch. Because of the higher risk associated with ComSwitch, the financial advisor has recommended that at most $25,000 should be invested in ComSwitch.

    a.   Formulate a linear programming model that can be used to determine the number of shares of Eastern Cable and the number of shares of ComSwitch that will meet the investment constraints and maximize the total return for the investment.

    b.   Graph the feasible region.

    c.   Determine the coordinates of each extreme point.

    d.   Find the optimal solution.

31.   Consider the following linear program:

$$\text{Min} \quad 3A + 4B$$
$$\text{s.t.}$$
$$1A + 3B \geq 6$$
$$1A + 1B \geq 4$$
$$A, B \geq 0$$

Identify the feasible region and find the optimal solution using the graphical solution procedure. What is the value of the objective function?

32. Identify the three extreme-point solutions for the M&D Chemicals problem (see Section 7.5). Identify the value of the objective function and the values of the slack and surplus variables at each extreme point.

33. Consider the following linear programming problem:

$$\text{Min} \quad A + 2B$$

s.t.

$$
\begin{aligned}
A + 4B &\le 21 \\
2A + B &\ge 7 \\
3A + 1.5B &\le 21 \\
-2A + 6B &\ge 0 \\
A, B &\ge 0
\end{aligned}
$$

a. Find the optimal solution using the graphical solution procedure and the value of the objective function.
b. Determine the amount of slack or surplus for each constraint.
c. Suppose the objective function is changed to max $5A + 2B$. Find the optimal solution and the value of the objective function.

34. Consider the following linear program:

$$\text{Min} \quad 2A + 2B$$

s.t.

$$
\begin{aligned}
1A + 3B &\le 12 \\
3A + 1B &\ge 13 \\
1A - 1B &= 3 \\
A, B &\ge 0
\end{aligned}
$$

a. Show the feasible region.
b. What are the extreme points of the feasible region?
c. Find the optimal solution using the graphical solution procedure.

35. For the linear program

$$\text{Min} \quad 6A + 4B$$

s.t.

$$
\begin{aligned}
2A + 1B &\ge 12 \\
1A + 1B &\ge 10 \\
1B &\le 4 \\
A, B &\ge 0
\end{aligned}
$$

a. Write the problem in standard form.
b. Solve the problem using the graphical solution procedure.
c. What are the values of the slack and surplus variables?

36. As part of a quality improvement initiative, Consolidated Electronics employees complete a three-day training program on teaming and a two-day training program on problem solving. The manager of quality improvement has requested that at least 8 training programs on teaming and at least 10 training programs on problem solving be offered during the next six months. In addition, senior-level management has specified that at least 25 training programs must be offered during this period. Consolidated Electronics uses a consultant to teach the training programs. During the next quarter, the consultant has 84 days of

training time available. Each training program on teaming costs $10,000 and each training program on problem solving costs $8000.

a. Formulate a linear programming model that can be used to determine the number of training programs on teaming and the number of training programs on problem solving that should be offered in order to minimize total cost.

b. Graph the feasible region.

c. Determine the coordinates of each extreme point.

d. Solve for the minimum-cost solution.

37. The New England Cheese Company produces two cheese spreads by blending mild cheddar cheese with extra sharp cheddar cheese. The cheese spreads are packaged in 12-ounce containers, which are then sold to distributors throughout the Northeast. The Regular blend contains 80% mild cheddar and 20% extra sharp, and the Zesty blend contains 60% mild cheddar and 40% extra sharp. This year, a local dairy cooperative offered to provide up to 8100 pounds of mild cheddar cheese for $1.20 per pound and up to 3000 pounds of extra sharp cheddar cheese for $1.40 per pound. The cost to blend and package the cheese spreads, excluding the cost of the cheese, is $0.20 per container. If each container of Regular is sold for $1.95 and each container of Zesty is sold for $2.20, how many containers of Regular and Zesty should New England Cheese produce?

38. Applied Technology, Inc. (ATI) produces bicycle frames using two fiberglass materials that improve the strength-to-weight ratio of the frames. The cost of the standard-grade material is $7.50 per yard and the cost of the professional-grade material is $9.00 per yard. The standard- and professional-grade materials contain different amounts of fiberglass, carbon fiber, and Kevlar, as shown in the following table:

|  | Standard Grade | Professional Grade |
| --- | --- | --- |
| Fiberglass | 84% | 58% |
| Carbon fiber | 10% | 30% |
| Kevlar | 6% | 12% |

ATI signed a contract with a bicycle manufacturer to produce a new frame with a carbon fiber content of at least 20% and a Kevlar content of not greater than 10%. To meet the required weight specification, a total of 30 yards of material must be used for each frame.

a. Formulate a linear program to determine the number of yards of each grade of fiberglass material that ATI should use in each frame in order to minimize total cost. Define the decision variables and indicate the purpose of each constraint.

b. Use the graphical solution procedure to determine the feasible region. What are the coordinates of the extreme points?

c. Compute the total cost at each extreme point. What is the optimal solution?

d. The distributor of the fiberglass material is currently overstocked with the professional-grade material. To reduce inventory, the distributor offered ATI the opportunity to purchase the professional-grade material for $8 per yard. Will the optimal solution change?

e. Suppose that the distributor further lowers the price of the professional-grade material to $7.40 per yard. Will the optimal solution change? What effect would an even lower price for the professional-grade material have on the optimal solution? Explain.

39. Innis Investments manages funds for a number of companies and wealthy clients. The investment strategy is tailored to each client's needs. For a new client, Innis has been authorized to invest up to $1.2 million in two investment funds: a stock fund and a money market

fund. Each unit of the stock fund costs $50 and provides an annual rate of return of 10%; each unit of the money market fund costs $100 and provides an annual rate of return of 4%.

The client wants to minimize risk subject to the requirement that the annual income from the investment be at least $60,000. According to Innis's risk measurement system, each unit invested in the stock fund has a risk index of 8, and each unit invested in the money market fund has a risk index of 3; the higher risk index associated with the stock fund simply indicates that it is the riskier investment. Innis's client also specifies that at least $300,000 be invested in the money market fund.

a. Determine how many units of each fund Innis should purchase for the client to minimize the total risk index for the portfolio.

b. How much annual income will this investment strategy generate?

c. Suppose the client desires to maximize annual return. How should the funds be invested?

40. Eastern Chemicals produces two types of lubricating fluids used in industrial manufacturing. Both products cost Eastern Chemicals $1 per gallon to produce. Based on an analysis of current inventory levels and outstanding orders for the next month, Eastern Chemicals' management specified that at least 30 gallons of product 1 and at least 20 gallons of product 2 must be produced during the next two weeks. Management also stated that an existing inventory of highly perishable raw material required in the production of both fluids must be used within the next two weeks. The current inventory of the perishable raw material is 80 pounds. Although more of this raw material can be ordered if necessary, any of the current inventory that is not used within the next two weeks will spoil—hence, the management requirement that at least 80 pounds be used in the next two weeks. Furthermore, it is known that product 1 requires 1 pound of this perishable raw material per gallon and product 2 requires 2 pounds of the raw material per gallon. Because Eastern Chemicals' objective is to keep its production costs at the minimum possible level, the firm's management is looking for a minimum-cost production plan that uses all the 80 pounds of perishable raw material and provides at least 30 gallons of product 1 and at least 20 gallons of product 2. What is the minimum-cost solution?

41. Southern Oil Company produces two grades of gasoline: regular and premium. The profit contributions are $0.30 per gallon for regular gasoline and $0.50 per gallon for premium gasoline. Each gallon of regular gasoline contains 0.3 gallons of grade A crude oil and each gallon of premium gasoline contains 0.6 gallons of grade A crude oil. For the next production period, Southern has 18,000 gallons of grade A crude oil available. The refinery used to produce the gasolines has a production capacity of 50,000 gallons for the next production period. Southern Oil's distributors have indicated that demand for the premium gasoline for the next production period will be at most 20,000 gallons.

a. Formulate a linear programming model that can be used to determine the number of gallons of regular gasoline and the number of gallons of premium gasoline that should be produced in order to maximize total profit contribution.

b. What is the optimal solution?

c. What are the values and interpretations of the slack variables?

d. What are the binding constraints?

42. Does the following linear program involve infeasibility, unbounded, and/or alternative optimal solutions? Explain.

$$\text{Max} \quad 4A + 8B$$
$$\text{s.t.}$$
$$2A + 2B \leq 10$$
$$-1A + 1B \geq 8$$
$$A, B \geq 0$$

**SELF** test

43. Does the following linear program involve infeasibility, unbounded, and/or alternative optimal solutions? Explain.

$$\text{Max} \quad 1A + 1B$$

s.t.

$$8A + 6B \geq 24$$
$$2B \geq 4$$
$$A, B \geq 0$$

44. Consider the following linear program:

$$\text{Max} \quad 1A + 1B$$

s.t.

$$5A + 3B \leq 15$$
$$3A + 5B \leq 15$$
$$A, B \geq 0$$

a. What is the optimal solution for this problem?
b. Suppose that the objective function is changed to $1A + 2B$. Find the new optimal solution.

45. Consider the following linear program:

$$\text{Max} \quad 1A - 2B$$

s.t.

$$-4A + 3B \leq 3$$
$$1A - 1B \leq 3$$
$$A, B \geq 0$$

a. Graph the feasible region for the problem.
b. Is the feasible region unbounded? Explain.
c. Find the optimal solution.
d. Does an unbounded feasible region imply that the optimal solution to the linear program will be unbounded?

46. The manager of a small independent grocery store is trying to determine the best use of her shelf space for soft drinks. The store carries national and generic brands and currently has 200 square feet of shelf space available. The manager wants to allocate at least 60% of the space to the national brands and, regardless of the profitability, allocate at least 10% of the space to the generic brands. How many square feet of space should the manager allocate to the national brands and the generic brands under the following circumstances?
a. The national brands are more profitable than the generic brands.
b. Both brands are equally profitable.
c. The generic brand is more profitable than the national brand.

47. Discuss what happens to the M&D Chemicals problem (see Section 7.5) if the cost per gallon for product A is increased to $3.00 per gallon. What would you recommend? Explain.

48. For the M&D Chemicals problem in Section 7.5, discuss the effect of management's requiring total production of 500 gallons for the two products. List two or three actions M&D should consider to correct the situation you encounter.

49. PharmaPlus operates a chain of 30 pharmacies. The pharmacies are staffed by licensed pharmacists and pharmacy technicians. The company currently employs 85 full-time-equivalent

pharmacists (combination of full time and part time) and 175 full-time-equivalent technicians. Each spring management reviews current staffing levels and makes hiring plans for the year. A recent forecast of the prescription load for the next year shows that at least 250 full-time-equivalent employees (pharmacists and technicians) will be required to staff the pharmacies. The personnel department expects 10 pharmacists and 30 technicians to leave over the next year. To accommodate the expected attrition and prepare for future growth, management states that at least 15 new pharmacists must be hired. In addition, PharmaPlus's new service quality guidelines specify no more than two technicians per licensed pharmacist. The average salary for licensed pharmacists is $40 per hour and the average salary for technicians is $10 per hour.

a. Determine a minimum-cost staffing plan for PharmaPlus. How many pharmacists and technicians are needed?

b. Given current staffing levels and expected attrition, how many new hires (if any) must be made to reach the level recommended in part (a)? What will be the impact on the payroll?

50. Expedition Outfitters manufactures a variety of specialty clothing for hiking, skiing, and mountain climbing. The company has decided to begin production on two new parkas designed for use in extremely cold weather: the Mount Everest Parka and the Rocky Mountain Parka. Expedition's manufacturing plant has 120 hours of cutting time and 120 hours of sewing time available for producing these two parkas. Each Mount Everest Parka requires 30 minutes of cutting time and 45 minutes of sewing time, and each Rocky Mountain Parka requires 20 minutes of cutting time and 15 minutes of sewing time. The labor and material cost is $150 for each Mount Everest Parka and $50 for each Rocky Mountain Parka, and the retail prices through the firm's mail order catalog are $250 for the Mount Everest Parka and $200 for the Rocky Mountain Parka. Because management believes that the Mount Everest Parka is a unique coat that will enhance the image of the firm, management specified that at least 20% of the total production must consist of this model. Assuming that Expedition Outfitters can sell as many coats of each type as it can produce, how many units of each model should it manufacture to maximize the total profit contribution?

51. English Motors, Ltd. (EML), developed a new all-wheel-drive sports utility vehicle. As part of the marketing campaign, EML produced a digitally recorded sales presentation to send to both owners of current EML four-wheel-drive vehicles as well as to owners of four-wheel-drive sports utility vehicles offered by competitors; EML refers to these two target markets as the current customer market and the new customer market. Individuals who receive the new promotion will also receive a coupon for a test drive of the new EML model for one weekend. A key factor in the success of the new promotion is the response rate, the percentage of individuals who receive the new promotion and test drive the new model. EML estimates that the response rate for the current customer market is 25% and the response rate for the new customer market is 20%. For the customers who test drive the new model, the sales rate is the percentage of individuals who make a purchase. Marketing research studies indicate that the sales rate is 12% for the current customer market and 20% for the new customer market. The cost for each promotion, excluding the test drive costs, is $4 for each promotion sent to the current customer market and $6 for each promotion sent to the new customer market. Management also specified that a minimum of 30,000 current customers should test drive the new model and a minimum of 10,000 new customers should test drive the new model. In addition, the number of current customers who test drive the new vehicle must be at least twice the number of new customers who test drive the new vehicle. If the marketing budget, excluding test drive costs, is $1.2 million, how many promotions should be sent to each group of customers in order to maximize total sales?

52. Creative Sports Design (CSD) manufactures a standard-size racket and an oversize racket. The firm's rackets are extremely light due to the use of a magnesium-graphite alloy that was invented by the firm's founder. Each standard-size racket uses 0.125 kilograms of the alloy and each oversize racket uses 0.4 kilograms; over the next two-week production period, only 80 kilograms of the alloy are available. Each standard-size racket uses 10 minutes of manufacturing time and each oversize racket uses 12 minutes. The profit contributions are $10 for each standard-size racket and $15 for each oversize racket, and 40 hours of manufacturing time are available each week. Management specified that at least 20% of the total production must be the standard-size racket. How many rackets of each type should CSD manufacture over the next two weeks to maximize the total profit contribution? Assume that because of the unique nature of its products, CSD can sell as many rackets as it can produce.

53. Management of High Tech Services (HTS) would like to develop a model that will help allocate its technicians' time between service calls to regular contract customers and new customers. A maximum of 80 hours of technician time is available over the two-week planning period. To satisfy cash flow requirements, at least $800 in revenue (per technician) must be generated during the two-week period. Technician time for regular customers generates $25 per hour. However, technician time for new customers only generates an average of $8 per hour because in many cases a new customer contact does not provide billable services. To ensure that new customer contacts are being maintained, the technician time spent on new customer contacts must be at least 60% of the time spent on regular customer contacts. Given these revenue and policy requirements, HTS would like to determine how to allocate technician time between regular customers and new customers so that the total number of customers contacted during the two-week period will be maximized. Technicians require an average of 50 minutes for each regular customer contact and 1 hour for each new customer contact.
    a. Develop a linear programming model that will enable HTS to allocate technician time between regular customers and new customers.
    b. Find the optimal solution.

54. Jackson Hole Manufacturing is a small manufacturer of plastic products used in the automotive and computer industries. One of its major contracts is with a large computer company and involves the production of plastic printer cases for the computer company's portable printers. The printer cases are produced on two injection molding machines. The M-100 machine has a production capacity of 25 printer cases per hour, and the M-200 machine has a production capacity of 40 cases per hour. Both machines use the same chemical material to produce the printer cases; the M-100 uses 40 pounds of the raw material per hour and the M-200 uses 50 pounds per hour. The computer company asked Jackson Hole to produce as many of the cases during the upcoming week as possible; it will pay $18 for each case Jackson Hole can deliver. However, next week is a regularly scheduled vacation period for most of Jackson Hole's production employees; during this time, annual maintenance is performed for all equipment in the plant. Because of the downtime for maintenance, the M-100 will be available for no more than 15 hours, and the M-200 will be available for no more than 10 hours. However, because of the high set-up cost involved with both machines, management requires that, if production is scheduled on either machine, the machine must be operated for at least 5 hours. The supplier of the chemical material used in the production process informed Jackson Hole that a maximum of 1000 pounds of the chemical material will be available for next week's production; the cost for this raw material is $6 per pound. In addition to the raw material cost, Jackson Hole estimates that the hourly costs of operating the M-100 and the M-200 are $50 and $75, respectively.

a. Formulate a linear programming model that can be used to maximize the contribution to profit.
b. Find the optimal solution.

# Case Problem 1    Workload Balancing

Digital Imaging (DI) produces photo printers for both the professional and consumer markets. The DI consumer division recently introduced two photo printers that provide color prints rivaling those produced by a professional processing lab. The DI-910 model can produce a 4″ × 6″ borderless print in approximately 37 seconds. The more sophisticated and faster DI-950 can even produce a 13″ × 19″ borderless print. Financial projections show profit contributions of $42 for each DI-910 and $87 for each DI-950.

The printers are assembled, tested, and packaged at DI's plant located in New Bern, North Carolina. This plant is highly automated and uses two manufacturing lines to produce the printers. Line 1 performs the assembly operation with times of 3 minutes per DI-910 printer and 6 minutes per DI-950 printer. Line 2 performs both the testing and packaging operations. Times are 4 minutes per DI-910 printer and 2 minutes per DI-950 printer. The shorter time for the DI-950 printer is a result of its faster print speed. Both manufacturing lines are in operation one 8-hour shift per day.

## Managerial Report

Perform an analysis for Digital Imaging in order to determine how many units of each printer to produce. Prepare a report to DI's president presenting your findings and recommendations. Include (but do not limit your discussion to) a consideration of the following:

1. The recommended number of units of each printer to produce to maximize the total contribution to profit for an 8-hour shift. What reasons might management have for not implementing your recommendation?
2. Suppose that management also states that the number of DI-910 printers produced must be at least as great as the number of DI-950 units produced. Assuming that the objective is to maximize the total contribution to profit for an 8-hour shift, how many units of each printer should be produced?
3. Does the solution you developed in part (2) balance the total time spent on line 1 and the total time spent on line 2? Why might this balance or lack of it be a concern to management?
4. Management requested an expansion of the model in part (2) that would provide a better balance between the total time on line 1 and the total time on line 2. Management wants to limit the difference between the total time on line 1 and the total time on line 2 to 30 minutes or less. If the objective is still to maximize the total contribution to profit, how many units of each printer should be produced? What effect does this workload balancing have on total profit in part (2)?
5. Suppose that in part (1) management specified the objective of maximizing the total number of printers produced each shift rather than total profit contribution. With this objective, how many units of each printer should be produced per shift? What effect does this objective have on total profit and workload balancing?

For each solution that you develop, include a copy of your linear programming model and graphical solution in the appendix to your report.

**Case Problem 2**    # Production Strategy

Better Fitness, Inc. (BFI) manufactures exercise equipment at its plant in Freeport, Long Island. It recently designed two universal weight machines for the home exercise market. Both machines use BFI-patented technology that provides the user with an extremely wide range of motion capability for each type of exercise performed. Until now, such capabilities have been available only on expensive weight machines used primarily by physical therapists.

At a recent trade show, demonstrations of the machines resulted in significant dealer interest. In fact, the number of orders that BFI received at the trade show far exceeded its manufacturing capabilities for the current production period. As a result, management decided to begin production of the two machines. The two machines, which BFI named the Body-Plus 100 and the BodyPlus 200, require different amounts of resources to produce.

The BodyPlus 100 consists of a frame unit, a press station, and a pec-dec station. Each frame produced uses 4 hours of machining and welding time and 2 hours of painting and finishing time. Each press station requires 2 hours of machining and welding time and 1 hour of painting and finishing time, and each pec-dec station uses 2 hours of machining and welding time and 2 hours of painting and finishing time. In addition, 2 hours are spent assembling, testing, and packaging each BodyPlus 100. The raw material costs are $450 for each frame, $300 for each press station, and $250 for each pec-dec station; packaging costs are estimated to be $50 per unit.

The BodyPlus 200 consists of a frame unit, a press station, a pec-dec station, and a leg-press station. Each frame produced uses 5 hours of machining and welding time and 4 hours of painting and finishing time. Each press station requires 3 hours machining and welding time and 2 hours of painting and finishing time, each pec-dec station uses 2 hours of machining and welding time and 2 hours of painting and finishing time, and each leg-press station requires 2 hours of machining and welding time and 2 hours of painting and finishing time. In addition, 2 hours are spent assembling, testing, and packaging each BodyPlus 200. The raw material costs are $650 for each frame, $400 for each press station, $250 for each pec-dec station, and $200 for each leg-press station; packaging costs are estimated to be $75 per unit.

For the next production period, management estimates that 600 hours of machining and welding time; 450 hours of painting and finishing time; and 140 hours of assembly, testing, and packaging time will be available. Current labor costs are $20 per hour for machining and welding time; $15 per hour for painting and finishing time; and $12 per hour for assembly, testing, and packaging time. The market in which the two machines must compete suggests a retail price of $2400 for the BodyPlus 100 and $3500 for the BodyPlus 200, although some flexibility may be available to BFI because of the unique capabilities of the new machines. Authorized BFI dealers can purchase machines for 70% of the suggested retail price.

BFI's president believes that the unique capabilities of the BodyPlus 200 can help position BFI as one of the leaders in high-end exercise equipment. Consequently, she states that the number of units of the BodyPlus 200 produced must be at least 25% of the total production.

## Managerial Report

Analyze the production problem at Better Fitness, Inc., and prepare a report for BFI's president presenting your findings and recommendations. Include (but do not limit your discussion to) a consideration of the following items:

1. The recommended number of BodyPlus 100 and BodyPlus 200 machines to produce

2. The effect on profits of the requirement that the number of units of the BodyPlus 200 produced must be at least 25% of the total production
3. Where efforts should be expended in order to increase contribution to profits

Include a copy of your linear programming model and graphical solution in an appendix to your report.

## Case Problem 3    Hart Venture Capital

Hart Venture Capital (HVC) specializes in providing venture capital for software development and Internet applications. Currently HVC has two investment opportunities: (1) Security Systems, a firm that needs additional capital to develop an Internet security software package, and (2) Market Analysis, a market research company that needs additional capital to develop a software package for conducting customer satisfaction surveys. In exchange for Security Systems stock, the firm asked HVC to provide $600,000 in year 1, $600,000 in year 2, and $250,000 in year 3 over the coming three-year period. In exchange for Market Analysis stock, the firm asked HVC to provide $500,000 in year 1, $350,000 in year 2, and $400,000 in year 3 over the same three-year period. HVC believes that both investment opportunities are worth pursuing. However, because of other investments, HVC is willing to commit at most $800,000 for both projects in the first year, at most $700,000 in the second year, and $500,000 in the third year.

HVC's financial analysis team reviewed both projects and recommended that the company's objective should be to maximize the net present value of the total investment in Security Systems and Market Analysis. The net present value takes into account the estimated value of the stock at the end of the three-year period as well as the capital outflows that are necessary during each of the three years. Using an 8% rate of return, HVC's financial analysis team estimates that 100% funding of the Security Systems project has a net present value of $1,800,000, and 100% funding of the Market Analysis project has a net present value of $1,600,000.

HVC has the option to fund any percentage of the Security Systems and Market Analysis projects. For example, if HVC decides to fund 40% of the Security Systems project, investments of 0.40($600,000) = $240,000 would be required in year 1, 0.40($600,000) = $240,000 would be required in year 2, and 0.40($250,000) = $100,000 would be required in year 3. In this case, the net present value of the Security Systems project would be 0.40($1,800,000) = $720,000. The investment amounts and the net present value for partial funding of the Market Analysis project would be computed in the same manner.

### Managerial Report

Perform an analysis of HVC's investment problem and prepare a report that presents your findings and recommendations. Be sure to include information on the following:

1. The recommended percentage of each project that HVC should fund and the net present value of the total investment
2. A capital allocation plan for Security Systems and Market Analysis for the coming three-year period and the total HVC investment each year
3. The effect, if any, on the recommended percentage of each project that HVC should fund if HVC is willing to commit an additional $100,000 during the first year
4. A capital allocation plan if an additional $100,000 is made available
5. Your recommendation as to whether HVC should commit the additional $100,000 in the first year

Provide model details and relevant computer output in a report appendix.

# Appendix 7.1  Solving Linear Programs with Excel 2010

In this appendix we will use an Excel worksheet to solve the RMC linear programming problem. We will enter the problem data for the RMC problem in the top part of the worksheet and develop the linear programming model in the bottom part of the worksheet. Note that Appendix A contains much more detail on how to formulate models in Excel.

## Formulation

Whenever we formulate a worksheet model of a linear program, we perform the following steps:

**Step 1.** Enter the problem data in the top part of the worksheet
**Step 2.** Specify cell locations for the decision variables
**Step 3.** Select a cell and enter a formula for computing the value of the objective function
**Step 4.** Select a cell and enter a formula for computing the left-hand side of each constraint
**Step 5.** Select a cell and enter a formula for computing the right-hand side of each constraint

The formula worksheet that we developed for the RMC problem using these five steps is shown in Figure 7.25. Let us review each of the preceding steps as they apply to the RMC problem.

**FIGURE 7.25**  EXCEL FORMULA WORKSHEET FOR THE RMC PROBLEM

WEB file

RMC

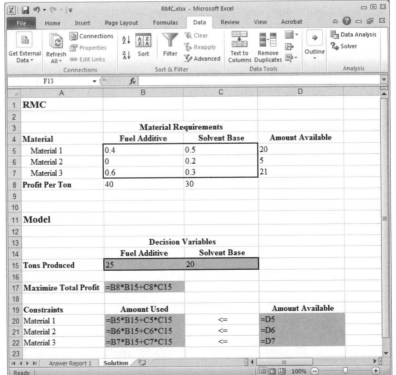

**Step 1.** Enter the problem data in the top part of the worksheet
Cells B5 to C7 show the material requirements per ton of each product.
Cells B8 and C8 show the profit contribution per ton for the two products.
Cells D5 to D7 show the maximum amounts available for each of the three materials.

**Step 2.** Specify cell locations for the decision variables
Cell B15 will contain the number of tons of fuel additive produced, and Cell C15 will contain the number of tons of solvent base produced.

**Step 3.** Select a cell and enter a formula for computing the value of the objective function
Cell B17: =B8*B15+C8*C15

**Step 4.** Select a cell and enter a formula for computing the left-hand side of each constraint. With three constraints, we have
Cell B20: =B5*B15+C5*C15
Cell B21: =C6*C15
Cell B22: =B7*B15+C7*C15

**Step 5.** Select a cell and enter a formula for computing the right-hand side of each constraint. With three constraints, we have
Cell D20: =D5
Cell D21: =D6
Cell D22: =D7

Note that descriptive labels make the model section of the worksheet easier to read and understand. For example, we added "Fuel Additive," "Solvent Base," and "Tons Produced" in rows 14 and 15 so that the values of the decision variables appearing in Cells B15 and C15 can be easily interpreted. In addition, we entered "Maximize Total Profit" in Cell A17 to indicate that the value of the objective function appearing in Cell B17 is the maximum profit contribution. In the constraint section of the worksheet we added the constraint names as well as the "<=" symbols to show the relationship that exists between the left-hand side and the right-hand side of each constraint. Although these descriptive labels are not necessary to use Excel Solver to find a solution to the RMC problem, the labels make it easier for the user to understand and interpret the optimal solution.

## Excel Solution

Excel 2010 contains an updated Solver capability that incorporates much of what was previously known as Premium Solver. Excel Solver, developed by Frontline Systems, can be used to solve all of the linear programming problems presented in this text.

The following steps describe how Excel Solver can be used to obtain the optimal solution to the RMC problem:

**Step 1.** Select the **Data** tab from the **Ribbon**

**Step 2.** Select **Solver** from the **Analysis Group** (see Figure 7.25, where the Analysis Group and Data tab are displayed in the Ribbon)

**Step 3.** When the **Solver Parameters** dialog box appears (see Figure 7.26):
Enter B17 into the **Set Objective** box
Select the **To: Max** option
Enter B15:C15 into the **By Changing Variable Cells** box
Select **Add**

**Step 4.** When the **Add Constraint** dialog box appears:
Enter B20:B22 in the **Cell Reference** box

**FIGURE 7.26**   EXCEL SOLVER PARAMETERS DIALOG BOX FOR THE RMC
PROBLEM

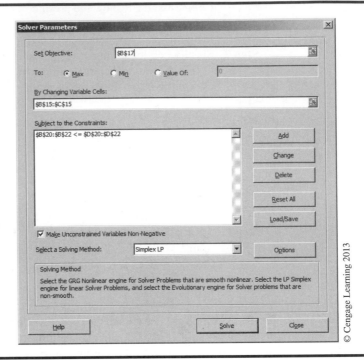

Select <=
Enter D20:D22 in the **Constraint** box
Click **OK**

**Step 5.** When the **Solver Parameters** dialog box reappears:
Click the checkbox for **Make Unconstrained Variables Non-negative**

**Step 6.** Select the **Select a Solving Method** drop-down button
Select **Simplex LP***

**Step 7.** Click **Solve**

**Step 8.** When the **Solver Results** dialog box appears:
Select **Keep Solver Solution**
Click **OK**

*The Excel Answer Report
that is similar to Figure 7.15
is generated from the **Solver
Results** dialog box. This is
created by clicking on
**Answer** in the **Reports**
group before clicking **OK** in
step 7. We will discuss the
Sensitivity Report in
Chapter 8.*

Figure 7.26 shows the completed Excel Solver Parameters dialog box, and Figure 7.27 shows the optimal solution in the worksheet. The optimal solution of 25 tons of fuel additive and 20 tons of solvent base is the same as we obtained using the graphical solution procedure. Solver also has an option to provide sensitivity analysis information. We discuss sensitivity analysis in Chapter 8.

In step 5 we selected the **Make Unconstrained Variables Non-negative** option in the **Solver Parameters** dialog box to avoid having to enter nonnegativity constraints for the decision variables. In general, whenever we want to solve a linear programming model in

---

*Because we know this is a linear program, the Simplex LP algorithm is the most efficient solution method.

**FIGURE 7.27**  EXCEL SOLUTION FOR THE RMC PROBLEM

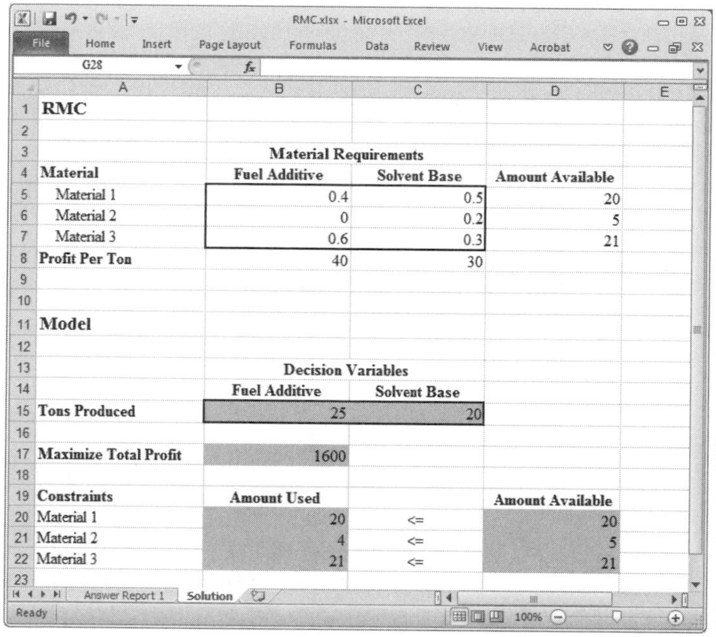

which the decision variables are all restricted to be nonnegative, we will select this option. In addition, in step 4 we entered all three less-than-or-equal-to constraints simultaneously by entering B20:B22 into the **Cell Reference** box, selecting <=, and entering D20:D22 into the **Constraint** box. Alternatively, we could have entered the three constraints one at a time.

The Solver Add-In should be found under the **Data** tab on the Excel Ribbon. If it does not appear here, you will have to add it by following the steps shown below.

**Step 1.**  Select the **File** tab from the Ribbon
**Step 2.**  Select **Options** from the **File** menu
**Step 3.**  Choose **Add-Ins** from the Excel Options screen
**Step 4.**  Click on **Go** next to **Manage: Excel Add-ins**
**Step 5.**  Click on the **Solver Add-in** checkbox

## Appendix 7.2  Solving Linear Programs with LINGO

In this appendix we describe how to use LINGO to solve the RMC problem. When you start LINGO, two windows are immediately displayed. The outer, or mainframe, window contains all the command menus and the command toolbar. The smaller window is the model window; this window is used to enter and edit the linear programming model you want to solve.

As with any model, it is good to document your LINGO model with comments. A comment in a LINGO model begins with an exclamation point and ends with a semicolon. If desired, a comment can span multiple lines.

The first item we enter is a comment describing the objective function. Recall that the objective function for the RMC problem is to maximize profit. Hence we enter the following comment:

```
! MAXIMIZE PROFIT;
```

*For the latest information on LINGO software see http://www.lindo.com.*

Next we press the Enter key and then type the objective function. The objective function for the RMC problem is Max $40F + 30S$. Thus, in the second line of the LINGO model window, we enter the following expression:

```
MAX = 40*F + 30*S;
```

Note that in LINGO the symbol * is used to denote multiplication and that the objective function, like a comment, ends with a semicolon. In general, each mathematical expression (objective function and constraints) in LINGO is terminated with a semicolon.

Next, we press the Enter key to move to a new line. The first constraint in the RMC problem is $0.4F + 0.5S \leq 20$, for material 1. Thus, in the third and fourth lines of the LINGO model window, we enter the following expressions:

```
!MATERIAL 1 CONSTRAINT;
0.4*F + 0.5*S <= 20;
```

Note that LINGO interprets the $<=$ symbol as $\leq$. Alternatively, we could enter $<$ instead of $<=$. As was the case when entering the objective function, a semicolon is required at the end of the first constraint. Pressing the Enter key moves us to a new line, and we continue the process by entering the remaining comments and constraints as shown here:

```
!MATERIAL 2 CONSTRAINT;
0.2*S <= 5;
!MATERIAL 3 CONSTRAINT;
0.6*F + 0.3*S <= 21;
```

The model window will now appear as follows:

```
!MAXIMIZE PROFIT;
MAX = 40*F + 30*S;
!MATERIAL 1 CONSTRAINT;
0.4*F + 0.5*S <= 20;
!MATERIAL 2 CONSTRAINT;
0.2*S <= 5;
!MATERIAL 3 CONSTRAINT;
0.6*F + 0.3*S <= 21;
```

If you make an error in entering the model, you can correct it at any time by simply positioning the cursor where you made the error and entering the necessary correction.

To solve the model, select the **Solve** command from the **LINGO** menu or press the **Solve** button on the toolbar at the top of the mainframe window. LINGO will begin the solution process by determining whether the model conforms to all syntax requirements. If the LINGO model doesn't pass these tests, you will be informed by an error message. If LINGO does not find any errors in the model input, it will begin to solve the model. As part of the solution process, LINGO displays a **Solver Status** window that allows you to monitor the progress of the solver. LINGO displays the solution in a new window titled "Solution Report." The output that appears in the **Solution Report** window for the RMC problem is shown in Figure 7.28.

**FIGURE 7.28**   SOLUTION TO THE RMC PROBLEM USING LINGO

```
Global optimal solution found.
Objective value:                              1600.000
Total solver iterations:                             2

               Variable            Value      Reduced Cost
                      F         25.00000          0.000000
                      S         20.00000          0.000000

               Row       Slack or Surplus        Dual Price
                 1            1600.000             1.000000
                 2            0.000000            33.33333
                 3            1.000000             0.000000
                 4            0.000000            44.44444
```

© Cengage Learning 2013

The first part of the output shown in Figure 7.28 indicates that an optimal solution has been found and that the value of the objective function is 1600. We see that the optimal solution is $F = 25$ and $S = 20$, and that the slack variables for the three constraints (rows 2–4) are 0, 1, and 0. We will discuss the use of the information in the Reduced Cost column and the Dual Price column in Chapter 8.

# CHAPTER 8

# Linear Programming: Sensitivity Analysis and Interpretation of Solution

**CONTENTS**

**Sensitivity analysis** is the study of how changes in the coefficients of a linear programming problem affect the optimal solution. Using sensitivity analysis, we can answer questions such as the following:

1. How will a change in an *objective function coefficient* affect the optimal solution?
2. How will a change in a *right-hand-side value* for a constraint affect the optimal solution?

Because sensitivity analysis is concerned with how these changes affect the optimal solution, sensitivity analysis does not begin until the optimal solution to the original linear programming problem has been obtained. For this reason, sensitivity analysis is often referred to as *postoptimality analysis*.

Our approach to sensitivity analysis parallels the approach used to introduce linear programming in Chapter 7. We introduce sensitivity analysis by using the graphical method for a linear programming problem with two decision variables. Then, we show how Excel Solver can be used to provide more complete sensitivity analysis information. Finally, we extend the discussion of problem formulation started in Chapter 7 by formulating and solving three larger linear programming problems. In discussing the solution for each of these problems, we focus on managerial interpretation of the optimal solution and sensitivity analysis information.

Sensitivity analysis and the interpretation of the optimal solution are important aspects of applying linear programming. The Q.M. in Action, Assigning Products to Worldwide Facilities at Eastman Kodak, shows some of the sensitivity analysis and interpretation issues encountered at Kodak in determining the optimal product assignments. Later in the chapter other Q.M. in Action features illustrate how Performance Analysis Corporation uses sensitivity analysis as part of an evaluation model for a chain of fast-food outlets, how General Electric Plastics uses a linear programming model involving thousands of variables and constraints to determine optimal production quantities, how Kimpton Hotels uses a linear program to set prices and room availability on Priceline, and how Duncan Industries Limited's linear programming model for tea distribution convinced management of the benefits of using quantitative analysis techniques to support the decision-making process.

## Q.M. *in* ACTION

### ASSIGNING PRODUCTS TO WORLDWIDE FACILITIES AT EASTMAN KODAK*

One of the major planning issues at Eastman Kodak involves the determination of which products should be manufactured at Kodak's facilities located throughout the world. The assignment of products to facilities is called the "world load." In determining the world load, Kodak faces a number of interesting trade-offs. For instance, not all manufacturing facilities are equally efficient for all products, and the margins by which some facilities are better varies from product to product. In addition to

manufacturing costs, the transportation costs and the effects of duty and duty drawbacks (refunds of duty taxes) can significantly affect the allocation decision.

To assist in determining the world load, Kodak developed a linear programming model that accounts for the physical nature of the distribution problem and the various costs (manufacturing, transportation, and duties) involved. The model's objective is to minimize the total cost subject to constraints such as satisfying demand and dealing with capacity constraints for each facility.

*Based on information provided by Greg Sampson of Eastman Kodak.

(*continued*)

The linear programming model is a static representation of the problem situation, and the real world is always changing. Thus, the linear programming model must be used in a dynamic way. For instance, when demand expectations change, the model can be used to determine the effect the change will have on the world load. Suppose that the currency of country A rises compared to the currency of country B. How should the world load be modified? In addition to using the linear programming model in a "how-to-react" mode, the model is useful in a more active mode by considering questions such as the following: Is it worthwhile for facility F to spend $d$ dollars to lower the unit manufacturing cost of product P from $x$ to $y$? The linear programming model helps Kodak evaluate the overall effect of possible changes at any facility.

In the final analysis, managers recognize that they cannot use the model by simply turning it on, reading the results, and executing the solution. The model's recommendation combined with managerial judgment provides the final decision.

 ## 8.1 Introduction to Sensitivity Analysis

Sensitivity analysis is important to decision makers because real-world problems exist in a changing environment. Prices of raw materials change, product demands change, production capacities change, stock prices change, and so on. If a linear programming model has been used in such an environment, we can expect some of the coefficients in the model to change over time. As a result, we will want to determine how these changes affect the optimal solution. Sensitivity analysis provides information needed to respond to such changes without requiring a complete solution of a revised linear program.

Recall the RMC problem introduced in Chapter 7. RMC wanted to determine the number of tons of fuel additive ($F$) and the number of tons of solvent base ($S$) to produce in order to maximize the total profit contribution for the two products. Three raw material constraints limit the amounts of the two products that can be produced. The RMC linear programming model is restated here:

$$
\begin{aligned}
\text{Max} \quad & 40F + 30S \\
\text{s.t.} \quad & \\
0.4F + 0.5 \quad & \leq 20 \quad \text{Material 1} \\
0.2S \quad & \leq 5 \quad \text{Material 2} \\
0.6F + 0.3S \quad & \leq 21 \quad \text{Material 3} \\
F, S \quad & \geq 0
\end{aligned}
$$

The optimal solution, $F = 25$ tons and $S = 20$ tons, provided a maximum profit contribution of $1600.

The optimal solution was based on profit contributions of $40 per ton for the fuel additive and $30 per ton for the solvent base. However, suppose that we later learn that a price reduction causes the profit contribution for the fuel additive to fall from $40 to $30 per ton. Sensitivity analysis can be used to determine whether producing 25 tons of fuel additive and 20 tons of solvent base is still best. If it is, solving a modified linear programming problem with $30F + 30S$ as the new objective function is not necessary.

Sensitivity analysis can also be used to determine which coefficients in a linear programming model are crucial. For example, suppose that management believes that the $30 per ton profit contribution for the solvent base is only a rough estimate of the profit contribution that will actually be obtained. If sensitivity analysis shows that 25 tons of fuel additive and 20 tons of solvent base will be the optimal solution as long as the profit contribution for the solvent base is between $20 and $50, management should feel comfortable with the $30 per ton estimate and the recommended production quantities. However, if sensitivity analysis shows that 25 tons of fuel additive and 20 tons of solvent base will be the optimal solution only if the profit contribution for the solvent base is between $29.90 and $30.20 per ton, management may want to review the accuracy of the $30 per ton estimate.

Another aspect of sensitivity analysis concerns changes in the right-hand-side values of the constraints. Recall that in the RMC problem the optimal solution used all available material 1 and material 3. What would happen to the optimal solution and total profit contribution if RMC could obtain additional quantities of either of these resources? Sensitivity analysis can help determine how much each added ton of material is worth and how many tons can be added before diminishing returns set in.

## 8.2  Objective Function Coefficients

Let us begin sensitivity analysis by using the graphical solution procedure to demonstrate how a change in an objective function coefficient can affect the optimal solution to a linear programming problem. We begin with the graphical solution to the original RMC problem shown in Figure 8.1. The feasible region is shaded. The objective function $40F + 30S$ takes on its maximum value at the extreme point $F = 25$ and $S = 20$. Thus, $F = 25$ and $S = 20$ is the optimal solution and $40(25) + 30(20) = 1600$ is the value of the optimal solution.

Now suppose RMC learns that a price reduction in the fuel additive has reduced its profit contribution to $30 per ton. With this reduction, RMC's management may question the desirability of maintaining the original optimal solution of $F = 25$ tons and $S = 20$ tons.

**FIGURE 8.1**  OPTIMAL SOLUTION TO THE ORIGINAL RMC PROBLEM

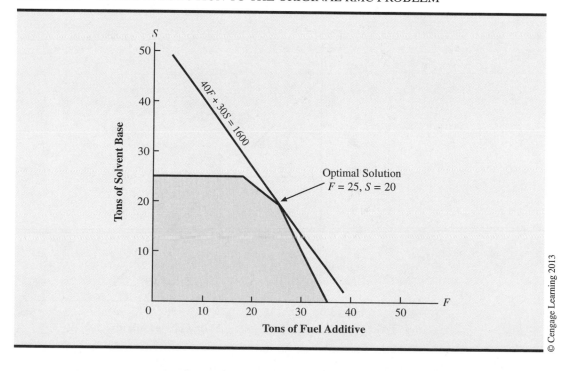

Perhaps a different solution is now optimal. The RMC linear program with the revised objective function is as follows:

$$\text{Max} \quad 30F + 30S$$

s.t.

$$
\begin{aligned}
0.4F + 0.5S &\le 20 \quad \text{Material 1} \\
0.2S &\le 5 \quad \text{Material 2} \\
0.6F + 0.3S &\le 21 \quad \text{Material 3} \\
F, S &\ge 0
\end{aligned}
$$

Note that only the objective function has changed. Because the constraints have not changed, the feasible region for the revised RMC problem remains the same as the original problem. The graphical solution to the RMC problem with the objective function $30F + 30S$ is shown in Figure 8.2. Note that the extreme point providing the optimal solution is still $F = 25$ and $S = 20$. Thus, although the total profit contribution decreased to $30(25) + 30(20) = 1350$, the decrease in the profit contribution for the fuel additive from \$40 per ton to \$30 per ton does not change the optimal solution $F = 25$ and $S = 20$.

Now let us suppose that a further price reduction causes the profit contribution for the fuel additive to be reduced to \$20 per ton. Is $F = 25$ and $S = 20$ still the optimal solution? Figure 8.3 shows the graphical solution to the RMC problem with the objective function revised to $20F + 30S$. The extreme point providing the optimal solution is now $F = 18.75$ and $S = 25$. The total profit contribution decreased to $20(18.75) + 30(25) = 1125$. However, in this case, we see that decreasing the profit contribution for the fuel additive to

**FIGURE 8.2**    REVISED OPTIMAL SOLUTION WITH THE RMC OBJECTIVE FUNCTION $30F + 30S$

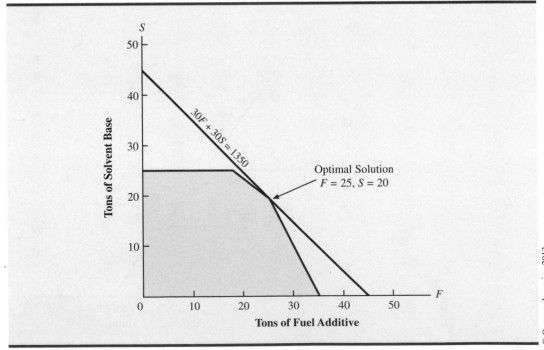

**FIGURE 8.3**    REVISED OPTIMAL SOLUTION WITH THE RMC OBJECTIVE FUNCTION
$20F + 30S$

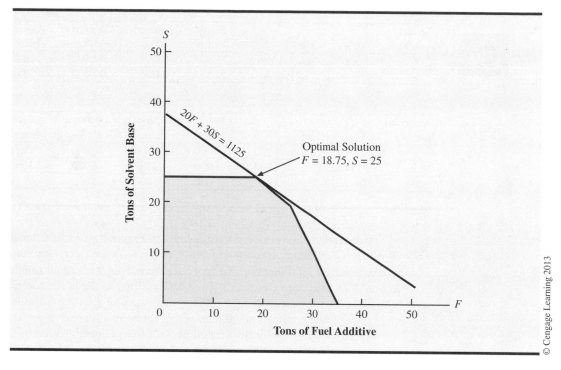

*The graphical solution is used here to help the reader visualize how changes to an objective function coefficient may or may not change the optimal solution.*

$20 per ton changes the optimal solution. The solution $F = 25$ tons and $S = 20$ tons is no longer optimal. The solution $F = 18.75$ and $S = 25$ now provides the optimal production quantities for RMC.

What do we learn from the graphical solutions in Figures 8.1, 8.2, and 8.3? Changing one objective function coefficient changes the slope of the objective function line but leaves the feasible region unchanged. If the change in the objective function coefficient is small, the extreme point that provided the optimal solution to the original problem may still provide the optimal solution. However, if the change in the objective function coefficient is large enough, a different extreme point will provide a new optimal solution.

*Computer solutions typically provide sensitivity analysis information.*

Fortunately, Excel can easily provide sensitivity analysis information about the objective function coefficients for the original RMC linear programming problem. You do not have to reformulate and re-solve the linear programming problem to obtain the sensitivity analysis information. Appendix 8.1 explains how to generate a Sensitivity Report using Excel Solver. A sensitivity report similar to the output provided by Excel for the original RMC linear programming problem is shown in Figure 8.4. In addition to all of the Excel Solver Sensitivity Report information, the report in Figure 8.4 also shows the variables we used in our model. This allows you to easily link the sensitivity report to the model under discussion. We shall use this style of sensitivity report throughout this chapter.

In the Variable Cells section of the sensitivity report, the column labeled Final Value contains the optimal values of the decision variables. For the RMC problem the optimal solution is to produce 25 tons of fuel additive and 20 tons of solvent base. Associated with each decision variable is a reduced cost. We will discuss reduced costs in more detail after introducing the concept of shadow prices later in this chapter.

**FIGURE 8.4**    SENSITIVITY REPORT FOR THE RMC PROBLEM

WEB file

RMC

Variable Cells

| Model Variable | Name | Final Value | Reduced Cost | Objective Coefficient | Allowable Increase | Allowable Decrease |
|---|---|---|---|---|---|---|
| F | Tons Produced Fuel Additive | 25.000 | 0.000 | 40.000 | 20.000 | 16.000 |
| S | Tons Produced Solvent Base | 20.000 | 0.000 | 30.000 | 20.000 | 10.000 |

Constraints

| Constraint Number | Name | Final Value | Shadow Price | Constraint R.H. Side | Allowable Increase | Allowable Decrease |
|---|---|---|---|---|---|---|
| 1 | Material 1 Amount Used | 20.000 | 33.333 | 20.000 | 1.500 | 6.000 |
| 2 | Material 2 Amount Used | 4.000 | 0.000 | 5.000 | 1E+30 | 1.000 |
| 3 | Material 3 Amount Used | 21.000 | 44.444 | 21.000 | 9.000 | 2.250 |

© Cengage Learning 2013

To the right of the Reduced Cost column in Figure 8.4, we find three columns labeled Objective Coefficient, Allowable Increase, and Allowable Decrease. For example, the objective function coefficient for the fuel additive is $40, with an allowable increase of $20 and an allowable decrease of $16. Therefore, as long as the profit contribution associated with fuel additive is between $40 + $20 = $60 and $40 − $16 = $24, the optimal solution of 25 tons of fuel additive and 20 tons of solvent base will not change. The value of $20 is often referred to as the **objective function coefficient allowable increase**, and the value of $16 is the **objective function coefficient allowable decrease**. The range between $24 and $60 is referred to as the **objective coefficient range** or **range of optimality** for the fuel additive variable. If the profit contribution for the fuel additive is outside this range, a different extreme point and a different solution will become optimal.

The objective function coefficient for the solvent base variable is $30. The allowable decrease of $10 and allowable increase of $20 for the solvent base variable show that the optimal solution will not change so long as the profit contribution for solvent base is between $30 + $20 = $50 and $30 − $10 = $20.

**NOTES AND COMMENTS**

**1.** The sensitivity analysis information provided for the objective function coefficients is based on the assumption that *only one objective function coefficient changes at a time* and that all other aspects of the original problem remain unchanged. Thus, an objective coefficient range is only applicable for changes to a single objective coefficient. We examine this issue in more depth in Section 8.4.

## ( 8.3 )   Right-Hand Sides

Let us expand the discussion of sensitivity analysis by considering how a change in the right-hand side of a constraint affects the feasible region and the optimal solution to a linear programming problem. As with sensitivity analysis for the objective function coefficients, we consider what happens when we make *one change at a time*. For example, suppose that in the RMC problem an additional 4.5 tons of material 3 becomes available.

In this case, the right-hand side of the third constraint increases from 21 tons to 25.5 tons. The revised RMC linear programming model is as follows:

$$\text{Max} \quad 40F + 30S$$
$$\text{s.t.}$$

$$0.4F + 0.5S \leq 20 \qquad \text{Material 1}$$
$$0.2S \leq 5 \qquad \text{Material 2}$$
$$0.6F + 0.3S \leq 25.5 \qquad \text{Material 3}$$
$$F, S \geq 0$$

*Sensitivity analysis for right-hand sides is based on the assumption that only one right-hand side changes at a time. All other aspects of the problem are assumed to be as stated in the original problem.*

The graphical solution to this problem is shown in Figure 8.5. Note how the feasible region expands because of the additional 4.5 tons of material 3. Application of the graphical solution procedure shows that the extreme point $F = 37.5$ tons and $S = 10$ tons is the new optimal solution. The value of the optimal solution is $40(37.5) + 30(10) = \$1800$. Recall that the optimal solution to the original RMC problem was $F = 25$ tons and $S = 20$ tons and the value of the optimal solution was \$1600. Thus, the additional 4.5 tons of material 3 in the revised problem provides a new optimal solution and increases the value of the optimal solution by $\$1800 - \$1600 = \$200$. On a per-ton basis, the additional 4.5 tons of material 3 increases the value of the optimal solution at the rate of $\$200/4.5 = \$44.44$ per ton.

*Shadow prices often provide the economic information that helps make decisions about acquiring additional resources.*

The **shadow price** is the change in the optimal objective function value per unit increase in the right-hand side of a constraint. Hence, the shadow price for the material 3 constraint is \$44.44 per ton. In other words, if we increase the right-hand side of the material 3 constraint by 1 ton, the value of the optimal solution will increase by \$44.44. Conversely, if we decrease the right-hand side of the material 3 constraint by 1 ton, the value of the optimal solution will decrease by \$44.44.

**FIGURE 8.5**   GRAPHICAL SOLUTION TO THE RMC PROBLEM WITH MATERIAL 3 CONSTRAINT $0.6F + 0.5S \leq 24.5$

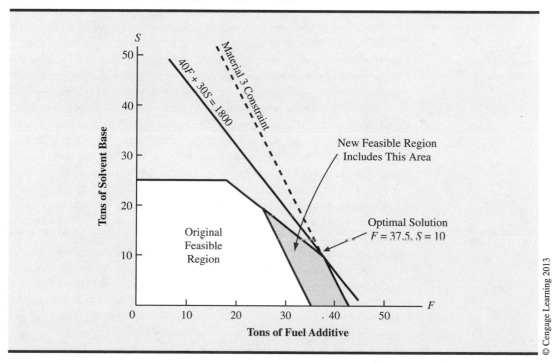

Fortunately, the sensitivity report for the original linear programming problem provides the shadow prices for all the constraints. *You do not have to reformulate and re-solve the linear programming problem to obtain the shadow price information.* The sensitivity report for the original RMC linear programming problem is shown in Figure 8.4.

Examine the Constraints section of the sensitivity report. The entries in the Final Value column indicate the number of tons of each material used in the optimal solution. Thus, RMC will use 20 tons of material 1, 4 tons of material 2, and 21 tons of material 3 in order to produce the optimal solution of 25 tons of fuel additive and 20 tons of solvent base.

The values in the Constraint R.H. Side column are the right-hand sides of the constraints for the RMC problem. The differences between the entries in the Constraint R.H. Side column and the Final Value column provide the values of the slack variables for the RMC problem. Thus, there are $20 - 20 = 0$ tons of slack for material 1, $5 - 4 = 1$ ton of slack for material 2, and $21 - 21 = 0$ tons of slack for material 3.

The column labeled Shadow Price provides the following information:

*Computer solutions typically provide the shadow price for each constraint.*

| Constraint | Shadow Price |
|---|---|
| Material 1 Amount Used | $33.33 |
| Material 2 Amount Used | $ 0.00 |
| Material 3 Amount Used | $44.44 |

Note that the shadow price for material 3, $44.44 per ton, agrees with the calculations we made using the graphical solution procedure. We also observe that the shadow price for the material 1 constraint indicates that the value of the optimal solution will increase at the rate of $33.33 per ton of material 1. Finally, note that the shadow price for the material 2 constraint is $0.00. The optimal solution to the RMC problem shows that material 2 has a slack of 1 ton. Thus, at the optimal solution, 1 ton of material 2 is unused. The shadow price of $0.00 tells us that additional tons of material 2 will simply add to the amount of slack for constraint 2 and will not change the value of the optimal solution.

We caution here that the value of a shadow price may be applicable only for small increases in the right-hand side. As more and more resources are obtained and as the right-hand side continues to increase, other constraints will become binding and limit the change in the value of the optimal solution. At some point, the shadow price can no longer be used to determine the improvement in the value of the optimal solution.

Now that we have introduced the concept of shadow prices, we can define the **reduced cost** associated with each variable. The reduced cost associated with a variable is equal to the shadow price for the nonnegativity constraint associated with the variable.[1] From Figure 8.4 we see that the reduced cost for both variables are zero. This makes sense. Consider fuel additive. The nonnegativity constraint associated with the fuel additive variable, $F$, is $F \geq 0$, so changing the nonnegativity constraint to $F \geq 1$ has no effect on the optimal solution value. Because increasing the right-hand side by one unit has no effect on the optimal objective function value, the shadow price (i.e., reduced cost) of this nonnegativity constraint is zero. A similar argument applies to the solvent base variable, $S$. Later we introduce a modified RMC problem that has a nonzero reduced cost to better explain this concept.

The last two columns in the Constraints section of the sensitivity report contain the **right-hand side allowable increase** and **allowable decrease** for each constraint. For example, consider the material 1 constraint with an allowable increase value of 1.5 and an allowable decrease value of 6. The values in the Allowable Increase and Allowable Decrease

---

[1]We also note that, if the value of a variable in an optimal solution is equal to the upper bound of the variable, then the reduced cost will be the shadow price of this upper-bound constraint.

*The range of feasibility is also sometimes referred to as the right-hand-side range.*

columns indicate that the shadow price of \$33.33 is applicable for increases up to $20 + 1.5 = 21.5$ tons and decreases down to $20 - 6 = 14$ tons. The values between 14 tons and 21.5 tons are often referred to as the **range of feasibility** for the material 1 constraint.

Note that unlike the objective function coefficient ranges, it is not true that the optimal solution will not change if you stay within the range of feasibility. The range of feasibility only implies that the same set of binding constraints will remain binding and hence that the shadow price will accurately predict what will happen to the optimal objective function value as the ride-hand-side is changed.

*Similar to sensitivity analysis for objective function coefficients, the sensitivity analysis for right-hand sides of constraints assumes that only one constraint right-hand side changes at a time.*

In summary, the range of feasibility information provides the limits where the shadow prices are applicable. For changes outside the range, the problem must be re-solved to find the new shadow price. Note that the sensitivity analysis information for right-hand sides of constraints is only applicable for changes to a single right-hand side. If two or more right-hand sides of constraints change at the same time, it is easiest to re-solve the problem to see the effect of these changes. This issue is discussed in more detail in Section 8.4.

The Q.M. in Action, Evaluating Efficiency at Performance Analysis Corporation, illustrates the use of shadow prices as part of an evaluation model for a chain of fast-food outlets. This type of model will be studied in more detail in the next chapter when we discuss an application referred to as *data envelopment analysis*.

---

## Q.M. in ACTION

### EVALUATING EFFICIENCY AT PERFORMANCE ANALYSIS CORPORATION*

Performance Analysis Corporation specializes in the use of management science to design more efficient and effective operations for a wide variety of chain stores. One such application uses linear programming methodology to provide an evaluation model for a chain of fast-food outlets.

According to the concept of Pareto optimality, a restaurant in a given chain is relatively inefficient if other restaurants in the same chain exhibit the following characteristics:

1. Operate in the same or worse environment
2. Produce at least the same level of *all* outputs
3. Utilize no more of *any* resource and *less* of at least one of the resources

To determine which of the restaurants are Pareto inefficient, Performance Analysis Corporation developed and solved a linear programming model. Model constraints involve requirements concerning the minimum acceptable levels of output and conditions imposed by uncontrollable elements in the environment, and the objective function calls for the minimization of the resources

necessary to produce the output. Solving the model produces the following output for each restaurant:

1. A score that assesses the level of so-called relative technical efficiency achieved by the particular restaurant over the time period in question.
2. The reduction in controllable resources or the increase of outputs over the time period in question needed for an inefficient restaurant to be rated as efficient.
3. A peer group of other restaurants with which each restaurant can be compared in the future.

Sensitivity analysis provides important managerial information. For example, for each constraint concerning a minimum acceptable output level, the shadow price tells the manager how much one more unit of output would increase the efficiency measure.

The analysis typically identifies 40% to 50% of the restaurants as underperforming, given the previously stated conditions concerning the inputs available and outputs produced. Performance Analysis Corporation finds that if all the relative inefficiencies identified are eliminated simultaneously, corporate profits typically increase approximately 5% to 10%. This increase is truly substantial given the large scale of operations involved.

*Based on information provided by Richard C. Morey of Performance Analysis Corporation.

---

### NOTES AND COMMENTS

**1.** Some texts and computer programs use the term *dual value* or *dual price* instead of *shadow price*. Often the meaning of these terms is identical to the definition given here for shadow price. However, you must be careful to understand exactly what is meant by the term being used.

---

## Cautionary Note on the Interpretation of Shadow Prices

As stated previously, the shadow price is the change in the value of the optimal solution per unit increase in the right-hand side of a constraint. When the right-hand side of the constraint represents the amount of a resource available, the shadow price is often interpreted as the maximum amount one should be willing to pay for one additional unit of the resource. However, such an interpretation is not always correct. To see why, we need to understand the difference between sunk and relevant costs. A **sunk cost** is one that is not affected by the decision made. It will be incurred no matter what values the decision variables assume. A **relevant cost** is one that depends on the decision made. The amount of a relevant cost will vary depending on the values of the decision variables.

   Let us reconsider the RMC problem. The amount of material 1 available is 20 tons. The cost of material 1 is a sunk cost if it must be paid regardless of the number of tons of fuel additive and solvent base produced. It would be a relevant cost if RMC only had to pay for the number of tons of material 1 actually used to produce fuel additive and solvent base. All relevant costs should be included in the objective function of a linear program. Sunk costs should not be included in the objective function. For RMC we have been assuming that the company has already paid for materials 1, 2, and 3. Therefore, the cost of the raw materials for RMC is a sunk cost and has not been included in the objective function.

   When the cost of a resource is *sunk*, the shadow price can be interpreted as the maximum amount the company should be willing to pay for one additional unit of the resource. When the cost of a resource used is relevant, the shadow price can be interpreted as the amount by which the value of the resource exceeds its cost. Thus, when the resource cost is relevant, the shadow price can be interpreted as the maximum premium over the normal cost that the company should be willing to pay for one unit of the resource.

*Only relevant costs should be included in the objective function.*

---

### NOTES AND COMMENTS

**1.** Most computer software packages for solving linear programs provide the optimal solution, shadow price information, the objective coefficient ranges, and the ranges of feasibility. The labels used for these ranges may vary, but the meaning is usually the same as what we have described here.

**2.** We defined the shadow price as the change in the optimal objective function value per unit increase in a right-hand side of a constraint. The negative of the shadow price gives the change in the optimal objective function value per unit decrease in the right-hand side.

**3.** Whenever one of the right-hand sides is at an endpoint of its range, the shadow price only provides one-sided information. In this case, the shadow price only predicts the change in the optimal value of the objective function for changes toward the interior of the range.

**4.** A condition called *degeneracy* can cause a subtle difference in how we interpret changes in the objective function coefficients beyond the endpoints of the objective coefficient range. Degeneracy occurs when the shadow price equals zero for one of the binding constraints.

Degeneracy does not affect the interpretation of changes toward the interior of the objective coefficient range. However, when degeneracy is present, changes beyond the endpoints of the range do not necessarily mean a different solution will be optimal. From a practical point of view, changes beyond the endpoints of the range necessitate resolving the problem.

5. Managers are frequently called on to provide an economic justification for new technology. Often the new technology is developed, or purchased, in order to conserve resources. The shadow price can be helpful in such cases because it can be used to determine the savings attributable to the new technology by showing the savings per unit of resource conserved.

## 8.4   Limitations of Classical Sensitivity Analysis

As we have seen, classical sensitivity analysis can provide useful information on the sensitivity of the solution to changes in the model input data. However, classical sensitivity analysis does have its limitations. In this section we discuss three such limitations: simultaneous changes in input data, changes in constraint coefficients, and nonintuitive shadow prices. We give examples of these three cases and discuss how to deal effectively with these through re-solving the model with changes. In fact, in our experience, it is rarely the case that one solves a model once and makes a recommendation. More often than not, a series of models are solved using a variety of input data sets before a final plan is adopted. With improved algorithms and more powerful computers, solving multiple runs of a model is extremely cost- and time-effective.

### Simultaneous Changes

Classical sensitivity analysis is based on the assumption that only one coefficient changes; it is assumed that all other coefficients will remain as stated in the original problem. Thus, the range analysis for the objective function coefficients and the constraint right-hand sides is only applicable for changes in a single coefficient. In many cases, however, we are interested in what would happen if two or more coefficients are changed simultaneously. The easiest way to examine the effect of simultaneous changes is to rerun the model. Computer solution methods such as Excel Solver make rerunning the model easy and fast for many applications.

Consider again the original RMC problem. Suppose RMC's accounting department reviews both the price and cost data for the two products. As a result, the profit contribution for the fuel additive is increased to $48 per ton and the profit contribution for the solvent base is decreased to $27 per ton. Figure 8.6 shows the answer report for this revised problem. The total profit has increased to $48(25) + $27(20) = $1740, but the optimal solution of 25 tons of fuel additive and 20 tons of solvent base has not changed.

Now suppose that the profit contribution for fuel additive is increased again to $55 per ton and the profit contribution for the solvent base remains at $27 per ton. If RMC produces 25 tons of fuel additive and 20 tons of solvent base, this will generate a profit of $55(25) + $27(20) = $1915. However, the answer report in Figure 8.7 shows that if we re-solve this problem with the new profit contribution values, the optimal solution changes. The optimal solution is to produce 35 tons of fuel additive and zero tons of solvent base. This optimal solution results in a profit of $55(35) + $27(0) = $1925.

Sensitivity analysis for the right-hand side of constraints has a similar limitation. The right-hand-side sensitivity analysis information is based on the assumption that only one right-hand side changes at a time. If two or more right-hand sides change simultaneously, the easiest way to observe the effect of these changes is to re-solve the model.

**FIGURE 8.6**　ANSWER REPORT FOR RMC PROBLEM WITH CHANGE IN PROFITS PER TON FOR FUEL ADDITIVE TO $48 AND SOLVENT BASE TO $27

Objective Cell (Max)

| Name | Original Value | Final Value |
|---|---|---|
| Maximize Total Profit | 0.000 | 1740.000 |

Variable Cells

| Model Variable | Name | Original Value | Final Value | Integer |
|---|---|---|---|---|
| A | Tons Produced Fuel Additive | 0.000 | 25.000 | Contin |
| B | Tons Produced Solvent Base | 0.000 | 20.000 | Contin |

Constraints

| Constraint Number | Name | Cell Value | Status | Slack |
|---|---|---|---|---|
| 1 | Material 1 Amount Used | 20.000 | Binding | 0.000 |
| 2 | Material 2 Amount Used | 4.000 | Not Binding | 1.000 |
| 3 | Material 3 Amount Used | 21.000 | Binding | 0.000 |

© Cengage Learning 2013

**FIGURE 8.7**　ANSWER REPORT FOR THE RMC PROBLEM WITH ADDITIONAL INCREASE IN PROFIT PER TON FOR FUEL ADDITIVE TO $55

Objective Cell (Max)

| Name | Original Value | Final Value |
|---|---|---|
| Maximize Total Profit | 0.000 | 1925.000 |

Variable Cells

| Model Variable | Name | Original Value | Final Value | Integer |
|---|---|---|---|---|
| A | Tons Produced Fuel Additive | 0.000 | 35.000 | Contin |
| B | Tons Produced Solvent Base | 0.000 | 0.000 | Contin |

Constraints

| Constraint Number | Name | Cell Value | Status | Slack |
|---|---|---|---|---|
| 1 | Material 1 Amount Used | 14.000 | Not Binding | 6.000 |
| 2 | Material 2 Amount Used | 0.000 | Not Binding | 5.000 |
| 3 | Material 3 Amount Used | 21.000 | Binding | 0.000 |

© Cengage Learning 2013

## Changes in Constraint Coefficients

Classical sensitivity analysis provides no information about changes resulting from a change in the coefficient of a variable in a constraint. We return to the RMC problem to illustrate this idea.

Suppose RMC is considering a different blending formula such that a ton of fuel additive uses 0.5 tons of material 1 instead of 0.4 tons. The constraint for material 1 would then change to

$$0.5F + 0.5S \le 20$$

Even though this is a single change in a coefficient in the model, there is no way to tell from classical sensitivity analysis what impact the change in the coefficient of $F$ will have on the

**FIGURE 8.8**   ANSWER REPORT FOR THE RMC PROBLEM WITH CHANGES TO CONSTRAINT
COEFFICIENTS

Objective Cell (Max)

| Name | Original Value | Final Value |
|---|---|---|
| Maximize Total Profit | 0.000 | 1500.000 |

Variable Cells

| Model Variable | Name | Original Value | Final Value | Integer |
|---|---|---|---|---|
| A | Tons Produced Fuel Additive | 0.000 | 30.000 | Contin |
| B | Tons Produced Solvent Base | 0.000 | 10.000 | Contin |

Constraints

| Constraint Number | Name | Cell Value | Status | Slack |
|---|---|---|---|---|
| 1 | Material 1 Amount Used | 20.000 | Binding | 0.000 |
| 2 | Material 2 Amount Used | 2.000 | Not Binding | 3.000 |
| 3 | Material 3 Amount Used | 21.000 | Binding | 0.000 |

© Cengage Learning 2013

solution. Instead, we must simply change the coefficient and rerun the model. The answer report appears in Figure 8.8. Note that it is optimal to produce 30 tons of fuel additive and 10 tons of solvent base. The optimal profit has also changed from $1600 to $40(30) + $30(10) = $1500. Changing to this new blending formula will cost RMC $1600 − $1500 = $100.

## Nonintuitive Shadow Prices

Constraints with variables naturally on both the left-hand and right-hand sides often lead to shadow prices that have a nonintuitve explanation. To illustrate such a case and how we may deal with it, let us again reconsider the RMC problem.

Suppose that after reviewing the solution to the original RMC problem (sensitivity report shown in Figure 8.4), management decides that it is concerned with solutions requiring greater production of fuel additive than solvent base. Management believes that the profit generated per ton of fuel additive could decrease in the future, so it is more comfortable producing a greater amount of solvent base than fuel additive. If management wants to specify that RMC produces at least as much solvent base as fuel additive, then we must add the constraint

$$S \geq F$$

This new constraint will require RMC to produce at least as many tons of solvent base as fuel additive. The sensitivity report generated from resolving this problem with the new constraint is shown in Figure 8.9. This shows that it is optimal to produce 22.222 tons of fuel additive and 22.222 tons of solvent base. The total profit using this optimal solution is $40(22.222) + $30(22.222) = $1556.

Let us consider the shadow price for the Min Solvent Base Required constraint. The shadow price of −8.89 indicates that a one-unit increase in the right-hand side of the Min Solvent Base Required constraint will lower profits by $8.89. Thus, what the shadow price is really telling us is what will happen to the value of the optimal solution if the constraint is changed to

$$S \geq F + 1$$

**FIGURE 8.9** SENSITIVITY REPORT FOR RMC PROBLEM WITH ADDITIONAL CONSTRAINT FOR MINIMUM SOLVENT BASE PRODUCTION REQUIRED

Variable Cells

| Model Variable | Name | Final Value | Reduced Cost | Objective Coefficient | Allowable Increase | Allowable Decrease |
|---|---|---|---|---|---|---|
| F | Tons Produced Fuel Additive | 22.222 | 0.000 | 40.000 | 1E+30 | 16.000 |
| S | Tons Produced Solvent Base | 22.222 | 0.000 | 30.000 | 20.000 | 70.000 |

Constraints

| Constraint Number | Name | Final Value | Shadow Price | Constraint R.H. Side | Allowable Increase | Allowable Decrease |
|---|---|---|---|---|---|---|
| 1 | Material 1 Amount Used | 20.000 | 77.778 | 20.000 | 1.000 | 20.000 |
| 2 | Material 2 Amount Used | 4.444 | 0.000 | 5.000 | 1E+30 | 0.556 |
| 3 | Material 3 Amount Used | 20.000 | 0.000 | 21.000 | 1E+30 | 1.000 |
| 4 | Min Solvent Base Required | 22.222 | −8.889 | 0.000 | 6.250 | 5.000 |

© Cengage Learning 2013

The interpretation for this shadow price of −8.89 is correctly stated as follows: If we are forced to produce 1 ton more of solvent base over and above the amount of fuel additive produced, total profits will decrease by $8.89. Conversely, if we relax the requirement by 1 ton ($S \geq F - 1$), total profits will increase by $8.89.

We might instead be more interested in what happens if we change the coefficient on $F$. For instance, what if management required RMC to produce an amount of solvent base that is at least 110% of the amount of fuel additive produce? In other words, the constraint would change to

$$S \geq 1.1F$$

The shadow price does *not* tell us what will happen in this case. Because we have changed the coefficient of $F$ from 1.0 to 1.1, this is the same as the case discussed in the previous section: a change in the constraint coefficient. Since there is no way to get this information from classical sensitivity analysis, we need to re-solve the problem using the constraint $S \geq 1.1F$. To test the sensitivity of the solution to changes in the minimum required percentage of solvent base required, we can re-solve the model replacing the coefficient of $F$ with any percentage of interest.

To get a feel for how the required percentage impacts total profit, we solved versions of this model varying the percentage from 100% to 200% in increments of 10%. In other words, we varied the coefficient of $F$ from 1.0 to 2.0 in increments of 0.1. The impact of changing this percentage is shown in Figure 8.10, and the results are shown in Table 8.1.

What have we learned from this analysis? Notice from Figure 8.10 that the slope of the graph becomes steeper for values larger than 130%. This indicates that there is a shift in the rate of deterioration in profit starting at 130%. Table 8.1 shows why this is the case. For all percentages larger than 130%, we produce 25 tons of solvent base. We are unable to produce additional solvent base due to the material 2 constraint. This is because the left-hand side of the material 2 constraint $0.2(25) = 5$, which is equal to the right-hand side. Thus, the material 2 constraint is binding whenever we produce 25 tons of material 2.

**FIGURE 8.10**   PROFIT FOR VARIOUS VALUES OF REQUIRED SOLVENT BASE AS A
PERCENTAGE OF FUEL ADDITIVE PRODUCED

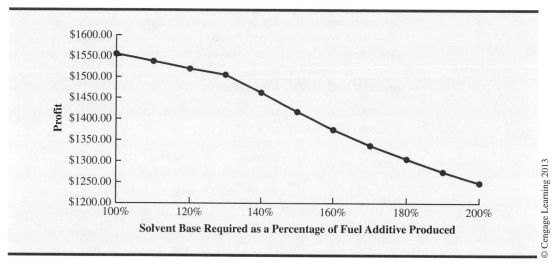

© Cengage Learning 2013

**TABLE 8.1**   SOLUTIONS FOR VARIOUS VALUES OF MINIMUM REQUIRED PRODUCTION
OF SOLVENT BASE AS A PERCENTAGE OF FUEL ADDITIVE PRODUCED

| Percent | Profit | Fuel Additive | Solvent Base |
|---|---|---|---|
| 100% | $1556.00 | 22.222 | 22.222 |
| 110% | $1537.00 | 21.053 | 23.158 |
| 120% | $1520.00 | 20.000 | 24.000 |
| 130% | $1505.00 | 19.048 | 24.762 |
| 140% | $1464.00 | 17.857 | 25.000 |
| 150% | $1417.00 | 16.667 | 25.000 |
| 160% | $1375.00 | 15.625 | 25.000 |
| 170% | $1338.00 | 14.706 | 25.000 |
| 180% | $1306.00 | 13.889 | 25.000 |
| 190% | $1275.00 | 13.158 | 25.000 |
| 200% | $1250.00 | 12.500 | 25.000 |

© Cengage Learning 2013

Management now knows that minimum percentage requirements between 100% and
130% result in modest profit losses. Minimum percentage requirements greater than 130%
result in greater profit losses. Greater minimum percentage requirements will result in
more significant profit losses because we are unable to produce more than 25 tons of solvent base due to the material 2 constraint

## 8.5   More Than Two Decision Variables

The graphical solution procedure is useful only for linear programs involving two decision
variables. In practice, the problems solved using linear programming usually involve large
numbers of variables and constraints. For instance, the Q.M. in Action, Determining Optimal

Production Quantities at GE Plastics, describes how a linear programming model with 3100 variables and 1100 constraints was solved in less than 10 seconds to determine the optimal production quantities at GE Plastics. In this section we discuss the formulation and computer solution for two linear programs with three decision variables. In doing so, we will show how to interpret the reduced-cost portion of the computer output and will also illustrate the interpretation of shadow prices for constraints that involve percentages.

## Modified RMC Problem

The RMC linear programming problem was introduced in Section 7.1. The original problem formulation is restated here:

$$\text{Max} \quad 40F + 30S$$

s.t.

$$
\begin{aligned}
0.4F + 0.5S &\leq 20 \quad \text{Material 1} \\
0.2S &\leq 5 \quad \text{Material 2} \\
0.6F + 0.3S &\leq 21 \quad \text{Material 3} \\
F, S &\geq 0
\end{aligned}
$$

Suppose that management also is considering producing a carpet cleaning fluid. Estimates are that each ton of carpet cleaning fluid will require 0.6 tons of material 1, 0.1 tons of material 2, and 0.3 tons of material 3. Because of the unique capabilities of the new product, RMC's management believes that the company will realize a profit contribution of $50 for each ton of carpet cleaning fluid produced during the current production period.

Let us consider the modifications in the original linear programming model that are needed to incorporate the effect of this additional decision variable. We let $C$ denote the number of tons of carpet cleaning fluid produced. After adding $C$ to the objective

---

**Q.M.** *in* ACTION

*DETERMINING OPTIMAL PRODUCTION QUANTITIES AT GE PLASTICS\**

General Electric Plastics (GEP) is a $5 billion global materials supplier of plastics and raw materials to many industries (e.g., automotive, computer, and medical equipment). GEP has plants all over the globe. In the past, GEP followed a pole-centric manufacturing approach wherein each product was manufactured in the geographic area (Americas, Europe, or Pacific) where it was to be delivered. When many of GEP's customers started shifting their manufacturing operations to the Pacific, a geographic imbalance was created between GEP's capacity and demand in the form of overcapacity in the Americas and undercapacity in the Pacific.

\*Based on R. Tyagi, P. Kalish, and K. Akbay, "GE Plastics Optimizes the Two-Echelon Global Fulfillment Network at Its High-Performance Polymers Division," *Interfaces* (September/October 2004): 359–366.

Recognizing that a pole-centric approach was no longer effective, GEP adopted a global approach to its manufacturing operations. Initial work focused on the high-performance polymers (HPP) division. Using a linear programming model, GEP was able to determine the optimal production quantities at each HPP plant to maximize the total contribution margin for the division. The model included demand constraints, manufacturing capacity constraints, and constraints that modeled the flow of materials produced at resin plants to the finishing plants and on to warehouses in three geographical regions (Americas, Europe, and Pacific). The mathematical model for a one-year problem has 3100 variables and 1100 constraints and can be solved in less than 10 seconds. The new system proved successful at the HPP division, and other GE Plastics divisions are adapting it for their supply chain planning.

**FIGURE 8.11**   SENSITIVITY REPORT FOR MODIFIED RMC PROBLEM

Variable Cells

| Model Variable | Name | Final Value | Reduced Cost | Objective Coefficient | Allowable Increase | Allowable Decrease |
|---|---|---|---|---|---|---|
| F | Tons Produced Fuel Additive | 27.500 | 0.000 | 40.000 | 60.000 | 6.667 |
| S | Tons Produced Solvent Base | 0.000 | −12.500 | 30.000 | 12.500 | 1E+30 |
| C | Tons Produced Carpet Cleaning Fluid | 15.000 | 0.000 | 50.000 | 10.000 | 16.667 |

Constraints

| Constraint Number | Name | Final Value | Shadow Price | Constraint R.H. Side | Allowable Increase | Allowable Decrease |
|---|---|---|---|---|---|---|
| 1 | Material 1 Amount Used | 20.000 | 75.000 | 20.000 | 14.000 | 6.000 |
| 2 | Material 2 Amount Used | 1.500 | 0.000 | 5.000 | 1E+30 | 3.500 |
| 3 | Material 3 Amount Used | 21.000 | 16.667 | 21.000 | 9.000 | 11.000 |

**WEB file**

**ModifiedRMC**

function and to each of the three constraints, we obtain the linear program for the modi-fied problem:

$$\text{Max} \quad 40F + 30S + 50C$$

s.t.

$$0.4F + 0.5S + 0.6C \leq 20 \quad \text{Material 1}$$
$$0.2S + 0.1C \leq 5 \quad \text{Material 2}$$
$$0.6F + 0.3S + 0.3C \leq 21 \quad \text{Material 3}$$
$$F, S, C \geq 0$$

Figure 8.11 shows the sensitivity report for this solution to the modified RMC problem. The optimal solution calls for the production of 27.5 tons of fuel additive, 0 tons of solvent base, and 15 tons of carpet cleaning fluid. The value of the optimal solution is $40(27.5) + $30(0) + $50(15) = $1850.

Note the information contained in the Reduced Costs column of the Variable Cells section. Recall that reduced costs are the shadow prices of the corresponding nonnegativ-ity constraints. As Figure 8.11 shows, the reduced costs for fuel additive and carpet clean-ing fluid variables are zero because increasing the right-hand side of these nonnegativity constraints would not change the optimal objective function value. However, the reduced cost for the solvent base decision variable is −12.50. This means that the shadow price for the nonnegativity constraint associated with the solvent base decision variable is −12.50. The interpretation for this value is that if the nonnegativity constraint, $S \geq 0$, was changed to $S \geq 1$, the optimal objective function value would decrease by $12.50. In other words, if we forced the production of at least 1 ton of solvent base, the profit for the optimal solution would decrease by $12.50.[2]

Figure 8.11 also shows that the shadow prices for material 1 amount used and material 3 amount used are 75.000 and 16.667, respectively, indicating that these two constraints are binding in the optimal solution. Thus, each additional ton of material 1 would increase the value of the optimal solution by $75 and each additional ton of material 3 would increase the value of the optimal solution by $16.67.

---

[2]Another interpretation for this is that if we "reduce the cost" of the objective function coefficient for solvent base by −12.50 [i.e., change the profit contribution from solvent base to $30 − (−$12.50) = $42.50)], then there is an optimal solution where we produce a nonzero amount of solvent base.

## Bluegrass Farms Problem

To provide additional practice in formulating and interpreting the computer solution for linear programs involving more than two decision variables, we consider a minimization problem involving three decision variables. Bluegrass Farms, located in Lexington, Kentucky, has been experimenting with a special diet for its racehorses. The feed components available for the diet are a standard horse feed product, an enriched oat product, and a new vitamin and mineral feed additive. The nutritional values in units per pound and the costs for the three feed components are summarized in Table 8.2; for example, each pound of the standard feed component contains 0.8 units of ingredient A, 1 unit of ingredient B, and 0.1 units of ingredient C. The minimum daily diet requirements for each horse are 3 units of ingredient A, 6 units of ingredient B, and 4 units of ingredient C. In addition, to control the weight of the horses, the total daily feed for a horse should not exceed 6 pounds. Bluegrass Farms would like to determine the minimum-cost mix that will satisfy the daily diet requirements.

To formulate a linear programming model for the Bluegrass Farms problem, we introduce three decision variables:

$S$ = number of pounds of the standard horse feed product

$E$ = number of pounds of the enriched oat product

$A$ = number of pounds of the vitamin and mineral feed additive

Using the data in Table 8.2, the objective function that will minimize the total cost associated with the daily feed can be written as follows:

$$\text{Min } 0.25S + 0.5E + 3A$$

Because the minimum daily requirement for ingredient A is 3 units, we obtain the constraint

$$0.8S + 0.2E \geq 3$$

The constraint for ingredient B is

$$1.0S + 1.5E + 3.0A \geq 6$$

and the constraint for ingredient C is

$$0.1S + 0.6E + 2.0A \geq 4$$

Finally, the constraint that restricts the mix to at most 6 pounds is

$$S + E + A \leq 6$$

**TABLE 8.2**   NUTRITIONAL VALUE AND COST DATA FOR THE BLUEGRASS
FARMS PROBLEM

| Feed Component | Standard | Enriched Oat | Additive |
|----------------|----------|--------------|----------|
| Ingredient A   | 0.8      | 0.2          | 0.0      |
| Ingredient B   | 1.0      | 1.5          | 3.0      |
| Ingredient C   | 0.1      | 0.6          | 2.0      |
| Cost per pound | $0.25    | $0.50        | $3.00    |

© Cengage Learning 2013

Combining all the constraints with the nonnegativity requirements enables us to write the complete linear programming model for the Bluegrass Farms problem as follows:

$$\text{Min}\quad 0.25S + 0.50E + 3A$$

s.t.

$$
\begin{aligned}
0.8S + 0.2E \qquad\quad &\geq 3 \quad \text{Ingredient A}\\
1.0S + 1.5E + 3.0A &\geq 6 \quad \text{Ingredient B}\\
0.1S + 0.6E + 2.0A &\geq 4 \quad \text{Ingredient C}\\
S + E + A &\leq 6 \quad \text{Weight}\\
S, E, A &\geq 0
\end{aligned}
$$

The sensitivity report for the Bluegrass Farms problem is shown in Figure 8.12. After rounding, we see that the optimal solution calls for a daily diet consisting of 3.51 pounds of the standard horse feed product, 0.95 pounds of the enriched oat product, and 1.54 pounds of the vitamin and mineral feed additive. Thus, with feed component costs of $0.25, $0.50, and $3.00, the total cost of the optimal diet is

$$
\begin{aligned}
3.51 \text{ pounds @ } \$0.25 \text{ per pound} &= \$0.88\\
0.95 \text{ pound @ } \$0.50 \text{ per pound} &= \$0.47\\
1.54 \text{ pounds @ } \$3.00 \text{ per pound} &= \underline{\$4.62}\\
\text{Total cost} &= \$5.97
\end{aligned}
$$

Looking at the Constraints section of the sensitivity report, we see that the final value for the Ingredient B LHS constraint is 9.554 and the right-hand side of this constraint is 6. Because this constraint is a greater-than-or-equal-to constraint, 3.554 is the surplus; the optimal solution exceeds the minimum daily diet requirement for ingredient B (6 units) by 3.554 units. Because the final values for the ingredient A and ingredient C constraints are

**FIGURE 8.12**   SENSITIVITY REPORT FOR THE BLUEGRASS FARMS PROBLEM

Variable Cells

| Model Variable | Name | Final Value | Reduced Cost | Objective Coefficient | Allowable Increase | Allowable Decrease |
|---|---|---|---|---|---|---|
| S | Number of Pounds Standard | 3.514 | 0.000 | 0.250 | 1E+30 | 0.643 |
| E | Number of Pounds Enriched Oat | 0.946 | 0.000 | 0.500 | 0.425 | 1E+30 |
| A | Number of Pounds Additive | 1.541 | 0.000 | 3.000 | 1E+30 | 1.478 |

Constraints

| Constraint Number | Name | Final Value | Shadow Price | Constraint R.H. Side | Allowable Increase | Allowable Decrease |
|---|---|---|---|---|---|---|
| 1 | Ingredient A | 3.000 | 1.216 | 3.000 | 0.368 | 1.857 |
| 2 | Ingredient B | 9.554 | 0.000 | 6.000 | 3.554 | 1E+30 |
| 3 | Ingredient C | 4.000 | 1.959 | 4.000 | 0.875 | 1.900 |
| 4 | Weight | 6.000 | −0.919 | 6.000 | 2.478 | 0.437 |

WEB file

Bluegrass

© Cengage Learning 2013

equal to the right-hand sides for these constraints, we see that the optimal diet just meets the minimum requirements for ingredients A and C. The final value for the weight constraint is equal to the right-hand side (6 pounds). This tells us that this constraint has a slack value of zero, which means that the optimal solution provides a total daily feed weight of 6 pounds.

The shadow price (after rounding) for ingredient A is 1.22. Thus, increasing the right-hand side of the ingredient A constraint by one unit will cause the solution value to increase by $1.22. Conversely, it is also correct to conclude that a decrease of one unit in the right-hand side of the ingredient A constraint will decrease the total cost by $1.22. Looking at the Allowable Increase and Allowable Decrease columns in the Constraints section of the sensitivity report, we see that these interpretations are correct as long as the right-hand side of the ingredient A constraint is between $3 - 1.857 = 1.143$ and $3 + 0.368 = 3.368$.

Suppose that the Bluegrass management is willing to reconsider its position regarding the maximum weight of the daily diet. The shadow price of $-0.92$ (after rounding) for the weight constraint shows that a one-unit increase in the right-hand side of constraint 4 will reduce total cost by $0.92. The Allowable Increase column in the sensitivity report shows that this interpretation is correct for increases in the right-hand side up to a maximum of $6 + 2.478 = 8.478$ pounds. Thus, the effect of increasing the right-hand side of the weight constraint from 6 to 8 pounds is a decrease in the total daily cost of $2 \times \$0.92$, or $1.84. Keep in mind that if this change were made, the feasible region would change, and we would obtain a new optimal solution.

Next we look at the Variable Cells section of the sensitivity report. The Allowable Decrease column shows a lower limit of $0.25 - 0.643 = -0.393$ for the objective function coefficient associated with the standard horse feed product variable, $S$. Clearly, in a real problem, the objective function coefficient of $S$ (the cost of the standard horse feed product) cannot take on a negative value. So, from a practical point of view, we can think of the lower limit for the objective function coefficient of $S$ as being zero. We can thus conclude that no matter how much the cost of the standard mix were to decrease, the optimal solution would not change. Even if Bluegrass Farms could obtain the standard horse feed product for free, the optimal solution would still specify a daily diet of 3.51 pounds of the standard horse feed product, 0.95 pounds of the enriched oat product, and 1.54 pounds of the vitamin and mineral feed additive. However, any decrease in the per-unit cost of the standard feed would result in a decrease in the total cost for the optimal daily diet.

Note from Figure 8.12 that the allowable increases for the objective function coefficients associated with standard horse feed product and additive are shown as 1E+30. This is the same notation as is used in Excel's Sensitivity Report; it means that these objective function coefficients have no upper limit. Even if the cost of additive were to increase, for example, from $3.00 to $13.00 per pound, the optimal solution would not change; the total cost of the solution, however, would increase by $10 (the amount of the increase) $\times 1.541$, or $15.41. You must always keep in mind that the interpretations we make using classical sensitivity analysis information are only appropriate if all other coefficients in the problem do not change. To consider simultaneous changes, we must re-solve the problem.

Linear programming has been successfully applied to a variety of applications. The Q.M. in Action, Kimpton Hotels Uses Optimization for Setting Prices on Priceline, provides an example from the hotel industry. The Q.M. in Action discusses how Kimpton Hotels uses linear programming and, specifically, the value of shadow prices, to set prices of rooms sold through Priceline.

*KIMPTON HOTELS USES OPTIMIZATION FOR SETTING PRICES ON PRICELINE\**

How to price rooms to maximize revenue is a problem faced by all hotels. If prices are set too low, demand will be higher, but total revenue may be lower than what would have been generated if the customer's willingness to pay was known. If the price is too high, demand may drop, resulting in empty rooms and lost revenue. Revenue management, sometimes called yield management, attempts to determine prices to charge and how many rooms to offer at each price so as to maximize revenue.

Kimpton Hotels owns over 40 boutique four-star hotels in the United States and Canada. Most of Kimpton's customers are business travelers who generally book later and are often willing to pay more than leisure travelers. The shorter lead time of business travelers presents a challenge for Kimpton, since it has less time to react by adjusting its prices when demand does not materialize.

Priceline.com is an Internet site that allows the user to specify the area he or she would like to visit, the dates of the visit, and the level of the hotel (three-star, four-

star, etc.) and to make a bid price for a room. Priceline searches a list of participating hotels for a hotel that matches the criteria specified by the user. This is known as opaque marketing because the hotel name is revealed to the user only when a match is found, at which point the user is committed. This opaqueness is important for the hotel, because it allows the hotel to segment the market and offer different prices without diluting its regularly posted prices.

Kimpton participates in the Priceline bidding process and has to submit prices and how many rooms are available at each price level over a specified set of dates. Using historical data, Kimpton predicts future demand and uses a technique known as dynamic programming to set prices. A linear program is then used to determine the number of rooms to offer at each price level. In particular, the shadow price on a room availability constraint is utilized to assess whether or not to offer another room at a given price in a given period. Since implementing this new optimization-based approach, rooms sold via Priceline have increased 11% and the average price for the rooms has increased by nearly 4%.

\*Based on C. Anderson, "Setting Prices on Priceline," *Interfaces* 39, no. 4 (July/August 2009): 307–315.

# 8.6 Electronic Communications Problem

The Electronic Communications problem is a maximization problem involving four decision variables, two less-than-or-equal-to constraints, one equality constraint, and one greater-than-or-equal-to constraint. We will use this problem to provide a summary of the process of formulating a mathematical model, using Excel to obtain an optimal solution, and interpreting the solution and sensitivity report information. In the next chapter we will continue to illustrate how linear programming can be applied by showing additional examples from the areas of marketing, finance, and production management.

Electronic Communications manufactures portable radio systems that can be used for two-way communications. The company's new product, which has a range of up to 25 miles, is suitable for use in a variety of business and personal applications. The distribution channels for the new radio are as follows:

1. Marine equipment distributors
2. Business equipment distributors
3. National chain of retail stores
4. Direct mail

Because of differing distribution and promotional costs, the profitability of the product will vary with the distribution channel. In addition, the advertising cost and the personal sales

**TABLE 8.3**   PROFIT, ADVERTISING COST, AND PERSONAL SALES TIME DATA
FOR THE ELECTRONIC COMMUNICATIONS PROBLEM

| Distribution Channel | Profit per Unit Sold | Advertising Cost per Unit Sold | Personal Sales Effort per Unit Sold |
|---|---|---|---|
| Marine distributors | $90 | $10 | 2 hours |
| Business distributors | $84 | $ 8 | 3 hours |
| National retail stores | $70 | $ 9 | 3 hours |
| Direct mail | $60 | $15 | None |

© Cengage Learning 2013

effort required will vary with the distribution channel. Table 8.3 summarizes the contribution to profit, advertising cost, and personal sales effort data for the Electronic Communications problem. The firm set the advertising budget at $5000. A maximum of 1800 hours of sales force time is available for allocation to the sales effort. Management also decided to produce exactly 600 units for the current production period. Finally, an ongoing contract with a national chain of retail stores requires that at least 150 units be distributed through this distribution channel.

Electronic Communications is now faced with the problem of determining the number of units that should be produced for each of the distribution channels in order to maximize the total contribution to profit. In addition to determining how many units should be allocated to each of the four distribution channels, Electronic Communications must also determine how to allocate the advertising budget and sales force effort to each of the four distribution channels.

## Problem Formulation

We will now write the objective function and the constraints for the Electronic Communications problem. We begin with the objective function.

Objective function: Maximize profit

Four constraints are needed to account for the following restrictions: (1) a limited advertising budget, (2) limited sales force availability, (3) a production requirement, and (4) a retail stores distribution requirement.

**Constraint 1** Advertising expenditure $\leq$ Budget

**Constraint 2** Sales time used $\leq$ Time available

**Constraint 3** Radios produced $=$ Management requirement

**Constraint 4** Retail distribution $\geq$ Contract requirement

These expressions provide descriptions of the objective function and the constraints. We are now ready to define the decision variables that will represent the decisions the manager must make. For the Electronic Communications problem, we introduce the following four decision variables:

$M$ = the number of units produced for the marine equipment distribution channel

$B$ = the number of units produced for the business equipment distribution channel

$R$ = the number of units produced for the national retail chain distribution channel

$D$ = the number of units produced for the direct mail distribution channel

Using the data in Table 8.3, we can write the objective function for maximizing the total contribution to profit associated with the radios as follows:

$$\text{Max } 90M + 84B + 70R + 60D$$

Let us now develop a mathematical statement of the constraints for the problem. For the advertising budget of $5000, the constraint that limits the amount of advertising expenditure can be written as follows:

$$10M + 8B + 9R + 15D \leq 5000$$

Similarly, with sales time limited to 1800 hours, we obtain the constraint

$$2M + 3B + 3R \leq 1800$$

Management's decision to produce exactly 600 units during the current production period is expressed as

$$M + B + R + D = 600$$

Finally, to account for the fact that the number of units distributed by the national chain of retail stores must be at least 150, we add the constraint

$$R \geq 150$$

Combining all of the constraints with the nonnegativity requirements enables us to write the complete linear programming model for the Electronic Communications problem as follows:

$$\text{Max} \quad 90M + 84B + 70R + 60D$$
$$\text{s.t.}$$

| | | | | | |
|---|---|---|---|---|---|
| $10M +$ | $8B +$ | $9R +$ | $15D \leq 5000$ | Advertising budget |
| $2M +$ | $3B +$ | $3R$ | $\leq 1800$ | Sales force availability |
| $M +$ | $B +$ | $R +$ | $D = \phantom{0}600$ | Production level |
| | | $R$ | $\geq \phantom{0}150$ | Retail stores requirement |
| $M, B, R, D \geq 0$ | | | | |

## Solution and Interpretation

Figure 8.13 shows the sensitivity report for the Electronic Communications problem. The optimal decisions are to produce 25 units for the marine distribution channel ($M = 25$), 425 units for the business equipment distribution channel ($B = 425$), 150 units for the retail chain distribution channel ($R = 150$), and no units for the direct mail distribution channel ($D = 0$). The optimal solution to the problem will provide a profit of $90(25) + $84(425) + $70(150) + $60(0) = $48,450. Consider the information contained in the

## FIGURE 8.13   SENSITIVITY REPORT FOR THE ELECTRONIC COMMUNICATIONS PROBLEM

Variable Cells

| Model Variable | Name | Final Value | Reduced Cost | Objective Coefficient | Allowable Increase | Allowable Decrease |
|---|---|---|---|---|---|---|
| M | Number of Units Produced Marine | 25.000 | 0.000 | 90.000 | 1E+30 | 6.000 |
| B | Number of Units Produced Business | 425.000 | 0.000 | 84.000 | 6.000 | 34.000 |
| R | Number of Units Produced Retail | 150.000 | 0.000 | 70.000 | 17.000 | 1E+30 |
| D | Number of Units Produced Direct Mail | 0.000 | −45.000 | 60.000 | 45.000 | 1E+30 |

Constraints

| Constraint Number | Name | Final Value | Shadow Price | Constraint R.H. Side | Allowable Increase | Allowable Decrease |
|---|---|---|---|---|---|---|
| 1 | Advertising Budget | 5000.000 | 3.000 | 5000.000 | 850.000 | 50.000 |
| 2 | Sales Force Availability | 1775.000 | 0.000 | 1800.000 | 1E+30 | 25.000 |
| 3 | Production Level | 600.000 | 60.000 | 600.000 | 3.571 | 85.000 |
| 4 | Retail Stores Requirement | 150.000 | −17.000 | 150.000 | 50.000 | 150.000 |

WEB file

Electronic

Reduced Cost column of the Variable Cells section of the sensitivity report in Figure 8.13. Recall that the reduced cost of a variable is the shadow price of the corresponding nonnegativity constraint. As the sensitivity analysis shows, the first three reduced costs are zero because the corresponding decision variables already have positive values in the optimal solution. However, the reduced cost of $-45$ for Number of Units Produced Direct Mail ($D$) tells us that profit will decrease by $45 for every unit produced for the direct mail channel. Stated another way, the objective function coefficient associated with $D$ would have to be reduced by at least $-$45 per unit [i.e., the profit contribution would have to be at least $60 - (-$45) = $105 per unit] before it would be profitable to use the direct mail distribution channel.

Next consider the Constraints section of the sensitivity report in Figure 8.13. The advertising budget constraint has a final value equal to the constraint right-hand side, indicating that the entire budget of $5000 has been used. The corresponding shadow price of 3 tells us that an additional dollar added to the advertising budget will increase the profit by $3. Thus, the possibility of increasing the advertising budget should be seriously considered by the firm. Comparing the final value to the right-hand-side value for the sales force availability, we see that this constraint has a slack value of $1800 - 1725 = 25$ hours. In other words, the allocated 1800 hours of sales time are adequate to distribute the radios produced, and 25 hours of sales time will remain unused. Because the production level constraint is an equality constraint, it is expected that the final value will equal the right-hand side for this constraint. However, the shadow price of 60 associated with this constraint shows that if the firm were to consider increasing the production level for the radios, the value of the objective function, or profit, would increase at the rate of $60 per radio produced. Finally, the final value is equal to the right-hand side for the retail stores requirement constraint shows that this constraint is binding. The negative shadow price indicates that increasing the commitment from 150 to 151 units will actually decrease the profit by $17. Thus, Electronic Communications may want to consider reducing its commitment to the retail store distribution channel. A *decrease* in the commitment will actually increase profit at the rate of $17 per unit.

We now consider the Allowable Increase and Allowable Decrease columns from the Variable Cells section of the sensitivity report shown in Figure 8.13. The allowable increases and decreases for the objective function coefficients are

| Name | Objective Coefficient | Allowable Increase | Allowable Decrease |
|------|------|------|------|
| Units Produced Marine | 90.000 | Infinite | 6.000 |
| Units Produced Business | 84.000 | 6.000 | 34.000 |
| Units Produced Retail | 70.000 | 17.000 | Infinite |
| Units Produced Direct Mail | 60.000 | 45.000 | Infinite |

The current solution, or strategy, remains optimal, provided that the objective function coefficients do not increase or decrease by more than the allowed amounts. Note in particular the range associated with the direct mail distribution channel coefficient. This information is consistent with the earlier observation for the Reduced Cost portion of the output. In both instances, we see that the per-unit profit would have to increase to $60 + $45 = $105 before the direct mail distribution channel could be in the optimal solution with a positive value.

Finally, the sensitivity analysis for the allowable increases and decreases of the right-hand side of the constraints can be taken from Figure 8.13 as follows:

| Name | Constraint R.H. Side | Allowable Increase | Allowable Decrease |
|------|------|------|------|
| Advertising Budget | 5000.000 | 850.000 | 50.000 |
| Sales Force Availability | 1800.000 | Infinite | 25.000 |
| Production Level | 600.000 | 3.571 | 85.000 |
| Retail Stores Requirement | 150.000 | 50.000 | 150.000 |

Several interpretations of these right-hand-side ranges are possible. In particular, recall that the shadow price for the advertising budget enabled us to conclude that each $1 increase in the budget would improve the profit by $3. The current advertising budget is $5000. The allowable increase on the advertising budget is $850 and this implies that there is value in increasing the budget up to an advertising budget of $5850. Increases above this level would not necessarily be beneficial. Also note that the shadow price of $-17$ for the retail stores requirement suggested the desirability of reducing this commitment. The allowable decrease for this constraint is 150, and this implies that the commitment could be reduced to zero and the value of the reduction would be at the rate of $17 per unit.

Again, the *sensitivity analysis* or *postoptimality analysis* provided by computer software packages for linear programming problems considers only *one change at a time*, with all other coefficients of the problem remaining as originally specified. As mentioned earlier, simultaneous changes are best handled by re-solving the problem.

Finally, recall that the complete solution to the Electronic Communications problem requested information not only on the number of units to be distributed over each channel, but also on the allocation of the advertising budget and the sales force effort to each distribution channel. Because the optimal solution is $M = 25$, $B = 425$, $R = 150$, and $D = 0$, we can simply evaluate each term in a given constraint to determine how much of the constraint

**TABLE 8.4**    PROFIT-MAXIMIZING STRATEGY FOR THE ELECTRONIC
COMMUNICATIONS PROBLEM

| Distribution Channel | Volume | Advertising Allocation | Sales Force Allocation (hours) |
|---|---|---|---|
| Marine distributors | 25 | $ 250 | 50 |
| Business distributors | 425 | 3400 | 1275 |
| National retail stores | 150 | 1350 | 450 |
| Direct mail | 0 | 0 | 0 |
| Totals | 600 | $5000 | 1775 |
| Projected total profit = $48,450 | | | |

© Cengage Learning 2013

resource is allocated to each distribution channel. For example, the advertising budget constraint of

$$10M + 8B + 9R + 15D \leq 5000$$

shows that $10M = 10(25) = \$250$, $8B = 8(425) = \$3400$, $9R = 9(150) = \$1350$, and $15D = 15(0) = \$0$. Thus, the advertising budget allocations are, respectively, $250, $3400, $1350, and $0 for each of the four distribution channels. Making similar calculations for the sales force constraint results in the managerial summary of the Electronic Communications optimal solution, as shown in Table 8.4.

## Summary

We began the chapter with a discussion of sensitivity analysis, the study of how changes in the coefficients of a linear program affect the optimal solution. First, we showed how a graphical method can be used to determine how a change in one of the objective function coefficients or a change in the right-hand-side value for a constraint will affect the optimal solution to the problem. Because graphical sensitivity analysis is limited to linear programs with two decision variables, we showed how to use a computer software package such as Excel Solver to produce a sensitivity report containing the same information.

We continued our discussion of problem formulation, sensitivity analysis, and the interpretation of the solution by introducing modifications of the RMC problem. We also discussed several limitations of classical sensitivity analysis, including issues related to simultaneous changes, changes in constraint coefficients, and nonintuitive shadow prices. Then, in order to provide additional practice in formulating and interpreting the solution for linear programs involving more than two decision variables, we introduced the Bluegrass Farms problem, a minimization problem involving three decision variables. In the last section we summarized all the work to date using the Electronic Communications problem, a maximization problem with four decision variables: two less-than-or-equal-to constraints, one equality constraint, and one greater-than-or-equal-to constraint.

The Q.M. in Action, Tea Production and Distribution at Duncan Industries Limited, illustrates the diversity of problem situations in which linear programming can be applied and the importance of sensitivity analysis. In the next chapter we will see many more applications of linear programming.

## TEA PRODUCTION AND DISTRIBUTION AT DUNCAN INDUSTRIES LIMITED*

In India, one of the largest tea producers in the world, approximately $1 billion of tea packets and loose tea are sold. Duncan Industries Limited (DIL), the third largest producer of tea in the Indian tea market, sells about $37.5 million of tea, almost all of which is sold in packets.

DIL has 16 tea gardens, 3 blending units, 6 packing units, and 22 depots. Tea from the gardens is sent to blending units, which then mix various grades of tea to produce blends such as Sargam, Double Diamond, and Runglee Rungliot. The blended tea is transported to packing units, where it is placed in packets of different sizes and shapes to produce about 120 different product lines. For example, one line is Sargam tea packed in 500-gram cartons, another line is Double Diamond packed in 100-gram polythene pouches, and so on. The tea is then shipped to the depots that supply 11,500 distributors, through whom the needs of approximately 325,000 retailers are satisfied.

*Based on Nilotpal Chakravarti, "Tea Company Steeped in OR," *OR/MS Today* (April 2000).

For the coming month, sales managers provide estimates of the demand for each line of tea at each depot. Using these estimates, a team of senior managers would determine the amounts of loose tea of each blend to ship to each packing unit, the quantity of each line of tea to be packed at each packing unit, and the amounts of packed tea of each line to be transported from each packing unit to the various depots. This process requires two to three days each month and often results in stock-outs of lines in demand at specific depots.

Consequently, a linear programming model involving approximately 7000 decision variables and 1500 constraints was developed to minimize the company's freight cost while satisfying demand, supply, and all operational constraints. The model was tested on past data and showed that stock-outs could be prevented at little or no additional cost. Moreover, the model was able to provide management with the ability to perform various what-if types of exercises, convincing managers of the potential benefits of using management science techniques to support the decision-making process.

## Glossary

**Sensitivity analysis** The study of how changes in the coefficients of a linear programming problem affect the optimal solution.

**Objective function coefficient allowable increase (decrease)** The allowable increase (decrease) of an objective function coefficient is the amount the coefficient may increase (decrease) without causing any change in the values of the decision variables in the optimal solution. The allowable increase/decrease for the objective function coefficients can be used to calculate the range of optimality.

**Objective coefficient range (range of optimality)** The range of values over which an objective function coefficient may vary without causing any change in the values of the decision variables in the optimal solution.

**Shadow price** The change in the optimal objective function value per unit increase in the right-hand side of a constraint.

**Reduced cost** If a variable is at its lower bound of zero, the reduced cost is equal to the shadow price of the nonnegativity constraint for that variable. In general, if a variable is at its lower or upper bound, the reduced cost is the shadow price for that simple lower or upper bound constraint.

**Range of feasibility** The range of values over which the shadow price is applicable.

**Right-hand-side allowable increase (decrease)** The allowable increase (decrease) of the right-hand side of a constraint is the amount the right-hand side may increase (decrease) without causing any change in the shadow price for that constraint. The allowable increase and decrease for the right-hand side can be used to calculate the range of feasibility for that constraint.

**Sunk cost** A cost that is not affected by the decision made. It will be incurred no matter what values the decision variables assume.

**Relevant cost** A cost that depends upon the decision made. The amount of a relevant cost will vary depending on the values of the decision variables.

## Problems

1. Consider the following linear program:

$$\text{Max} \quad 3A + 2B$$
$$\text{s.t.}$$
$$1A + 1B \le 10$$
$$3A + 1B \le 24$$
$$1A + 2B \le 16$$
$$A, B \ge 0$$

a. Use the graphical solution procedure to find the optimal solution.
b. Assume that the objective function coefficient for A changes from 3 to 5. Does the optimal solution change? Use the graphical solution procedure to find the new optimal solution.
c. Assume that the objective function coefficient for A remains 3, but the objective function coefficient for B changes from 2 to 4. Does the optimal solution change? Use the graphical solution procedure to find the new optimal solution.
d. The sensitivity report for the linear program in part (a) provides the following objective coefficient range information:

| Variable | Objective Coefficient | Allowable Increase | Allowable Decrease |
|---|---|---|---|
| A | 3.000 | 3.000 | 1.000 |
| B | 2.000 | 1.000 | 1.000 |

Use this objective coefficient range information to answer parts (b) and (c).

2. Consider the linear program in Problem 1. The value of the optimal solution is 27. Suppose that the right-hand side for constraint 1 is increased from 10 to 11.
a. Use the graphical solution procedure to find the new optimal solution.
b. Use the solution to part (a) to determine the shadow price for constraint 1.
c. The sensitivity report for the linear program in Problem 1 provides the following right-hand-side range information:

| Constraint | Constraint R.H. Side | Allowable Increase | Allowable Decrease |
|---|---|---|---|
| 1 | 10.000 | 1.200 | 2.000 |
| 2 | 24.000 | 6.000 | 6.000 |
| 3 | 16.000 | Infinite | 3.000 |

What does the right-hand-side range information for constraint 1 tell you about the shadow price for constraint 1?

d. The shadow price for constraint 2 is 0.5. Using this shadow price and the right-hand-side range information in part (c), what conclusion can you draw about the effect of changes to the right-hand side of constraint 2?

3. Consider the following linear program:

$$\text{Min} \quad 8X + 12Y$$

s.t.

$$1X + 3Y \geq 9$$
$$2X + 2Y \geq 10$$
$$6X + 2Y \geq 18$$
$$X, Y \geq 0$$

a. Use the graphical solution procedure to find the optimal solution.
b. Assume that the objective function coefficient for $X$ changes from 8 to 6. Does the optimal solution change? Use the graphical solution procedure to find the new optimal solution.
c. Assume that the objective function coefficient for $X$ remains 8, but the objective function coefficient for $Y$ changes from 12 to 6. Does the optimal solution change? Use the graphical solution procedure to find the new optimal solution.
d. The sensitivity report for the linear program in part (a) provides the following objective coefficient range information:

| Variable | Objective Coefficient | Allowable Increase | Allowable Decrease |
|---|---|---|---|
| $X$ | 8.000 | 4.000 | 4.000 |
| $Y$ | 12.000 | 12.000 | 4.000 |

How would this objective coefficient range information help you answer parts (b) and (c) prior to resolving the problem?

4. Consider the linear program in Problem 3. The value of the optimal solution is 48. Suppose that the right-hand side for constraint 1 is increased from 9 to 10.
a. Use the graphical solution procedure to find the new optimal solution.
b. Use the solution to part (a) to determine the shadow price for constraint 1.
c. The sensitivity report for the linear program in Problem 3 provides the following right-hand-side range information:

| Constraint | Constraint R.H. Side | Allowable Increase | Allowable Decrease |
|---|---|---|---|
| 1 | 9.000 | 2.000 | 4.000 |
| 2 | 10.000 | 8.000 | 1.000 |
| 3 | 18.000 | 4.000 | Infinite |

What does the right-hand-side range information for constraint 1 tell you about the shadow price for constraint 1?
d. The shadow price for constraint 2 is 3. Using this shadow price and the right-hand-side range information in part (c), what conclusion can be drawn about the effect of changes to the right-hand side of constraint 2?

5. Refer to the Kelson Sporting Equipment problem (Chapter 7, Problem 24). Letting

$$R = \text{number of regular gloves}$$
$$C = \text{number of catcher's mitts}$$

leads to the following formulation:

$$\begin{aligned} \text{Max} \quad & 5R + 8C \\ \text{s.t.} \quad & \\ & R + \tfrac{3}{2}C \leq 900 \quad \text{Cutting and sewing} \\ & \tfrac{1}{2}R + \tfrac{1}{3}C \leq 300 \quad \text{Finishing} \\ & \tfrac{1}{8}R + \tfrac{1}{4}C \leq 100 \quad \text{Packaging and shipping} \\ & R, C \geq 0 \end{aligned}$$

The sensitivity report is shown in Figure 8.14.
   a. What is the optimal solution, and what is the value of the total profit contribution?
   b. Which constraints are binding?
   c. What are the shadow prices for the resources? Interpret each.
   d. If overtime can be scheduled in one of the departments, where would you recommend doing so?

6. Refer to the sensitivity information for the Kelson Sporting Equipment problem in Figure 8.14 (see Problem 5).
   a. Determine the objective coefficient ranges.
   b. Interpret the ranges in part (a).
   c. Interpret the right-hand-side ranges.
   d. How much will the value of the optimal solution improve if 20 extra hours of packaging and shipping time are made available?

7. Investment Advisors, Inc., is a brokerage firm that manages stock portfolios for a number of clients. A particular portfolio consists of $U$ shares of U.S. Oil and $H$ shares of Huber Steel. The annual return for U.S. Oil is $3 per share and the annual return for

**FIGURE 8.14** SENSITIVITY REPORT FOR THE KELSON SPORTING EQUIPMENT PROBLEM

Variable Cells

| Model Variable | Name | Final Value | Reduced Cost | Objective Coefficient | Allowable Increase | Allowable Decrease |
|---|---|---|---|---|---|---|
| R | Gloves Standard | 500.000 | 0.000 | 5.000 | 7.000 | 1.000 |
| C | Gloves Deluxe | 150.000 | 0.000 | 8.000 | 2.000 | 4.667 |

Constraints

| Constraint Number | Name | Final Value | Shadow Price | Constraint R.H. Side | Allowable Increase | Allowable Decrease |
|---|---|---|---|---|---|---|
| 1 | Cutting and Dyeing Hours Used | 725.000 | 0.000 | 900.000 | 1E+30 | 175.000 |
| 2 | Finishing Hours Used | 300.000 | 3.000 | 300.000 | 100.000 | 166.667 |
| 3 | Packaging and Shipping Hours Used | 100.000 | 28.000 | 100.000 | 35.000 | 25.000 |

Huber Steel is $5 per share. U.S. Oil sells for $25 per share and Huber Steel sells for $50 per share. The portfolio has $80,000 to be invested. The portfolio risk index (0.50 per share of U.S. Oil and 0.25 per share for Huber Steel) has a maximum of 700. In addition, the portfolio is limited to a maximum of 1000 shares of U.S. Oil. The linear programming formulation that will maximize the total annual return of the portfolio is as follows:

$$\text{Max} \quad 3U + 5H \qquad \text{Maximize total annual return}$$

s.t.

$$25U + 50H \leq 80{,}000 \quad \text{Funds available}$$
$$0.50U + 0.25H \leq 700 \quad \text{Risk maximum}$$
$$1U \leq 1000 \quad \text{U.S. Oil maximum}$$
$$U, H \geq 0$$

The sensitivity report for this problem is shown in Figure 8.15.
a. What is the optimal solution, and what is the value of the total annual return?
b. Which constraints are binding? What is your interpretation of these constraints in terms of the problem?
c. What are the shadow prices for the constraints? Interpret each.
d. Would it be beneficial to increase the maximum amount invested in U.S. Oil? Why or why not?

8. Refer to Figure 8.15, which shows the sensitivity report for Problem 7.
a. How much would the return for U.S. Oil have to increase before it would be beneficial to increase the investment in this stock?
b. How much would the return for Huber Steel have to decrease before it would be beneficial to reduce the investment in this stock?
c. How much would the total annual return be reduced if the U.S. Oil maximum were reduced to 900 shares?

9. Recall the Tom's, Inc., problem (Chapter 7, Problem 28). Letting

$$W = \text{jars of Western Foods Salsa}$$
$$M = \text{jars of Mexico City Salsa}$$

**FIGURE 8.15** SENSITIVITY REPORT FOR THE INVESTMENT ADVISORS PROBLEM

Variable Cells

| Model Variable | Name | Final Value | Reduced Cost | Objective Coefficient | Allowable Increase | Allowable Decrease |
|---|---|---|---|---|---|---|
| U | U.S. Oil | 800.000 | 0.000 | 3.000 | 7.000 | 0.500 |
| H | Huber | 1200.000 | 0.000 | 5.000 | 1.000 | 3.500 |

Constraints

| Constraint Number | Name | Final Value | Shadow Price | Constraint R.H. Side | Allowable Increase | Allowable Decrease |
|---|---|---|---|---|---|---|
| 1 | Funds available | 80000.000 | 0.093 | 80000.000 | 60000.000 | 15000.000 |
| 2 | Risk maximum | 700.000 | 1.333 | 700.000 | 75.000 | 300.000 |
| 3 | U.S. Oil maximum | 800.000 | 0.000 | 1000.000 | 1E+30 | 200.000 |

**FIGURE 8.16** SENSITIVITY REPORT FOR THE TOM'S INC., PROBLEM

Variable Cells

| Model Variable | Name | Final Value | Reduced Cost | Objective Coefficient | Allowable Increase | Allowable Decrease |
|---|---|---|---|---|---|---|
| W | Western Foods Salsa | 560.000 | 0.000 | 1.000 | 0.250 | 0.107 |
| M | Mexico City Salsa | 240.000 | 0.000 | 1.250 | 1.150 | 3.250 |

Constraints

| Constraint Number | Name | Final Value | Shadow Price | Constraint R.H. Side | Allowable Increase | Allowable Decrease |
|---|---|---|---|---|---|---|
| 1 | Whole tomatoes | 4480.000 | 0.125 | 4480.000 | 1120.000 | 160.000 |
| 2 | Tomato sauce | 1920.000 | 0.000 | 2080.000 | 1E+30 | 160.000 |
| 3 | Tomato paste | 1600.000 | 0.188 | 1600.000 | 40.000 | 320.000 |

leads to the formulation:

$$\text{Max} \quad 1W + 1.25M$$

s.t.

$$5W + 7M \leq 4480 \quad \text{Whole tomatoes}$$
$$3W + 1M \leq 2080 \quad \text{Tomato sauce}$$
$$2W + 2M \leq 1600 \quad \text{Tomato paste}$$
$$W, M \geq 0$$

The sensitivity report is shown in Figure 8.16.
a. What is the optimal solution, and what are the optimal production quantities?
b. Specify the objective coefficient ranges.
c. What are the shadow prices for each constraint? Interpret each.
d. Identify each of the right-hand-side ranges.

10. Recall the Innis Investments problem (Chapter 7, Problem 39). Letting

$$S = \text{units purchased in the stock fund}$$

$$M = \text{units purchased in the money market fund}$$

leads to the following formulation:

$$\text{Min} \quad 8S + 3M$$

s.t.

$$50S + 100M \leq 1,200,000 \quad \text{Funds available}$$
$$5S + 4M \geq 60,000 \quad \text{Annual income}$$
$$M \geq 3,000 \quad \text{Units in money market}$$
$$S, M \geq 0$$

The sensitivity report is shown in Figure 8.17.
a. What is the optimal solution, and what is the minimum total risk?
b. Specify the objective coefficient ranges.
c. How much annual income will be earned by the portfolio?
d. What is the rate of return for the portfolio?
e. What is the shadow price for the funds available constraint?
f. What is the marginal rate of return on extra funds added to the portfolio?

**FIGURE 8.17** SENSITIVITY REPORT FOR THE INNIS INVESTMENTS PROBLEM

Variable Cells

| Model Variable | Name | Final Value | Reduced Cost | Objective Coefficient | Allowable Increase | Allowable Decrease |
|---|---|---|---|---|---|---|
| S | Units in Stock Fund | 4000.000 | 0.000 | 8.000 | 1E+30 | 4.250 |
| M | Units in Money Market Fund | 10000.000 | 0.000 | 3.000 | 3.400 | 1E+30 |

Constraints

| Constraint Number | Name | Final Value | Shadow Price | Constraint R.H. Side | Allowable Increase | Allowable Decrease |
|---|---|---|---|---|---|---|
| 1 | Funds Available | 1200000.000 | −0.057 | 1200000.000 | 300000.000 | 420000.000 |
| 2 | Annual Income | 60000.000 | 2.167 | 60000.000 | 42000.000 | 12000.000 |
| 3 | Units in Money Market | 10000.000 | 0.000 | 3000.000 | 7000.000 | 1E+30 |

11. Refer to Problem 10 and the sensitivity report shown in Figure 8.17.
    a. Suppose the risk index for the stock fund (the objective function coefficient for $S$) increases from its current value of 8 to 12. How does the optimal solution change, if at all?
    b. Suppose the risk index for the money market fund (the objective function coefficient for $M$) increases from its current value of 3 to 3.5. How does the optimal solution change, if at all?
    c. Suppose the objective function coefficient for $S$ increases to 12 and the objective function coefficient for $M$ increases to 3.5. Can you determine how the optimal solution will change using the information in Figure 8.17?

12. Quality Air Conditioning manufactures three home air conditioners: an economy model, a standard model, and a deluxe model. The profits per unit are $63, $95, and $135, respectively. The production requirements per unit are as follows:

| | Number of Fans | Number of Cooling Coils | Manufacturing Time (hours) |
|---|---|---|---|
| Economy | 1 | 1 | 8 |
| Standard | 1 | 2 | 12 |
| Deluxe | 1 | 4 | 14 |

For the coming production period, the company has 200 fan motors, 320 cooling coils, and 2400 hours of manufacturing time available. How many economy models ($E$), standard models ($S$), and deluxe models ($D$) should the company produce in order to maximize profit? The linear programming model for the problem is as follows.

$$\text{Max} \quad 63E + 95S + 135D$$
$$\text{s.t.}$$
$$1E + 1S + 1D \le 200 \quad \text{Fan motors}$$
$$1E + 2S + 4D \le 320 \quad \text{Cooling coils}$$
$$8E + 12S + 14D \le 2400 \quad \text{Manufacturing time}$$
$$E, S, D \ge 0$$

**FIGURE 8.18**   SENSITIVITY REPORT FOR THE QUALITY AIR CONDITIONING PROBLEM

Variable Cells

| Model Variable | Name | Final Value | Reduced Cost | Objective Coefficient | Allowable Increase | Allowable Decrease |
|---|---|---|---|---|---|---|
| E | Economy Models | 80.000 | 0.000 | 63.000 | 12.000 | 15.500 |
| S | Standard Models | 120.000 | 0.000 | 95.000 | 31.000 | 8.000 |
| D | Deluxe Models | 0.000 | −24.000 | 135.000 | 24.000 | 1E+30 |

Constraints

| Constraint Number | Name | Final Value | Shadow Price | Constraint R.H. Side | Allowable Increase | Allowable Decrease |
|---|---|---|---|---|---|---|
| 1 | Fan Motors | 200.000 | 31.000 | 200.000 | 80.000 | 40.000 |
| 2 | Cooling Coils | 320.000 | 32.000 | 320.000 | 80.000 | 120.000 |
| 3 | Manufacturing Time | 2080.000 | 0.000 | 2400.000 | 1E+30 | 320.000 |

The sensitivity report is shown in Figure 8.18.

a. What is the optimal solution, and what is the value of the objective function?

b. Which constraints are binding?

c. Which constraint shows extra capacity? How much?

d. If the profit for the deluxe model were increased to $150 per unit, would the optimal solution change? Use the information in Figure 8.18 to answer this question.

13. Refer to the sensitivity report in Figure 8.18.

a. Identify the range of optimality for each objective function coefficient.

b. Suppose the profit for the economy model is increased by $6 per unit, the profit for the standard model is decreased by $2 per unit, and the profit for the deluxe model is increased by $4 per unit. What will the new optimal solution be?

c. Identify the range of feasibility for the right-hand-side values.

d. If the number of fan motors available for production is increased by 100, will the shadow price for that constraint change? Explain.

14. Digital Controls, Inc. (DCI) manufactures two models of a radar gun used by police to monitor the speed of automobiles. Model A has an accuracy of plus or minus 1 mile per hour, whereas the smaller model B has an accuracy of plus or minus 3 miles per hour. For the next week, the company has orders for 100 units of model A and 150 units of model B. Although DCI purchases all the electronic components used in both models, the plastic cases for both models are manufactured at a DCI plant in Newark, New Jersey. Each model A case requires 4 minutes of injection-molding time and 6 minutes of assembly time. Each model B case requires 3 minutes of injection-molding time and 8 minutes of assembly time. For next week the Newark plant has 600 minutes of injection-molding time available and 1080 minutes of assembly time available. The manufacturing cost is $10 per case for model A and $6 per case for model B. Depending upon demand and the time available at the Newark plant, DCI occasionally purchases cases for one or both models from an outside supplier in order to fill customer orders that could not be filled otherwise. The purchase cost is $14 for each model A case and $9 for each model B case. Management wants to develop a minimum cost plan that will determine how many cases of each model should be produced at the Newark plant and how many cases of each model should be purchased. The following decision variables were used to formulate a linear programming model for this problem:

$AM$ = number of cases of model A manufactured

$BM$ = number of cases of model B manufactured

$AP$ = number of cases of model A purchased

$BP$ = number of cases of model B purchased

The linear programming model that can be used to solve this problem is as follows:

$$\text{Min} \quad 10AM + 6BM + 14AP + 9BP$$

s.t.

| | | | | | |
|---|---|---|---|---|---|
| $1AM +$ | | $+ \ 1AP +$ | | $= \ 100$ | Demand for model A |
| | $1BM +$ | | $1BP =$ | $150$ | Demand for model B |
| $4AM + 3BM$ | | | | $\leq \ 600$ | Injection molding time |
| $6AM + 8BM$ | | | | $\leq 1080$ | Assembly time |
| $AM, BM, AP, BP \geq 0$ | | | | | |

The sensitivity report is shown in Figure 8.19.

a. What is the optimal solution and what is the optimal value of the objective function?

b. Which constraints are binding?

c. What are the shadow prices? Interpret each.

d. If you could change the right-hand side of one constraint by one unit, which one would you choose? Why?

15. Refer to the sensitivity report for Problem 14 in Figure 8.19.

a. Interpret the ranges of optimality for the objective function coefficients.

b. Suppose that the manufacturing cost increases to $11.20 per case for model A. What is the new optimal solution?

c. Suppose that the manufacturing cost increases to $11.20 per case for model A and the manufacturing cost for model B decreases to $5 per unit. Would the optimal solution change?

**FIGURE 8.19**   SENSITIVITY REPORT FOR THE DIGITAL CONTROLS, INC., PROBLEM

Variable Cells

| Model Variable | Name | Final Value | Reduced Cost | Objective Coefficient | Allowable Increase | Allowable Decrease |
|---|---|---|---|---|---|---|
| AM | Models A Manufactured | 100.000 | 0.000 | 10.000 | 1.750 | 1E+30 |
| BM | Models B Manufactured | 60.000 | 0.000 | 6.000 | 3.000 | 2.333 |
| AP | Models A Purchased | 0.000 | 1.750 | 14.000 | 1E+30 | 1.750 |
| BP | Models B Purchased | 90.000 | 0.000 | 9.000 | 2.333 | 3.000 |

Constraints

| Constraint Number | Name | Final Value | Shadow Price | Constraint R.H. Side | Allowable Increase | Allowable Decrease |
|---|---|---|---|---|---|---|
| 1 | Demand for model A | 100.000 | 12.250 | 100.000 | 11.429 | 100.000 |
| 2 | Demand for model B | 150.000 | 9.000 | 150.000 | 1E+30 | 90.000 |
| 3 | Injection molding time | 580.000 | 0.000 | 600.000 | 1E+30 | 20.000 |
| 4 | Assembly time | 1080.000 | -0.375 | 1080.000 | 53.333 | 480.000 |

16.  Tucker Inc. produces high-quality suits and sport coats for men. Each suit requires 1.2 hours of cutting time and 0.7 hours of sewing time, uses 6 yards of material, and provides a profit contribution of $190. Each sport coat requires 0.8 hours of cutting time and 0.6 hours of sewing time, uses 4 yards of material, and provides a profit contribution of $150. For the coming week, 200 hours of cutting time, 180 hours of sewing time, and 1200 yards of fabric material are available. Additional cutting and sewing time can be obtained by scheduling overtime for these operations. Each hour of overtime for the cutting operation increases the hourly cost by $15, and each hour of overtime for the sewing operation increases the hourly cost by $10. A maximum of 100 hours of overtime can be scheduled. Marketing requirements specify a minimum production of 100 suits and 75 sport coats. Let

$$S = \text{number of suits produced}$$
$$SC = \text{number of sport coats produced}$$
$$D1 = \text{hours of overtime for the cutting operation}$$
$$D2 = \text{hours of overtime for the sewing operation}$$

The sensitivity report is shown in Figure 8.20.

a.  What is the optimal solution, and what is the total profit? What is the plan for the use of overtime?

b.  A price increase for suits is being considered that would result in a profit contribution of $210 per suit. If this price increase is undertaken, how will the optimal solution change?

c.  Discuss the need for additional material during the coming week. If a rush order for material can be placed at the usual price plus an extra $8 per yard for handling, would you recommend that the company consider placing a rush order for material? What is the maximum price Tucker would be willing to pay for an additional yard of material? How many additional yards of material should Tucker consider ordering?

d.  Suppose the minimum production requirement for suits is lowered to 75. Would this change help or hurt profit? Explain.

**FIGURE 8.20    SENSITIVITY REPORT FOR THE TUCKER INC. PROBLEM**

Variable Cells

| Model Variable | Name | Final Value | Reduced Cost | Objective Coefficient | Allowable Increase | Allowable Decrease |
|---|---|---|---|---|---|---|
| S | Suits Produced | 100.000 | 0.000 | 190.000 | 35.000 | 1E+30 |
| SC | Coats Produced | 150.000 | 0.000 | 150.000 | 1E+30 | 23.333 |
| D1 | Overtime for Cutting | 40.000 | 0.000 | −15.000 | 15.000 | 172.500 |
| D2 | Overtime for Sewing | 0.000 | −10.000 | −10.000 | 10.000 | 1E+30 |

Constraints

| Constraint Number | Name | Final Value | Shadow Price | Constraint R.H. Side | Allowable Increase | Allowable Decrease |
|---|---|---|---|---|---|---|
| 1 | Cutting time | 200.000 | 15.000 | 200.000 | 40.000 | 60.000 |
| 2 | Sewing time | 160.000 | 0.000 | 180.000 | 1E+30 | 20.000 |
| 3 | Material | 1200.000 | 34.500 | 1200.000 | 133.333 | 200.000 |
| 4 | Overtime | 40.000 | 0.000 | 100.000 | 1E+30 | 60.000 |
| 5 | Suit minimum | 100.000 | −35.000 | 100.000 | 50.000 | 100.000 |
| 6 | Sport coat minimum | 150.000 | 0.000 | 75.000 | 75.000 | 1E+30 |

17. The Porsche Club of America sponsors driver education events that provide high-performance driving instruction on actual racetracks. Because safety is a primary consideration at such events, many owners elect to install roll bars in their cars. Deegan Industries manufactures two types of roll bars for Porsches. Model DRB is bolted to the car using existing holes in the car's frame. Model DRW is a heavier roll bar that must be welded to the car's frame. Model DRB requires 20 pounds of a special high-alloy steel, 40 minutes of manufacturing time, and 60 minutes of assembly time. Model DRW requires 25 pounds of the special high-alloy steel, 100 minutes of manufacturing time, and 40 minutes of assembly time. Deegan's steel supplier indicated that at most 40,000 pounds of the high-alloy steel will be available next quarter. In addition, Deegan estimates that 2000 hours of manufacturing time and 1600 hours of assembly time will be available next quarter. The profit contributions are $200 per unit for model DRB and $280 per unit for model DRW. The linear programming model for this problem is as follows:

$$\text{Max} \quad 200DRB + 280DRW$$

s.t.

$$
\begin{array}{llll}
20DRB + & 25DRW \le & 40,000 & \text{Steel available} \\
40DRB + & 100DRW \le & 120,000 & \text{Manufacturing minutes} \\
60DRB + & 40DRW \le & 96,000 & \text{Assembly minutes} \\
& DRB, DRW \ge 0 &
\end{array}
$$

The sensitivity report is shown in Figure 8.21.

a. What are the optimal solution and the total profit contribution?
b. Another supplier offered to provide Deegan Industries with an additional 500 pounds of the steel alloy at $2 per pound. Should Deegan purchase the additional pounds of the steel alloy? Explain.
c. Deegan is considering using overtime to increase the available assembly time. What would you advise Deegan to do regarding this option? Explain.
d. Because of increased competition, Deegan is considering reducing the price of model DRB such that the new contribution to profit is $175 per unit. How would this change in price affect the optimal solution? Explain.
e. If the available manufacturing time is increased by 500 hours, will the shadow price for the manufacturing time constraint change? Explain.

**FIGURE 8.21** SENSITIVITY REPORT FOR THE DEEGAN INDUSTRIES PROBLEM

Variable Cells

| Model Variable | Name | Final Value | Reduced Cost | Objective Coefficient | Allowable Increase | Allowable Decrease |
|---|---|---|---|---|---|---|
| DRB | Model DRB | 1000.000 | 0.000 | 200.000 | 24.000 | 88.000 |
| DRW | Model DRW | 800.000 | 0.000 | 280.000 | 220.000 | 30.000 |

Constraints

| Constraint Number | Name | Final Value | Shadow Price | Constraint R.H. Side | Allowable Increase | Allowable Decrease |
|---|---|---|---|---|---|---|
| 1 | Steel available | 40000.000 | 8.800 | 40000.000 | 909.091 | 10000.000 |
| 2 | Manufacturing minutes | 120000.000 | 0.600 | 120000.000 | 40000.000 | 5714.286 |
| 3 | Assembly minutes | 92000.000 | 0.000 | 96000.000 | 1E+30 | 4000.000 |

18. Davison Electronics manufactures two LCD television monitors, identified as model A and model B. Each model has its lowest possible production cost when produced on Davison's new production line. However, the new production line does not have the capacity to handle the total production of both models. As a result, at least some of the production must be routed to a higher-cost, old production line. The following table shows the minimum production requirements for next month, the production line capacities in units per month, and the production cost per unit for each production line:

| Model | Production Cost per Unit | | Minimum Production Requirements |
|-------|---------|----------|-------------|
|       | New Line | Old Line | |
| A | $30 | $50 | 50,000 |
| B | $25 | $40 | 70,000 |
| Production Line Capacity | 80,000 | 60,000 | |

Let

$$AN = \text{Units of model A produced on the new production line}$$
$$AO = \text{Units of model A produced on the old production line}$$
$$BN = \text{Units of model B produced on the new production line}$$
$$BO = \text{Units of model B produced on the old production line}$$

Davison's objective is to determine the minimum cost production plan. The sensitivity report is shown in Figure 8.22.

a. Formulate the linear programming model for this problem using the following four constraints:

**Constraint 1:** Minimum production for model A
**Constraint 2:** Minimum production for model B

**FIGURE 8.22**   SENSITIVITY REPORT FOR THE DAVISON ELECTRONICS PROBLEM

Variable Cells

| Model Variable | Name | Final Value | Reduced Cost | Objective Coefficient | Allowable Increase | Allowable Decrease |
|------|------|-------------|--------------|----------------------|--------------------|--------------------|
| AN | Model A Produced on New Line | 50000.000 | 0.000 | 30.000 | 5.000 | 1E+30 |
| AO | Model A Produced on Old Line | 0.000 | 5.000 | 50.000 | 1E+30 | 5.000 |
| BN | Model B Produced on New Line | 30000.000 | 0.000 | 25.000 | 15.000 | 5.000 |
| BO | Model B Produced on Old Line | 40000.000 | 0.000 | 40.000 | 5.000 | 15.000 |

Constraints

| Constraint Number | Name | Final Value | Shadow Price | Constraint R.H. Side | Allowable Increase | Allowable Decrease |
|-------------------|------|-------------|--------------|---------------------|--------------------|--------------------|
| 1 | Min production for A | 50000.000 | 45.000 | 50000.000 | 20000.000 | 40000.000 |
| 2 | Min production for B | 70000.000 | 40.000 | 70000.000 | 20000.000 | 40000.000 |
| 3 | Capacity of new production line | 80000.000 | −15.000 | 80000.000 | 40000.000 | 20000.000 |
| 4 | Capacity of old production line | 40000.000 | 0.000 | 60000.000 | 1E+30 | 20000.000 |

**Constraint 3:** Capacity of the new production line
**Constraint 4:** Capacity of the old production line

b. Using the sensitivity analysis information in Figure 8.22, what is the optimal solution and what is the total production cost associated with this solution?

c. Which constraints are binding? Explain.

d. The production manager noted that the only constraint with a negative shadow price is the constraint on the capacity of the new production line. The manager's interpretation of the shadow price was that a one-unit increase in the right-hand side of this constraint would actually increase the total production cost by $15 per unit. Do you agree with this interpretation? Would an increase in capacity for the new production line be desirable? Explain.

e. Would you recommend increasing the capacity of the old production line? Explain.

f. The production cost for model A on the old production line is $50 per unit. How much would this cost have to change to make it worthwhile to produce model A on the old production line? Explain.

g. Suppose that the minimum production requirement for model B is reduced from 70,000 units to 60,000 units. What effect would this change have on the total production cost? Explain.

19. Better Products, Inc., manufactures three products on two machines. In a typical week, 40 hours are available on each machine. The profit contribution and production time in hours per unit are as follows:

| Category | Product 1 | Product 2 | Product 3 |
|---|---|---|---|
| Profit/unit | $30 | $50 | $20 |
| Machine 1 time/unit | 0.5 | 2.0 | 0.75 |
| Machine 2 time/unit | 1.0 | 1.0 | 0.5 |

Two operators are required for machine 1; thus, 2 hours of labor must be scheduled for each hour of machine 1 time. Only one operator is required for machine 2. A maximum of 100 labor-hours is available for assignment to the machines during the coming week. Other production requirements are that product 1 cannot account for more than 50% of the units produced and that product 3 must account for at least 20% of the units produced.

a. How many units of each product should be produced to maximize the total profit contribution? What is the projected weekly profit associated with your solution?

b. How many hours of production time will be scheduled on each machine?

c. What is the value of an additional hour of labor?

d. Assume that labor capacity can be increased to 120 hours. Would you be interested in using the additional 20 hours available for this resource? Develop the optimal product mix, assuming that the extra hours are made available.

20. Adirondack Savings Bank (ASB) has $1 million in new funds that must be allocated to home loans, personal loans, and automobile loans. The annual rates of return for the three types of loans are 7% for home loans, 12% for personal loans, and 9% for automobile loans. The bank's planning committee has decided that at least 40% of the new funds must be allocated to home loans. In addition, the planning committee has specified that the amount allocated to personal loans cannot exceed 60% of the amount allocated to automobile loans.

a. Formulate a linear programming model that can be used to determine the amount of funds ASB should allocate to each type of loan in order to maximize the total annual return for the new funds.

b. How much should be allocated to each type of loan? What is the total annual return? What is the annual percentage return?

c. If the interest rate on home loans increased to 9%, would the amount allocated to each type of loan change? Explain.

d. Suppose the total amount of new funds available was increased by $10,000. What effect would this have on the total annual return? Explain.

e. Assume that ASB has the original $1 million in new funds available and that the planning committee has agreed to relax the requirement that at least 40% of the new funds must be allocated to home loans by 1%. How much would the annual return change? How much would the annual percentage return change?

21. Round Tree Manor is a hotel that provides two types of rooms with three rental classes: Super Saver, Deluxe, and Business. The profit per night for each type of room and rental class is as follows:

|  |  | Rental Class | | |
| --- | --- | --- | --- | --- |
|  |  | **Super Saver** | **Deluxe** | **Business** |
| **Room** | Type I | $30 | $35 | — |
|  | Type II | $20 | $30 | $40 |

Type I rooms do not have wireless Internet access and are not available for the Business rental class.

Round Tree's management makes a forecast of the demand by rental class for each night in the future. A linear programming model developed to maximize profit is used to determine how many reservations to accept for each rental class. The demand forecast for a particular night is 130 rentals in the Super Saver class, 60 rentals in the Deluxe class, and 50 rentals in the Business class. Round Tree has 100 Type I rooms and 120 Type II rooms.

a. Use linear programming to determine how many reservations to accept in each rental class and how the reservations should be allocated to room types. Is the demand by any rental class not satisfied? Explain.

b. How many reservations can be accommodated in each rental class?

c. Management is considering offering a free breakfast to anyone upgrading from a Super Saver reservation to Deluxe class. If the cost of the breakfast to Round Tree is $5, should this incentive be offered?

d. With a little work, an unused office area could be converted to a rental room. If the conversion cost is the same for both types of rooms, would you recommend converting the office to a Type I or a Type II room? Why?

e. Could the linear programming model be modified to plan for the allocation of rental demand for the next night? What information would be needed and how would the model change?

22. Industrial Designs has been awarded a contract to design a label for a new wine produced by Lake View Winery. The company estimates that 150 hours will be required to complete the project. The firm's three graphic designers available for assignment to this project are Lisa, a senior designer and team leader; David, a senior designer; and Sarah, a junior designer. Because Lisa has worked on several projects for Lake View Winery, management specified that Lisa must be assigned at least 40% of the total number of hours assigned to the two senior designers. To provide label-designing experience for Sarah, Sarah must be assigned at least 15% of the total project time. However, the number of hours assigned to Sarah must not exceed 25% of the total number of hours assigned to the two senior

designers. Due to other project commitments, Lisa has a maximum of 50 hours available to work on this project. Hourly wage rates are $30 for Lisa, $25 for David, and $18 for Sarah.

a. Formulate a linear program that can be used to determine the number of hours each graphic designer should be assigned to the project in order to minimize total cost.

b. How many hours should each graphic designer be assigned to the project? What is the total cost?

c. Suppose Lisa could be assigned more than 50 hours. What effect would this have on the optimal solution? Explain.

d. If Sarah were not required to work a minimum number of hours on this project, would the optimal solution change? Explain.

23. Vollmer Manufacturing makes three components for sale to refrigeration companies. The components are processed on two machines: a shaper and a grinder. The times (in minutes) required on each machine are as follows:

|           | Machine |         |
| --------- | ------- | ------- |
| Component | Shaper  | Grinder |
| 1         | 6       | 4       |
| 2         | 4       | 5       |
| 3         | 4       | 2       |

The shaper is available for 120 hours, and the grinder is available for 110 hours. No more than 200 units of component 3 can be sold, but up to 1000 units of each of the other components can be sold. In fact, the company already has orders for 600 units of component 1 that must be satisfied. The profit contributions for components 1, 2, and 3 are $8, $6, and $9, respectively.

a. Formulate and solve for the recommended production quantities.

b. What are the objective coefficient ranges for the three components? Interpret these ranges for company management.

c. What are the right-hand-side ranges? Interpret these ranges for company management.

d. If more time could be made available on the grinder, how much would it be worth?

e. If more units of component 3 can be sold by reducing the sales price by $4, should the company reduce the price?

24. National Insurance Associates carries an investment portfolio of stocks, bonds, and other investment alternatives. Currently $200,000 of funds are available and must be considered for new investment opportunities. The four stock options National is considering and the relevant financial data are as follows:

|                                  | Stock |       |       |       |
| -------------------------------- | ----- | ----- | ----- | ----- |
|                                  | A     | B     | C     | D     |
| Price per share                  | $100  | $50   | $80   | $40   |
| Annual rate of return            | 0.12  | 0.08  | 0.06  | 0.10  |
| Risk measure per dollar invested | 0.10  | 0.07  | 0.05  | 0.08  |

The risk measure indicates the relative uncertainty associated with the stock in terms of its realizing the projected annual return; higher values indicate greater risk. The risk measures are provided by the firm's top financial advisor.

National's top management has stipulated the following investment guidelines: The annual rate of return for the portfolio must be at least 9%, and no one stock can account for more than 50% of the total dollar investment.

a.  Use linear programming to develop an investment portfolio that minimizes risk.
b.  If the firm ignores risk and uses a maximum return-on-investment strategy, what is the investment portfolio?
c.  What is the dollar difference between the portfolios in parts (a) and (b)? Why might the company prefer the solution developed in part (a)?

25.  Georgia Cabinets manufactures kitchen cabinets that are sold to local dealers throughout the Southeast. Because of a large backlog of orders for oak and cherry cabinets, the company decided to contract with three smaller cabinetmakers to do the final finishing operation. For the three cabinetmakers, the number of hours required to complete all the oak cabinets, the number of hours required to complete all the cherry cabinets, the number of hours available for the final finishing operation, and the cost per hour to perform the work are shown here:

|  | Cabinetmaker 1 | Cabinetmaker 2 | Cabinetmaker 3 |
|---|---|---|---|
| Hours required to complete all the oak cabinets | 50 | 42 | 30 |
| Hours required to complete all the cherry cabinets | 60 | 48 | 35 |
| Hours available | 40 | 30 | 35 |
| Cost per hour | $36 | $42 | $55 |

For example, Cabinetmaker 1 estimates that it will take 50 hours to complete all the oak cabinets and 60 hours to complete all the cherry cabinets. However, Cabinetmaker 1 only has 40 hours available for the final finishing operation. Thus, Cabinetmaker 1 can only complete 40/50 = 0.80, or 80%, of the oak cabinets if it worked only on oak cabinets. Similarly, Cabinetmaker 1 can only complete 40/60 = 0.67, or 67%, of the cherry cabinets if it worked only on cherry cabinets.

a.  Formulate a linear programming model that can be used to determine the percentage of the oak cabinets and the percentage of the cherry cabinets that should be given to each of the three cabinetmakers in order to minimize the total cost of completing both projects.
b.  Solve the model formulated in part (a). What percentage of the oak cabinets and what percentage of the cherry cabinets should be assigned to each cabinetmaker? What is the total cost of completing both projects?
c.  If Cabinetmaker 1 has additional hours available, would the optimal solution change? Explain.
d.  If Cabinetmaker 2 has additional hours available, would the optimal solution change? Explain.
e.  Suppose Cabinetmaker 2 reduced its cost to $38 per hour. What effect would this change have on the optimal solution? Explain.

26.  Benson Electronics manufactures three components used to produce cell phones and other communication devices. In a given production period, demand for the three components may exceed Benson's manufacturing capacity. In this case, the company meets demand by purchasing the components from another manufacturer at an increased cost per unit.

Benson's manufacturing cost per unit and purchasing cost per unit for the three components are as follows:

| Source | Component 1 | Component 2 | Component 3 |
|---|---|---|---|
| Manufacture | $4.50 | $5.00 | $2.75 |
| Purchase | $6.50 | $8.80 | $7.00 |

Manufacturing times in minutes per unit for Benson's three departments are as follows:

| Department | Component 1 | Component 2 | Component 3 |
|---|---|---|---|
| Production | 2 | 3 | 4 |
| Assembly | 1 | 1.5 | 3 |
| Testing & Packaging | 1.5 | 2 | 5 |

For instance, each unit of component 1 that Benson manufactures requires 2 minutes of production time, 1 minute of assembly time, and 1.5 minutes of testing and packaging time. For the next production period, Benson has capacities of 360 hours in the production department, 250 hours in the assembly department, and 300 hours in the testing and packaging department.

a. Formulate a linear programming model that can be used to determine how many units of each component to manufacture and how many units of each component to purchase. Assume that component demands that must be satisfied are 6000 units for component 1, 4000 units for component 2, and 3500 units for component 3. The objective is to minimize the total manufacturing and purchasing costs.

b. What is the optimal solution? How many units of each component should be manufactured and how many units of each component should be purchased?

c. Which departments are limiting Benson's manufacturing quantities? Use the shadow price to determine the value of an *extra hour* in each of these departments.

d. Suppose that Benson had to obtain one additional unit of component 2. Discuss what the shadow price for the component 2 constraint tells us about the cost to obtain the additional unit.

27. Cranberries can be harvested using either a "wet" method or a "dry" method. Dry-harvested cranberries can be sold at a premium, while wet-harvested cranberries are used mainly for cranberry juice and bring in less revenue. Fresh Made Cranberry Cooperative must decide how much of its cranberry crop should be harvested wet and how much should be dry harvested. Fresh Made has 5000 barrels of cranberries that can be harvested using either the wet or dry method. Dry cranberries are sold for $32.50 per barrel and wet cranberries are sold for $17.50 per barrel. Once harvested, cranberries must be processed through several operations before they can be sold. Both wet and dry cranberries must go through dechaffing and cleaning operations. The dechaffing and the cleaning operations can each be run 24 hours per day for the 6-week season (for a total of 1008 hours). Each barrel of dry cranberries requires 0.18 hours in the dechaffing operation and 0.32 hours in the cleaning operation. Wet cranberries require 0.04 hours in the dechaffing operation and 0.10 hours in the cleaning operation. Wet cranberries must also go through a drying process. The drying process can also be operated 24 hours per day for the 6-week season, and each barrel of wet cranberries must be dried for 0.22 hours.

a. Develop a linear program that Fresh Made can use to determine the optimal amount of cranberries to dry harvest and wet harvest.

b. Solve the linear program in part (a). How many barrels should be dry harvested? How many barrels should be wet harvested?

    c.   Suppose that Fresh Made can increase its dechaffing capacity by using an outside firm for this operation. Fresh Made will still use its own dechaffing operation as much as possible, but it can purchase additional capacity from this outside firm for $500 per hour. Should Fresh Made purchase additional dechaffing capacity? Why or why not?

    d.   Interpret the shadow price for the constraint corresponding to the cleaning operation. How would you explain the meaning of this shadow price to management?

28.  The Pfeiffer Company manages approximately $15 million for clients. For each client, Pfeiffer chooses a mix of three investment vehicles: a growth stock fund, an income fund, and a money market fund. Each client has different investment objectives and different tolerances for risk. To accommodate these differences, Pfeiffer places limits on the percentage of each portfolio that may be invested in the three funds and assigns a portfolio risk index to each client.

    Here's how the system works for Dennis Hartmann, one of Pfeiffer's clients. Based on an evaluation of Hartmann's risk tolerance, Pfeiffer has assigned Hartmann's portfolio a risk index of 0.05. Furthermore, to maintain diversity, the fraction of Hartmann's portfolio invested in the growth and income funds must be at least 10% for each, and at least 20% must be in the money market fund.

    The risk ratings for the growth, income, and money market funds are 0.10, 0.05, and 0.01, respectively. A portfolio risk index is computed as a weighted average of the risk ratings for the three funds, where the weights are the fraction of the portfolio invested in each of the funds. Hartmann has given Pfeiffer $300,000 to manage. Pfeiffer is currently forecasting a yield of 20% on the growth fund, 10% on the income fund, and 6% on the money market fund.

    a.   Develop a linear programming model to select the best mix of investments for Hartmann's portfolio.

    b.   Solve the model you developed in part (a).

    c.   How much may the yields on the three funds vary before it will be necessary for Pfeiffer to modify Hartmann's portfolio?

    d.   If Hartmann were more risk tolerant, how much of a yield increase could he expect? For instance, what if his portfolio risk index is increased to 0.06?

    e.   If Pfeiffer revised the yield estimate for the growth fund downward to 0.10, how would you recommend modifying Hartmann's portfolio?

    f.   What information must Pfeiffer maintain on each client in order to use this system to manage client portfolios?

    g.   On a weekly basis Pfeiffer revises the yield estimates for the three funds. Suppose Pfeiffer has 50 clients. Describe how you would envision Pfeiffer making weekly modifications in each client's portfolio and allocating the total funds managed among the three investment funds.

29.  La Jolla Beverage Products is considering producing a wine cooler that would be a blend of a white wine, a rosé wine, and fruit juice. To meet taste specifications, the wine cooler must consist of at least 50% white wine, at least 20% and no more than 30% rosé, and exactly 20% fruit juice. La Jolla purchases the wine from local wineries and the fruit juice from a processing plant in San Francisco. For the current production period, 10,000 gallons of white wine and 8000 gallons of rosé wine can be purchased; an unlimited amount of fruit juice can be ordered. The costs for the wine are $1.00 per gallon for the white and $1.50 per gallon for the rosé; the fruit juice can be purchased for $0.50 per gallon. La Jolla Beverage Products can sell all of the wine cooler it can produce for $2.50 per gallon.

    a.   Is the cost of the wine and fruit juice a sunk cost or a relevant cost in this situation? Explain.

    b.   Formulate a linear program to determine the blend of the three ingredients that will maximize the total profit contribution. Solve the linear program to determine the number of gallons of each ingredient La Jolla should purchase and the total profit contribution it will realize from this blend.

c. If La Jolla could obtain additional amounts of the white wine, should it do so? If so, how much should it be willing to pay for each additional gallon, and how many additional gallons would it want to purchase?

d. If La Jolla Beverage Products could obtain additional amounts of the rosé wine, should it do so? If so, how much should it be willing to pay for each additional gallon, and how many additional gallons would it want to purchase?

e. Interpret the shadow price for the constraint corresponding to the requirement that the wine cooler must contain at least 50% white wine. What is your advice to management given this shadow price?

f. Interpret the shadow price for the constraint corresponding to the requirement that the wine cooler must contain exactly 20% fruit juice. What is your advice to management given this shadow price?

30. The program manager for Channel 10 would like to determine the best way to allocate the time for the 11:00–11:30 evening news broadcast. Specifically, she would like to determine the number of minutes of broadcast time to devote to local news, national news, weather, and sports. Over the 30-minute broadcast, 10 minutes are set aside for advertising. The station's broadcast policy states that at least 15% of the time available should be devoted to local news coverage; the time devoted to local news or national news must be at least 50% of the total broadcast time; the time devoted to the weather segment must be less than or equal to the time devoted to the sports segment; the time devoted to the sports segment should be no longer than the total time spent on the local and national news; and at least 20% of the time should be devoted to the weather segment. The production costs per minute are $300 for local news, $200 for national news, $100 for weather, and $100 for sports.

a. Formulate and solve a linear program that can determine how the 20 available minutes should be used to minimize the total cost of producing the program.

b. Interpret the shadow price for the constraint corresponding to the available time. What advice would you give the station manager given this shadow price?

c. Interpret the shadow price for the constraint corresponding to the requirement that at least 15% of the available time should be devoted to local coverage. What advice would you give the station manager given this shadow price?

d. Interpret the shadow price for the constraint corresponding to the requirement that the time devoted to the local and the national news must be at least 50% of the total broadcast time. What advice would you give the station manager given this shadow price?

e. Interpret the shadow price for the constraint corresponding to the requirement that the time devoted to the weather segment must be less than or equal to the time devoted to the sports segment. What advice would you give the station manager given this shadow price?

31. Gulf Coast Electronics is ready to award contracts for printing its annual report. For the past several years, the four-color annual report has been printed by Johnson Printing and Lakeside Litho. A new firm, Benson Printing, inquired into the possibility of doing a portion of the printing. The quality and service level provided by Lakeside Litho has been extremely high; in fact, only 0.5% of Gulf Coast's annual reports have had to be discarded because of quality problems. Johnson Printing has also had a high quality level historically, producing an average of only 1% unacceptable reports. Because Gulf Coast Electronics has had no experience with Benson Printing, it estimated Benson's defective rate to be 10%. Gulf Coast would like to determine how many reports should be printed by each firm to obtain 75,000 acceptable-quality reports. To ensure that Benson Printing will receive some of the contract, management specified that the number of reports awarded to Benson

Printing must be at least 10% of the volume given to Johnson Printing. In addition, the total volume assigned to Benson Printing, Johnson Printing, and Lakeside Litho should not exceed 30,000, 50,000, and 50,000 copies, respectively. Because of the long-term relationship with Lakeside Litho, management also specified that at least 30,000 reports should be awarded to Lakeside Litho. The cost per copy is $2.45 for Benson Printing, $2.50 for Johnson Printing, and $2.75 for Lakeside Litho.

a. Formulate and solve a linear program for determining how many copies should be assigned to each printing firm to minimize the total cost of obtaining 75,000 acceptable-quality reports.

b. Suppose that the quality level for Benson Printing is much better than estimated. What effect, if any, would this quality level have?

c. Suppose that management is willing to reconsider its requirement that Lakeside Litho be awarded at least 30,000 reports. What effect, if any, would this consideration have?

32. PhotoTech, Inc., a manufacturer of rechargeable batteries for digital cameras, signed a contract with a digital photography company to produce three different lithium-ion battery packs for a new line of digital cameras. The contract calls for the following:

| Battery Pack | Production Quantity |
|---|---|
| PT-100 | 200,000 |
| PT-200 | 100,000 |
| PT-300 | 150,000 |

PhotoTech can manufacture the battery packs at manufacturing plants located in the Philippines and Mexico. The unit cost of the battery packs differs at the two plants because of differences in production equipment and wage rates. The unit costs for each battery pack at each manufacturing plant are as follows:

| | Plant | |
|---|---|---|
| Product | Philippines | Mexico |
| PT-100 | $0.95 | $0.98 |
| PT-200 | $0.98 | $1.06 |
| PT-300 | $1.34 | $1.15 |

The PT-100 and PT-200 battery packs are produced using similar production equipment available at both plants. However, each plant has a limited capacity for the total number of PT-100 and PT-200 battery packs produced. The combined PT-100 and PT-200 production capacities are 175,000 units at the Philippines plant and 160,000 units at the Mexico plant. The PT-300 production capacities are 75,000 units at the Philippines plant and 100,000 units at the Mexico plant. The cost of shipping from the Philippines plant is $0.18 per unit, and the cost of shipping from the Mexico plant is $0.10 per unit.

a. Develop a linear program that PhotoTech can use to determine how many units of each battery pack to produce at each plant in order to minimize the total production and shipping cost associated with the new contract.

b. Solve the linear program developed in part (a) to determine the optimal production plan.

c. Use sensitivity analysis to determine how much the production and/or shipping cost per unit would have to change in order to produce additional units of the PT-100 in the Philippines plant.

d. Use sensitivity analysis to determine how much the production and/or shipping cost per unit would have to change in order to produce additional units of the PT-200 in the Mexico plant.

# Case Problem 1    Product Mix

TJ's, Inc., makes three nut mixes for sale to grocery chains located in the Southeast. The three mixes, referred to as the Regular Mix, the Deluxe Mix, and the Holiday Mix, are made by mixing different percentages of five types of nuts.

In preparation for the fall season, TJ's purchased the following shipments of nuts at the prices shown:

| Type of Nut | Shipment Amount (pounds) | Cost per Shipment |
|---|---|---|
| Almond | 6000 | $7500 |
| Brazil | 7500 | $7125 |
| Filbert | 7500 | $6750 |
| Pecan | 6000 | $7200 |
| Walnut | 7500 | $7875 |

The Regular Mix consists of 15% almonds, 25% Brazil nuts, 25% filberts, 10% pecans, and 25% walnuts. The Deluxe Mix consists of 20% of each type of nut, and the Holiday Mix consists of 25% almonds, 15% Brazil nuts, 15% filberts, 25% pecans, and 20% walnuts.

TJ's accountant analyzed the cost of packaging materials, sales price per pound, and so forth, and determined that the profit contribution per pound is $1.65 for the Regular Mix, $2.00 for the Deluxe Mix, and $2.25 for the Holiday Mix. These figures do not include the cost of specific types of nuts in the different mixes because that cost can vary greatly in the commodity markets.

Customer orders already received are summarized here:

| Type of Mix | Orders (pounds) |
|---|---|
| Regular | 10,000 |
| Deluxe | 3,000 |
| Holiday | 5,000 |

Because demand is running high, TJ's expects to receive many more orders than can be satisfied.

TJ's is committed to using the available nuts to maximize profit over the fall season; nuts not used will be given to the Free Store. Even if it is not profitable to do so, TJ's president indicated that the orders already received must be satisfied.

## Managerial Report

Perform an analysis of TJ's product mix problem, and prepare a report for TJ's president that summarizes your findings. Be sure to include information and analysis on the following:

1. The cost per pound of the nuts included in the Regular, Deluxe, and Holiday mixes
2. The optimal product mix and the total profit contribution
3. Recommendations regarding how the total profit contribution can be increased if additional quantities of nuts can be purchased
4. A recommendation as to whether TJ's should purchase an additional 1000 pounds of almonds for $1000 from a supplier who overbought
5. Recommendations on how profit contribution could be increased (if at all) if TJ's does not satisfy all existing orders

## Case Problem 2   Investment Strategy

J. D. Williams, Inc., is an investment advisory firm that manages more than $120 million in funds for its numerous clients. The company uses an asset allocation model that recommends the portion of each client's portfolio to be invested in a growth stock fund, an income fund, and a money market fund. To maintain diversity in each client's portfolio, the firm places limits on the percentage of each portfolio that may be invested in each of the three funds. General guidelines indicate that the amount invested in the growth fund must be between 20% and 40% of the total portfolio value. Similar percentages for the other two funds stipulate that between 20% and 50% of the total portfolio value must be in the income fund and at least 30% of the total portfolio value must be in the money market fund.

In addition, the company attempts to assess the risk tolerance of each client and adjust the portfolio to meet the needs of the individual investor. For example, Williams just contracted with a new client who has $800,000 to invest. Based on an evaluation of the client's risk tolerance, Williams assigned a maximum risk index of 0.05 for the client. The firm's risk indicators show the risk of the growth fund at 0.10, the income fund at 0.07, and the money market fund at 0.01. An overall portfolio risk index is computed as a weighted average of the risk rating for the three funds, where the weights are the fraction of the client's portfolio invested in each of the funds.

Additionally, Williams is currently forecasting annual yields of 18% for the growth fund, 12.5% for the income fund, and 7.5% for the money market fund. Based on the information provided, how should the new client be advised to allocate the $800,000 among the growth, income, and money market funds? Develop a linear programming model that will provide the maximum yield for the portfolio. Use your model to develop a managerial report.

### Managerial Report

1. Recommend how much of the $800,000 should be invested in each of the three funds. What is the annual yield you anticipate for the investment recommendation?
2. Assume that the client's risk index could be increased to 0.055. How much would the yield increase, and how would the investment recommendation change?
3. Refer again to the original situation, where the client's risk index was assessed to be 0.05. How would your investment recommendation change if the annual yield for the growth fund were revised downward to 16% or even to 14%?
4. Assume that the client expressed some concern about having too much money in the growth fund. How would the original recommendation change if the amount invested in the growth fund is not allowed to exceed the amount invested in the income fund?
5. The asset allocation model you developed may be useful in modifying the portfolios for all of the firm's clients whenever the anticipated yields for the three funds are periodically revised. What is your recommendation as to whether use of this model is possible?

## Case Problem 3   Truck Leasing Strategy

Reep Construction recently won a contract for the excavation and site preparation of a new rest area on the Pennsylvania Turnpike. In preparing his bid for the job, Bob Reep, founder and president of Reep Construction, estimated that it would take four months to perform the work and that 10, 12, 14, and 8 trucks would be needed in months 1 through 4, respectively.

The firm currently has 20 trucks of the type needed to perform the work on the new project. These trucks were obtained last year when Bob signed a long-term lease with PennState Leasing. Although most of these trucks are currently being used on existing jobs, Bob estimates that one truck will be available for use on the new project in month 1, two trucks will be available in month 2, three trucks will be available in month 3, and one truck will be available in month 4. Thus, to complete the project, Bob will have to lease additional trucks.

The long-term leasing contract with PennState charges a monthly cost of $600 per truck. Reep Construction pays its truck drivers $20 an hour, and daily fuel costs are approximately $100 per truck. All maintenance costs are paid by PennState Leasing. For planning purposes, Bob estimates that each truck used on the new project will be operating eight hours a day, five days a week for approximately four weeks each month.

Bob does not believe that current business conditions justify committing the firm to additional long-term leases. In discussing the short-term leasing possibilities with PennState Leasing, Bob learned that he can obtain short-term leases of one to four months. Short-term leases differ from long-term leases in that the short-term leasing plans include the cost of both a truck and a driver. Maintenance costs for short-term leases also are paid by PennState Leasing. The following costs for each of the four months cover the lease of a truck and driver:

| Length of Lease | Cost per Month |
| --- | --- |
| 1 | $4000 |
| 2 | $3700 |
| 3 | $3225 |
| 4 | $3040 |

Bob Reep would like to acquire a lease that minimizes the cost of meeting the monthly trucking requirements for his new project, but he also takes great pride in the fact that his company has never laid off employees. Bob is committed to maintaining his no-layoff policy; that is, he will use his own drivers even if costs are higher.

## Managerial Report

Perform an analysis of Reep Construction's leasing problem and prepare a report for Bob Reep that summarizes your findings. Be sure to include information on and analysis of the following items:

1. The optimal leasing plan
2. The costs associated with the optimal leasing plan
3. The cost for Reep Construction to maintain its current policy of no layoffs

# Appendix 8.1    Sensitivity Analysis with Excel

In Appendix 7.1 we showed how Excel Solver can be used to solve a linear program by using it to solve the RMC problem. We used reports similar to Excel's Answer Report in Chapter 7, but these reports do not contain the sensitivity analysis information discussed in this chapter. Let us now see how Excel can be used to provide sensitivity analysis information.

When Excel Solver has found the optimal solution to a linear program, the **Solver Results** dialog box (see Figure 8.23) will appear on the screen. If only the solution is desired, simply

**FIGURE 8.23**    EXCEL SOLVER RESULTS DIALOG BOX TO PRODUCE SENSITIVITY
REPORT

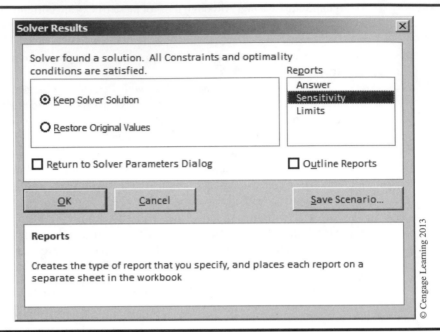

click **OK**. To obtain the optimal solution and the sensitivity analysis output, you must select
**Sensitivity** in the **Reports** box before clicking **OK**; the Sensitivity Report is created on
another worksheet in the same Excel workbook. Following this procedure for the RMC problem, we obtained the optimal solution shown in Figure 8.24. Figure 8.25 shows the Sensitivity Report as generated by Excel Solver. Note that there are no columns for Model
Variables or Constraint Numbers as shown in the reports in Chapter 8. The Cell columns in
Figure 8.25 correspond to the location of the decision variables and constraints in the Excel
model (Figure 8.24).

## Appendix 8.2    Sensitivity Analysis with LINGO

In Appendix 7.2 we showed how LINGO can be used to solve a linear program by using it
to solve the RMC problem. A copy of the Solution Report is shown in Figure 8.26. As we
discussed previously, the value of the objective function is 1600, the optimal solution is
$F = 25$ and $S = 20$, and the values of the slack variables corresponding to the three constraints (rows 2–4) are 0.0, 1.0, and 0.0. Now, let us consider the information in the Reduced
Cost column and the Dual Price column.

For the RMC problem, the reduced costs for both decision variables are zero because
both variables are at a positive value. LINGO reports a *dual price* rather than a shadow price.
For a maximization problem, the dual price and shadow price are identical. For a minimization problem, the dual price is equal to the negative of the shadow price. When interpreting
the LINGO output for a minimization problem, multiply the dual prices by $-1$, treat the resulting number as a shadow price, and interpret the number as described in Section 8.3. The
nonzero dual prices of 33.3333 for constraint 1 (material 1 constraint in row 2) and 44.4444

**FIGURE 8.24**    EXCEL SOLUTION FOR THE RMC PROBLEM

WEB file

RMC

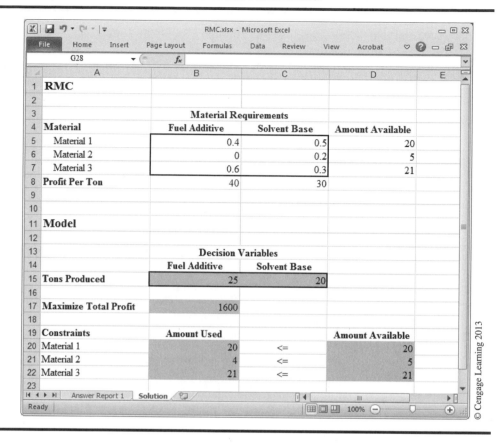

**FIGURE 8.25**    EXCEL SOLVER SENSITIVITY REPORT FOR THE RMC PROBLEM

Adjustable Cells

| Cell | Name | Final Value | Reduced Cost | Objective Coefficient | Allowable Increase | Allowable Decrease |
|------|------|-------------|--------------|-----------------------|--------------------|--------------------|
| $B$15 | Tons Produced Fuel Additive | 25.000 | 0.000 | 40.000 | 20.000 | 16.000 |
| $C$15 | Tons Produced Solvent Base | 20.000 | 0.000 | 30.000 | 20.000 | 10.000 |

Constraints

| Cell | Name | Final Value | Shadow Price | Constraint R.H. Side | Allowable Increase | Allowable Decrease |
|------|------|-------------|--------------|----------------------|--------------------|--------------------|
| $B$20 | Material 1 Amount Used | 20.000 | 33.333 | 20.000 | 1.500 | 6.000 |
| $B$21 | Material 2 Amount Used | 4.000 | 0.000 | 5.000 | 1E+30 | 1.000 |
| $B$22 | Material 3 Amount Used | 21.000 | 44.444 | 21.000 | 9.000 | 2.250 |

*LINGO always takes the absolute value of the reduced cost.*

for constraint 3 (material 3 constraint in row 4) tell us that an additional ton of material 1 increases the value of the optimal solution by $33.33 and an additional ton of material 3 increases the value of the optimal solution by $44.44.

© Cengage Learning 2013

**FIGURE 8.26**   LINGO SOLUTION REPORT FOR THE RMC PROBLEM

```
Global optimal solution found.          1600.000
Objective value:                              2
Total solver iterations:

Model Title: RMC CORPORATION

        Variable              Value            Reduced Cost
    --------------        --------------     -----------------
            F                25.00000                0.00000
            S                20.00000                0.00000

          Row            Slack/Surplus           Dual Price
    --------------        --------------     -----------------
            1              1600.00000                1.00000
            2                 0.00000               33.33333
            3                 1.00000                0.00000
            4                 0.00000               44.44444
```

Next, let us consider how LINGO can be used to compute the range of optimality for each objective function coefficient and the range of feasibility for each of the dual prices. By default, range computations are not enabled in LINGO. To enable range computations, perform the following steps:

**Step 1.** Choose the **LINGO** menu
**Step 2.** Select **Options**
**Step 3.** When the **LINGO Options** dialog box appears:
   Select the **General Solver** tab
   Choose **Prices and Ranges** in the Dual Computations box
   Click **Apply**
   Click **OK**

You will now have to re-solve the RMC problem in order for LINGO to perform the range computations. After re-solving the problem, close or minimize the **Solution Report** window. To display the range information, select the **Range** command from the **LINGO** menu. LINGO displays the range information in a new window titled **Range Report**. The output that appears in the Range Report window for the RMC problem is shown in Figure 8.27.

We will use the information in the Objective Coefficient Ranges section of the range report to compute the range of optimality for the objective function coefficients. For example, the current objective function coefficient for $F$ (fuel additive) is 40. Note that the corresponding allowable increase is 20.0 and the corresponding allowable decrease is 16.0. Thus the range of optimality for the contribution to profit for $F$, the objective function coefficient for $F$, is $40.0 - 16.0 = 24.0$ to $40.0 + 20.0 = 60.0$. Using $PF$ to denote the contribution to profit for fuel additive, the range of optimality for $PF$ is $24.0 \leq PF \leq 60.0$. Similarly, with an allowable increase of 20.0 and an allowable decrease of 10.0, the range of optimality for $PS$, the profit contribution for solvent is $20.0 \leq PS \leq 50.0$.

**FIGURE 8.27**   LINGO RANGE REPORT FOR THE RMC PROBLEM

Ranges in which the basis is unchanged:

OBJECTIVE COEFFICIENT RANGES

| Variable | Current Coefficient | Allowable Increase | Allowable Decrease |
|----------|--------------------|--------------------|--------------------|
| F | 40.00000 | 20.00000 | 16.00000 |
| S | 30.00000 | 20.00000 | 10.00000 |

RIGHTHAND SIDE RANGES

| Row | Current RHS | Allowable Increase | Allowable Decrease |
|-----|-------------|--------------------|--------------------|
| 2 | 20.00000 | 1.50000 | 6.00000 |
| 3 | 5.00000 | INFINITY | 1.00000 |
| 4 | 21.00000 | 9.00000 | 2.25000 |

© Cengage Learning 2013

To compute the range of feasibility for each dual price, we will use the information in the Righthand Side Ranges section of the Range Report. For example, the current right-hand-side value for material 1 constraint (row 2) is 20, the allowable increase is 1.5, and the allowable decrease is 6.0. Because the dual price for this constraint is 33.33 (shown in the LINGO Solution Report), we can conclude that an additional ton will increase the objective function by $33.33 per ton. From the range information given, we see that after rounding, the dual price of $33.33 is valid for increases up to 20.0 + 1.5 = 21.5 and decreases to 20.0 − 6.0 = 14.0. Thus, the range of feasibility for material 1 is 14.0 to 21.5. The ranges of feasibility for the other constraints can be determined in a similar manner.

# CHAPTER 9

# Linear Programming Applications in Marketing, Finance, and Operations Management

## CONTENTS

Linear programming has proven to be one of the most successful quantitative approaches to decision making. Applications have been reported in almost every industry. These applications include production scheduling, media selection, financial planning, capital budgeting, supply chain design, product mix, staffing, and blending.

The Q.M. in Action, A Marketing Planning Model at Marathon Oil Company, provides an example of the use of linear programming by showing how Marathon uses a large-scale linear programming model to solve a wide variety of planning problems. Later in the chapter other Q.M. in Action features illustrate how General Electric uses linear programming for deciding on investments in solar energy; how Jeppesen Sanderson uses linear programming to optimize production of flight manuals; and how the Kellogg Company uses a large-scale linear programming model to integrate production, distribution, and inventory planning.

In this chapter we present a variety of applications from the traditional business areas of marketing, finance, and operations management. Modeling, computer solution, and interpretation of output are emphasized. A mathematical model is developed for each problem studied, and solutions obtained using Excel Solver are presented for most of the applications. In the chapter appendix we illustrate the use of Excel Solver by solving a financial planning problem.

---

## Q.M. *in* ACTION

### A MARKETING PLANNING MODEL AT MARATHON OIL COMPANY*

Marathon Oil Company has four refineries within the United States, operates 50 light product terminals, and has product demand at more than 95 locations. The Supply and Transportation Division faces the problem of determining which refinery should supply which terminal and, at the same time, determining which products should be transported via pipeline, barge, or tanker to minimize cost. Product demand must be satisfied, and the supply capability of each refinery must not be exceeded. To help solve this difficult problem, Marathon Oil developed a marketing planning model.

The marketing planning model is a large-scale linear programming model that takes into account sales not only at Marathon product terminals but also at all exchange locations. An exchange contract is an agreement with other oil product marketers that involves exchanging or trading

Marathon's products for theirs at different locations. All pipelines, barges, and tankers within Marathon's marketing area are also represented in the linear programming model. The objective of the model is to minimize the cost of meeting a given demand structure, taking into account sales price, pipeline tariffs, exchange contract costs, product demand, terminal operating costs, refining costs, and product purchases.

The marketing planning model is used to solve a wide variety of planning problems that vary from evaluating gasoline blending economics to analyzing the economics of a new terminal or pipeline. With daily sales of about 10 million gallons of refined light product, a savings of even one-thousandth of a cent per gallon can result in significant long-term savings. At the same time, what may appear to be a savings in one area, such as refining or transportation, may actually add to overall costs when the effects are fully realized throughout the system. The marketing planning model allows a simultaneous examination of this total effect.

---

*Based on information provided by Robert W. Wernert at Marathon Oil Company, Findlay, Ohio.

# 9.1  Marketing Applications

Applications of linear programming in marketing are numerous. In this section we discuss applications in media selection and marketing research.

## Media Selection

Media selection applications of linear programming are designed to help marketing managers allocate a fixed advertising budget to various advertising media. Potential media include newspapers, magazines, radio, television, and direct mail. In these applications, the objective is to maximize reach, frequency, and quality of exposure. Restrictions on the allowable allocation usually arise during consideration of company policy, contract requirements, and media availability. In the application that follows, we illustrate how a media selection problem might be formulated and solved using a linear programming model.

Relax-and-Enjoy Lake Development Corporation is developing a lakeside community at a privately owned lake. The primary market for the lakeside lots and homes includes all middle- and upper-income families within approximately 100 miles of the development. Relax-and-Enjoy employed the advertising firm of Boone, Phillips, and Jackson (BP&J) to design the promotional campaign.

After considering possible advertising media and the market to be covered, BP&J recommended that the first month's advertising be restricted to five media. At the end of the month, BP&J will then reevaluate its strategy based on the month's results. BP&J collected data on the number of potential customers reached, the cost per advertisement, the maximum number of times each medium is available, and the exposure quality rating for each of the five media. The quality rating is measured in terms of an exposure quality unit, a measure of the relative value of one advertisement in each of the media. This measure, based on BP&J's experience in the advertising business, takes into account factors such as audience demographics (age, income, and education of the audience reached), image presented, and quality of the advertisement. The information collected is presented in Table 9.1.

**TABLE 9.1**   ADVERTISING MEDIA ALTERNATIVES FOR THE RELAX-AND-ENJOY LAKE DEVELOPMENT CORPORATION

| Advertising Media | Number of Potential Customers Reached | Cost ($) per Advertisement | Maximum Times Available per Month* | Exposure Quality Units |
|---|---|---|---|---|
| 1. Daytime TV (1 min), station WKLA | 1000 | 1500 | 15 | 65 |
| 2. Evening TV (30 sec), station WKLA | 2000 | 3000 | 10 | 90 |
| 3. Daily newspaper (full page), *The Morning Journal* | 1500 | 400 | 25 | 40 |
| 4. Sunday newspaper magazine (½ page color), *The Sunday Press* | 2500 | 1000 | 4 | 60 |
| 5. Radio, 8:00 A.M. or 5:00 P.M. news (30 sec), station KNOP | 300 | 100 | 30 | 20 |

*The maximum number of times the medium is available is either the maximum number of times the advertising medium occurs (e.g., four Sundays per month) or the maximum number of times BP&J recommends that the medium be used.

*In Section 7.1 we provided some general guidelines for modeling linear programming problems. You may want to review Section 7.1 before proceeding with the linear programming applications in this chapter.*

Relax-and-Enjoy provided BP&J with an advertising budget of $30,000 for the first month's campaign. In addition, Relax-and-Enjoy imposed the following restrictions on how BP&J may allocate these funds: At least 10 television commercials must be used, at least 50,000 potential customers must be reached, and no more than $18,000 may be spent on television advertisements. What advertising media selection plan should be recommended?

The decision to be made is how many times to use each medium. We begin by defining the decision variables:

$$DTV = \text{number of times daytime TV is used}$$
$$ETV = \text{number of times evening TV is used}$$
$$DN = \text{number of times daily newspaper is used}$$
$$SN = \text{number of times Sunday newspaper is used}$$
$$R = \text{number of times radio is used}$$

The data on quality of exposure in Table 9.1 show that each daytime TV ($DTV$) advertisement is rated at 65 exposure quality units. Thus, an advertising plan with $DTV$ advertisements will provide a total of $65DTV$ exposure quality units. Continuing with the data in Table 9.1, we find evening TV ($ETV$) rated at 90 exposure quality units, daily newspaper ($DN$) rated at 40 exposure quality units, Sunday newspaper ($SN$) rated at 60 exposure quality units, and radio ($R$) rated at 20 exposure quality units. With the objective of maximizing the total exposure quality units for the overall media selection plan, the objective function becomes

$$\text{Max} \quad 65DTV + 90ETV + 40DN + 60SN + 20R \qquad \text{Exposure quality}$$

We now formulate the constraints for the model from the information given:

$$
\begin{array}{rcll}
DTV & \leq & 15 & \left.\begin{array}{l}\\\\\\\\\\\end{array}\right.\\
ETV & \leq & 10 & \\
DN & \leq & 25 & \left.\begin{array}{l}\text{Availability}\\\text{of media}\end{array}\right.\\
SN & \leq & 4 & \\
R & \leq & 30 & \\
1500DTV + 3000ETV + 400DN + 1000SN + 100R & \leq & 30{,}000 & \text{Budget}\\
DTV + ETV & \geq & 10 & \left.\begin{array}{l}\text{Television}\\\text{restrictions}\end{array}\right.\\
1500DTV + 3000ETV & \leq & 18{,}000 & \\
1000DTV + 2000ETV + 1500DN + 2500SN + 300R & \geq & 50{,}000 & \text{Customers reached}\\
DTV, ETV, DN, SN, R & \geq & 0 &
\end{array}
$$

*Care must be taken to ensure the linear programming model accurately reflects the real problem. Always review your formulation thoroughly before attempting to solve the model.*

The optimal solution to this five-variable, nine-constraint linear programming model is shown in Figure 9.1; a summary is presented in Table 9.2.

The optimal solution calls for advertisements to be distributed among daytime TV, daily newspaper, Sunday newspaper, and radio. The maximum number of exposure quality units is $65(10) + 90(0) + 40(25) + 60(2) + 20(30) = 2370$, and the total number of customers reached is 61,500. Note that in the constraint section the simple bound constraints on the availability of media are not listed. However, for each variable at its bound, the Reduced Cost gives the shadow price for that constraint. So, for example, the reduced cost of 65 for

*Problem 1 provides practice at formulating a similar media selection model.*

evening TV indicates that forcing the use of this type of ad would actually drop exposure quality by 65 points. On the other hand, allowing another daily newspaper ad (26 instead of a limit of 25) would increase exposure quality by 16 units. Note that the budget constraint has a shadow price of 0.060. Therefore, a $1.00 increase in the advertising budget will lead

**FIGURE 9.1**     SENSITIVITY REPORT FOR THE RELAX-AND-ENJOY LAKE
DEVELOPMENT CORPORATION PROBLEM

Variable Cells

| Model Variable | Name | Final Value | Reduced Cost | Objective Coefficient | Allowable Increase | Allowable Decrease |
|---|---|---|---|---|---|---|
| DTV | Ads Placed DTV | 10.000 | 0.000 | 65.000 | 25.000 | 65.000 |
| EVT | Ads Placed ETV | 0.000 | −65.000 | 90.000 | 65.000 | 1E+30 |
| DN | Ads Placed DN | 25.000 | 16.000 | 40.000 | 1E+30 | 16.000 |
| SN | Ads Placed SN | 2.000 | 0.000 | 60.000 | 40.000 | 16.667 |
| R | Ads Placed R | 30.000 | 14.000 | 20.000 | 1E+30 | 14.000 |

Constraints

| Constraint Number | Name | Final Value | Shadow Price | Constraint R.H. Side | Allowable Increase | Allowable Decrease |
|---|---|---|---|---|---|---|
| 1 | Budget | 30000.000 | 0.060 | 30000.000 | 2000.000 | 2000.000 |
| 2 | Num TV Ads | 10.000 | −25.000 | 10.000 | 1.333 | 1.333 |
| 3 | TV Budget | 15000.000 | 0.000 | 18000.000 | 1E+30 | 3000.000 |
| 4 | Customers Reached | 61500.000 | 0.000 | 50000.000 | 11500.000 | 1E+30 |

*More complex media selection models may include considerations such as the reduced exposure quality value for repeat media usage, cost discounts for repeat media usage, audience overlap by different media, and/or timing recommendations for the advertisements.*

to an increase of 0.06 exposure quality units. The shadow price of −25.000 for the number of TV ads indicates that reducing the number of required television commercials by 1 will increase the exposure quality of the advertising plan by 25 units. Thus, Relax-and-Enjoy should consider reducing the requirement of having at least 10 television commercials.

A possible shortcoming of this model is that, even if the exposure quality measure were not subject to error, it offers no guarantee that maximization of total exposure quality will lead to a maximization of profit or of sales (a common surrogate for profit). However, this issue is not a shortcoming of linear programming; rather, it is a shortcoming of the use of exposure quality as a criterion. If we could directly measure the effect of an advertisement on profit, we could use total profit as the objective to be maximized.

**TABLE 9.2**     ADVERTISING PLAN FOR THE RELAX-AND-ENJOY
LAKE DEVELOPMENT CORPORATION

| Media | Frequency | Budget |
|---|---|---|
| Daytime TV | 10 | $15,000 |
| Daily newspaper | 25 | 10,000 |
| Sunday newspaper | 2 | 2,000 |
| Radio | 30 | 3,000 |
| | | $30,000 |

Exposure quality units = 2370
Total customers reached = 61,500

## NOTES AND COMMENTS

1. The media selection model required subjective evaluations of the exposure quality for the media alternatives. Marketing managers may have substantial data concerning exposure quality, but the final coefficients used in the objective

function may also include considerations based primarily on managerial judgment.

2. The media selection model presented in this section uses exposure quality as the objective function and places a constraint on the number of

customers reached. An alternative formulation of this problem would be to use the number of customers reached as the objective function and add a constraint indicating the minimum total exposure quality required for the media plan.

## Marketing Research

An organization conducts marketing research to learn about consumer characteristics, attitudes, and preferences. Marketing research firms that specialize in providing such information often do the actual research for client organizations. Typical services offered by a marketing research firm include designing the study, conducting market surveys, analyzing the data collected, and providing summary reports and recommendations for the client. In the research design phase, targets or quotas may be established for the number and types of respondents to be surveyed. The marketing research firm's objective is to conduct the survey so as to meet the client's needs at a minimum cost.

Market Survey, Inc. (MSI) specializes in evaluating consumer reaction to new products, services, and advertising campaigns. A client firm requested MSI's assistance in ascertaining consumer reaction to a recently marketed household product. During meetings with the client, MSI agreed to conduct door-to-door personal interviews to obtain responses from households with children and households without children. In addition, MSI agreed to conduct both day and evening interviews. Specifically, the client's contract called for MSI to conduct 1000 interviews under the following quota guidelines:

1. Interview at least 400 households with children.
2. Interview at least 400 households without children.
3. The total number of households interviewed during the evening must be at least as great as the number of households interviewed during the day.
4. At least 40% of the interviews for households with children must be conducted during the evening.
5. At least 60% of the interviews for households without children must be conducted during the evening.

Because the interviews for households with children take additional interviewer time and because evening interviewers are paid more than daytime interviewers, the cost varies with the type of interview. Based on previous research studies, estimates of the interview costs are as follows:

| | Interview Cost | |
|---|---|---|
| **Household** | **Day** | **Evening** |
| Children | $20 | $25 |
| No children | $18 | $20 |

What is the household, time-of-day interview plan that will satisfy the contract requirements at a minimum total interviewing cost?

In formulating the linear programming model for the MSI problem, we utilize the following decision-variable notation:

$$DC = \text{the number of daytime interviews of households with children}$$

$$EC = \text{the number of evening interviews of households with children}$$

$DNC$ = the number of daytime interviews of households without children

$ENC$ = the number of evening interviews of households without children

We begin the linear programming model formulation by using the cost-per-interview data to develop the objective function:

$$\text{Min} \quad 20DC + 25EC + 18DNC + 20ENC$$

The constraint requiring a total of 1000 interviews is

$$DC + EC + DNC + ENC = 1000$$

The five specifications concerning the types of interviews are as follows:

- Households with children:

$$DC + EC \geq 400$$

- Households without children:

$$DNC + ENC \geq 400$$

- At least as many evening interviews as day interviews:

$$EC + ENC \geq DC + DNC$$

The usual format for linear programming model formulation places all decision variables on the left side of the inequality and a constant (possibly zero) on the right side. Thus, we rewrite this constraint as

$$-DC + EC - DNC + ENC \geq 0$$

- At least 40% of interviews of households with children during the evening:
$$EC \geq 0.4(DC + EC) \quad \text{or} \quad -0.4DC + 0.6EC \geq 0$$

- At least 60% of interviews of households without children during the evening:
$$ENC \geq 0.6(DNC + ENC) \quad \text{or} \quad -0.6DNC + 0.4ENC \geq 0$$

When we add the nonnegativity requirements, the four-variable and six-constraint linear programming model becomes

Min     $20DC + 25EC + 18DNC + 20ENC$

s.t.

| | | | | | |
|---|---|---|---|---|---|
| $DC +$ | $EC +$ | $DNC +$ | $ENC = 1000$ | Total interviews |
| $DC +$ | $EC$ | | $\geq 400$ | Households with children |
| | | $DNC +$ | $ENC \geq 400$ | Households without children |
| $-DC +$ | $EC -$ | $DNC +$ | $ENC \geq 0$ | Evening interviews |
| $-0.4DC +$ | $0.6EC$ | | $\geq 0$ | Evening interviews in households with children |
| | | $-0.6DNC +$ | $0.4ENC \geq 0$ | Evening interviews in households without children |

$$DC, EC, DNC, ENC \geq 0$$

The sensitivity report based on Excel Solver is shown in Figure 9.2. The solution reveals that the minimum cost of $20(240) + 25(160) + 18(240) + 20(360) = \$20{,}320$ occurs with the following interview schedule:

**Market**

| Household | Number of Interviews | | |
|---|---|---|---|
| | **Day** | **Evening** | **Totals** |
| Children | 240 | 160 | 400 |
| No children | 240 | 360 | 600 |
| Totals | 480 | 520 | 1000 |

Hence, 480 interviews will be scheduled during the day and 520 during the evening. Households with children will be covered by 400 interviews, and households without children will be covered by 600 interviews.

Selected sensitivity analysis information from Figure 9.2 shows a shadow price of 19.200 for the Total Interviews constraint. This indicates that the total interviewing cost will increase by $19.20 if the number of interviews is increased from 1000 to 1001. Thus, $19.20 is the incremental cost of obtaining additional interviews. It also is the savings that could be realized by reducing the number of interviews from 1000 to 999.

In this solution, exactly 400 households with children are interviewed and we exceed the minimum requirement on households without children by 200 (600 versus the minimum required of 400). The shadow price of 5.000 for the fifth constraint indicates that if one more household (with children) than the minimum requirement must be interviewed during the evening, the total interviewing cost will go up by $5.00. Similarly, the sixth constraint shows that requiring one more household (without children) to be interviewed during the evening will increase costs by $2.00.

**FIGURE 9.2**   SENSITIVITY REPORT FOR THE MARKET SURVEY PROBLEM

Variable Cells

| Model Variable | Name | Final Value | Reduced Cost | Objective Coefficient | Allowable Increase | Allowable Decrease |
|---|---|---|---|---|---|---|
| DC | Children Day | 240.000 | 0.000 | 20.000 | 5.000 | 4.667 |
| EC | Children Evening | 160.000 | 0.000 | 25.000 | 1E+30 | 5.000 |
| DNC | No Children Day | 240.000 | 0.000 | 18.000 | 2.000 | 1E+30 |
| ENC | No Children Evening | 360.000 | 0.000 | 20.000 | 4.667 | 2.000 |

Constraints

| Constraint Number | Name | Final Value | Shadow Price | Constraint R.H. Side | Allowable Increase | Allowable Decrease |
|---|---|---|---|---|---|---|
| 1 | Total Interviews | 1000.000 | 19.200 | 1000.000 | 1E+30 | 200.000 |
| 2 | Children | 400.000 | 2.800 | 400.000 | 100.000 | 400.000 |
| 3 | No Children | 600.000 | 0.000 | 400.000 | 200.000 | 1E+30 |
| 4 | Eve. Interviews | 520.000 | 0.000 | 0.000 | 40.000 | 1E+30 |
| 5 | Eve. Children | 160.000 | 5.000 | 0.000 | 240.000 | 20.000 |
| 6 | Eve. No Children | 360.000 | 2.000 | 0.000 | 240.000 | 20.000 |

# 9.2   Financial Applications

In finance, linear programming can be applied in problem situations involving capital budgeting, make-or-buy decisions, asset allocation, portfolio selection, financial planning, and many more. In this section we describe a portfolio selection problem and a problem involving funding of an early retirement program.

## Portfolio Selection

Portfolio selection problems involve situations in which a financial manager must select specific investments—for example, stocks and bonds—from a variety of investment alternatives. Managers of mutual funds, credit unions, insurance companies, and banks frequently encounter this type of problem. The objective function for portfolio selection problems usually is maximization of expected return or minimization of risk. The constraints usually reflect restrictions on the type of permissible investments, state laws, company policy, maximum permissible risk, and so on. Problems of this type have been formulated and solved using a variety of mathematical programming techniques. In this section we formulate and solve a portfolio selection problem as a linear program.

Consider the case of Welte Mutual Funds, Inc., located in New York City. Welte just obtained $100,000 by converting industrial bonds to cash and is now looking for other investment opportunities for these funds. Based on Welte's current investments, the firm's top financial analyst recommends that all new investments be made in the oil industry, in the steel industry, or in government bonds. Specifically, the analyst identified five investment opportunities and projected their annual rates of return. The investments and rates of return are shown in Table 9.3.

Management of Welte imposed the following investment guidelines:

1.  Neither industry (oil or steel) should receive more than $50,000.
2.  Government bonds should be at least 25% of the steel industry investments.
3.  The investment in Pacific Oil, the high-return but high-risk investment, cannot be more than 60% of the total oil industry investment.

What portfolio recommendations—investments and amounts—should be made for the available $100,000? Given the objective of maximizing projected return subject to the budgetary and managerially imposed constraints, we can answer this question by formulating and solving a linear programming model of the problem. The solution will provide investment recommendations for the management of Welte Mutual Funds.

**TABLE 9.3**   INVESTMENT OPPORTUNITIES FOR WELTE MUTUAL FUNDS

| Investment | Projected Rate of Return (%) |
| --- | --- |
| Atlantic Oil | 7.3 |
| Pacific Oil | 10.3 |
| Midwest Steel | 6.4 |
| Huber Steel | 7.5 |
| Government bonds | 4.5 |

Let

$$A = \text{dollars invested in Atlantic Oil}$$
$$P = \text{dollars invested in Pacific Oil}$$
$$M = \text{dollars invested in Midwest Steel}$$
$$H = \text{dollars invested in Huber Steel}$$
$$G = \text{dollars invested in government bonds}$$

Using the projected rates of return shown in Table 9.3, we write the objective function for maximizing the total return for the portfolio as

$$\text{Max} \quad 0.073A + 0.103P + 0.064M + 0.075H + 0.045G$$

The constraint specifying investment of the available \$100,000 is

$$A + P + M + H + G = 100,000$$

The requirements that neither the oil nor the steel industry should receive more than \$50,000 are

$$A + P \leq 50,000$$
$$M + H \leq 50,000$$

The requirement that government bonds be at least 25% of the steel industry investment is expressed as

$$G \geq 0.25(M + H) \quad \text{or} \quad -0.25M - 0.25H + G \geq 0$$

Finally, the constraint that Pacific Oil cannot be more than 60% of the total oil industry investment is

$$P \leq 0.60(A + P) \quad \text{or} \quad -0.60A + 0.40P \leq 0$$

By adding the nonnegativity restrictions, we obtain the complete linear programming model for the Welte Mutual Funds investment problem:

Max   $0.073A + 0.103P + 0.064M + 0.075H + 0.045G$
s.t.

| | | | | | | |
|---|---|---|---|---|---|---|
| $A +$ | $P +$ | $M +$ | $H +$ | $G =$ | 100,000 | Available funds |
| $A +$ | $P$ | | | $\leq$ | 50,000 | Oil industry maximum |
| | | $M +$ | $H$ | $\leq$ | 50,000 | Steel industry maximum |
| | | $- \; 0.25M -$ | $0.25H +$ | $G \geq$ | 0 | Government bonds minimum |
| $-0.6A +$ | $0.4P$ | | | $\leq$ | 0 | Pacific Oil restriction |

$$A, P, M, H, G \geq 0$$

The sensitivity based on Excel Solver for this linear program is shown in Figure 9.3. Table 9.4 shows how the funds are divided among the securities. Note that the optimal solution indicates that the portfolio should be diversified among all the investment opportunities except

**FIGURE 9.3**   SENSITIVITY REPORT FOR THE WELTE MUTUAL FUNDS PROBLEM

Variable Cells

| Model Variable | Name | Final Value | Reduced Cost | Objective Coefficient | Allowable Increase | Allowable Decrease |
|---|---|---|---|---|---|---|
| A | Atlantic Oil Amount Invested | 20000.000 | 0.000 | 0.073 | 0.030 | 0.055 |
| P | Pacific Oil Amount Invested | 30000.000 | 0.000 | 0.103 | 1E+30 | 0.030 |
| M | Midwest Steel Amount Invested | 0.000 | −0.011 | 0.064 | 0.011 | 1E+30 |
| H | Huber Steel Amount Invested | 40000.000 | 0.000 | 0.075 | 0.0275 | 0.011 |
| G | Gov't Bonds Amount Invested | 10000.000 | 0.000 | 0.045 | 0.030 | 1E+30 |

Constraints

| Constraint Number | Name | Final Value | Shadow Price | Constraint R.H. Side | Allowable Increase | Allowable Decrease |
|---|---|---|---|---|---|---|
| 1 | Avl. Funds | 100000.000 | 0.069 | 100000.000 | 12500.000 | 50000.000 |
| 2 | Oil Max | 50000.000 | 0.022 | 50000.000 | 50000.000 | 12500.000 |
| 3 | Steel Max | 40000.000 | 0.000 | 50000.000 | 1E+30 | 10000.000 |
| 4 | Gov't Bonds | 10000.000 | −0.024 | 0.000 | 50000.000 | 12500.000 |
| 5 | Pacific Oil | 30000.000 | 0.030 | 0.000 | 20000.000 | 30000.000 |

© Cengage Learning 2013

Midwest Steel. The projected annual return for this portfolio is 0.073(20000) + 0.103(30000) + 0.064(0) + 0.075(40000) + 0.045(10000) = $8000, which is an overall return of 8%.

The optimal solution shows the shadow price for the third constraint is zero. The reason is that the steel industry maximum constraint is not binding; increases in the steel industry limit of $50,000 will not improve the value of the optimal solution. Indeed, the final value for the left hand side of the third constraint shows that the current steel industry investment is $10,000 below its limit of $50,000. The shadow prices for the other constraints are nonzero, indicating that these constraints are binding.

The shadow price of 0.069 for the first constraint shows that the optimal value of objective function can be increased by 0.069 if one more dollar can be made available for the portfolio investment. If more funds can be obtained at a cost of less than 6.9%, management should consider obtaining them. However, if a return in excess of 6.9% can be obtained by investing funds elsewhere (other than in these five securities), management should question the wisdom of investing the entire $100,000 in this portfolio.

**TABLE 9.4**   OPTIMAL PORTFOLIO SELECTION FOR WELTE MUTUAL FUNDS

| Investment | Amount | Expected Annual Return |
|---|---|---|
| Atlantic Oil | $ 20,000 | $1460 |
| Pacific Oil | 30,000 | 3090 |
| Huber Steel | 40,000 | 3000 |
| Government bonds | 10,000 | 450 |
| Totals | $100,000 | $8000 |

Expected annual return of $8000
Overall rate of return = 8%

© Cengage Learning 2013

*The shadow price for the available funds constraint provides information on the rate of return from additional investment funds.*

Similar interpretations can be given to the other shadow prices. Note that the shadow price for the government bonds constraint is −0.024. This result indicates that increasing the value on the right-hand side of the constraint by one unit can be expected to decrease the value of the optimal solution by 0.024. In terms of the optimal portfolio, then, if Welte invests one more dollar in government bonds (beyond the minimum requirement), the total return will decrease by $0.024. To see why this decrease occurs, note again from the shadow price for the first constraint that the marginal return on the funds invested in the portfolio is 6.9% (the average return is 8%). The rate of return on government bonds is 4.5%. Thus, the cost of investing one more dollar in government bonds is the difference between the marginal return on the portfolio and the marginal return on government bonds: 6.9% − 4.5% = 2.4%.

*Practice formulating a variation of the Welte problem by working Problem 9.*

Note that the optimal solution shows that Midwest Steel should not be included in the portfolio ($M = 0$). The associated reduced cost for $M$ of −0.011 tells us that the objective function value will decrease by 0.011 for every dollar we invest in Midwest Steel. Stated differently, the coefficient for Midwest Steel would have to increase by 0.011 before considering the Midwest Steel investment alternative would be advisable. With such an increase the Midwest Steel return would be 0.064 + 0.011 = 0.075, making this investment just as desirable as the currently used Huber Steel investment alternative.

Finally, a simple modification of the Welte linear programming model permits us to determine the fraction of available funds invested in each security. That is, we divide each of the right-hand-side values by 100,000. Then the optimal values for the variables will give the fraction of funds that should be invested in each security for a portfolio of any size.

## NOTES AND COMMENTS

1. The optimal solution to the Welte Mutual Funds problem indicates that $20,000 is to be spent on the Atlantic Oil stock. If Atlantic Oil sells for $75 per share, we would have to purchase exactly 266⅔ shares in order to spend exactly $20,000. The difficulty of purchasing fractional shares can be handled by purchasing the largest possible integer number of shares with the allotted funds (e.g., 266 shares of Atlantic Oil). This approach guarantees that the budget constraint will not be violated. This approach, of course, introduces the possibility that the solution will no longer be optimal, but the danger is

slight if a large number of securities are involved. In cases where the analyst believes that the decision variables *must* have integer values, the problem must be formulated as an integer linear programming model. Integer linear programming is the topic of Chapter 11.

2. Financial portfolio theory stresses obtaining a proper balance between risk and return. In the Welte problem, we explicitly considered return in the objective function. Risk is controlled by choosing constraints that ensure diversity among oil and steel stocks and a balance between government bonds and the steel industry investment.

## Financial Planning

Linear programming has been used for a variety of investment planning applications. The Q.M. in Action, General Electric Uses Linear Programming for Solar Energy Investment Decisions, describes how linear programming is used to guide GE's investment in solar energy.

### GENERAL ELECTRIC USES LINEAR PROGRAMMING FOR SOLAR ENERGY INVESTMENT DECISIONS*

With growing concerns about the environment and our ability to continue to utilize limited nonrenewable sources for energy, companies have begun to place much more emphasis on renewable forms of energy. Water, wind, and solar energy are renewable forms of energy that have become the focus of considerable investment by companies.

General Electric (GE) has products in a variety of areas within the energy sector. One such area of interest to GE is solar energy. Solar energy is a relatively new concept with rapidly changing technologies; for example, solar cells and solar power systems. Solar cells can convert sunlight directly into electricity. Concentrating solar power systems focus a larger area of sunlight into a small beam that can be used as a heat source for conventional power generation. Solar cells can be placed on rooftops and hence can be used by both commercial and residential customers, whereas solar power systems are mostly used in commercial settings. In recent years, GE has invested in several solar cell technologies.

Uncertainties in technology development, costs, and demand for solar energy make determining the appropriate amount of production capacity in which to invest a difficult problem. GE uses a set of decision support tools to solve this problem. A detailed descriptive analytical model is used to estimate the cost of newly developed or proposed solar cells. Statistical models developed for new product introductions are used to estimate annual solar demand 10 to 15 years into the future. Finally, the cost and demand estimates are used in a multiperiod linear program to determine the best production capacity investment plan.

The linear program finds an optimal expansion plan by taking into account inventory, capacity, production, and budget constraints. Because of the high level of uncertainty, the linear program is solved over multiple future scenarios. A solution to each individual scenario is found and evaluated in the other scenarios to assess the risk associated with that plan. GE planning analysts have used these tools to support management's strategic investment decisions in the solar energy sector.

*Based on B. G. Thomas and S. Bollapragada, "General Electric Uses an Integrated Framework for Product Costing, Demand Forecasting and Capacity Planning for New Photovoltaic Technology Products," *Interfaces* 40, no. 5 (September/October 2010): 353–367.

Hewlitt Corporation established an early retirement program as part of its corporate restructuring. At the close of the voluntary sign-up period, 68 employees had elected early retirement. As a result of these early retirements, the company incurs the following obligations over the next eight years:

| Year | 1 | 2 | 3 | 4 | 5 | 6 | 7 | 8 |
|---|---|---|---|---|---|---|---|---|
| Cash Requirement | 430 | 210 | 222 | 231 | 240 | 195 | 225 | 255 |

The cash requirements (in thousands of dollars) are due at the beginning of each year.

The corporate treasurer must determine how much money must be set aside today to meet the eight yearly financial obligations as they come due. The financing plan for the retirement program includes investments in government bonds as well as savings. The investments in government bonds are limited to three choices:

| Bond | Price | Rate (%) | Years to Maturity |
|---|---|---|---|
| 1 | $1150 | 8.875 | 5 |
| 2 | 1000 | 5.500 | 6 |
| 3 | 1350 | 11.750 | 7 |

The government bonds have a par value of $1000, which means that even with different prices each bond pays $1000 at maturity. The rates shown are based on the par value. For purposes of planning, the treasurer assumed that any funds not invested in bonds will be placed in savings and earn interest at an annual rate of 4%.

We define the decision variables as follows:

$F$ = total dollars required to meet the retirement plan's eight-year obligation

$B_1$ = units of bond 1 purchased at the beginning of year 1

$B_2$ = units of bond 2 purchased at the beginning of year 1

$B_3$ = units of bond 3 purchased at the beginning of year 1

$S_i$ = amount placed in savings at the beginning of year $i$ for $i = 1, \ldots, 8$

The objective function is to minimize the total dollars needed to meet the retirement plan's eight-year obligation, or

$$\text{Min}\quad F$$

A key feature of this type of financial planning problem is that a constraint must be formulated for each year of the planning horizon. In general, each constraint takes the form

$$\begin{pmatrix} \text{Funds available at} \\ \text{the beginning of the year} \end{pmatrix} - \begin{pmatrix} \text{Funds invested in bonds} \\ \text{and placed in savings} \end{pmatrix} = \begin{pmatrix} \text{Cash obligation for} \\ \text{the current year} \end{pmatrix}$$

The funds available at the beginning of year 1 are given by $F$. With a current price of $1150 for bond 1 and investments expressed in thousands of dollars, the total investment for $B_1$ units of bond 1 would be $1.15B_1$. Similarly, the total investment in bonds 2 and 3 would be $1B_2$ and $1.35B_3$, respectively. The investment in savings for year 1 is $S_1$. Using these results and the first-year obligation of 430, we obtain the constraint for year 1:

$$F - 1.15B_1 - 1B_2 - 1.35B_3 - S_1 = 430 \quad \text{Year 1}$$

Investments in bonds can take place only in this first year, and the bonds will be held until maturity.

The funds available at the beginning of year 2 include the investment returns of 8.875% on the par value of bond 1, 5.5% on the par value of bond 2, 11.75% on the par value of bond 3, and 4% on savings. The new amount to be invested in savings for year 2 is $S_2$. With an obligation of 210, the constraint for year 2 is

$$0.08875B_1 + 0.055B_2 + 0.1175B_3 + 1.04S_1 - S_2 = 210 \quad \text{Year 2}$$

Similarly, the constraints for years 3 to 8 are

$$0.08875B_1 + 0.055B_2 + 0.1175B_3 + 1.04S_2 - S_3 = 222 \quad \text{Year 3}$$
$$0.08875B_1 + 0.055B_2 + 0.1175B_3 + 1.04S_3 - S_4 = 231 \quad \text{Year 4}$$
$$0.08875B_1 + 0.055B_2 + 0.1175B_3 + 1.04S_4 - S_5 = 240 \quad \text{Year 5}$$
$$1.08875B_1 + 0.055B_2 + 0.1175B_3 + 1.04S_5 - S_6 = 195 \quad \text{Year 6}$$
$$1.055B_2 + 0.1175B_3 + 1.04S_6 - S_7 = 225 \quad \text{Year 7}$$
$$1.1175B_3 + 1.04S_7 - S_8 = 255 \quad \text{Year 8}$$

*We do not consider future investments in bonds because the future price of bonds depends on interest rates and cannot be known in advance.*

Note that the constraint for year 6 shows that funds available from bond 1 are $1.08875B_1$. The coefficient of 1.08875 reflects the fact that bond 1 matures at the end of year 5. As a result, the par value plus the interest from bond 1 during year 5 is available at the beginning of year 6. Also, because bond 1 matures in year 5 and becomes available for use at the beginning of year 6, the variable $B_1$ does not appear in the constraints for years 7 and 8. Note the similar interpretation for bond 2, which matures at the end of year 6 and has

**FIGURE 9.4** SENSITIVITY REPORT FOR THE HEWLITT CORPORATION CASH REQUIREMENTS PROBLEM

Variable Cells

| Model Variable | Name | Final Value | Reduced Cost | Objective Coefficient | Allowable Increase | Allowable Decrease |
|---|---|---|---|---|---|---|
| F | Dollars Needed | 1728.794 | 0.000 | 1.000 | 1E+30 | 1.000 |
| B1 | Bond 1 - Year 1 | 144.988 | 0.000 | 0.000 | 0.067 | 0.013 |
| B2 | Bond 2 - Year 2 | 187.856 | 0.000 | 0.000 | 0.013 | 0.020 |
| B3 | Bond 3 - Year 3 | 228.188 | 0.000 | 0.000 | 0.023 | 0.750 |
| S1 | Savings Year 1 | 636.148 | 0.000 | 0.000 | 0.110 | 0.055 |
| S2 | Savings Year 2 | 501.606 | 0.000 | 0.000 | 0.143 | 0.057 |
| S3 | Savings Year 3 | 349.682 | 0.000 | 0.000 | 0.211 | 0.059 |
| S4 | Savings Year 4 | 182.681 | 0.000 | 0.000 | 0.414 | 0.061 |
| S5 | Savings Year 5 | 0.000 | 0.064 | 0.000 | 1E+30 | 0.064 |
| S6 | Savings Year 6 | 0.000 | 0.013 | 0.000 | 1E+30 | 0.013 |
| S7 | Savings Year 7 | 0.000 | 0.021 | 0.000 | 1E+30 | 0.021 |
| S8 | Savings Year 8 | 0.000 | 0.671 | 0.000 | 1E+30 | 0.671 |

**WEB** file

Hewlitt

Constraints

| Constraint Number | Name | Final Value | Shadow Price | Constraint R.H. Side | Allowable Increase | Allowable Decrease |
|---|---|---|---|---|---|---|
| 1 | Year 1 Flow | 430.000 | 1.000 | 430.000 | 1E+30 | 1728.794 |
| 2 | Year 2 Flow | 210.000 | 0.962 | 210.000 | 1E+30 | 661.594 |
| 3 | Year 3 Flow | 222.000 | 0.925 | 222.000 | 1E+30 | 521.670 |
| 4 | Year 4 Flow | 231.000 | 0.889 | 231.000 | 1E+30 | 363.669 |
| 5 | Year 5 Flow | 240.000 | 0.855 | 240.000 | 1E+30 | 189.988 |
| 6 | Year 6 Flow | 195.000 | 0.760 | 195.000 | 2149.928 | 157.856 |
| 7 | Year 7 Flow | 225.000 | 0.719 | 225.000 | 3027.962 | 198.188 |
| 8 | Year 8 Flow | 255.000 | 0.671 | 255.000 | 1583.882 | 255.000 |

© Cengage Learning 2013

the par value plus interest available at the beginning of year 7. In addition, bond 3 matures at the end of year 7 and has the par value plus interest available at the beginning of year 8.

Finally, note that a variable $S_8$ appears in the constraint for year 8. The retirement fund obligation will be completed at the beginning of year 8, so we anticipate that $S_8$ will be zero and no funds will be put into savings. However, the formulation includes $S_8$ in the event that the bond income plus interest from the savings in year 7 exceed the 255 cash requirement for year 8. Thus, $S_8$ is a surplus variable that shows any funds remaining after the eight-year cash requirements have been satisfied.

The optimal solution and sensitivity report based on Excel Solver is shown in Figure 9.4. With an objective function value of $F = 1728.794$, the total investment required to meet the retirement plan's eight-year obligation is $1,728,794. Using the current prices of $1150, $1000, and $1350 for each of the bonds, respectively, we can summarize the initial investments in the three bonds as follows:

| Bond | Units Purchased | Investment Amount |
|---|---|---|
| 1 | $B_1 = 144.988$ | $1150(144.988) = \$166,736$ |
| 2 | $B_2 = 187.856$ | $1000(187.856) = \$187,856$ |
| 3 | $B_3 = 228.188$ | $1350(228.188) = \$308,054$ |

The solution also shows that \$636,148 (see $S_1$) will be placed in savings at the beginning of the first year. By starting with \$1,728,794, the company can make the specified bond and savings investments and have enough left over to meet the retirement program's first-year cash requirement of \$430,000.

The optimal solution in Figure 9.4 shows that the decision variables $S_1$, $S_2$, $S_3$, and $S_4$ all are greater than zero, indicating that investments in savings are required in each of the first four years. However, interest from the bonds plus the bond maturity incomes will be sufficient to cover the retirement program's cash requirements in years 5 through 8.

*In this application, the shadow price can be thought of as the present value of each dollar in the cash requirement. For example, each dollar that must be paid in year 8 has a present value of \$0.671.*

The shadow prices have an interesting interpretation in this application. Each right-hand-side value corresponds to the payment that must be made in that year. Note that the shadow prices are positive, indicating that increasing the requirements in any year causes the needed cash to increase. However, *reducing* the payment in any year would be beneficial because the total funds required for the retirement program's obligation would be less. Note that the shadow prices show that reductions in required funds are more beneficial in the early years, with decreasing benefits in subsequent years. As a result, Hewlitt would benefit by reducing cash requirements in the early years even if it had to make equivalently larger cash payments in later years.

## NOTES AND COMMENTS

1. The optimal solution for the Hewlitt Corporation problem shows fractional numbers of government bonds at 144.988, 187.856, and 228.188 units, respectively. However, fractional bond units usually are not available. If we were conservative and rounded up to 145, 188, and 229 units, respectively, the total funds required for the eight-year retirement program obligation would be approximately \$1254 more than the total funds indicated by the objective function. Because of the magnitude of the funds involved, rounding up probably would provide a workable solution. If an optimal integer solution were required, the methods of integer linear programming covered in Chapter 11 would have to be used.

2. We implicitly assumed that interest from the government bonds is paid annually. Investments such as treasury notes actually provide interest payments every six months. In such cases, the model can be reformulated using six-month periods, with interest and/or cash payments occurring every six months.

## 9.3 Operations Management Applications

Linear programming applications developed for production and operations management include scheduling, staffing, inventory control, and capacity planning. In this section we describe examples of make-or-buy decisions, production scheduling, and workforce assignments.

### A Make-or-Buy Decision

We illustrate the use of a linear programming model to determine how much of each of several component parts a company should manufacture and how much it should purchase from an outside supplier. Such a decision is referred to as a make-or-buy decision.

The Janders Company markets various business and engineering products. Currently, Janders is preparing to introduce two new calculators: one for the business market, called the Financial Manager, and one for the engineering market, called the Technician. Each calculator has three components: a base, an electronic cartridge, and a faceplate or top. The same base is used for both calculators, but the cartridges and tops are different. All

**TABLE 9.5** MANUFACTURING COSTS AND PURCHASE PRICES FOR JANDERS CALCULATOR COMPONENTS

| | Cost per Unit | |
| | Manufacture | |
| Component | (regular time) | Purchase |
|---|---|---|
| Base | $0.50 | $0.60 |
| Financial cartridge | $3.75 | $4.00 |
| Technician cartridge | $3.30 | $3.90 |
| Financial top | $0.60 | $0.65 |
| Technician top | $0.75 | $0.78 |

© Cengage Learning 2013

components can be manufactured by the company or purchased from outside suppliers. The manufacturing costs and purchase prices for the components are summarized in Table 9.5.

Company forecasters indicate that 3000 Financial Manager calculators and 2000 Technician calculators will be needed. However, manufacturing capacity is limited. The company has 200 hours of regular manufacturing time and 50 hours of overtime that can be scheduled for the calculators. Overtime involves a premium at the additional cost of $9 per hour. Table 9.6 shows manufacturing times (in minutes) for the components.

The problem for Janders is to determine how many units of each component to manufacture and how many units of each component to purchase. We define the decision variables as follows:

$$BM = \text{number of bases manufactured}$$
$$BP = \text{number of bases purchased}$$
$$FCM = \text{number of Financial cartridges manufactured}$$
$$FCP = \text{number of Financial cartridges purchased}$$
$$TCM = \text{number of Technician cartridges manufactured}$$
$$TCP = \text{number of Technician cartridges purchased}$$
$$FTM = \text{number of Financial tops manufactured}$$
$$FTP = \text{number of Financial tops purchased}$$
$$TTM = \text{number of Technician tops manufactured}$$
$$TTP = \text{number of Technician tops purchased}$$

One additional decision variable is needed to determine the hours of overtime that must be scheduled:

$$OT = \text{number of hours of overtime to be scheduled}$$

**TABLE 9.6** MANUFACTURING TIMES IN MINUTES PER UNIT FOR JANDERS CALCULATOR COMPONENTS

| Component | Manufacturing Time |
|---|---|
| Base | 1.0 |
| Financial cartridge | 3.0 |
| Technician cartridge | 2.5 |
| Financial top | 1.0 |
| Technician top | 1.5 |

© Cengage Learning 2013

The objective function is to minimize the total cost, including manufacturing costs, purchase costs, and overtime costs. Using the cost-per-unit data in Table 9.5 and the overtime premium cost rate of $9 per hour, we write the objective function as

$$\text{Min} \quad 0.5BM + 0.6BP + 3.75FCM + 4FCP + 3.3TCM + 3.9TCP + 0.6FTM$$
$$+ \ 0.65FTP + 0.75TTM + 0.78TTP + 9OT$$

The first five constraints specify the number of each component needed to satisfy the demand for 3000 Financial Manager calculators and 2000 Technician calculators. A total of 5000 base components are needed, with the number of other components depending on the demand for the particular calculator. The five demand constraints are

$$
\begin{array}{llll}
BM + BP & = 5000 & \text{Bases} \\
FCM + FCP & = 3000 & \text{Financial cartridges} \\
TCM + TCP & = 2000 & \text{Technician cartridges} \\
FTM + FTP & = 3000 & \text{Financial tops} \\
TTM + TTP & = 2000 & \text{Technician tops}
\end{array}
$$

Two constraints are needed to guarantee that manufacturing capacities for regular time and overtime cannot be exceeded. The first constraint limits overtime capacity to 50 hours, or

$$OT \le 50$$

The second constraint states that the total manufacturing time required for all components must be less than or equal to the total manufacturing capacity, including regular time plus overtime. The manufacturing times for the components are expressed in minutes, so we state the total manufacturing capacity constraint in minutes, with the 200 hours of regular time capacity becoming $60(200) = 12{,}000$ minutes. The actual overtime required is unknown at this point, so we write the overtime as $60OT$ minutes. Using the manufacturing times from Table 9.6, we have

$$BM + 3FCM + 2.5TCM + FTM + 1.5TTM \le 12{,}000 + 60OT$$

Moving the decision variable for overtime to the left-hand side of the constraint provides the manufacturing capacity constraint:

$$BM + 3FCM + 2.5TCM + FTM + 1.5TTM - 60OT \le 12{,}000$$

The complete formulation of the Janders make-or-buy problem with all decision variables greater than or equal to zero is

Min   $0.5BM + 0.6BP + 3.75FCM + 4FCP + 3.3TCM + 3.9TCP$
        $+ 0.6FTM + 0.65FTP + 0.75TTM + 0.78TTP + 9OT$

s.t.

$$
\begin{array}{llll}
BM & + & BP = & 5000 & \text{Bases} \\
FCM & + & FCP = & 3000 & \text{Financial cartridges} \\
TCM & + & TCP = & 2000 & \text{Technician cartridges} \\
FTM & + & FTP = & 3000 & \text{Financial tops} \\
TTM & + & TTP = & 2000 & \text{Technician tops} \\
& & OT \le & 50 & \text{Overtime hours} \\
\end{array}
$$
$$BM + 3FCM + 2.5TCM + FTM + 1.5TTM - 60OT \le 12{,}000 \quad \text{Manufacturing capacity}$$

**FIGURE 9.5**   SENSITIVITY REPORT FOR THE JANDERS MAKE-OR-BUY PROBLEM

**Janders**

Variable Cells

| Model Variable | Name | Final Value | Reduced Cost | Objective Coefficient | Allowable Increase | Allowable Decrease |
|---|---|---|---|---|---|---|
| BM | Base Make | 5000.000 | 0.000 | 0.500 | 0.017 | 1E+30 |
| BP | Base Purchase | 0.000 | 0.017 | 0.600 | 1E+30 | 0.017 |
| FCM | Fin. Cart. Make | 666.667 | 0.000 | 3.750 | 0.100 | 0.050 |
| FCP | Fin. Cart. Purchase | 2333.333 | 0.000 | 4.000 | 0.050 | 0.100 |
| TCM | Tech. Cart. Make | 2000.000 | 0.000 | 3.300 | 0.392 | 1E+30 |
| TCP | Tech. Cart. Purchase | 0.000 | 0.392 | 3.900 | 1E+30 | 0.392 |
| FTM | Fin. Top Make | 0.000 | 0.033 | 0.600 | 1E+30 | 0.033 |
| FTP | Fin. Top Purchase | 3000.000 | 0.000 | 0.650 | 0.033 | 1E+30 |
| TTM | Tech. Top Make | 0.000 | 0.095 | 0.750 | 1E+30 | 0.095 |
| TTP | Tech. Top Purchase | 2000.000 | 0.000 | 0.780 | 0.095 | 1E+30 |
| OT | Overtime Used | 0.000 | 4.000 | 9.000 | 1E+30 | 4.000 |

Constraints

| Constraint Number | Name | Final Value | Shadow Price | Constraint R.H. Side | Allowable Increase | Allowable Decrease |
|---|---|---|---|---|---|---|
| 1 | Base Available | 5000.0000 | 0.583 | 5000.000 | 2000.000 | 5000.000 |
| 2 | Fin. Cart. Available | 3000.0000 | 4.000 | 3000.000 | 1E+30 | 2333.333 |
| 3 | Tech. Cart. Available | 2000.0000 | 3.508 | 2000.000 | 800.000 | 2000.000 |
| 4 | Fin. Top Available | 3000.0000 | 0.650 | 3000.000 | 1E+30 | 3000.000 |
| 5 | Tech. Top Available | 2000.0000 | 0.780 | 2000.000 | 1E+30 | 2000.000 |
| 6 | Overtime Time Used | 0.0000 | 0.000 | 0.000 | 1E+30 | 50.000 |
| 7 | Mfg. Time Time Used | 12000.0000 | −0.083 | 0.000 | 7000.000 | 2000.000 |

© Cengage Learning 2013

The sensitivity report based on Excel Solver for this 11-variable, 7-constraint linear program is shown in Figure 9.5. The optimal solution indicates that all 5000 bases (*BM*), 666.67 Financial Manager cartridges (*FCM*), and 2000 Technician cartridges (*TCM*) should be manufactured. The remaining 2333.333 Financial Manager cartridges (*FCP*), all the Financial Manager tops (*FTP*), and all Technician tops (*TTP*) should be purchased. No overtime manufacturing is necessary. This plan results in a total cost of 0.5(5000) + 0.6(0) + 3.75(666.67) + 4(2333.333) + 3.3(2000) + 3.9(0) + 0.6(0) + 0.65(3000) + 0.75(0) + 0.78(2000) + 9(0) = $24,443.33.

*The same units of measure must be used for both the left-hand side and right-hand side of the constraint. In this case, minutes are used.*

Sensitivity analysis provides some additional information about the unused overtime capacity. The Reduced Costs column shows that the overtime (*OT*) premium would have to decrease by $4 per hour before overtime production should be considered. That is, if the overtime premium is $9 − $4 = $5 or less, Janders may want to replace some of the purchased components with components manufactured on overtime.

The shadow price for the manufacturing capacity constraint time (constraint 7) is −0.083. This price indicates that an additional hour of manufacturing capacity is worth $0.083 per minute or ($0.083)(60) = $5 per hour. The right-hand-side range for constraint 7 shows that this conclusion is valid until the amount of regular time increases to 19,000 minutes, or 316.7 hours.

Sensitivity analysis also indicates that a change in prices charged by the outside suppliers can affect the optimal solution. For instance, the objective coefficient range for *BP* is 0.600 − 0.017 = 0.583 to no upper limit. If the purchase price for bases remains at $0.583

or more, the number of bases purchased (*BP*) will remain at zero. However, if the purchase price drops below \$0.583, Janders should begin to purchase rather than manufacture the base component. Similar sensitivity analysis conclusions about the purchase price ranges can be drawn for the other components.

## NOTES AND COMMENTS

1. The proper interpretation of the shadow price for manufacturing capacity (constraint 7) in the Janders problem is that an additional hour of manufacturing capacity is worth (\$0.083)(60) = \$5 per hour. Thus, the company should be willing to pay a premium of \$5 per hour over and above the current regular time cost per hour, which is already included in the manufacturing cost of the product. Thus, if the regular time cost is \$18 per hour, Janders should be willing to pay up to \$18 + \$5 = \$23 per hour to obtain additional labor capacity.

## Production Scheduling

One of the most important applications of linear programming deals with multiperiod planning such as production scheduling. The solution to a production scheduling problem enables the manager to establish an efficient low-cost production schedule for one or more products over several time periods (weeks or months). Essentially, a production scheduling problem can be viewed as a product-mix problem for each of several periods in the future. The manager must determine the production levels that will allow the company to meet product demand requirements, given limitations on production capacity, labor capacity, and storage space, while minimizing total production costs.

One advantage of using linear programming for production scheduling problems is that they recur. A production schedule must be established for the current month, then again for the next month, for the month after that, and so on. When looking at the problem each month, the production manager will find that, although demand for the products has changed, production times, production capacities, storage space limitations, and so on are roughly the same. Thus, the production manager is basically re-solving the same problem handled in previous months, and a general linear programming model of the production scheduling procedure may be frequently applied. Once the model has been formulated, the manager can simply supply the data—demand, capacities, and so on—for the given production period and use the linear programming model repeatedly to develop the production schedule. The Q.M. in Action, Optimizing Production of Flight Manuals at Jeppesen Sanderson, Inc., describes how linear programming is used to minimize the cost of producing weekly revisions to flight manuals.

**Q.M.** *in* ACTION

### OPTIMIZING PRODUCTION OF FLIGHT MANUALS AT JEPPESEN SANDERSON, INC.*

Jeppesen Sanderson, Inc., manufactures and distributes flight manuals that contain safety information to more than 300,000 pilots and 4000 airlines. Every week Jeppesen mails between 5 and 30 million pages of chart revisions to 200,000 customers worldwide and receives about 1500 new orders each week. In the late 1990s, its customer service deteriorated as its existing production and supporting systems failed to keep up with this level of activity. To meet customer service goals, Jeppesen turned to optimization-based decision support tools for production planning.

*Based on E. Katok, W. Tarantino, and R. Tiedman, "Improving Performance and Flexibility at Jeppesen: The World's Leading Aviation-Information Company," *Interfaces* (January/February 2001): 7–29.

(*continued*)

Jeppesen developed a large-scale linear program called Scheduler to minimize the cost of producing the weekly revisions. Model constraints included capacity constraints and numerous internal business rules. The model includes 250,000 variables and 40,000–50,000 constraints. Immediately after introducing the model, Jeppesen established a new record for the number of consecutive weeks with 100% on-time revisions. Scheduler decreased tardiness of revisions from approximately 9% to 3% and dramatically improved customer satisfaction. Even more importantly, Scheduler provided a model of the production system for Jeppesen to use in strategic economic analysis. Overall, the use of optimization techniques at Jeppesen resulted in cost reductions of nearly 10% and a 24% increase in profit.

Let us consider the case of the Bollinger Electronics Company, which produces two different electronic components for a major airplane engine manufacturer. The airplane engine manufacturer notifies the Bollinger sales office each quarter of its monthly requirements for components for each of the next three months. The monthly requirements for the components may vary considerably depending on the type of engine the airplane engine manufacturer is producing. The order shown in Table 9.7 has just been received for the next three-month period.

After the order is processed, a demand statement is sent to the production control department. The production control department must then develop a three-month production plan for the components. In arriving at the desired schedule, the production manager will want to identify the following:

1. Total production cost
2. Inventory holding cost
3. Change-in-production-level costs

In the remainder of this section, we show how to formulate a linear programming model of the production and inventory process for Bollinger Electronics to minimize the total cost.

To develop the model, we let $x_{im}$ denote the production volume in units for product $i$ in month $m$. Here $i = 1, 2$, and $m = 1, 2, 3$; $i = 1$ refers to component 322A, $i = 2$ refers to component 802B, $m = 1$ refers to April, $m = 2$ refers to May, and $m = 3$ refers to June. The purpose of the double subscript is to provide a more descriptive notation. We could simply use $x_6$ to represent the number of units of product 2 produced in month 3, but $x_{23}$ is more descriptive, identifying directly the product and month represented by the variable.

If component 322A costs $20 per unit produced and component 802B costs $10 per unit produced, the total production cost part of the objective function is

$$\text{Total production cost} = 20x_{11} + 20x_{12} + 20x_{13} + 10x_{21} + 10x_{22} + 10x_{23}$$

Because the production cost per unit is the same each month, we don't need to include the production costs in the objective function; that is, regardless of the production schedule selected, the total production cost will remain the same. In other words, production costs are not relevant costs for the production scheduling decision under consideration. In cases in which the production cost per unit is expected to change each month, the variable

**TABLE 9.7**    THREE-MONTH DEMAND SCHEDULE FOR BOLLINGER ELECTRONICS COMPANY

| Component | April | May | June |
|---|---|---|---|
| 322A | 1000 | 3000 | 5000 |
| 802B | 1000 | 500 | 3000 |

production costs per unit per month must be included in the objective function. The solution for the Bollinger Electronics problem will be the same regardless of whether these costs are included; therefore, we included them so that the value of the linear programming objective function will include all the costs associated with the problem.

To incorporate the relevant inventory holding costs into the model, we let $s_{im}$ denote the inventory level for product $i$ at the end of month $m$. Bollinger determined that on a monthly basis, inventory holding costs are 1.5% of the cost of the product; that is, $(0.015)(\$20) = \$0.30$ per unit for component 322A and $(0.015)(\$10) = \$0.15$ per unit for component 802B. A common assumption made in using the linear programming approach to production scheduling is that monthly ending inventories are an acceptable approximation to the average inventory levels throughout the month. Making this assumption, we write the inventory holding cost portion of the objective function as

$$\text{Inventory holding cost} = 0.30s_{11} + 0.30s_{12} + 0.30s_{13} + 0.15s_{21} + 0.15s_{22} + 0.15s_{23}$$

To incorporate the costs of fluctuations in production levels from month to month, we need to define two additional variables:

$$I_m = \text{increase in the total production level necessary during month } m$$
$$D_m = \text{decrease in the total production level necessary during month } m$$

After estimating the effects of employee layoffs, turnovers, reassignment training costs, and other costs associated with fluctuating production levels, Bollinger estimates that the cost associated with increasing the production level for any month is $0.50 per unit increase. A similar cost associated with decreasing the production level for any month is $0.20 per unit. Thus, we write the third portion of the objective function as

$$\text{Change-in-production-level costs} = 0.50I_1 + 0.50I_2 + 0.50I_3$$
$$+ 0.20D_1 + 0.20D_2 + 0.20D_3$$

Note that the cost associated with changes in production level is a function of the change in the total number of units produced in month $m$ compared to the total number of units produced in month $m - 1$. In other production scheduling applications, fluctuations in production level might be measured in terms of machine-hours or labor-hours required rather than in terms of the total number of units produced.

Combining all three costs, the complete objective function becomes

$$\begin{aligned}
\text{Min} \quad & 20x_{11} + 20x_{12} + 20x_{13} + 10x_{21} + 10x_{22} + 10x_{23} + 0.30s_{11} \\
& + 0.30s_{12} + 0.30s_{13} + 0.15s_{21} + 0.15s_{22} + 0.15s_{23} + 0.50I_1 \\
& + 0.50I_2 + 0.50I_3 + 0.20D_1 + 0.20D_2 + 0.20D_3
\end{aligned}$$

We now consider the constraints. First, we must guarantee that the schedule meets customer demand. Because the units shipped can come from the current month's production or from inventory carried over from previous months, the demand requirement takes the form

$$\begin{pmatrix} \text{Ending} \\ \text{inventory} \\ \text{from previous} \\ \text{month} \end{pmatrix} + \begin{pmatrix} \text{Current} \\ \text{production} \end{pmatrix} - \begin{pmatrix} \text{Ending} \\ \text{inventory} \\ \text{for this} \\ \text{month} \end{pmatrix} = \begin{pmatrix} \text{This month's} \\ \text{demand} \end{pmatrix}$$

Suppose that the inventories at the beginning of the three-month scheduling period were 500 units for component 322A and 200 units for component 802B. The demand for both products in the first month (April) was 1000 units, so the constraints for meeting demand in the first month become

$$500 + x_{11} - s_{11} = 1000$$
$$200 + x_{21} - s_{21} = 1000$$

Moving the constants to the right-hand side, we have

$$x_{11} - s_{11} = 500$$
$$x_{21} - s_{21} = 800$$

Similarly, we need demand constraints for both products in the second and third months. We write them as follows:

**Month 2**

$$s_{11} + x_{12} - s_{12} = 3000$$
$$s_{21} + x_{22} - s_{22} = 500$$

**Month 3**

$$s_{12} + x_{13} - s_{13} = 5000$$
$$s_{22} + x_{23} - s_{23} = 3000$$

If the company specifies a minimum inventory level at the end of the three-month period of at least 400 units of component 322A and at least 200 units of component 802B, we can add the constraints

$$s_{13} \geq 400$$
$$s_{23} \geq 200$$

Suppose that we have the additional information on machine, labor, and storage capacity shown in Table 9.8. Machine, labor, and storage space requirements are given in Table 9.9. To reflect these limitations, the following constraints are necessary:

**TABLE 9.8**  MACHINE, LABOR, AND STORAGE CAPACITIES FOR BOLLINGER ELECTRONICS

| Month | Machine Capacity (hours) | Labor Capacity (hours) | Storage Capacity (square feet) |
|-------|--------------------------|------------------------|--------------------------------|
| April | 400 | 300 | 10,000 |
| May | 500 | 300 | 10,000 |
| June | 600 | 300 | 10,000 |

© Cengage Learning 2013

**TABLE 9.9**  MACHINE, LABOR, AND STORAGE REQUIREMENTS FOR COMPONENTS 322A AND 802B

| Component | Machine (hours/unit) | Labor (hours/unit) | Storage (square feet/unit) |
|-----------|----------------------|--------------------|----------------------------|
| 322A | 0.10 | 0.05 | 2 |
| 802B | 0.08 | 0.07 | 3 |

## Machine Capacity

$$0.10x_{11} + 0.08x_{21} \leq 400 \quad \text{Month 1}$$
$$0.10x_{12} + 0.08x_{22} \leq 500 \quad \text{Month 2}$$
$$0.10x_{13} + 0.08x_{23} \leq 600 \quad \text{Month 3}$$

## Labor Capacity

$$0.05x_{11} + 0.07x_{21} \leq 300 \quad \text{Month 1}$$
$$0.05x_{12} + 0.07x_{22} \leq 300 \quad \text{Month 2}$$
$$0.05x_{13} + 0.07x_{23} \leq 300 \quad \text{Month 3}$$

## Storage Capacity

$$2s_{11} + 3s_{21} \leq 10{,}000 \quad \text{Month 1}$$
$$2s_{12} + 3s_{22} \leq 10{,}000 \quad \text{Month 2}$$
$$2s_{13} + 3s_{23} \leq 10{,}000 \quad \text{Month 3}$$

One final set of constraints must be added to guarantee that $I_m$ and $D_m$ will reflect the increase or decrease in the total production level for month $m$. Suppose that the production levels for March, the month before the start of the current production scheduling period, had been 1500 units of component 322A and 1000 units of component 802B for a total production level of $1500 + 1000 = 2500$ units. We can find the amount of the change in production for April from the relationship

$$\text{April production} - \text{March production} = \text{Change}$$

Using the April production variables, $x_{11}$ and $x_{21}$, and the March production of 2500 units, we have

$$(x_{11} + x_{21}) - 2500 = \text{Change}$$

Note that the change can be positive or negative. A positive change reflects an increase in the total production level, and a negative change reflects a decrease in the total production level. We can use the increase in production for April, $I_1$, and the decrease in production for April, $D_1$, to specify the constraint for the change in total production for the month of April:

$$(x_{11} + x_{21}) - 2500 = I_1 - D_1$$

Of course, we cannot have an increase in production and a decrease in production during the same one-month period; thus, either $I_1$ or $D_1$ will be zero. If April requires 3000 units of production, $I_1 = 500$ and $D_1 = 0$. If April requires 2200 units of production, $I_1 = 0$ and $D_1 = 300$. This approach of denoting the change in production level as the difference between two nonnegative variables, $I_1$ and $D_1$, permits both positive and negative changes in the total production level. If a single variable (say, $c_m$) had been used to represent the change in production level, only positive changes would be possible because of the nonnegativity requirement.

Using the same approach in May and June (always subtracting the previous month's total production from the current month's total production), we obtain the constraints for the second and third months of the production scheduling period:

$$(x_{12} + x_{22}) - (x_{11} + x_{21}) = I_2 - D_2$$
$$(x_{13} + x_{23}) - (x_{12} + x_{22}) = I_3 - D_3$$

Placing the variables on the left-hand side and the constants on the right-hand side yields the complete set of what are commonly referred to as production-smoothing constraints:

$$
\begin{aligned}
x_{11} + x_{21} & & - I_1 + D_1 = 2500 \\
-x_{11} - x_{21} + x_{12} + x_{22} & & - I_2 + D_2 = 0 \\
-x_{12} - x_{22} + x_{13} + x_{23} & - I_3 + D_3 = 0
\end{aligned}
$$

The initially small, two-product, three-month scheduling problem has now developed into an 18-variable, 20-constraint linear programming problem. Note that in this problem we were concerned only with one type of machine process, one type of labor, and one type of storage area. Actual production scheduling problems usually involve several machine types, several labor grades, and/or several storage areas, requiring large-scale linear programs. For instance, a problem involving 100 products over a 12-month period could have more than 1000 variables and constraints.

*Problem 19 involves a production scheduling application with labor-smoothing constraints.*

Figure 9.6 shows the optimal solution to the Bollinger Electronics production scheduling problem. Table 9.10 contains a portion of the managerial report based on the optimal solution.

Consider the monthly variation in the production and inventory schedule shown in Table 9.10. Recall that the inventory cost for component 802B is one-half the inventory cost

**TABLE 9.10**   MINIMUM COST PRODUCTION SCHEDULE INFORMATION FOR THE BOLLINGER ELECTRONICS PROBLEM

| Activity | April | May | June |
|---|---|---|---|
| Production | | | |
|     Component 322A | 500 | 3200 | 5200 |
|     Component 802B | 2500 | 2000 | 0 |
|      Totals | 3000 | 5200 | 5200 |
| Ending inventory | | | |
|     Component 322A | 0 | 200 | 400 |
|     Component 802B | 1700 | 3200 | 200 |
| Machine usage | | | |
|     Scheduled hours | 250 | 480 | 520 |
|     Slack capacity hours | 150 | 20 | 80 |
| Labor usage | | | |
|     Scheduled hours | 200 | 300 | 260 |
|     Slack capacity hours | 100 | 0 | 40 |
| Storage usage | | | |
|     Scheduled storage | 5100 | 10,000 | 1400 |
|     Slack capacity | 4900 | 0 | 8600 |
| Total production, inventory, and production-smoothing cost = $225,295 | | | |

**FIGURE 9.6**   SENSITIVITY REPORT FOR THE BOLLINGER ELECTRONICS PROBLEM

Variable Cells

| Model Variable | Name | Final Value | Reduced Cost | Objective Coefficient | Allowable Increase | Allowable Decrease |
|---|---|---|---|---|---|---|
| X11 | 322A April Production | 500.000 | 0.000 | 20.000 | 1E+30 | 0.172 |
| X12 | 322A May Production | 3200.000 | 0.000 | 20.000 | 0.093 | 0.100 |
| X13 | 322A June Production | 5200.000 | 0.000 | 20.000 | 0.100 | 0.093 |
| S11 | 322A April Ending Inv | 0.000 | 0.172 | 0.300 | 1E+30 | 0.172 |
| S12 | 322A May Ending Inv | 200.000 | 0.000 | 0.300 | 0.093 | 0.100 |
| S13 | 322A June Ending Inv | 400.000 | 0.000 | 0.300 | 1E+30 | 20.728 |
| X21 | 802B April Production | 2500.000 | 0.000 | 10.000 | 0.130 | 0.050 |
| X22 | 802B May Production | 2000.000 | 0.000 | 10.000 | 0.050 | 0.130 |
| X23 | 802B June Production | 0.000 | 0.128 | 10.000 | 1E+30 | 0.128 |
| S21 | 802B April Ending Inv | 1700.000 | 0.000 | 0.150 | 0.130 | 0.050 |
| S22 | 802B May Ending Inv | 3200.000 | 0.000 | 0.150 | 0.128 | 10.450 |
| S23 | 802B June Ending Inv | 200.000 | 0.000 | 0.150 | 1E+30 | 10.450 |
| I1 | Increase April | 500.000 | 0.000 | 0.500 | 0.130 | 0.050 |
| I2 | Increase May | 2200.000 | 0.000 | 0.500 | 0.033 | 0.192 |
| I3 | Increase June | 0.000 | 0.072 | 0.500 | 1E+30 | 0.072 |
| D1 | Decrease April | 0.000 | 0.700 | 0.200 | 1E+30 | 0.700 |
| D2 | Decrease May | 0.000 | 0.700 | 0.200 | 1E+30 | 0.700 |
| D3 | Decrease June | 0.000 | 0.628 | 0.200 | 1E+30 | 0.628 |

Constraints

| Constraint Number | Name | Final Value | Shadow Price | Constraint R.H. Side | Allowable Increase | Allowable Decrease |
|---|---|---|---|---|---|---|
| 1 | 322A/April Balance Equation | 1000.000 | 20.000 | 1000.000 | 1500.000 | 500.000 |
| 2 | 802B/April Balance Equation | 1000.000 | 10.000 | 1000.000 | 1428.571 | 500.000 |
| 3 | 322A/May Balance Equation | 3000.000 | 20.128 | 3000.000 | 600.000 | 0.000 |
| 4 | 802B/May Balance Equation | 500.000 | 10.150 | 500.000 | 1428.571 | 500.000 |
| 5 | 322A/June Balance Equation | 5000.000 | 20.428 | 5000.000 | 0.000 | 257.143 |
| 6 | 802B/June Balance Equation | 3000.000 | 10.300 | 3000.000 | 0.000 | 500.000 |
| 7 | 322A Ending Inventory | 400.000 | 20.728 | 400.000 | 0.000 | 257.143 |
| 8 | 802B Ending Inventory | 200.000 | 10.450 | 200.000 | 0.000 | 200.000 |
| 9 | Mach/Apr Used | 250.000 | 0.000 | 400.000 | 1E+30 | 150.000 |
| 10 | Mach/May Used | 480.000 | 0.000 | 500.000 | 1E+30 | 20.000 |
| 11 | Mach/June Used | 520.000 | 0.000 | 600.000 | 1E+30 | 80.000 |
| 12 | Labor/Apr Used | 200.000 | 0.000 | 300.000 | 1E+30 | 100.000 |
| 13 | Labor/May Used | 300.000 | −1.111 | 300.000 | 18.000 | 1.00044E-13 |
| 14 | Labor/June Used | 260.000 | 0.000 | 300.000 | 1E+30 | 40.000 |
| 15 | Storage/Apr Used | 5100.000 | 0.000 | 10000.000 | 1E+30 | 4900.000 |
| 16 | Storage/May Used | 10000.000 | 0.000 | 10000.000 | 1E+30 | 0.000 |
| 17 | Storage/June Used | 1400.000 | 0.000 | 10000.000 | 1E+30 | 8600.000 |
| 18 | April Difference | 500.000 | −0.500 | 0.000 | 500.000 | 1E+30 |
| 19 | May Difference | 2200.000 | −0.500 | 0.000 | 2200.000 | 1E+30 |
| 20 | June Difference | 0.000 | −0.428 | 0.000 | 257.143 | 0.000 |

WEB file

**Bollinger**

© Cengage Learning 2013

*Linear programming models for production scheduling are often very large. Thousands of decision variables and constraints are necessary when the problem involves numerous products, machines, and time periods. Data collection for large-scale models can be more time-consuming than either the formulation of the model or the development of the computer solution.*

for component 322A. Therefore, as might be expected, component 802B is produced heavily in the first month (April) and then held in inventory for the demand that will occur in future months. Component 322A tends to be produced when needed, and only small amounts are carried in inventory.

The costs of increasing and decreasing the total production volume tend to smooth the monthly variations. In fact, the minimum-cost schedule calls for a 500-unit increase in total production in April and a 2200-unit increase in total production in May. The May production level of 5200 units is then maintained during June.

The machine usage section of the report shows ample machine capacity in all three months. However, labor capacity is at full utilization in the month of May (see constraint 13 in Figure 9.6). The shadow price shows that an additional hour of labor capacity in May will decrease the optimal cost by approximately $1.11.

A linear programming model of a two-product, three-month production system can provide valuable information in terms of identifying a minimum-cost production schedule. In larger production systems, where the number of variables and constraints is too large to track manually, linear programming models can provide a significant advantage in developing cost-saving production schedules. The Q.M. in Action, Optimizing Production, Inventory, and Distribution at the Kellogg Company, illustrates the use of a large-scale multiperiod linear program for production planning and distribution.

## Workforce Assignment

Workforce assignment problems frequently occur when production managers must make decisions involving staffing requirements for a given planning period. Workforce assignments often have some flexibility, and at least some personnel can be assigned to more than one department or work center. Such is the case when employees have been cross-trained on two or more jobs or, for instance, when sales personnel can be transferred between stores. In the following application, we show how linear programming can be used to determine not only an optimal product mix, but also an optimal workforce assignment.

McCormick Manufacturing Company produces two products with contributions to profit per unit of $10 and $9, respectively. The labor requirements per unit produced and the total hours of labor available from personnel assigned to each of four departments are shown in Table 9.11. Assuming that the number of hours available in each department is fixed, we can formulate McCormick's problem as a standard product-mix linear program with the following decision variables:

$$P_1 = \text{units of product 1}$$
$$P_2 = \text{units of product 2}$$

---

**Q.M.** *in* ACTION

*OPTIMIZING PRODUCTION, INVENTORY, AND DISTRIBUTION AT THE KELLOGG COMPANY\**

The Kellogg Company is the largest cereal producer in the world and a leading producer of convenience foods,

*Based on G. Brown, J. Keegan, B. Vigus, and K. Wood, "The Kellogg Company Optimizes Production, Inventory, and Distribution," Interfaces* (November/December 2001): 1–15.

such as Kellogg's Pop-Tarts and Nutri-Grain cereal bars. Kellogg produces more than 40 different cereals at plants in 19 countries, on six continents. The company markets its products in more than 160 countries and employs more than 15,600 people in its worldwide organization.

*(continued)*

In the cereal business alone, Kellogg coordinates the production of about 80 products using a total of approximately 90 production lines and 180 packaging lines.

Kellogg has a long history of using linear programming for production planning and distribution. The Kellogg Planning System (KPS) is a large-scale, multi-period linear program. The operational version of KPS makes production, packaging, inventory, and distribution decisions on a weekly basis. The primary objective of the system is to minimize the total cost of meeting estimated demand; to deal with constraints involving processing line capacities and packaging line capacities; and to satisfy safety stock requirements.

A tactical version of KPS helps to establish plant budgets and make capacity-expansion and consolidation decisions on a monthly basis. The tactical version was recently used to guide a consolidation of production capacity that resulted in projected savings of \$35 to \$40 million per year. Because of the success Kellogg has had using KPS in its North American operations, the company is now introducing KPS into Latin America and is studying the development of a global KPS model.

The linear program is

$$\text{Max} \quad 10P_1 + 9P_2$$
$$\text{s.t.}$$
$$0.65P_1 + 0.95P_2 \leq 6500$$
$$0.45P_1 + 0.85P_2 \leq 6000$$
$$1.00P_1 + 0.70P_2 \leq 7000$$
$$0.15P_1 + 0.30P_2 \leq 1400$$
$$P_1, P_2 \geq 0$$

The answer report to the linear programming model is shown in Figure 9.7. The product mix calls for approximately 5744 units of product 1, 1795 units of product 2, and a total profit of \$73,590. With this optimal solution, departments 3 and 4 are operating at capacity, and departments 1 and 2 have a slack of approximately 1062 and 1890 hours, respectively. We would anticipate that the product mix would change and that the total profit would increase if the workforce assignment could be revised so that the slack, or unused hours, in departments 1 and 2 could be transferred to the departments currently working at capacity. However, the production manager may be uncertain as to how the workforce should be reallocated among the four departments. Let us expand the linear programming model to include decision variables that will help determine the optimal workforce assignment in addition to the profit-maximizing product mix.

**TABLE 9.11**  DEPARTMENTAL LABOR-HOURS PER UNIT AND TOTAL HOURS AVAILABLE FOR THE MCCORMICK MANUFACTURING COMPANY

| | Labor-Hours per Unit | | |
|---|---|---|---|
| **Department** | **Product 1** | **Product 2** | **Total Hours Available** |
| 1 | 0.65 | 0.95 | 6500 |
| 2 | 0.45 | 0.85 | 6000 |
| 3 | 1.00 | 0.70 | 7000 |
| 4 | 0.15 | 0.30 | 1400 |

**FIGURE 9.7**    ANSWER REPORT FOR THE McCORMICK MANUFACTURING COMPANY
PROBLEM WITH NO WORKFORCE TRANSFERS PERMITTED

**WEB file**

**McCormick**

Objective Cell (Max)

| Name | Original Value | Final Value |
|---|---|---|
| Max Profit | 0.000 | 73589.744 |

Variable Cells

| Model Variable | Name | Original Value | Final Value | Integer |
|---|---|---|---|---|
| P1 | Product 1 | 0.000 | 5743.590 | Contin |
| P2 | Product 2 | 0.000 | 1794.872 | Contin |

Constraints

| Constraint Number | Name | Cell Value | Status | Slack |
|---|---|---|---|---|
| 1 | Dept 1 Hours | 5438.462 | Not Binding | 1061.538 |
| 2 | Dept 2 Hours | 4110.256 | Not Binding | 1889.744 |
| 3 | Dept 3 Hours | 7000.000 | Binding | 0.000 |
| 4 | Dept 4 Hours | 1400.000 | Binding | 0.000 |

© Cengage Learning 2013

Suppose that McCormick has a cross-training program that enables some employees to be transferred between departments. By taking advantage of the cross-training skills, a limited number of employees and labor-hours may be transferred from one department to another. For example, suppose that the cross-training permits transfers as shown in Table 9.12. Row 1 of this table shows that some employees assigned to department 1 have cross-training skills that permit them to be transferred to department 2 or 3. The right-hand column shows that, for the current production planning period, a maximum of 400 hours can be transferred from department 1. Similar cross-training transfer capabilities and capacities are shown for departments 2, 3, and 4.

When workforce assignments are flexible, we do not automatically know how many hours of labor should be assigned to or be transferred from each department. We need to add decision variables to the linear programming model to account for such changes.

*The right-hand sides are now treated as decision variables.*

$b_i$ = the labor-hours allocated to department $i$ for $i$ = 1, 2, 3, and 4

$t_{ij}$ = the labor-hours transferred from department $i$ to department $j$

**TABLE 9.12**    CROSS-TRAINING ABILITY AND CAPACITY INFORMATION

| From Department | Cross-Training Transfers Permitted to Department | | | | Maximum Hours Transferable |
|---|---|---|---|---|---|
| | 1 | 2 | 3 | 4 | |
| 1 | — | yes | yes | — | 400 |
| 2 | — | — | yes | yes | 800 |
| 3 | — | — | — | yes | 100 |
| 4 | yes | yes | — | — | 200 |

© Cengage Learning 2013

With the addition of decision variables $b_1$, $b_2$, $b_3$, and $b_4$, we write the capacity restrictions for the four departments as follows:

$$0.65P_1 + 0.95P_2 \leq b_1$$
$$0.45P_1 + 0.85P_2 \leq b_2$$
$$1.00P_1 + 0.70P_2 \leq b_3$$
$$0.15P_1 + 0.30P_2 \leq b_4$$

Because $b_1$, $b_2$, $b_3$, and $b_4$ are now decision variables, we follow the standard practice of placing these variables on the left side of the inequalities, and the first four constraints of the linear programming model become

$$0.65P_1 + 0.95P_2 - b_1 \qquad\qquad\quad \leq 0$$
$$0.45P_1 + 0.85P_2 \qquad - b_2 \qquad\quad \leq 0$$
$$1.00P_1 + 0.70P_2 \qquad\qquad - b_3 \quad \leq 0$$
$$0.15P_1 + 0.30P_2 \qquad\qquad\qquad - b_4 \leq 0$$

The labor-hours ultimately allocated to each department must be determined by a series of labor balance equations, or constraints, that include the number of hours initially assigned to each department plus the number of hours transferred into the department minus the number of hours transferred out of the department. Using department 1 as an example, we determine the workforce allocation as follows:

$$b_1 = \left(\begin{array}{c} \text{Hours} \\ \text{initially in} \\ \text{department 1} \end{array}\right) + \left(\begin{array}{c} \text{Hours} \\ \text{transferred into} \\ \text{department 1} \end{array}\right) - \left(\begin{array}{c} \text{Hours} \\ \text{transferred out of} \\ \text{department 1} \end{array}\right)$$

Table 9.11 shows 6500 hours initially assigned to department 1. We use the transfer decision variables $t_{i1}$ to denote transfers into department 1 and $t_{1j}$ to denote transfers from department 1. Table 9.12 shows that the cross-training capabilities involving department 1 are restricted to transfers from department 4 (variable $t_{41}$) and transfers to either department 2 or department 3 (variables $t_{12}$ and $t_{13}$). Thus, we can express the total workforce allocation for department 1 as

$$b_1 = 6500 + t_{41} - t_{12} - t_{13}$$

Moving the decision variables for the workforce transfers to the left-hand side, we have the labor balance equation or constraint

$$b_1 - t_{41} + t_{12} + t_{13} = 6500$$

This form of constraint will be needed for each of the four departments. Thus, the following labor balance constraints for departments 2, 3, and 4 would be added to the model:

$$b_2 - t_{12} - t_{42} + t_{23} + t_{24} = 6000$$
$$b_3 - t_{13} - t_{23} + t_{34} \qquad\quad = 7000$$
$$b_4 - t_{24} - t_{34} + t_{41} + t_{42} = 1400$$

Finally, Table 9.12 shows the number of hours that may be transferred from each department is limited, indicating that a transfer capacity constraint must be added for each of the four departments. The additional constraints are

$$t_{12} + t_{13} \leq 400$$
$$t_{23} + t_{24} \leq 800$$
$$t_{34} \phantom{+ t_{24}} \leq 100$$
$$t_{41} + t_{42} \leq 200$$

The complete linear programming model has two product decision variables ($P_1$ and $P_2$), four department workforce assignment variables ($b_1$, $b_2$, $b_3$, and $b_4$), seven transfer variables ($t_{12}$, $t_{13}$, $t_{23}$, $t_{24}$, $t_{34}$, $t_{41}$, and $t_{42}$), and 12 constraints. Figure 9.8 shows the optimal solution to this linear program based on Excel Solver.

**FIGURE 9.8**    ANSWER REPORT FOR THE McCORMICK MANUFACTURING COMPANY PROBLEM

**WEB file**

**McCormickMod**

Objective Cell (Max)

| Name | Original Value | Final Value |
|---|---|---|
| Max Profit | 0.000 | 84011.299 |

Variable Cells

| Model Name | Name | Original Value | Final Value | Integer |
|---|---|---|---|---|
| P1 | Product 1 | 0.000 | 6824.859 | Contin |
| P2 | Product 2 | 0.000 | 1751.412 | Contin |
| B1 | Dept 1 Hours Allocated | 0.000 | 6100.000 | Contin |
| B2 | Dept 2 Hours Allocated | 0.000 | 5200.000 | Contin |
| B3 | Dept 3 Hours Allocated | 0.000 | 8050.847 | Contin |
| B4 | Dept 4 Hours Allocated | 0.000 | 1549.153 | Contin |
| T12 | From 1 To 2 | 0.000 | 0.000 | Contin |
| T13 | From 1 To 3 | 0.000 | 400.000 | Contin |
| T23 | From 2 To 3 | 0.000 | 650.847 | Contin |
| T24 | From 2 To 4 | 0.000 | 149.153 | Contin |
| T34 | From 3 To 4 | 0.000 | 0.000 | Contin |
| T41 | From 4 To 1 | 0.000 | 0.000 | Contin |
| T42 | From 4 To 2 | 0.000 | 0.000 | Contin |

Constraints

| Constraint Number | Name | Cell Value | Status | Slack |
|---|---|---|---|---|
| 1 | Dept 1 Hours | 6100.000 | Binding | 0.000 |
| 2 | Dept 2 Hours | 4559.887 | Not Binding | 640.113 |
| 3 | Dept 3 Hours | 8050.847 | Binding | 0.000 |
| 4 | Dept 4 Hours | 1549.153 | Binding | 0.000 |
| 5 | Dept 1 Hours Allocated | 6100.000 | Binding | 0.000 |
| 6 | Dept 2 Hours Allocated | 5200.000 | Binding | 0.000 |
| 7 | Dept 3 Hours Allocated | 8050.847 | Binding | 0.000 |
| 8 | Dept 4 Hours Allocated | 1549.153 | Binding | 0.000 |
| 9 | From 1 Total | 400.000 | Binding | 0.000 |
| 10 | From 2 Total | 800.000 | Binding | 0.000 |
| 11 | From 3 Total | 0.000 | Not Binding | 100.000 |
| 12 | From 4 Total | 0.000 | Not Binding | 200.000 |

*Variations in the workforce assignment model could be used in situations such as allocating raw material resources to products, allocating machine time to products, and allocating salesforce time to stores or sales territories.*

McCormick's profit can be increased by $84,011 - $73,590 = $10,421 by taking advantage of cross-training and workforce transfers. The optimal product mix of 6825 units of product 1 and 1751 units of product 2 can be achieved if $t_{13} = 400$ hours are transferred from department 1 to department 3; $t_{23} = 651$ hours are transferred from department 2 to department 3; and $t_{24} = 149$ hours are transferred from department 2 to department 4. The resulting workforce assignments for departments 1–4 would provide 6100, 5200, 8051, and 1549 hours, respectively, after rounding.

If a manager has the flexibility to assign personnel to different departments, reduced workforce idle time, improved workforce utilization, and improved profit should result. The linear programming model in this section automatically assigns employees and labor-hours to the departments in the most profitable manner.

## Blending Problems

Blending problems arise whenever a manager must decide how to blend two or more resources to produce one or more products. In these situations, the resources contain one or more essential ingredients that must be blended into final products that will contain specific percentages of each. In most of these applications, then, management must decide how much of each resource to purchase to satisfy product specifications and product demands at minimum cost.

Blending problems occur frequently in the petroleum industry (e.g., blending crude oil to produce different octane gasolines), the chemical industry (e.g., blending chemicals to produce fertilizers and weed killers), and the food industry (e.g., blending ingredients to produce soft drinks and soups). In this section we illustrate how to apply linear programming to a blending problem in the petroleum industry.

The Grand Strand Oil Company produces regular and premium gasoline for independent service stations in the southeastern United States. The Grand Strand refinery manufactures the gasoline products by blending three petroleum components. The gasolines are sold at different prices, and the petroleum components have different costs. The firm wants to determine how to mix or blend the three components into the two gasoline products and maximize profits.

Data available show that regular gasoline can be sold for $2.90 per gallon and premium gasoline for $3.00 per gallon. For the current production planning period, Grand Strand can obtain the three petroleum components at the cost per gallon and in the quantities shown in Table 9.13.

Product specifications for the regular and premium gasolines restrict the amounts of each component that can be used in each gasoline product. Table 9.14 lists the product specifications. Current commitments to distributors require Grand Strand to produce at least 10,000 gallons of regular gasoline.

**TABLE 9.13**  PETROLEUM COST AND SUPPLY FOR THE GRAND STRAND BLENDING PROBLEM

| Petroleum Component | Cost/Gallon | Maximum Available |
|---|---|---|
| 1 | $2.50 | 5,000 gallons |
| 2 | $2.60 | 10,000 gallons |
| 3 | $2.84 | 10,000 gallons |

**TABLE 9.14**   PRODUCT SPECIFICATIONS FOR THE GRAND STRAND
BLENDING PROBLEM

| Product | Specifications |
|---------|----------------|
| Regular gasoline | At most 30% component 1 |
| | At least 40% component 2 |
| | At most 20% component 3 |
| Premium gasoline | At least 25% component 1 |
| | At most 45% component 2 |
| | At least 30% component 3 |

The Grand Strand blending problem is to determine how many gallons of each component should be used in the regular gasoline blend and how many should be used in the premium gasoline blend. The optimal blending solution should maximize the firm's profit, subject to the constraints on the available petroleum supplies shown in Table 9.13, the product specifications shown in Table 9.14, and the required 10,000 gallons of regular gasoline.

We define the decision variables as

$$x_{ij} = \text{gallons of component } i \text{ used in gasoline } j,$$
$$\text{where } i = 1, 2, \text{ or } 3 \text{ for components } 1, 2, \text{ or } 3,$$
$$\text{and } j = r \text{ if regular or } j = p \text{ if premium}$$

The six decision variables are

$$x_{1r} = \text{gallons of component 1 in regular gasoline}$$
$$x_{2r} = \text{gallons of component 2 in regular gasoline}$$
$$x_{3r} = \text{gallons of component 3 in regular gasoline}$$
$$x_{1p} = \text{gallons of component 1 in premium gasoline}$$
$$x_{2p} = \text{gallons of component 2 in premium gasoline}$$
$$x_{3p} = \text{gallons of component 3 in premium gasoline}$$

The total number of gallons of each type of gasoline produced is the sum of the number of gallons produced using each of the three petroleum components.

**Total Gallons Produced**

$$\text{Regular gasoline} = x_{1r} + x_{2r} + x_{3r}$$
$$\text{Premium gasoline} = x_{1p} + x_{2p} + x_{3p}$$

The total gallons of each petroleum component are computed in a similar fashion.

**Total Petroleum Component Use**

$$\text{Component 1} = x_{1r} + x_{1p}$$
$$\text{Component 2} = x_{2r} + x_{2p}$$
$$\text{Component 3} = x_{3r} + x_{3p}$$

We develop the objective function of maximizing the profit contribution by identifying the difference between the total revenue from both gasolines and the total cost of the three petroleum components. By multiplying the $2.90 per gallon price by the total gallons of regular gasoline, the $3.00 per gallon price by the total gallons of premium gasoline, and the component cost per gallon figures in Table 9.13 by the total gallons of each component used, we obtain the objective function:

$$\text{Max} \quad 2.90(x_{1r} + x_{2r} + x_{3r}) + 3.00(x_{1p} + x_{2p} + x_{3p})$$
$$- 2.50(x_{1r} + x_{1p}) - 2.60(x_{2r} + x_{2p}) - 2.84(x_{3r} + x_{3p})$$

When we combine terms, the objective function becomes

$$\text{Max} \quad 0.40x_{1r} + 0.30x_{2r} + 0.06x_{3r} + 0.50x_{1p} + 0.40x_{2p} + 0.16x_{3p}$$

The limitations on the availability of the three petroleum components are

$$x_{1r} + x_{1p} \leq 5{,}000 \quad \text{Component 1}$$
$$x_{2r} + x_{2p} \leq 10{,}000 \quad \text{Component 2}$$
$$x_{3r} + x_{3p} \leq 10{,}000 \quad \text{Component 3}$$

Six constraints are now required to meet the product specifications stated in Table 9.14. The first specification states that component 1 can account for no more than 30% of the total gallons of regular gasoline produced. That is,

$$x_{1r} \leq 0.30(x_{1r} + x_{2r} + x_{3r})$$

Rewriting this constraint with the variables on the left-hand side and a constant on the right-hand side yields

$$0.70x_{1r} - 0.30x_{2r} - 0.30x_{3r} \leq 0$$

The second product specification listed in Table 9.14 becomes

$$x_{2r} \geq 0.40(x_{1r} + x_{2r} + x_{3r})$$

and thus

$$-0.40x_{1r} + 0.60x_{2r} - 0.40x_{3r} \geq 0$$

Similarly, we write the four remaining blending specifications listed in Table 9.14 as

$$-0.20x_{1r} - 0.20x_{2r} + 0.80x_{3r} \leq 0$$
$$+0.75x_{1p} - 0.25x_{2p} - 0.25x_{3p} \geq 0$$
$$-0.45x_{1p} + 0.55x_{2p} - 0.45x_{3p} \leq 0$$
$$-0.30x_{1p} - 0.30x_{2p} + 0.70x_{3p} \geq 0$$

The constraint for at least 10,000 gallons of regular gasoline is

$$x_{1r} + x_{2r} + x_{3r} \geq 10{,}000$$

The complete linear programming model with 6 decision variables and 10 constraints is

$$
\begin{aligned}
\text{Max} \quad & 0.40x_{1r} + 0.30x_{2r} + 0.06x_{3r} + 0.50x_{1p} + 0.40x_{2p} + 0.16x_{3p} \\
\text{s.t.} \quad &
\end{aligned}
$$

$$
\begin{array}{llr}
x_{1r} & + \quad x_{1p} & \leq \ 5{,}000 \\
x_{2r} & + \quad x_{2p} & \leq 10{,}000 \\
x_{3r} & + \quad x_{3p} & \leq 10{,}000 \\
0.70x_{1r} - 0.30x_{2r} - 0.30x_{3r} & & \leq \quad 0 \\
-0.40x_{1r} + 0.60x_{2r} - 0.40x_{3r} & & \geq \quad 0 \\
-0.20x_{1r} - 0.20x_{2r} + 0.80x_{3r} & & \leq \quad 0 \\
0.75x_{1p} - 0.25x_{2p} - 0.25x_{3p} & \geq \quad 0 \\
-0.45x_{1p} + 0.55x_{2p} - 0.45x_{3p} & \leq \quad 0 \\
-0.30x_{1p} - 0.30x_{2p} + 0.70x_{3p} & \geq \quad 0 \\
x_{1r} + \quad x_{2r} + \quad x_{3r} & & \geq 10{,}000 \\
x_{1r}, x_{2r}, x_{3r}, x_{1p}, x_{2p}, x_{3p} \geq 0 &
\end{array}
$$

The optimal solution to the Grand Strand blending problem is shown in Figure 9.9. The optimal solution, which provides a profit of $7100, is summarized in Table 9.15. The optimal blending strategy shows that 10,000 gallons of regular gasoline should be produced. The regular gasoline will be manufactured as a blend of 8000 gallons of component 2 and 2000 gallons of component 3. The 15,000 gallons of premium gasoline will be manufactured as a blend of 5000 gallons of component 1, 2000 gallons of component 2, and 8000 gallons of component 3.

*Try Problem 15 as another example of a blending model.*

The interpretation of the slack and surplus variables associated with the product specification constraints (constraints 4–9) in Figure 9.9 needs some clarification. If the constraint is a $\leq$ constraint, the value of the slack variable can be interpreted as the gallons of component use below the maximum amount of the component use specified by the constraint. For example, the slack of 3000.000 for constraint 4 shows that component 1 use is 3000 gallons below the maximum amount of component 1 that could have been used in the production of 10,000 gallons of regular gasoline. If the product specification constraint is a $\geq$ constraint, a surplus variable shows the gallons of component use above the minimum amount of component use specified by the blending constraint. For example, the surplus of 4000.000 for constraint 5 shows that component 2 use is 4000 gallons above the minimum amount of component 2 that must be used in the production of 10,000 gallons of regular gasoline.

**TABLE 9.15**    GRAND STRAND GASOLINE BLENDING SOLUTION

| | Gallons of Component (percentage) | | | |
| --- | --- | --- | --- | --- |
| **Gasoline** | **Component 1** | **Component 2** | **Component 3** | **Total** |
| Regular | 0 (0.0%) | 8000 (80%) | 2000 (20%) | 10,000 |
| Premium | 5000 (33⅓%) | 2000 (13⅓%) | 8000 (53⅓%) | 15,000 |

**FIGURE 9.9**   ANSWER REPORT FOR THE GRAND STRAND BLENDING PROBLEM

Objective Cell (Max)

| Name | Original Value | Final Value |
|------|----------------|-------------|
| Max Profit | 0.000 | 7100.000 |

**Grand**

Variable Cells

| Model Variable | Name | Original Value | Final Value | Integer |
|----------------|------|----------------|-------------|---------|
| X1R | Regular Component 1 | 0.000 | 0.000 | Contin |
| X2R | Regular Component 2 | 0.000 | 8000.000 | Contin |
| X3R | Regular Component 3 | 0.000 | 2000.000 | Contin |
| X1P | Premium Component 1 | 0.000 | 5000.000 | Contin |
| X2P | Premium Component 2 | 0.000 | 2000.000 | Contin |
| X3P | Premium Component 3 | 0.000 | 8000.000 | Contin |

Constraints

| Constraint Number | Name | Cell Value | Status | Slack |
|-------------------|------|------------|--------|-------|
| 1 | Total Component 1 | 5000.000 | Binding | 0.000 |
| 2 | Total Component 2 | 10000.000 | Binding | 0.000 |
| 3 | Total Component 3 | 10000.000 | Binding | 0.000 |
| 4 | Max Comp 1 Regular | 0.000 | Not Binding | 3000.000 |
| 5 | Min Comp 2 Regular | 8000.000 | Not Binding | 4000.000 |
| 6 | Max Comp 3 Regular | 2000.000 | Binding | 0.000 |
| 7 | Min Comp 1 Premium | 5000.000 | Not Binding | 1250.000 |
| 8 | Max Comp 2 Premium | 2000.000 | Not Binding | 4000.000 |
| 9 | Min Comp 3 Premium | 8000.000 | Not Binding | 3500.000 |
| 10 | Regular Total | 10000.000 | Binding | 0.000 |

© Cengage Learning 2013

## NOTES AND COMMENTS

1. A convenient way to define the decision variables in a blending problem is to use a matrix in which the rows correspond to the raw materials and the columns correspond to the final products. For example, in the Grand Strand blending problem, we define the decision variables as follows:

This approach has two advantages: (1) It provides a systematic way to define the decision variables for any blending problem; and (2) it provides a visual image of the decision variables in terms of how they are related to the raw materials, products, and each other.

|  |  | **Final Products** | |
|--|--|----------------|--|
|  |  | **Regular Gasoline** | **Premium Gasoline** |
| **Raw Materials** | **Component 1** | $x_{1r}$ | $x_{1p}$ |
|  | **Component 2** | $x_{2r}$ | $x_{2p}$ |
|  | **Component 3** | $x_{3r}$ | $r_{3p}$ |

## Summary

In this chapter we presented a broad range of applications that demonstrate how to use linear programming to assist in the decision-making process. We formulated and solved problems from marketing, finance, and operations management, and interpreted the computer output.

Many of the illustrations presented in this chapter are scaled-down versions of actual situations in which linear programming has been applied. In real-world applications, the problem may not be so concisely stated, the data for the problem may not be as readily available, and the problem most likely will involve numerous decision variables and/or constraints. However, a thorough study of the applications in this chapter is a good place to begin in applying linear programming to real problems.

## Problems

*Note:* The following problems have been designed to give you an understanding and appreciation of the broad range of problems that can be formulated as linear programs. You should be able to formulate a linear programming model for each of the problems. However, you will need access to a linear programming computer package to develop the solutions and make the requested interpretations.

1. The Westchester Chamber of Commerce periodically sponsors public service seminars and programs. Currently, promotional plans are under way for this year's program. Advertising alternatives include television, radio, and newspaper. Audience estimates, costs, and maximum media usage limitations are as shown:

| Constraint | Television | Radio | Newspaper |
|---|---|---|---|
| Audience per advertisement | 100,000 | 18,000 | 40,000 |
| Cost per advertisement | $2000 | $300 | $600 |
| Maximum media usage | 10 | 20 | 10 |

To ensure a balanced use of advertising media, radio advertisements must not exceed 50% of the total number of advertisements authorized. In addition, television should account for at least 10% of the total number of advertisements authorized.

a. If the promotional budget is limited to $18,200, how many commercial messages should be run on each medium to maximize total audience contact? What is the allocation of the budget among the three media, and what is the total audience reached?

b. By how much would audience contact increase if an extra $100 were allocated to the promotional budget?

2. The management of Hartman Company is trying to determine the amount of each of two products to produce over the coming planning period. The following information concerns labor availability, labor utilization, and product profitability:

| Department | Product (hours/unit) 1 | Product (hours/unit) 2 | Labor-Hours Available |
|---|---|---|---|
| A | 1.00 | 0.35 | 100 |
| B | 0.30 | 0.20 | 36 |
| C | 0.20 | 0.50 | 50 |
| Profit contribution/unit | $30.00 | $15.00 | |

a. Develop a linear programming model of the Hartman Company problem. Solve the model to determine the optimal production quantities of products 1 and 2.

b. In computing the profit contribution per unit, management doesn't deduct labor costs because they are considered fixed for the upcoming planning period. However, suppose that overtime can be scheduled in some of the departments. Which departments would you recommend scheduling for overtime? How much would you be willing to pay per hour of overtime in each department?

c. Suppose that 10, 6, and 8 hours of overtime may be scheduled in departments A, B, and C, respectively. The cost per hour of overtime is $18 in department A, $22.50 in department B, and $12 in department C. Formulate a linear programming model that can be used to determine the optimal production quantities if overtime is made available. What are the optimal production quantities, and what is the revised total contribution to profit? How much overtime do you recommend using in each department? What is the increase in the total contribution to profit if overtime is used?

3. The employee credit union at State University is planning the allocation of funds for the coming year. The credit union makes four types of loans to its members. In addition, the credit union invests in risk-free securities to stabilize income. The various revenue-producing investments together with annual rates of return are as follows:

| Type of Loan/Investment | Annual Rate of Return (%) |
|---|---|
| Automobile loans | 8 |
| Furniture loans | 10 |
| Other secured loans | 11 |
| Signature loans | 12 |
| Risk-free securities | 9 |

The credit union will have $2 million available for investment during the coming year. State laws and credit union policies impose the following restrictions on the composition of the loans and investments:

- Risk-free securities may not exceed 30% of the total funds available for investment.
- Signature loans may not exceed 10% of the funds invested in all loans (automobile, furniture, other secured, and signature loans).
- Furniture loans plus other secured loans may not exceed the automobile loans.
- Other secured loans plus signature loans may not exceed the funds invested in risk-free securities.

How should the $2 million be allocated to each of the loan/investment alternatives to maximize total annual return? What is the projected total annual return?

4. The Bahama Nut Company sells three different half-pound bags of peanut mixes: Party Nuts, Mixed, and Premium Mix. These generate per-bag revenue of $1.00, $2.10, and $3.63, respectively. The tables below show the makeup of each mix, the available ingredients for the next week, and the cost of each ingredient.

| | Ingredients | | | |
|---|---|---|---|---|
| | Peanuts | Cashews | Brazil Nuts | Hazelnuts |
| Party Nuts | 100% | | | |
| Mixed | 55% | 25% | 10% | 10% |
| Premium Mix | | 40% | 20% | 40% |

| | Pounds Available | Cost per Pound |
|---|---|---|
| Peanuts | 500 | $1.50 |
| Cashews | 180 | $5.35 |
| Brazil nuts | 100 | $6.25 |
| Hazelnuts | 80 | $7.50 |

Develop a linear programming model to help Bahama determine how many bags of each type to produce to maximize contribution to profit. How many bags of each type should be produced and what is the maximal profit? Which constraints are binding?

5. Ajax Fuels, Inc., is developing a new additive for airplane fuels. The additive is a mixture of three ingredients: A, B, and C. For proper performance, the total amount of additive (amount of A, amount of B, amount of C) must be at least 10 ounces per gallon of fuel. However, for safety reasons, the amount of additive must not exceed 15 ounces per gallon of fuel. The mix or blend of the three ingredients is critical. At least 1 ounce of ingredient A must be used for every ounce of ingredient B. The amount of ingredient C must be at least one-half the amount of ingredient A. If the costs per ounce for ingredients A, B, and C are $0.10, $0.03, and $0.09, respectively, find the minimum-cost mixture of A, B, and C for each gallon of airplane fuel.

6. G. Kunz and Sons, Inc., manufactures two products used in the heavy equipment industry. Both products require manufacturing operations in two departments. The following are the production time (in hours) and profit contribution figures for the two products:

| | | Labor-Hours | |
|---|---|---|---|
| Product | Profit per Unit | Dept. A | Dept. B |
| 1 | $25 | 6 | 12 |
| 2 | $20 | 8 | 10 |

For the coming production period, Kunz has available a total of 900 hours of labor that can be allocated to either of the two departments. Find the production plan and labor allocation (hours assigned in each department) that will maximize the total contribution to profit.

7. As part of the settlement for a class action lawsuit, Hoxworth Corporation must provide sufficient cash to make the following annual payments (in thousands of dollars):

| Year | 1 | 2 | 3 | 4 | 5 | 6 |
|---|---|---|---|---|---|---|
| Payment | 190 | 215 | 240 | 285 | 315 | 460 |

The annual payments must be made at the beginning of each year. The judge will approve an amount that, along with earnings on its investment, will cover the annual payments. Investment of the funds will be limited to savings (at 4% annually) and government securities, at prices and rates currently quoted in *The Wall Street Journal*.

Hoxworth wants to develop a plan for making the annual payments by investing in the following securities (par value = $1000). Funds not invested in these securities will be placed in savings.

| Security | Current Price | Rate (%) | Years to Maturity |
|---|---|---|---|
| 1 | $1055 | 6.750 | 3 |
| 2 | $1000 | 5.125 | 4 |

Assume that interest is paid annually. The plan will be submitted to the judge and, if approved, Hoxworth will be required to pay a trustee the amount that will be required to fund the plan.

a. Use linear programming to find the minimum cash settlement necessary to fund the annual payments.

b. Use the shadow price to determine how much more Hoxworth should be willing to pay now to reduce the payment at the beginning of year 6 to $400,000.

c. Use the shadow price to determine how much more Hoxworth should be willing to pay to reduce the year 1 payment to $150,000.

d. Suppose that the annual payments are to be made at the end of each year. Reformulate the model to accommodate this change. How much would Hoxworth save if this change could be negotiated?

8. The Clark County Sheriff's Department schedules police officers for 8-hour shifts. The beginning times for the shifts are 8:00 A.M., noon, 4:00 P.M., 8:00 P.M., midnight, and 4:00 A.M. An officer beginning a shift at one of these times works for the next 8 hours. During normal weekday operations, the number of officers needed varies depending on the time of day. The department staffing guidelines require the following minimum number of officers on duty:

| Time of Day | Minimum Officers On Duty |
|---|---|
| 8:00 A.M.–Noon | 5 |
| Noon–4:00 P.M. | 6 |
| 4:00 P.M.–8:00 P.M. | 10 |
| 8:00 P.M.–Midnight | 7 |
| Midnight–4:00 A.M. | 4 |
| 4:00 A.M.–8:00 A.M. | 6 |

Determine the number of police officers that should be scheduled to begin the 8-hour shifts at each of the six times (8:00 A.M., noon, 4:00 P.M., 8:00 P.M., midnight, and 4:00 A.M.) to minimize the total number of officers required. (*Hint:* Let $x_1$ = the number of officers beginning work at 8:00 A.M., $x_2$ = the number of officers beginning work at noon, and so on.)

9. Reconsider the Welte Mutual Funds problem from Section 9.2. Define your decision variables as the fraction of funds invested in each security. Also, modify the constraints limiting investments in the oil and steel industries as follows: No more than 50% of the total funds invested in stock (oil and steel) may be invested in the oil industry, and no more than 50% of the funds invested in stock (oil and steel) may be invested in the steel industry.

a. Solve the revised linear programming model. What fraction of the portfolio should be invested in each type of security?

b. How much should be invested in each type of security?

c. What are the total earnings for the portfolio?

d. What is the marginal rate of return on the portfolio? That is, how much more could be earned by investing one more dollar in the portfolio?

10. An investment advisor at Shore Financial Services wants to develop a model that can be used to allocate investment funds among four alternatives: stocks, bonds, mutual funds, and cash. For the coming investment period, the company developed estimates of the annual rate of return and the associated risk for each alternative. Risk is measured using an index between 0 and 1, with higher risk values denoting more volatility and thus more uncertainty.

| Investment | Annual Rate of Return (%) | Risk |
|---|---|---|
| Stocks | 10 | 0.8 |
| Bonds | 3 | 0.2 |
| Mutual funds | 4 | 0.3 |
| Cash | 1 | 0.0 |

Because cash is held in a money market fund, the annual return is lower, but it carries essentially no risk. The objective is to determine the portion of funds allocated to each investment alternative in order to maximize the total annual return for the portfolio subject to the risk level the client is willing to tolerate.

Total risk is the sum of the risk for all investment alternatives. For instance, if 40% of a client's funds are invested in stocks, 30% in bonds, 20% in mutual funds, and 10% in cash, the total risk for the portfolio would be $0.40(0.8) + 0.30(0.2) + 0.20(0.3) + 0.10(0.0) = 0.44$. An investment advisor will meet with each client to discuss the client's investment objectives and to determine a maximum total risk value for the client. A maximum total risk value of less than 0.3 would be assigned to a conservative investor; a maximum total risk value of between 0.3 and 0.5 would be assigned to a moderate tolerance to risk; and a maximum total risk value greater than 0.5 would be assigned to a more aggressive investor.

Shore Financial Services specified additional guidelines that must be applied to all clients. The guidelines are as follows:

- No more than 75% of the total investment may be in stocks.
- The amount invested in mutual funds must be at least as much as invested in bonds.
- The amount of cash must be at least 10%, but no more than 30% of the total investment funds.

a. Suppose the maximum risk value for a particular client is 0.4. What is the optimal allocation of investment funds among stocks, bonds, mutual funds, and cash? What is the annual rate of return and the total risk for the optimal portfolio?

b. Suppose the maximum risk value for a more conservative client is 0.18. What is the optimal allocation of investment funds for this client? What is the annual rate of return and the total risk for the optimal portfolio?

c. Another more aggressive client has a maximum risk value of 0.7. What is the optimal allocation of investment funds for this client? What is the annual rate of return and the total risk for the optimal portfolio?

d. Refer to the solution for the more aggressive client in part (c). Would this client be interested in having the investment advisor increase the maximum percentage allowed in stocks or decrease the requirement that the amount of cash must be at least 10% of the funds invested? Explain.

e. What is the advantage of defining the decision variables as is done in this model rather than stating the amount to be invested and expressing the decision variables directly in dollar amounts?

11. Edwards Manufacturing Company purchases two component parts from three different suppliers. The suppliers have limited capacity, and no one supplier can meet all the company's needs. In addition, the suppliers charge different prices for the components. Component price data (in price per unit) are as follows:

| | **Supplier** | | |
|---|---|---|---|
| **Component** | **1** | **2** | **3** |
| 1 | $12 | $13 | $14 |
| 2 | $10 | $11 | $10 |

Each supplier has a limited capacity in terms of the total number of components it can supply. However, as long as Edwards provides sufficient advance orders, each supplier can devote its capacity to component 1, component 2, or any combination of the two components, if the total number of units ordered is within its capacity. Supplier capacities are as follows:

| Supplier | 1 | 2 | 3 |
|---|---|---|---|
| Capacity | 600 | 1000 | 800 |

If the Edwards production plan for the next period includes 1000 units of component 1 and 800 units of component 2, what purchases do you recommend? That is, how many units of each component should be ordered from each supplier? What is the total purchase cost for the components?

12. The Atlantic Seafood Company (ASC) is a buyer and distributor of seafood products that are sold to restaurants and specialty seafood outlets throughout the Northeast. ASC has a frozen storage facility in New York City that serves as the primary distribution point for all products. One of the ASC products is frozen large black tiger shrimp, which are sized at 16–20 pieces per pound. Each Saturday ASC can purchase more tiger shrimp or sell the tiger shrimp at the existing New York City warehouse market price. The ASC goal is to buy tiger shrimp at a low weekly price and sell it later at a higher price. ASC currently has 20,000 pounds of tiger shrimp in storage. Space is available to store a maximum of 100,000 pounds of tiger shrimp each week. In addition, ASC developed the following estimates of tiger shrimp prices for the next four weeks:

| Week | Price/lb. |
|---|---|
| 1 | $6.00 |
| 2 | $6.20 |
| 3 | $6.65 |
| 4 | $5.55 |

ASC would like to determine the optimal buying/storing/selling strategy for the next four weeks. The cost to store a pound of shrimp for one week is $0.15, and to account for unforeseen changes in supply or demand, management also indicated that 25,000 pounds of tiger shrimp must be in storage at the end of week 4. Determine the optimal buying/storing/selling strategy for ASC. What is the projected four-week profit?

13. Romans Food Market, located in Saratoga, New York, carries a variety of specialty foods from around the world. Two of the store's leading products use the Romans Food Market name: Romans Regular Coffee and Romans DeCaf Coffee. These coffees are blends of Brazilian Natural and Colombian Mild coffee beans, which are purchased from a distributor located in New York City. Because Romans purchases large quantities, the coffee beans may be purchased on an as-needed basis for a price 10% higher than the market price the distributor pays for the beans. The current market price is $0.47 per pound for Brazilian Natural and $0.62 per pound for Colombian Mild. The compositions of each coffee blend are as follows:

| | Blend | |
|---|---|---|
| Bean | Regular | DeCaf |
| Brazilian Natural | 75% | 40% |
| Colombian Mild | 25% | 60% |

Romans sells the Regular blend for $3.60 per pound and the DeCaf blend for $4.40 per pound. Romans would like to place an order for the Brazilian and Colombian coffee beans that will enable the production of 1000 pounds of Romans Regular coffee and 500 pounds of Romans DeCaf coffee. The production cost is $0.80 per pound for the Regular blend.

Because of the extra steps required to produce DeCaf, the production cost for the DeCaf blend is $1.05 per pound. Packaging costs for both products are $0.25 per pound. Formulate a linear programming model that can be used to determine the pounds of Brazilian Natural and Colombian Mild that will maximize the total contribution to profit. What is the optimal solution, and what is the contribution to profit?

14. The production manager for the Classic Boat Corporation must determine how many units of the Classic 21 model to produce over the next four quarters. The company has a beginning inventory of 100 Classic 21 boats, and demand for the four quarters is 2000 units in quarter 1, 4000 units in quarter 2, 3000 units in quarter 3, and 1500 units in quarter 4. The firm has limited production capacity in each quarter. That is, up to 4000 units can be produced in quarter 1, 3000 units in quarter 2, 2000 units in quarter 3, and 4000 units in quarter 4. Each boat held in inventory in quarters 1 and 2 incurs an inventory holding cost of $250 per unit; the holding cost for quarters 3 and 4 is $300 per unit. The production costs for the first quarter are $10,000 per unit; these costs are expected to increase by 10% each quarter because of increases in labor and material costs. Management specified that the ending inventory for quarter 4 must be at least 500 boats.

   a. Formulate a linear programming model that can be used to determine the production schedule that will minimize the total cost of meeting demand in each quarter subject to the production capacities in each quarter and also to the required ending inventory in quarter 4.

   b. Solve the linear program formulated in part (a). Then develop a table that will show for each quarter the number of units to manufacture, the ending inventory, and the costs incurred.

   c. Interpret each of the shadow prices corresponding to the constraints developed to meet demand in each quarter. Based on these shadow prices, what advice would you give the production manager?

   d. Interpret each of the shadow prices corresponding to the production capacity in each quarter. Based on each of these shadow prices, what advice would you give the production manager?

15. Bay Oil produces two types of fuels (regular and super) by mixing three ingredients. The major distinguishing feature of the two products is the octane level required. Regular fuel must have a minimum octane level of 90 while super must have a level of at least 100. The cost per barrel, octane levels, and available amounts (in barrels) for the upcoming two-week period are shown in the following table. Likewise, the maximum demand for each end product and the revenue generated per barrel are shown.

| Input | Cost/Barrel | Octane | Available (barrels) |
|---|---|---|---|
| 1 | $16.50 | 100 | 110,000 |
| 2 | $14.00 | 87 | 350,000 |
| 3 | $17.50 | 110 | 300,000 |

| | Revenue/Barrel | Max Demand (barrels) |
|---|---|---|
| Regular | $18.50 | 350,000 |
| Super | $20.00 | 500,000 |

Develop and solve a linear programming model to maximize contribution to profit. What is the optimal contribution to profit?

16. The Ferguson Paper Company produces rolls of paper for use in cash registers. The rolls, which are 200 feet long, are produced in widths of 1½, 2½, and 3½ inches. The production process provides 200-foot rolls in 10-inch widths only. The firm must therefore cut the rolls to the desired final product sizes. The seven cutting alternatives and the amount of waste generated by each are as follows:

| Cutting Alternative | Number of Rolls | | | Waste (inches) |
| --- | --- | --- | --- | --- |
| | 1½ in. | 2½ in. | 3½ in. | |
| 1 | 6 | 0 | 0 | 1 |
| 2 | 0 | 4 | 0 | 0 |
| 3 | 2 | 0 | 2 | 0 |
| 4 | 0 | 1 | 2 | ½ |
| 5 | 1 | 3 | 0 | 1 |
| 6 | 1 | 2 | 1 | 0 |
| 7 | 4 | 0 | 1 | ½ |

The minimum requirements for the three products are

| Roll Width (inches) | 1½ | 2½ | 3½ |
| --- | --- | --- | --- |
| Units | 1000 | 2000 | 4000 |

a.  If the company wants to minimize the number of 10-inch rolls that must be manufactured, how many 10-inch rolls will be processed on each cutting alternative? How many rolls are required, and what is the total waste (inches)?

b.  If the company wants to minimize the waste generated, how many 10-inch rolls will be processed on each cutting alternative? How many rolls are required, and what is the total waste (inches)?

c.  What are the differences between parts (a) and (b) of this problem? In this case, which objective do you prefer? Explain. What types of situations would make the other objective more desirable?

17. Frandec Company manufactures, assembles, and rebuilds material handling equipment used in warehouses and distribution centers. One product, called a Liftmaster, is assembled from four components: a frame, a motor, two supports, and a metal strap. Frandec's production schedule calls for 5000 Liftmasters to be made next month. Frandec purchases the motors from an outside supplier, but the frames, supports, and straps may be either manufactured by the company or purchased from an outside supplier. Manufacturing and purchase costs per unit are shown.

| Component | Manufacturing Cost | Purchase Cost |
| --- | --- | --- |
| Frame | $38.00 | $51.00 |
| Support | $11.50 | $15.00 |
| Strap | $ 6.50 | $ 7.50 |

Three departments are involved in the production of these components. The time (in minutes per unit) required to process each component in each department and the available capacity (in hours) for the three departments are as follows:

| Component | | Department | |
| --- | --- | --- | --- |
| | Cutting | Milling | Shaping |
| Frame | 3.5 | 2.2 | 3.1 |
| Support | 1.3 | 1.7 | 2.6 |
| Strap | 0.8 | — | 1.7 |
| Capacity (hours) | 350 | 420 | 680 |

    a.   Formulate and solve a linear programming model for this make-or-buy application. How many of each component should be manufactured and how many should be purchased?

    b.   What is the total cost of the manufacturing and purchasing plan?

    c.   How many hours of production time are used in each department?

    d.   How much should Frandec be willing to pay for an additional hour of time in the shaping department?

    e.   Another manufacturer has offered to sell frames to Frandec for $45 each. Could Frandec improve its position by pursuing this opportunity? Why or why not?

18.  The Two-Rivers Oil Company near Pittsburgh transports gasoline to its distributors by truck. The company recently contracted to supply gasoline distributors in southern Ohio, and it has $600,000 available to spend on the necessary expansion of its fleet of gasoline tank trucks. Three models of gasoline tank trucks are available.

| Truck Model | Capacity (gallons) | Purchase Cost | Monthly Operating Cost, Including Depreciation |
|---|---|---|---|
| Super Tanker | 5000 | $67,000 | $550 |
| Regular Line | 2500 | $55,000 | $425 |
| Econo-Tanker | 1000 | $46,000 | $350 |

The company estimates that the monthly demand for the region will be 550,000 gallons of gasoline. Because of the size and speed differences of the trucks, the number of deliveries or round trips possible per month for each truck model will vary. Trip capacities are estimated at 15 trips per month for the Super Tanker, 20 trips per month for the Regular Line, and 25 trips per month for the Econo-Tanker. Based on maintenance and driver availability, the firm does not want to add more than 15 new vehicles to its fleet. In addition, the company has decided to purchase at least three of the new Econo-Tankers for use on short-run, low-demand routes. As a final constraint, the company does not want more than half the new models to be Super Tankers.

    a.   If the company wishes to satisfy the gasoline demand with a minimum monthly operating expense, how many models of each truck should be purchased?

    b.   If the company did not require at least three Econo-Tankers and did not limit the number of Super Tankers to at most half the new models, how many models of each truck should be purchased?

19.  The Silver Star Bicycle Company will be manufacturing both men's and women's models of its Easy-Pedal bicycles during the next two months. Management wants to develop a production schedule indicating how many bicycles of each model should be produced in each month. Current demand forecasts call for 150 men's and 125 women's models to be shipped during the first month and 200 men's and 150 women's models to be shipped during the second month. Additional data are shown:

| Model | Production Costs | Labor Requirements (hours) | | Current Inventory |
|---|---|---|---|---|
| | | Manufacturing | Assembly | |
| Men's | $120 | 2.0 | 1.5 | 20 |
| Women's | $ 90 | 1.6 | 1.0 | 30 |

Last month the company used a total of 1000 hours of labor. The company's labor relations policy will not allow the combined total hours of labor (manufacturing plus assembly) to increase or decrease by more than 100 hours from month to month. In addition, the company charges monthly inventory at the rate of 2% of the production cost based on the inventory levels at the end of the month. The company would like to have at least 25 units of each model in inventory at the end of the two months.

a. Establish a production schedule that minimizes production and inventory costs and satisfies the labor-smoothing, demand, and inventory requirements. What inventories will be maintained, and what are the monthly labor requirements?

b. If the company changed the constraints so that monthly labor increases and decreases could not exceed 50 hours, what would happen to the production schedule? How much will the cost increase? What would you recommend?

20. Filtron Corporation produces filtration containers used in water treatment systems. Although business has been growing, the demand each month varies considerably. As a result, the company utilizes a mix of part-time and full-time employees to meet production demands. Although this approach provides Filtron with great flexibility, it resulted in increased costs and morale problems among employees. For instance, if Filtron needs to increase production from one month to the next, additional part-time employees have to be hired and trained, and costs go up. If Filtron has to decrease production, the workforce has to be reduced and Filtron incurs additional costs in terms of unemployment benefits and decreased morale. Best estimates are that increasing the number of units produced from one month to the next will increase production costs by $1.25 per unit, and that decreasing the number of units produced will increase production costs by $1.00 per unit. In February Filtron produced 10,000 filtration containers but only sold 7500 units; 2500 units are currently in inventory. The sales forecasts for March, April, and May are for 12,000 units, 8000 units, and 15,000 units, respectively. In addition, Filtron has the capacity to store up to 3000 filtration containers at the end of any month. Management would like to determine the number of units to be produced in March, April, and May that will minimize the total cost of the monthly production increases and decreases.

21. Star Power Company is a power company in the Midwest region of the United States. Star buys and sells energy on the spot market. Star can store power in a high-capacity battery that can store up to 60 kWh (kilowatt hours). During a particular period, Star can buy or sell electricity at the market price known as LMP (Locational Marginal Price). The maximum rate that power can be injected or withdrawn from the battery is 20 kWh per period. Star has forecasted the following LMP's for the next 10 periods:

| Period | LMP ($/kWh) |
|--------|-------------|
| 1 | $ 5 |
| 2 | $27 |
| 3 | $ 2 |
| 4 | $25 |
| 5 | $22 |
| 6 | $29 |
| 7 | $24 |
| 8 | $20 |
| 9 | $61 |
| 10 | $66 |

The battery is full at the beginning of period 1; that is, at the start of the planning horizon, the battery contains 60 kWh of electricity.

a. Develop a linear programming model Star Power can use to determine when to buy and sell electricity in order to maximize profit over these 10 weeks. What is the maximum achievable profit?

b. Your solution to part (a) should result in a battery level of 0 at the end of period 10. Why does this make sense? Modify your model with the requirement that the battery should be full (60 kWh) at the end of period 10. How does this impact the optimal profit?

c. To further investigate the impact of requirements on the battery level at the end of period 10, solve your model from part (b) with the constraint on the ending battery level varying from 0 kWh to 60 kWh in increments of 10 kWh. Develop a graph with profit on the vertical axis and required ending battery level on the horizontal axis. Given that Star has not forecasted LMPs for periods 11, 12, and so on, what ending battery level do you recommend that Star use in its optimization model?

22. TriCity Manufacturing (TCM) makes Styrofoam cups, plates, and sandwich and meal containers. Next week's schedule calls for the production of 80,000 small sandwich containers, 80,000 large sandwich containers, and 65,000 meal containers. To make these containers, Styrofoam sheets are melted and formed into final products using three machines: M1, M2, and M3. Machine M1 can process Styrofoam sheets with a maximum width of 12 inches. The width capacity of machine M2 is 16 inches, and the width capacity of machine M3 is 20 inches. The small sandwich containers require 10-inch-wide Styrofoam sheets; thus, these containers can be produced on each of the three machines. The large sandwich containers require 12-inch-wide sheets; thus, these containers can also be produced on each of the three machines. However, the meal containers require 16-inch-wide Styrofoam sheets, so the meal containers cannot be produced on machine M1. Waste is incurred in the production of all three containers because Styrofoam is lost in the heating and forming process as well as in the final trimming of the product. The amount of waste generated varies depending upon the container produced and the machine used. The following table shows the waste in square inches for each machine and product combination. The waste material is recycled for future use.

| Machine | Small Sandwich | Large Sandwich | Meal |
|---------|----------------|----------------|------|
| M1 | 20 | 15 | — |
| M2 | 24 | 28 | 18 |
| M3 | 32 | 35 | 36 |

Production rates also depend upon the container produced and the machine used. The following table shows the production rates in units per minute for each machine and product combination. Machine capacities are limited for the next week. Time available is 35 hours for machine M1, 35 hours for machine M2, and 40 hours for machine M3.

| Machine | Small Sandwich | Large Sandwich | Meal |
|---------|----------------|----------------|------|
| M1 | 30 | 25 | — |
| M2 | 45 | 40 | 30 |
| M3 | 60 | 52 | 44 |

a. Costs associated with reprocessing the waste material have been increasing. Thus, TCM would like to minimize the amount of waste generated in meeting next week's production schedule. Formulate a linear programming model that can be used to determine the best production schedule.

b. Solve the linear program formulated in part (a) to determine the production schedule. How much waste is generated? Which machines, if any, have idle capacity?

23. EZ-Windows, Inc., manufactures replacement windows for the home remodeling business. In January, the company produced 15,000 windows and ended the month with 9000 windows in inventory. EZ-Windows' management team would like to develop a production schedule for the next three months. A smooth production schedule is obviously desirable because it maintains the current workforce and provides a similar month-to-month operation. However, given the sales forecasts, the production capacities, and the storage capabilities as shown, the management team does not think a smooth production schedule with the same production quantity each month is possible.

|                     | February | March  | April  |
|---------------------|----------|--------|--------|
| Sales forecast      | 15,000   | 16,500 | 20,000 |
| Production capacity | 14,000   | 14,000 | 18,000 |
| Storage capacity    | 6,000    | 6,000  | 6,000  |

The company's cost accounting department estimates that increasing production by one window from one month to the next will increase total costs by $1.00 for each unit increase in the production level. In addition, decreasing production by one unit from one month to the next will increase total costs by $0.65 for each unit decrease in the production level. Ignoring production and inventory carrying costs, formulate and solve a linear programming model that will minimize the cost of changing production levels while still satisfying the monthly sales forecasts.

24. Morton Financial must decide on the percentage of available funds to commit to each of two investments, referred to as A and B, over the next four periods. The following table shows the amount of new funds available for each of the four periods, as well as the cash expenditure required for each investment (negative values) or the cash income from the investment (positive values). The data shown (in thousands of dollars) reflect the amount of expenditure or income if 100% of the funds available in any period are invested in either A or B. For example, if Morton decides to invest 100% of the funds available in any period in investment A, it will incur cash expenditures of $1000 in period 1, $800 in period 2, $200 in period 3, and income of $200 in period 4. Note, however, that if Morton made the decision to invest 80% in investment A, the cash expenditures or income would be 80% of the values shown.

|        | New Investment     | Investment |        |
|--------|--------------------|------------|--------|
| Period | Funds Available    | A          | B      |
| 1      | $1500              | −$1000     | −$800  |
| 2      | $ 400              | −$ 800     | −$500  |
| 3      | $ 500              | −$ 200     | −$300  |
| 4      | $ 100              | −$ 200     | −$300  |

The amount of funds available in any period is the sum of the new investment funds for the period, the new loan funds, the savings from the previous period, the cash income from investment A, and the cash income from investment B. The funds available in any period can be used to pay the loan and interest from the previous period, can be placed in savings, can be used to pay the cash expenditures for investment A, or can be used to pay the cash expenditures for investment B.

Assume an interest rate of 10% per period for savings and an interest rate of 18% per period on borrowed funds. Let

$$S_t = \text{the savings for period } t$$
$$L_t = \text{the new loan funds for period } t$$

Then, in any period $t$, the savings income from the previous period is $1.1S_{t-1}$ and the loan and interest expenditure from the previous period is $1.18L_{t-1}$.

At the end of period 4, investment A is expected to have a cash value of \$3200 (assuming a 100% investment in A), and investment B is expected to have a cash value of \$2500 (assuming a 100% investment in B). Additional income and expenses at the end of period 4 will be income from savings in period 4 less the repayment of the period 4 loan plus interest.

Suppose that the decision variables are defined as

$$x_1 = \text{the proportion of investment A undertaken}$$
$$x_2 = \text{the proportion of investment B undertaken}$$

For example, if $x_1 = 0.5$, \$500 would be invested in investment A during the first period, and all remaining cash flows and ending investment A values would be multiplied by 0.5. The same holds for investment B. The model must include constraints $x_1 \leq 1$ and $x_2 \leq 1$ to make sure that no more than 100% of the investments can be undertaken.

If no more than \$200 can be borrowed in any period, determine the proportions of investments A and B and the amount of savings and borrowing in each period that will maximize the cash value for the firm at the end of the four periods.

25. Western Family Steakhouse offers a variety of low-cost meals and quick service. Other than management, the steakhouse operates with two full-time employees who work 8 hours per day. The rest of the employees are part-time employees who are scheduled for 4-hour shifts during peak meal times. On Saturdays the steakhouse is open from 11:00 A.M. to 10:00 P.M. Management wants to develop a schedule for part-time employees that will minimize labor costs and still provide excellent customer service. The average wage rate for the part-time employees is \$7.60 per hour. The total number of full-time and part-time employees needed varies with the time of day as shown.

| Time | Total Number of Employees Needed |
|------|------|
| 11:00 A.M.–Noon | 9 |
| Noon–1:00 P.M. | 9 |
| 1:00 P.M.–2:00 P.M. | 9 |
| 2:00 P.M.–3:00 P.M. | 3 |
| 3:00 P.M.–4:00 P.M. | 3 |
| 4:00 P.M.–5:00 P.M. | 3 |
| 5:00 P.M.–6:00 P.M. | 6 |
| 6:00 P.M.–7:00 P.M. | 12 |
| 7:00 P.M.–8:00 P.M. | 12 |
| 8:00 P.M.–9:00 P.M. | 7 |
| 9:00 P.M.–10:00 P.M. | 7 |

One full-time employee comes on duty at 11:00 A.M., works 4 hours, takes an hour off, and returns for another 4 hours. The other full-time employee comes to work at 1:00 P.M. and works the same 4-hours-on, 1-hour-off, 4-hours-on pattern.

a. Develop a minimum-cost schedule for part-time employees.
b. What is the total payroll for the part-time employees? How many part-time shifts are needed? Use the surplus variables to comment on the desirability of scheduling at least some of the part-time employees for 3-hour shifts.
c. Assume that part-time employees can be assigned either a 3-hour or a 4-hour shift. Develop a minimum-cost schedule for the part-time employees. How many part-time shifts are needed, and what is the cost savings compared to the previous schedule?

## Case Problem 1 Planning an Advertising Campaign

The Flamingo Grill is an upscale restaurant located in St. Petersburg, Florida. To help plan an advertising campaign for the coming season, Flamingo's management team hired the advertising firm of Haskell & Johnson (HJ). The management team requested HJ's recommendation concerning how the advertising budget should be distributed across television, radio, and newspaper advertisements. The budget has been set at $279,000.

In a meeting with Flamingo's management team, HJ consultants provided the following information about the industry exposure effectiveness rating per ad, their estimate of the number of potential new customers reached per ad, and the cost for each ad:

| Advertising Media | Exposure Rating per Ad | New Customers per Ad | Cost per Ad |
|---|---|---|---|
| Television | 90 | 4000 | $10,000 |
| Radio | 25 | 2000 | $ 3000 |
| Newspaper | 10 | 1000 | $ 1000 |

The exposure rating is viewed as a measure of the value of the ad to both existing customers and potential new customers. It is a function of such things as image, message recall, visual and audio appeal, and so on. As expected, the more expensive television advertisement has the highest exposure effectiveness rating along with the greatest potential for reaching new customers.

At this point, the HJ consultants pointed out that the data concerning exposure and reach were only applicable to the first few ads in each medium. For television, HJ stated that the exposure rating of 90 and the 4000 new customers reached per ad were reliable for the first 10 television ads. After 10 ads, the benefit is expected to decline. For planning purposes, HJ recommended reducing the exposure rating to 55 and the estimate of the potential new customers reached to 1500 for any television ads beyond 10. For radio ads, the preceding data are reliable up to a maximum of 15 ads. Beyond 15 ads, the exposure rating declines to 20 and the number of new customers reached declines to 1200 per ad. Similarly, for newspaper ads, the preceding data are reliable up to a maximum of 20; the exposure rating declines to 5 and the potential number of new customers reached declines to 800 for additional ads.

Flamingo's management team accepted maximizing the total exposure rating across all media as the objective of the advertising campaign. Because of management's concern with attracting new customers, management stated that the advertising campaign must reach at least 100,000 new customers. To balance the advertising campaign and make use of all advertising media, Flamingo's management team also adopted the following guidelines:

- Use at least twice as many radio advertisements as television advertisements.
- Use no more than 20 television advertisements.
- The television budget should be at least $140,000.
- The radio advertising budget is restricted to a maximum of $99,000.
- The newspaper budget is to be at least $30,000.

HJ agreed to work with these guidelines and provide a recommendation as to how the $279,000 advertising budget should be allocated among television, radio, and newspaper advertising.

## Managerial Report

Develop a model that can be used to determine the advertising budget allocation for the Flamingo Grill. Include a discussion of the following items in your report:

1. A schedule showing the recommended number of television, radio, and newspaper advertisements and the budget allocation for each medium. Show the total exposure and indicate the total number of potential new customers reached.
2. A discussion of how the total exposure would change if an additional $10,000 were added to the advertising budget.
3. A discussion of the ranges for the objective function coefficients. What do the ranges indicate about how sensitive the recommended solution is to HJ's exposure rating coefficients?
4. The resulting media schedule if the objective of the advertising campaign was to maximize the number of potential new customers reached instead of maximizing the total exposure rating.
5. A comparison of the two media schedules resulting from items 1 and 4, respectively. What is your recommendation for the Flamingo Grill's advertising campaign?

## Case Problem 2    Phoenix Computer

Phoenix Computer manufactures and sells personal computers directly to customers. Orders are accepted by phone and through the company's website. Phoenix will be introducing several new laptop models over the next few months, and management recognizes a need to develop technical support personnel to specialize in the new laptop systems. One option being considered is to hire new employees and put them through a three-month training program. Another option is to put current customer service specialists through a two-month training program on the new laptop models. Phoenix estimates that the need for laptop specialists will grow from 0 to 100 during the months of May through September as follows: May—20; June—30; July—85; August—85; and September—100. After September, Phoenix expects that maintaining a staff of 100 laptop specialists will be sufficient.

The annual salary for a new employee is estimated to be $27,000 whether the person is hired to enter the training program or to replace a current employee who is entering the training program. The annual salary for the current Phoenix employees who are being considered for the training program is approximately $36,000. The cost of the three-month training program is $1500 per person, and the cost of the two-month training program is $1000 per person. Note that the length of the training program means that a lag will occur between the time when a new person is hired and the time a new laptop specialist is available. The number of current employees who will be available for training is limited. Phoenix estimates that the following numbers can be made available in the coming months: March—15; April—20; May—0; June—5; and July—10. The training center has the capacity to start new three-month and two-month training classes each month; however, the total number of students (new and current employees) that begin training each month cannot exceed 25.

Phoenix needs to determine the number of new hires that should begin the three-month training program each month and the number of current employees that should begin the two-month training program each month. The objective is to satisfy staffing needs during May through September at the lowest possible total cost; that is, minimize the incremental salary cost and the total training cost.

It is currently January, and Phoenix Computer would like to develop a plan for hiring new employees and determining the mix of new hires and current employees to place in the training program.

## Managerial Report

Perform an analysis of the Phoenix Computer problem and prepare a report that summarizes your findings. Be sure to include information on and analysis of the following items:

1. The incremental salary and training cost associated with hiring a new employee and training him/her to be a laptop specialist.
2. The incremental salary and training cost associated with putting a current employee through the training program. (Don't forget that a replacement must be hired when the current employee enters the program.)
3. Recommendations regarding the hiring and training plan that will minimize the salary and training costs over the February through August period as well as answers to these questions: What is the total cost of providing technical support for the new laptop models? How much higher will monthly payroll costs be in September than in January?

## Case Problem 3    Textile Mill Scheduling

The Scottsville Textile Mill[1] produces five different fabrics. Each fabric can be woven on one or more of the mill's 38 looms. The sales department's forecast of demand for the next month is shown in Table 9.16, along with data on the selling price per yard, variable cost per yard, and purchase price per yard. The mill operates 24 hours a day and is scheduled for 30 days during the coming month.

The mill has two types of looms: dobbie and regular. The dobbie looms are more versatile and can be used for all five fabrics. The regular looms can produce only three of the fabrics. The mill has a total of 38 looms: 8 are dobbie and 30 are regular. The rate of production for each fabric on each type of loom is given in Table 9.17. The time required to change over from producing one fabric to another is negligible and does not have to be considered.

The Scottsville Textile Mill satisfies all demand with either its own fabric or fabric purchased from another mill. Fabrics that cannot be woven at the Scottsville Mill because of limited loom capacity will be purchased from another mill. The purchase price of each fabric is also shown in Table 9.16.

---

[1] This case is based on the Calhoun Textile Mill Case by Jeffrey D. Camm, P. M. Dearing, and Suresh K. Tadisnia, 1987.

**TABLE 9.16**   MONTHLY DEMAND, SELLING PRICE, VARIABLE COST, AND PURCHASE PRICE DATA FOR SCOTTSVILLE TEXTILE MILL FABRICS

| Fabric | Demand (yards) | Selling Price ($/yard) | Variable Cost ($/yard) | Purchase Price ($/yard) |
|--------|----------------|------------------------|------------------------|-------------------------|
| 1 | 16,500 | 0.99 | 0.66 | 0.80 |
| 2 | 22,000 | 0.86 | 0.55 | 0.70 |
| 3 | 62,000 | 1.10 | 0.49 | 0.60 |
| 4 | 7,500 | 1.24 | 0.51 | 0.70 |
| 5 | 62,000 | 0.70 | 0.50 | 0.70 |

© Cengage Learning 2013

**TABLE 9.17**   LOOM PRODUCTION RATES FOR THE SCOTTSVILLE TEXTILE MILL

| | Loom Rate (yards/hour) | |
|--------|--------|---------|
| Fabric | Dobbie | Regular |
| 1 | 4.63 | — |
| 2 | 4.63 | — |
| 3 | 5.23 | 5.23 |
| 4 | 5.23 | 5.23 |
| 5 | 4.17 | 4.17 |

*Note:* Fabrics 1 and 2 can be manufactured only on the dobbie loom.

© Cengage Learning 2013

## Managerial Report

Develop a model that can be used to schedule production for the Scottsville Textile Mill, and, at the same time, determine how many yards of each fabric must be purchased from another mill. Include a discussion and analysis of the following items in your report:

1. The final production schedule and loom assignments for each fabric.
2. The projected total contribution to profit.
3. A discussion of the value of additional loom time. (The mill is considering purchasing a ninth dobbie loom. What is your estimate of the monthly profit contribution of this additional loom?)
4. A discussion of the objective coefficients' ranges.
5. A discussion of how the objective of minimizing total costs would provide a different model than the objective of maximizing total profit contribution. (How would the interpretation of the objective coefficients' ranges differ for these two models?)

## Case Problem 4   Workforce Scheduling

Davis Instruments has two manufacturing plants located in Atlanta, Georgia. Product demand varies considerably from month to month, causing Davis extreme difficulty in workforce scheduling. Recently Davis started hiring temporary workers supplied by Work-Force Unlimited, a company that specializes in providing temporary employees for firms in the greater Atlanta area. WorkForce Unlimited offered to provide temporary employees under three contract options that differ in terms of the length of employment and the cost. The three options are summarized:

| Option | Length of Employment | Cost |
|--------|---------------------|------|
| 1 | One month | $2000 |
| 2 | Two months | $4800 |
| 3 | Three months | $7500 |

The longer contract periods are more expensive because WorkForce Unlimited experiences greater difficulty finding temporary workers who are willing to commit to longer work assignments.

Over the next six months, Davis projects the following needs for additional employees:

| Month | January | February | March | April | May | June |
|-------|---------|----------|-------|-------|-----|------|
| **Employees Needed** | 10 | 23 | 19 | 26 | 20 | 14 |

Each month, Davis can hire as many temporary employees as needed under each of the three options. For instance, if Davis hires five employees in January under Option 2, WorkForce Unlimited will supply Davis with five temporary workers who will work two months: January and February. For these workers, Davis will have to pay 5($4800) = $24,000. Because of some merger negotiations under way, Davis does not want to commit to any contractual obligations for temporary employees that extend beyond June.

Davis's quality control program requires each temporary employee to receive training at the time of hire. The training program is required even if the person worked for Davis Instruments in the past. Davis estimates that the cost of training is $875 each time a temporary employee is hired. Thus, if a temporary employee is hired Davis will incur a training cost of $875 in the first month of hire, but will incur no additional training cost if the employee is on a two- or three-month contract.

## Managerial Report

Develop a model that can be used to determine the number of temporary employees Davis should hire each month under each contract plan in order to meet the projected needs at a minimum total cost. Include the following items in your report:

1. A schedule that shows the number of temporary employees that Davis should hire each month for each contract option.
2. A summary table that shows the number of temporary employees that Davis should hire under each contract option, the associated contract cost for each option, and the associated training cost for each option. Provide summary totals showing the total number of temporary employees hired, total contract costs, and total training costs.
3. An explanation of how reducing the cost to train each temporary employee to $700 per month affects the hiring plan. Discuss the implications that this effect on the hiring plan has for identifying methods for reducing training costs. How much of a reduction in training costs would be required to change the hiring plan based on a training cost of $875 per temporary employee?
4. A recommendation regarding the decision to hire additional full-time employees if Davis can hire 10 full-time employees at the beginning of January in order to satisfy part of the labor requirements over the next six months. Assume that Davis

can hire full-time employees at $16.50 per hour, including fringe benefits, and that full-time and temporary employees both work approximately 160 hours per month. What effect would does the hiring of additional full-time employees have on total labor and training costs over the six-month period as compared to hiring only temporary employees?

## Case Problem 5    Duke Energy Coal Allocation[2]

Duke Energy manufactures and distributes electricity to customers in the United States and Latin America. Duke Energy acquired Cinergy Corporation in 2005, which had generating facilities and energy customers in Indiana, Kentucky, and Ohio. For these customers Cinergy has been spending $725 to $750 million each year for the fuel needed to operate its coal-fired and gas-fired power plants; 92% to 95% of the fuel used is coal. In this region, Duke Energy uses 10 coal-burning generating plants: 5 located inland and 5 located on the Ohio River. Some plants have more than one generating unit. Duke Energy uses 28–29 million tons of coal per year at a cost of approximately $2 million every day in this region.

Duke Energy purchases coal using fixed-tonnage or variable-tonnage contracts from mines in Indiana (49%), West Virginia (20%), Ohio (12%), Kentucky (11%), Illinois (5%), and Pennsylvania (3%). Duke Energy must purchase all of the coal contracted for on fixed-tonnage contracts, but on variable-tonnage contracts it can purchase varying amounts up to the limit specified in the contract. The coal is shipped from the mines to Duke Energy's generating facilities in Ohio, Kentucky, and Indiana. The cost of coal varies from $19 to $35 per ton, and transportation/delivery charges range from $1.50 to $5.00 per ton.

A model is used to determine the megawatt-hours (mWh) of electricity that each generating unit is expected to produce and to provide a measure of each generating unit's efficiency, referred to as the heat rate. The heat rate is the total British thermal units [BTUs] required to produce 1 kilowatt-hour (kWh) of electrical power.

### Coal Allocation Model

Duke Energy uses a linear programming model, called the coal allocation model, to allocate coal to its generating facilities. The objective of the coal allocation model is to determine the lowest-cost method for purchasing and distributing coal to the generating units. The supply/availability of the coal is determined by the contracts with the various mines, and the demand for coal at the generating units is determined indirectly by the megawatt-hours of electricity each unit must produce.

The cost to process coal, called the add-on cost, depends upon the characteristics of the coal (moisture content, ash content, BTU content, sulfur content, and grindability) and the efficiency of the generating unit. The add-on cost plus the transportation cost are added to the purchase cost of the coal to determine the total cost to purchase and use the coal.

### Current Problem

Duke Energy signed three fixed-tonnage contracts and four variable-tonnage contracts. The company would like to determine the least-cost way to allocate the coal available through

---

[2] The authors are indebted to Thomas Mason and David Bossee of Duke Energy Corporation, formerly Cinergy Corp., for their contribution to this case problem.

these contracts to five generating units. The relevant data for the three fixed-tonnage contracts are as follows:

| Supplier | Number of Tons Contracted For | Cost ($/ton) | BTU/lb |
|----------|------------------------------|--------------|--------|
| RAG | 350,000 | 22 | 13,000 |
| Peabody Coal Sales | 300,000 | 26 | 13,300 |
| American Coal Sales | 275,000 | 22 | 12,600 |

For example, the contract signed with RAG requires Duke Energy to purchase 350,000 tons of coal at a price of $22 per ton; each pound of this particular coal provides 13,000 BTUs.

The data for the four variable-tonnage contracts follow:

| Supplier | Number of Tons Available | Cost ($/ton) | BTU/lb |
|----------|--------------------------|--------------|--------|
| Consol, Inc. | 200,000 | 32 | 12,250 |
| Cyprus Amax | 175,000 | 35 | 12,000 |
| Addington Mining | 200,000 | 31 | 12,000 |
| Waterloo | 180,000 | 33 | 11,300 |

For example, the contract with Consol, Inc., enables Duke Energy to purchase up to 200,000 tons of coal at a cost of $32 per ton; each pound of this coal provides 12,250 BTUs.

The number of megawatt-hours of electricity that each generating unit must produce and the heat rate provided are as follows:

| Generating Unit | Electricity Produced (mWh) | Heat Rate (BTU per kWh) |
|-----------------|----------------------------|--------------------------|
| Miami Fort Unit 5 | 550,000 | 10,500 |
| Miami Fort Unit 7 | 500,000 | 10,200 |
| Beckjord Unit 1 | 650,000 | 10,100 |
| East Bend Unit 2 | 750,000 | 10,000 |
| Zimmer Unit 1 | 1,100,000 | 10,000 |

For example, Miami Fort Unit 5 must produce 550,000 megawatt-hours of electricity, and 10,500 BTUs are needed to produce each kilowatt-hour.

The transportation cost and the add-on cost in dollars per ton are shown here:

| Supplier | Transportation Cost ($/ton) | | | | |
|----------|:---:|:---:|:---:|:---:|:---:|
| | Miami Fort Unit 5 | Miami Fort Unit 7 | Beckjord Unit 1 | East Bend Unit 2 | Zimmer Unit 1 |
| RAG | 5.00 | 5.00 | 4.75 | 5.00 | 4.75 |
| Peabody | 3.75 | 3.75 | 3.50 | 3.75 | 3.50 |
| American | 3.00 | 3.00 | 2.75 | 3.00 | 2.75 |
| Consol | 3.25 | 3.25 | 2.85 | 3.25 | 2.85 |
| Cyprus | 5.00 | 5.00 | 4.75 | 5.00 | 4.75 |
| Addington | 2.25 | 2.25 | 2.00 | 2.25 | 2.00 |
| Waterloo | 2.00 | 2.00 | 1.60 | 2.00 | 1.60 |

| | Add-On Cost ($/ton) | | | | |
| Supplier | Miami Fort Unit 5 | Miami Fort Unit 7 | Beckjord Unit 1 | East Bend Unit 2 | Zimmer Unit 1 |
|---|---|---|---|---|---|
| RAG | 10.00 | 10.00 | 10.00 | 5.00 | 6.00 |
| Peabody | 10.00 | 10.00 | 11.00 | 6.00 | 7.00 |
| American | 13.00 | 13.00 | 15.00 | 9.00 | 9.00 |
| Consol | 10.00 | 10.00 | 11.00 | 7.00 | 7.00 |
| Cyprus | 10.00 | 10.00 | 10.00 | 5.00 | 6.00 |
| Addington | 5.00 | 5.00 | 6.00 | 4.00 | 4.00 |
| Waterloo | 11.00 | 11.00 | 11.00 | 7.00 | 9.00 |

## Managerial Report

Prepare a report that summarizes your recommendations regarding Duke Energy's coal allocation problem. Be sure to include information and analysis for the following issues:

1. Determine how much coal to purchase from each of the mining companies and how it should be allocated to the generating units. What is the cost to purchase, deliver, and process the coal?
2. Compute the average cost of coal in cents per million BTUs for each generating unit (a measure of the cost of fuel for the generating units).
3. Compute the average number of BTUs per pound of coal received at each generating unit (a measure of the energy efficiency of the coal received at each unit).
4. Suppose that Duke Energy can purchase an additional 80,000 tons of coal from American Coal Sales as an "all or nothing deal" for $30 per ton. Should Duke Energy purchase the additional 80,000 tons of coal?
5. Suppose that Duke Energy learns that the energy content of the coal from Cyprus Amax is actually 13,000 BTUs per pound. Should Duke Energy revise its procurement plan?
6. Duke Energy has learned from its trading group that Duke Energy can sell 50,000 megawatt-hours of electricity over the grid (to other electricity suppliers) at a price of $30 per megawatt-hour. Should Duke Energy sell the electricity? If so, which generating units should produce the additional electricity?

## Appendix 9.1    Excel Solution of Hewlitt Corporation Financial Planning Problem

In Appendix 7.1 we showed how Excel could be used to solve the RMC linear programming problem. To illustrate the use of Excel in solving a more complex linear programming problem, we show the solution to the Hewlitt Corporation financial planning problem presented in Section 9.2.

The spreadsheet formulation and solution of the Hewlitt Corporation problem are shown in Figure 9.10. As described in Appendix 7.1, our practice is to put the data required for the problem in the top part of the worksheet and build the model in the bottom part of the worksheet. The model consists of a set of cells for the decision variables, a cell for the objective function, a set of cells for the left-hand-side functions, and a set of cells for the right-hand sides of the constraints. The cells for the decision variables are also enclosed by a boldface line. Descriptive labels are used to make the spreadsheet easy to read.

**FIGURE 9.10**   EXCEL SOLUTION FOR THE HEWLITT CORPORATION PROBLEM

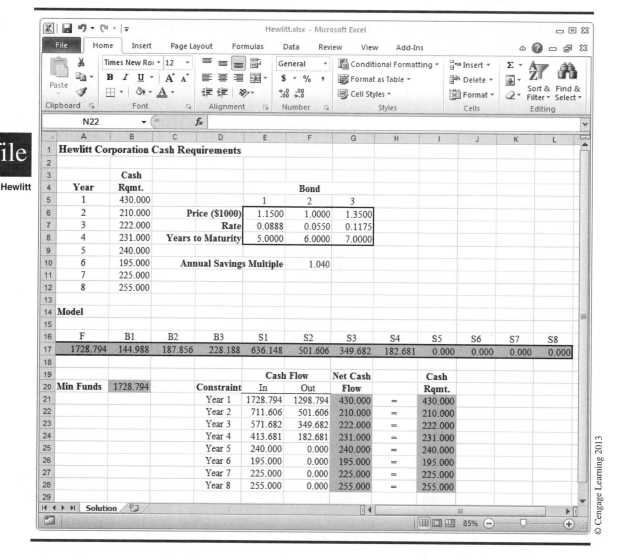

## Formulation

The data and descriptive labels are contained in cells A1:G12. The cells in the bottom portion of the spreadsheet contain the key elements of the model required by the Excel Solver.

**Decision Variables**   Cells A17:L17 are reserved for the decision variables. The optimal values (rounded to three places), are shown to be $F = 1728.794$, $B_1 = 144.988$, $B_2 = 187.856$, $B_3 = 228.188$, $S_1 = 636.148$, $S_2 = 501.606$, $S_3 = 349.682$, $S_4 = 182.681$, and $S_5 = S_6 = S_7 = S_8 = 0$.

**Objective Function**   The formula $= A17$ has been placed into cell B20 to reflect the total funds required. It is simply the value of the decision variable, $F$. The total funds required by the optimal solution are shown to be $1,728,794.

**Left-Hand Sides**   The left-hand sides for the eight constraints represent the annual net cash flow. They are placed into cells G21:G28.

Cell G21 $= $ E21 $-$ F21 (Copy to G22:G28)

For this problem, some of the left-hand-side cells reference other cells that contain formulas. These referenced cells provide Hewlitt's cash flow in and cash flow out for each of the eight years.[3] The cells and their formulas are as follows:

Cell E21 = A17

Cell E22 = SUMPRODUCT($E$7:$G$7,$B$17:$D$17)+$F$10*E17

Cell E23 = SUMPRODUCT($E$7:$G$7,$B$17:$D$17)+$F$10*F17

Cell E24 = SUMPRODUCT($E$7:$G$7,$B$17:$D$17)+$F$10*G17

Cell E25 = SUMPRODUCT($E$7:$G$7,$B$17:$D$17)+$F$10*H17

Cell E26 = (1+E7)*B17+F7*C17+G7*D17+F10*I17

Cell E27 = (1+F7)*C17+G7*D17+F10*J17

Cell E28 = (1+G7)*D17+F10*K17

Cell F21 = SUMPRODUCT(E6:G6,B17:D17)+E17

Cell F22 = F17

Cell F23 = G17

Cell F24 = H17

Cell F25 = I17

Cell F26 = J17

Cell F27 = K17

Cell F28 = L17

**Right-Hand Sides**    The right-hand sides for the eight constraints represent the annual cash requirements. They are placed into cells I21:I28.

Cell I21 = B5 (Copy to I22:I28)

## Excel Solution

We are now ready to use the information in the worksheet to determine the optimal solution to the Hewlitt Corporation problem. The following steps describe how to use Excel to obtain the optimal solution:

**Step 1.** Select the **Data** tab from the **Ribbon**

**Step 2.** Select **Solver** from the **Analysis** group

**Step 3.** When the **Solver Parameters** dialog box appears (see Figure 9.11):
Enter B20 in the Set **Objective Cell** box
Select the To**: Min** option
Enter A17:L17 in the **By Changing Variable Cells** box

**Step 4**. Select **Add**
When the **Add Constraint** dialog box appears:
Enter G21:G28 in the left-hand box of the **Cell Reference** box
From the middle drop-down button, select =
Enter I21:I28 in **Constraint** box
Click **OK**

---

[3] The cash flow in is the sum of the positive terms in each constraint equation in the mathematical model, and the cash flow out is the sum of the negative terms in each constraint equation.

**FIGURE 9.11**    EXCEL SOLVER PARAMETERS DIALOG BOX FOR THE HEWLITT
CORPORATION PROBLEM

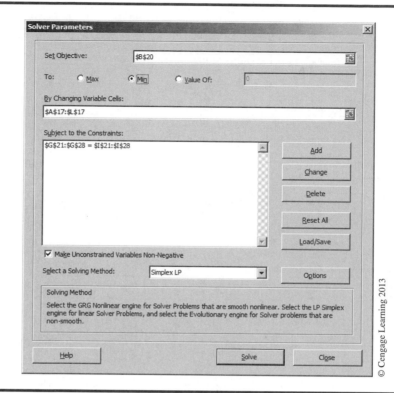

**Step 5.** When the **Solver Parameters** dialog box reappears (see Figure 9.11):
Click the checkbox for **Make Unconstrained Variables Non-negative**
**Step 6.** Select the **Select a Solving Method** drop-down button
Select **Simplex LP**
**Step 7.** Choose **Solve**
**Step 8.** When the **Solver Results** dialog box appears:
Select **Keep Solver Solution**
Select **Sensitivity** in the **Reports** box
Click **OK**

The Solver Parameters dialog box is shown in Figure 9.11. The optimal solution is shown in Figure 9.10; the accompanying sensitivity report is shown in Figure 9.12.

## Discussion

Recall that the Excel sensitivity report uses the term *shadow price* to describe the *change* in value of the solution per unit increase in the right-hand side of a constraint. LINGO uses the term *dual price* to describe the *improvement* in value of the solution per unit increase in the right-hand side of a constraint. For maximization problems, the shadow price and dual price are the same; for minimization problems, the shadow price and dual price have opposite signs.

**FIGURE 9.12** EXCEL SOLVER SENSITIVITY REPORT FOR THE HEWLITT CORPORATION PROBLEM

Variable Cells

| Cell | Name | Final Value | Reduced Cost | Objective Coefficient | Allowable Increase | Allowable Decrease |
|---|---|---|---|---|---|---|
| $A$17 | Dollers Needed | 1728.794 | 0.000 | 1.000 | 1E+30 | 1.000 |
| $B$17 | Bond 1 - Year 1 | 144.988 | 0.000 | 0.000 | 0.0670 | 0.013 |
| $C$17 | Bond 2 - Year 2 | 187.856 | 0.000 | 0.000 | 0.0128 | 0.020 |
| $D$17 | Bond 3 - Year 3 | 228.188 | 0.000 | 0.000 | 0.0229 | 0.750 |
| $E$17 | Savings Year 1 | 636.148 | 0.000 | 0.000 | 0.1096 | 0.055 |
| $F$17 | Savings Year 2 | 501.606 | 0.000 | 0.000 | 0.1433 | 0.057 |
| $G$17 | Savings Year 3 | 349.682 | 0.000 | 0.000 | 0.2109 | 0.059 |
| $H$17 | Savings Year 4 | 182.681 | 0.000 | 0.000 | 0.4136 | 0.061 |
| $I$17 | Savings Year 5 | 0.000 | 0.064 | 0.000 | 1E+30 | 0.064 |
| $J$17 | Savings Year 6 | 0.000 | 0.013 | 0.000 | 1E+30 | 0.013 |
| $K$17 | Savings Year 7 | 0.000 | 0.021 | 0.000 | 1E+30 | 0.021 |
| $L$17 | Savings Year 8 | 0.000 | 0.671 | 0.000 | 1E+30 | 0.671 |

Constraints

| Cell | Name | Final Value | Shadow Price | Constraint R.H. Side | Allowable Increase | Allowable Decrease |
|---|---|---|---|---|---|---|
| $G$21 | Year 1 Flow | 430.000 | 1.000 | 430.000 | 1E+30 | 1728.794 |
| $G$22 | Year 2 Flow | 210.000 | 0.962 | 210.000 | 1E+30 | 661.594 |
| $G$23 | Year 3 Flow | 222.000 | 0.925 | 222.000 | 1E+30 | 521.670 |
| $G$24 | Year 4 Flow | 231.000 | 0.889 | 231.000 | 1E+30 | 363.669 |
| $G$25 | Year 5 Flow | 240.000 | 0.855 | 240.000 | 1E+30 | 189.988 |
| $G$26 | Year 6 Flow | 195.000 | 0.760 | 195.000 | 2149.928 | 157.856 |
| $G$27 | Year 7 Flow | 225.000 | 0.719 | 225.000 | 3027.962 | 198.188 |
| $G$28 | Year 8 Flow | 225.000 | 0.671 | 225.000 | 1583.882 | 255.000 |

# CHAPTER 10

# Distribution and Network Models

The models discussed in this chapter belong to a special class of linear programming problems called *network flow* problems. We begin by discussing models commonly encountered when dealing with problems related to supply chains, specifically transportation and transshipment problems. We then consider three other types of network problems: assignment problems, shortest-route problems, and maximal flow problems.

In each case, we present a graphical representation of the problem in the form of a *network*. We then show how the problem can be formulated and solved as a linear program. In the last section of the chapter we present a production and inventory problem that is an interesting application of the transshipment problem.

 ## 10.1 Supply Chain Models

A **supply chain** describes the set of all interconnected resources involved in producing and distributing a product. For instance, a supply chain for automobiles could include raw material producers, automotive-parts suppliers, distribution centers for storing automotive parts, assembly plants, and car dealerships. All the materials needed to produce a finished automobile must flow through the supply chain. In general, supply chains are designed to satisfy customer demand for a product at minimum cost. Those that control the supply chain must make decisions such as where to produce the product, how much should be produced, and where it should be sent. We will look at two specific types of problems common in supply chain models that can be solved using linear programing: transportation problems and transshipment problems.

### Transportation Problem

The **transportation problem** arises frequently in planning for the distribution of goods and services from several supply locations to several demand locations. Typically, the quantity of goods available at each supply location (origin) is limited, and the quantity of goods needed at each of several demand locations (destinations) is known. The usual objective in a transportation problem is to minimize the cost of shipping goods from the origins to the destinations.

Let us illustrate by considering a transportation problem faced by Foster Generators. This problem involves the transportation of a product from three plants to four distribution centers. Foster Generators operates plants in Cleveland, Ohio; Bedford, Indiana; and York, Pennsylvania. Production capacities over the next three-month planning period for one particular type of generator are as follows:

| Origin | Plant | Three-Month Production Capacity (units) |
|--------|-------|------------------------|
| 1 | Cleveland | 5,000 |
| 2 | Bedford | 6,000 |
| 3 | York | 2,500 |
| | **Total** | 13,500 |

The firm distributes its generators through four regional distribution centers located in Boston, Chicago, St. Louis, and Lexington; the three-month forecast of demand for the distribution centers is as follows:

| Destination | Distribution Center | Three-Month Demand Forecast (units) |
|---|---|---|
| 1 | Boston | 6,000 |
| 2 | Chicago | 4,000 |
| 3 | St. Louis | 2,000 |
| 4 | Lexington | 1,500 |
| | **Total** | 13,500 |

Management would like to determine how much of its production should be shipped from each plant to each distribution center. Figure 10.1 shows graphically the 12 distribution routes Foster can use. Such a graph is called a **network**; the circles are referred to as

**FIGURE 10.1**  THE NETWORK REPRESENTATION OF THE FOSTER GENERATORS TRANSPORTATION PROBLEM

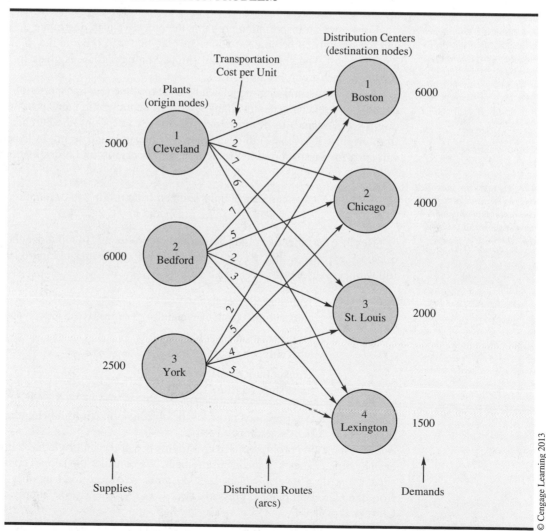

**TABLE 10.1**    TRANSPORTATION COST PER UNIT FOR THE FOSTER GENERATORS TRANSPORTATION PROBLEM

| Origin | Destination | | | |
| --- | --- | --- | --- | --- |
| | **Boston** | **Chicago** | **St. Louis** | **Lexington** |
| Cleveland | 3 | 2 | 7 | 6 |
| Bedford | 7 | 5 | 2 | 3 |
| York | 2 | 5 | 4 | 5 |

© Cengage Learning 2013

**nodes** and the lines connecting the nodes as **arcs**. Each origin and destination is represented by a node, and each possible shipping route is represented by an arc. The amount of the supply is written next to each origin node, and the amount of the demand is written next to each destination node. The goods shipped from the origins to the destinations represent the flow in the network. Note that the direction of flow (from origin to destination) is indicated by the arrows.

*Try Problem 1 for practice in developing a network model of a transportation problem.*

For Foster's transportation problem, the objective is to determine the routes to be used and the quantity to be shipped via each route that will provide the minimum total transportation cost. The cost for each unit shipped on each route is given in Table 10.1 and is shown on each arc in Figure 10.1.

A linear programming model can be used to solve this transportation problem. We use double-subscripted decision variables, with $x_{11}$ denoting the number of units shipped from origin 1 (Cleveland) to destination 1 (Boston), $x_{12}$ denoting the number of units shipped from origin 1 (Cleveland) to destination 2 (Chicago), and so on. In general, the decision variables for a transportation problem having $m$ origins and $n$ destinations are written as follows:

*The first subscript identifies the "from" node of the corresponding arc and the second subscript identifies the "to" node of the arc.*

$$x_{ij} = \text{number of units shipped from origin } i \text{ to destination } j$$
$$\text{where } i = 1, 2, \ldots, m \text{ and } j = 1, 2, \ldots, n$$

Because the objective of the transportation problem is to minimize the total transportation cost, we can use the cost data in Table 10.1 or on the arcs in Figure 10.1 to develop the following cost expressions:

Transportation costs for
units shipped from Cleveland $= 3x_{11} + 2x_{12} + 7x_{13} + 6x_{14}$

Transportation costs for
units shipped from Bedford $\quad = 7x_{21} + 5x_{22} + 2x_{23} + 3x_{24}$

Transportation costs for
units shipped from York $\quad\quad = 2x_{31} + 5x_{32} + 4x_{33} + 5x_{34}$

The sum of these expressions provides the objective function showing the total transportation cost for Foster Generators.

Transportation problems need constraints because each origin has a limited supply and each destination has a demand requirement. We consider the supply constraints first. The capacity at the Cleveland plant is 5000 units. With the total number of units shipped from the Cleveland plant expressed as $x_{11} + x_{12} + x_{13} + x_{14}$, the supply constraint for the Cleveland plant is

$$x_{11} + x_{12} + x_{13} + x_{14} \leq 5000 \quad \text{Cleveland supply}$$

With three origins (plants), the Foster transportation problem has three supply constraints. Given the capacity of 6000 units at the Bedford plant and 2500 units at the York plant, the two additional supply constraints are

$$x_{21} + x_{22} + x_{23} + x_{24} \leq 6000 \quad \text{Bedford supply}$$
$$x_{31} + x_{32} + x_{33} + x_{34} \leq 2500 \quad \text{York supply}$$

With the four distribution centers as the destinations, four demand constraints are needed to ensure that destination demands will be satisfied:

*To obtain a feasible solution, the total supply must be greater than or equal to the total demand.*

$$x_{11} + x_{21} + x_{31} = 6000 \quad \text{Boston demand}$$
$$x_{12} + x_{22} + x_{32} = 4000 \quad \text{Chicago demand}$$
$$x_{13} + x_{23} + x_{33} = 2000 \quad \text{St. Louis demand}$$
$$x_{14} + x_{24} + x_{34} = 1500 \quad \text{Lexington demand}$$

Combining the objective function and constraints into one model provides a 12-variable, 7-constraint linear programming formulation of the Foster Generators transportation problem:

$$\text{Min} \quad 3x_{11} + 2x_{12} + 7x_{13} + 6x_{14} + 7x_{21} + 5x_{22} + 2x_{23} + 3x_{24} + 2x_{31} + 5x_{32} + 4x_{33} + 5x_{34}$$

s.t.

$$
\begin{array}{llll}
x_{11} + x_{12} + x_{13} + x_{14} & & & \leq 5000 \\
x_{21} + x_{22} + x_{23} + x_{24} & & & \leq 6000 \\
x_{31} + x_{32} + x_{33} + x_{34} & & & \leq 2500 \\
x_{11} \qquad\qquad + x_{21} \qquad\qquad + x_{31} & & & = 6000 \\
x_{12} \qquad\qquad + x_{22} \qquad\qquad + x_{32} & & & = 4000 \\
x_{13} \qquad\qquad + x_{23} \qquad\qquad + x_{33} & & & = 2000 \\
x_{14} \qquad\qquad + x_{24} \qquad\qquad + x_{34} & & & = 1500 \\
\end{array}
$$

$$x_{ij} \geq 0 \quad \text{for } i = 1, 2, 3 \text{ and } j = 1, 2, 3, 4$$

Comparing the linear programming formulation to the network in Figure 10.1 leads to several observations: All the information needed for the linear programming formulation is on the network. Each node has one constraint and each arc has one variable. The sum of the variables corresponding to arcs from an origin node must be less than or equal to the origin's supply, and the sum of the variables corresponding to the arcs into a destination node must be equal to the destination's demand.

*Can you now use Excel to solve a linear programming model of a transportation problem? Try Problem 2.*

We solved the Foster Generators problem using Excel Solver. The optimal objective function values and optimal decision variable values are shown in Figure 10.2, which indicates that the minimum total transportation cost is $39,500. The values for the decision variables show the optimal amounts to ship over each route. For example, 3500 units should be shipped from Cleveland to Boston, and 1500 units should be shipped from Cleveland to Chicago. Other values of the decision variables indicate the remaining shipping quantities and routes. Table 10.2 shows the minimum cost transportation schedule, and Figure 10.3 summarizes the optimal solution on the network.

## Problem Variations

The Foster Generators problem illustrates use of the basic transportation model. Variations of the basic transportation model may involve one or more of the following situations:

1. Total supply not equal to total demand
2. Maximization objective function
3. Route capacities or route minimums
4. Unacceptable routes

**FIGURE 10.2**    OPTIMAL SOLUTION FOR THE FOSTER GENERATORS TRANSPORTATION
PROBLEM

Objective Cell (Min)

| Name | Original Value | Final Value |
|------|----------------|-------------|
| Minimize Total Cost | 0.000 | 39500.000 |

Variable Cells

| Model Variable | Name | Original Value | Final Value | Integer |
|----------------|------|----------------|-------------|---------|
| X11 | Cleveland to Boston | 0.000 | 3500.000 | Contin |
| X12 | Cleveland to Chicago | 0.000 | 1500.000 | Contin |
| X13 | Cleveland to St. Louis | 0.000 | 0.000 | Contin |
| X14 | Cleveland to Lexington | 0.000 | 0.000 | Contin |
| X21 | Bedford to Boston | 0.000 | 0.000 | Contin |
| X22 | Bedford to Chicago | 0.000 | 2500.000 | Contin |
| X23 | Bedford to St. Louis | 0.000 | 2000.000 | Contin |
| X24 | Bedford to Lexington | 0.000 | 1500.000 | Contin |
| X31 | York to Boston | 0.000 | 2500.000 | Contin |
| X32 | York to Chicago | 0.000 | 0.000 | Contin |
| X33 | York to St. Louis | 0.000 | 0.000 | Contin |
| X34 | York to Lexington | 0.000 | 0.000 | Contin |

**WEB** file

Foster

© Cengage Learning 2013

**TABLE 10.2**    OPTIMAL SOLUTION TO THE FOSTER GENERATORS TRANSPORTATION
PROBLEM

| Route | | Units | Cost | Total |
|-------|----|-------|------|-------|
| From | To | Shipped | per Unit | Cost |
| Cleveland | Boston | 3500 | $3 | $10,500 |
| Cleveland | Chicago | 1500 | $2 | $ 3,000 |
| Bedford | Chicago | 2500 | $5 | $12,500 |
| Bedford | St. Louis | 2000 | $2 | $ 4,000 |
| Bedford | Lexington | 1500 | $3 | $ 4,500 |
| York | Boston | 2500 | $2 | $ 5,000 |
| | | | | $39,500 |

© Cengage Learning 2013

With slight modifications in the linear programming model, we can easily accommodate
these situations.

**Total Supply Not Equal to Total Demand**    Often *the total supply is not equal to the
total demand.* If total supply exceeds total demand, no modification in the linear programming formulation is necessary. Excess supply will appear as slack in the linear programming solution. Slack for any particular origin can be interpreted as the unused supply or
amount not shipped from the origin.

If total supply is less than total demand, the linear programming model of a transportation problem will not have a feasible solution. In this case, we modify the network representation by adding a **dummy origin** with a supply equal to the difference between the
total demand and the total supply. With the addition of the dummy origin and an arc from

*Whenever total supply is
less than total demand, the
model does not determine
how the unsatisfied demand
is handled (e.g., backorders).
The manager must handle
this aspect of the problem.*

**FIGURE 10.3** NETWORK DIAGRAM FOR THE OPTIMAL SOLUTION TO THE FOSTER GENERATORS TRANSPORTATION PROBLEM

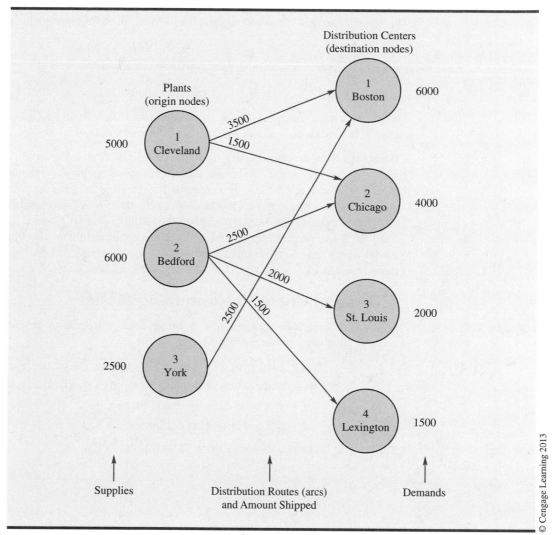

the dummy origin to each destination, the linear programming model will have a feasible solution. A zero cost per unit is assigned to each arc leaving the dummy origin so that the value of the optimal solution for the revised problem will represent the shipping cost for the units actually shipped (no shipments actually will be made from the dummy origin). When the optimal solution is implemented, the destinations showing shipments being received from the dummy origin will be the destinations experiencing a shortfall or unsatisfied demand.

*Try Problem 6 for practice with a case in which demand is greater than supply with a maximization objective.*

**Maximization Objective Function** In some transportation problems, the objective is to find a solution that maximizes profit or revenue. Using the values for profit or revenue per unit as coefficients in the objective function, we simply solve a maximization rather than a minimization linear program. This change does not affect the constraints.

**Route Capacities or Route Minimums** The linear programming formulation of the transportation problem also can accommodate capacities or minimum quantities for one or more of the routes. For example, suppose that in the Foster Generators problem the York–Boston route (origin 3 to destination 1) had a capacity of 1000 units because of limited space availability on its normal mode of transportation. With $x_{31}$ denoting the amount shipped from York to Boston, the route capacity constraint for the York–Boston route would be

$$x_{31} \leq 1000$$

Similarly, route minimums can be specified. For example,

$$x_{22} \geq 2000$$

would guarantee that a previously committed order for a Bedford–Chicago delivery of at least 2000 units would be maintained in the optimal solution.

**Unacceptable Routes**   Finally, establishing a route from every origin to every destination may not be possible. To handle this situation, we simply drop the corresponding arc from the network and remove the corresponding variable from the linear programming formulation. For example, if the Cleveland–St. Louis route were unacceptable or unusable, the arc from Cleveland to St. Louis could be dropped in Figure 10.1, and $x_{13}$ could be removed from the linear programming formulation. Solving the resulting 11-variable, 7-constraint model would provide the optimal solution while guaranteeing that the Cleveland–St. Louis route is not used.

## A General Linear Programming Model

To show the general linear programming model for a transportation problem with $m$ origins and $n$ destinations, we use the following notation:

$$x_{ij} = \text{number of units shipped from origin } i \text{ to destination } j$$
$$c_{ij} = \text{cost per unit of shipping from origin } i \text{ to destination } j$$
$$s_i = \text{supply or capacity in units at origin } i$$
$$d_j = \text{demand in units at destination } j$$

The general linear programming model is as follows:

$$\text{Min} \quad \sum_{i=1}^{m} \sum_{j=1}^{n} c_{ij} x_{ij}$$

s.t.

$$\sum_{j=1}^{n} x_{ij} \leq s_i \qquad i = 1, 2, \ldots, m \quad \text{Supply}$$

$$\sum_{i=1}^{m} x_{ij} = d_j \qquad j = 1, 2, \ldots, n \quad \text{Demand}$$

$$x_{ij} \geq 0 \qquad \text{for all } i \text{ and } j$$

As mentioned previously, we can add constraints of the form $x_{ij} \leq L_{ij}$ if the route from origin $i$ to destination $j$ has capacity $L_{ij}$. A transportation problem that includes constraints of this type is called a **capacitated transportation problem**. Similarly, we can add route minimum constraints of the form $x_{ij} \geq M_{ij}$ if the route from origin $i$ to destination $j$ must handle at least $M_{ij}$ units.

The Q.M. in Action, Optimizing Freight Car Assignments at Union Pacific, describes how Union Pacific railroad used an optimization model to solve a transportation problem of assigning empty freight cars to customer requests.

**Q.M.** *in* ACTION

*OPTIMIZING FREIGHT CAR ASSIGNMENTS AT UNION PACIFIC\**

Union Pacific (UP) is one of the largest railroads in North America. It owns over 100,000 freight cars, which it uses to service its customers via a network of over 30,000 miles of railroad track. In response to customer demand, UP moves empty freight cars to its customer locations, where the cars are loaded. UP then transports the loaded cars to destinations designated by the customers.

At any point in time, Union Pacific may have hundreds of customer requests for empty freight cars to transport their products. Empty freight cars are typically scattered throughout UP's rail network at previous delivery destinations. A day-to-day decision faced by UP operations managers is how to assign these empty freight cars to current freight car requests from its customers. The assignments need to be cost effective but also must meet the customers' needs in terms of service time.

*\*Based on A. Narisetty et al., "An Optimization Model for Empty Freight Car Assignment at Union Pacific Railroad," Interfaces 38, no. 2 (March/ April 2008): 89–102.*

UP partnered with researchers from Purdue University to develop an optimization model to assist with the empty freight car assignment problem. In order to be useful, the model had to be simple enough to be solved quickly and had to run within UP's existing information systems. A transportation model was developed, with supply being the empty freight cars at their current locations and demand being the current and forecasted requests at the customer locations. The objective function includes not just the cost of transporting the cars, but other factors such as early and late delivery penalties and customer priority. This allows the managers to trade off a variety of factors with the cost of assignments to ensure that the proper level of service is achieved. The model outputs the number of empty cars to move from each current location to the locations of customers requesting cars. The model is used on a daily basis for operations planning and is also used to study the potential impact of changes in operational policies.

## Transshipment Problem

The **transshipment problem** is an extension of the transportation problem in which intermediate nodes, referred to as *transshipment nodes*, are added to account for locations such as warehouses. In this more general type of distribution problem, shipments may be made between any pair of the three general types of nodes: origin nodes, transshipment nodes, and destination nodes. For example, the transshipment problem permits shipments of goods from origins to intermediate nodes and on to destinations, from one origin to another origin, from one intermediate location to another, from one destination location to another, and directly from origins to destinations.

As was true for the transportation problem, the supply available at each origin is limited, and the demand at each destination is specified. The objective in the transshipment problem is to determine how many units should be shipped over each arc in the network so that all destination demands are satisfied with the minimum possible transportation cost.

*Try Problem 11, part (a), for practice in developing a network representation of a transshipment problem.*

Let us consider the transshipment problem faced by Ryan Electronics. Ryan is an electronics company with production facilities in Denver and Atlanta. Components produced at either facility may be shipped to either of the firm's regional warehouses, which are located in Kansas City and Louisville. From the regional warehouses, the firm supplies retail outlets in Detroit, Miami, Dallas, and New Orleans. The key features of the problem are shown in the network model depicted in Figure 10.4. Note that the supply at each origin and demand at each destination are shown in the left and right margins, respectively. Nodes 1 and 2 are the origin nodes; nodes 3 and 4 are the transshipment nodes; and nodes 5, 6, 7, and 8 are the destination nodes. The transportation cost per unit for each distribution route is shown in Table 10.3 and on the arcs of the network model in Figure 10.4.

**FIGURE 10.4**    NETWORK REPRESENTATION OF THE RYAN ELECTRONICS
TRANSSHIPMENT PROBLEM

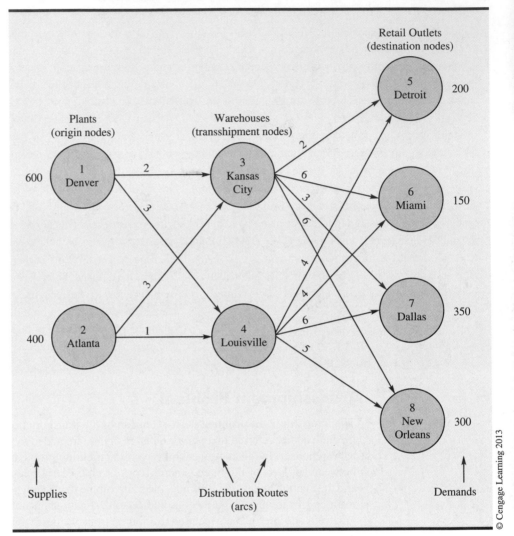

**TABLE 10.3**    TRANSPORTATION COST PER UNIT FOR THE RYAN ELECTRONICS
TRANSSHIPMENT PROBLEM

| | Warehouse | |
|---|---|---|
| **Plant** | **Kansas City** | **Louisville** |
| Denver | 2 | 3 |
| Atlanta | 3 | 1 |

| | Retail Outlet | | | |
|---|---|---|---|---|
| **Warehouse** | **Detroit** | **Miami** | **Dallas** | **New Orleans** |
| Kansas City | 2 | 6 | 3 | 6 |
| Louisville | 4 | 4 | 6 | 5 |

As with the transportation problem, we can formulate a linear programming model of the transshipment problem from a network representation. Again, we need a constraint for each node and a variable for each arc. Let $x_{ij}$ denote the number of units shipped from node $i$ to node $j$. For example, $x_{13}$ denotes the number of units shipped from the Denver plant to the Kansas City warehouse, $x_{14}$ denotes the number of units shipped from the Denver plant to the Louisville warehouse, and so on. Because the supply at the Denver plant is 600 units, the amount shipped from the Denver plant must be less than or equal to 600. Mathematically, we write this supply constraint as

$$x_{13} + x_{14} \leq 600$$

Similarly, for the Atlanta plant we have

$$x_{23} + x_{24} \leq 400$$

We now consider how to write the constraints corresponding to the two transshipment nodes. For node 3 (the Kansas City warehouse), we must guarantee that the number of units shipped out must equal the number of units shipped into the warehouse. If

$$\text{Number of units shipped out of node 3} = x_{35} + x_{36} + x_{37} + x_{38}$$

and

$$\text{Number of units shipped into node 3} = x_{13} + x_{23}$$

we obtain

$$x_{35} + x_{36} + x_{37} + x_{38} = x_{13} + x_{23}$$

Placing all the variables on the left-hand side provides the constraint corresponding to node 3 as

$$- x_{13} - x_{23} + x_{35} + x_{36} + x_{37} + x_{38} = 0$$

Similarly, the constraint corresponding to node 4 is

$$- x_{14} - x_{24} + x_{45} + x_{46} + x_{47} + x_{48} = 0$$

To develop the constraints associated with the destination nodes, we recognize that for each node the amount shipped to the destination must equal the demand. For example, to satisfy the demand for 200 units at node 5 (the Detroit retail outlet), we write

$$x_{35} + x_{45} = 200$$

Similarly, for nodes 6, 7, and 8, we have

$$x_{36} + x_{46} = 150$$
$$x_{37} + x_{47} = 350$$
$$x_{38} + x_{48} = 300$$

*Try Problem 11, parts (b) and (c), for practice in developing the linear programming model and in solving a transshipment problem on the computer.*

As usual, the objective function reflects the total shipping cost over the 12 shipping routes. Combining the objective function and constraints leads to a 12-variable, 8-constraint linear programming model of the Ryan Electronics transshipment problem (see Figure 10.5). Figure 10.6 shows the optimal solution from the answer report, and Table 10.4 summarizes the optimal solution.

As mentioned at the beginning of this section, in the transshipment problem, arcs may connect any pair of nodes. All such shipping patterns are possible in a transshipment

**FIGURE 10.5**   LINEAR PROGRAMMING FORMULATION OF THE RYAN ELECTRONICS
TRANSSHIPMENT PROBLEM

$$\text{Min } 2x_{13} + 3x_{14} + 3x_{23} + 1x_{24} + 2x_{35} + 6x_{36} + 3x_{37} + 6x_{38} + 4x_{45} + 4x_{46} + 6x_{47} + 5x_{48}$$

s.t.

$$
\begin{array}{llll}
x_{13} + x_{14} & & & \leq 600 \quad \rbrace \text{ Origin node} \\
\quad\quad\quad x_{23} + x_{24} & & & \leq 400 \quad \rbrace \text{ constraints} \\
-x_{13} \quad\quad - x_{23} \quad\quad + x_{35} + x_{36} + x_{37} + x_{38} & & = 0 \quad \rbrace \text{ Transshipment node} \\
\quad - x_{14} \quad\quad - x_{24} \quad\quad\quad + x_{45} + x_{46} + x_{47} + x_{48} & = 0 \quad \rbrace \text{ constraints} \\
\quad\quad\quad\quad\quad x_{35} \quad\quad\quad\quad\quad\quad + x_{45} & = 200 \quad \rbrace \\
\quad\quad\quad\quad\quad\quad x_{36} \quad\quad\quad\quad\quad\quad + x_{46} & = 150 \quad \rbrace \text{ Destination node} \\
\quad\quad\quad\quad\quad\quad\quad x_{37} \quad\quad\quad\quad\quad\quad + x_{47} & = 350 \quad \rbrace \text{ constraints} \\
\quad\quad\quad\quad\quad\quad\quad\quad x_{38} \quad\quad\quad\quad\quad\quad + x_{48} & = 300 \quad \rbrace
\end{array}
$$

$$x_{ij} \geq 0 \quad \text{for all } i \text{ and } j$$

© Cengage Learning 2013

**FIGURE 10.6**   OPTIMAL SOLUTION FOR THE RYAN ELECTRONICS TRANSSHIPMENT
PROBLEM

Objective Cell (Min)

| Name | Original Value | Final Value |
|---|---|---|
| Minimize Total Cost | 0.000 | 5200.000 |

Variable Cells

| Model Variable | Name | Original Value | Final Value | Integer |
|---|---|---|---|---|
| X13 | Denver–Kansas City | 0.000 | 550.000 | Contin |
| X14 | Denver–Louisville | 0.000 | 50.000 | Contin |
| X23 | Atlanta–Kansas City | 0.000 | 0.000 | Contin |
| X24 | Atlanta–Louisville | 0.000 | 400.000 | Contin |
| X35 | Kansas City–Detroit | 0.000 | 200.000 | Contin |
| X36 | Kansas City–Miami | 0.000 | 0.000 | Contin |
| X37 | Kansas City–Dallas | 0.000 | 350.000 | Contin |
| X38 | Kansas City–New Orleans | 0.000 | 0.000 | Contin |
| X45 | Louisville–Detroit | 0.000 | 0.000 | Contin |
| X46 | Louisville–Miami | 0.000 | 150.000 | Contin |
| X47 | Louisville–Dallas | 0.000 | 0.000 | Contin |
| X48 | Louisville–New Orleans | 0.000 | 300.000 | Contin |

**WEB** file

**Ryan**

© Cengage Learning 2013

problem. We still require only one constraint per node, but the constraint must include a
variable for every arc entering or leaving the node. For origin nodes, the sum of the shipments out minus the sum of the shipments in must be less than or equal to the origin supply. For destination nodes, the sum of the shipments in minus the sum of the shipments out
must equal demand. For transshipment nodes, the sum of the shipments out must equal the
sum of the shipments in, as before.

    For an illustration of this more general type of transshipment problem, let us modify
the Ryan Electronics problem. Suppose that it is possible to ship directly from Atlanta to
New Orleans at $4 per unit and from Dallas to New Orleans at $1 per unit. The network
model corresponding to this modified Ryan Electronics problem is shown in Figure 10.7,

**TABLE 10.4** OPTIMAL SOLUTION TO THE RYAN ELECTRONICS TRANSSHIPMENT
PROBLEM

| Route | | | | |
|---|---|---|---|---|
| **From** | **To** | **Units Shipped** | **Cost per Unit** | **Total Cost** |
| Denver | Kansas City | 550 | $2 | $1100 |
| Denver | Louisville | 50 | $3 | $ 150 |
| Atlanta | Louisville | 400 | $1 | $ 400 |
| Kansas City | Detroit | 200 | $2 | $ 400 |
| Kansas City | Dallas | 350 | $3 | $1050 |
| Louisville | Miami | 150 | $4 | $ 600 |
| Louisville | New Orleans | 300 | $5 | $1500 |
| | | | | $5200 |

© Cengage Learning 2013

**FIGURE 10.7** NETWORK REPRESENTATION OF THE MODIFIED RYAN ELECTRONICS
TRANSSHIPMENT PROBLEM

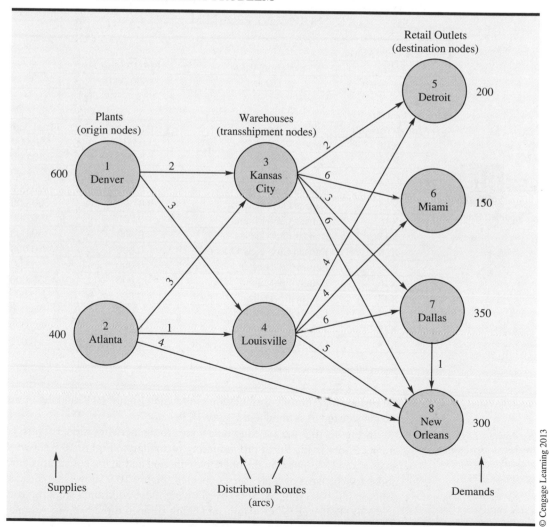

© Cengage Learning 2013

**FIGURE 10.8** LINEAR PROGRAMMING FORMULATION OF THE MODIFIED RYAN ELECTRONICS
TRANSSHIPMENT PROBLEM

Min $2x_{13} + 3x_{14} + 3x_{23} + 1x_{24} + 2x_{35} + 6x_{36} + 3x_{37} + 6x_{38} + 4x_{45} + 4x_{46} + 6x_{47} + 5x_{48} + 4x_{28} + 1x_{78}$

s.t.

$$
\begin{aligned}
x_{13} + x_{14} && \le 600 \quad &\} \text{ Origin node constraints} \\
x_{23} + x_{24} + x_{28} && \le 400 \\
-x_{13} \quad - x_{23} \quad + x_{35} + x_{36} + x_{37} + x_{38} && = 0 \quad &\} \text{ Transshipment node} \\
- x_{14} \quad - x_{24} \quad + x_{45} + x_{46} + x_{47} + x_{48} && = 0 \quad & \text{ constraints} \\
x_{35} \quad + x_{45} && = 200 \\
x_{36} \quad + x_{46} && = 150 \quad &\} \text{ Destination node} \\
x_{37} \quad + x_{47} \quad - x_{78} && = 350 \quad & \text{ constraints} \\
x_{38} \quad + x_{48} + x_{28} + x_{78} && = 300
\end{aligned}
$$

$x_{ij} \ge 0$ for all $i$ and $j$

© Cengage Learning 2013

**FIGURE 10.9** OPTIMAL SOLUTION FOR THE MODIFIED RYAN ELECTRONICS
TRANSSHIPMENT PROBLEM

Objective Cell (Min)

| Name | Original Value | Final Value |
|------|----------------|-------------|
| Total Cost | 0.000 | 4600.000 |

Variable Cells

| Model Variable | Name | Original Value | Final Value | Integer |
|----------------|------|----------------|-------------|---------|
| X13 | Denver–Kansas City | 0.000 | 550.000 | Contin |
| X14 | Denver–Louisville | 0.000 | 50.000 | Contin |
| X23 | Atlanta–Kansas City | 0.000 | 0.000 | Contin |
| X24 | Atlanta–Louisville | 0.000 | 100.000 | Contin |
| X35 | Kansas City–Detroit | 0.000 | 200.000 | Contin |
| X36 | Kansas City–Miami | 0.000 | 0.000 | Contin |
| X37 | Kansas City–Dallas | 0.000 | 350.000 | Contin |
| X38 | Kansas City–New Orleans | 0.000 | 0.000 | Contin |
| X45 | Louisville–Detroit | 0.000 | 0.000 | Contin |
| X46 | Louisville–Miami | 0.000 | 150.000 | Contin |
| X47 | Louisville–Dallas | 0.000 | 0.000 | Contin |
| X48 | Louisville–New Orleans | 0.000 | 0.000 | Contin |
| X28 | Atlanta–New Orleans | 0.000 | 300.000 | Contin |
| X78 | Dallas–New Orleans | 0.000 | 0.000 | Contin |

**WEB file**

**Modified Ryan**

© Cengage Learning 2013

the linear programming formulation is shown in Figure 10.8, and the optimal solution from
the answer report is shown in Figure 10.9.

*Try Problem 12 for practice
working with transshipment
problems with this more
general structure.*

In Figure 10.7 we added two new arcs to the network model. Thus, two new variables
are necessary in the linear programming formulation. Figure 10.8 shows that the new variables $x_{28}$ and $x_{78}$ appear in the objective function and in the constraints corresponding to the
nodes to which the new arcs are connected. Figure 10.9 shows that the value of the optimal
solution has been reduced \$600 by allowing these additional shipping routes. The value of
$x_{28} = 300$ indicates that 300 units are being shipped directly from Atlanta to New Orleans.

The value of $x_{78} = 0$ indicates that no units are shipped from Dallas to New Orleans in this solution.[1]

## Problem Variations

As with transportation problems, transshipment problems may be formulated with several variations, including

1. Total supply not equal to total demand
2. Maximization objective function
3. Route capacities or route minimums
4. Unacceptable routes

The linear programming model modifications required to accommodate these variations are identical to the modifications required for the transportation problem. When we add one or more constraints of the form $x_{ij} \leq L_{ij}$ to show that the route from node $i$ to node $j$ has capacity $L_{ij}$, we refer to the transshipment problem as a **capacitated transshipment problem**.

## A General Linear Programming Model

To show the general linear programming model for the transshipment problem, we use the following notation:

$$x_{ij} = \text{number of units shipped from node } i \text{ to node } j$$
$$c_{ij} = \text{cost per unit of shipping from node } i \text{ to node } j$$
$$s_i = \text{supply at origin node } i$$
$$d_j = \text{demand at destination node } j$$

The general linear programming model for the transshipment problem is as follows:

$$\text{Min} \quad \sum_{\text{all arcs}} c_{ij} x_{ij}$$

s.t.

$$\sum_{\text{arcs out}} x_{ij} - \sum_{\text{arcs in}} x_{ij} \leq s_i \quad \text{Origin nodes } i$$

$$\sum_{\text{arcs out}} x_{ij} - \sum_{\text{arcs in}} x_{ij} = 0 \quad \text{Transshipment nodes}$$

$$\sum_{\text{arcs in}} x_{ij} - \sum_{\text{arcs out}} x_{ij} = d_j \quad \text{Destination nodes } j$$

$$x_{ij} \geq 0 \text{ for all } i \text{ and } j$$

The Q.M. in Action, Product Sourcing Heuristic at Procter & Gamble, describes a transshipment model used by Procter & Gamble to help make strategic decisions related to sourcing and distribution.

---

[1]This is an example of a linear programming with alternate optimal solutions. The solution $x_{13} = 600$, $x_{14} = 0$, $x_{23} = 0$, $x_{24} = 150$, $x_{28} = 250$, $x_{35} = 200$, $x_{36} = 0$, $x_{37} = 400$, $x_{38} = 0$, $x_{45} = 0$, $x_{46} = 150$, $x_{47} = 0$, $x_{48} = 0$, $x_{78} = 50$ is also optimal. Thus, in this solution both new routes are used: $x_{28} = 250$ units are shipped from Atlanta to New Orleans and $x_{78} = 50$ units are shipped from Dallas to New Orleans.

## NOTES AND COMMENTS

1. Supply chain models used in practice usually lead to large linear programs. Problems with 100 origins and 100 destinations are not unusual. Such a problem would involve $(100)(100) = 10,000$ variables.

2. To handle a situation in which some routes may be unacceptable, we stated that you could drop the corresponding arc from the network and remove the corresponding variable from the linear programming formulation. Another approach often used is to assign an extremely large objective function cost coefficient to any unacceptable arc. If the problem has already been formulated, another option is to add a constraint to the formulation that sets the variable you want to remove equal to zero.

3. The optimal solution to a transportation model will consist of integer values for the decision variables as long as all supply and demand values are integers. The reason is the special mathematical structure of the linear programming model. Each variable appears in exactly one supply and one demand constraint, and all coefficients in the constraint equations are 1 or 0.

4. In the general linear programming formulation of the transshipment problem, the constraints for the destination nodes are often written as

$$\sum_{\text{arcs out}} x_{ij} - \sum_{\text{arcs in}} x_{ij} = -d_j$$

The advantage of writing the constraints this way is that the left-hand side of each constraint then represents the flow out of the node minus the flow in.

## Q.M. *in* ACTION

### PRODUCT SOURCING HEURISTIC AT PROCTER & GAMBLE*

A few years ago Procter & Gamble (P&G) embarked on a major strategic planning initiative called the North American Product Sourcing Study. P&G wanted to consolidate its product sources and optimize its distribution system design throughout North America. A decision support system used to aid in this project was called the Product Sourcing Heuristic (PSH) and was based on a transshipment model much like the ones described in this chapter.

In a preprocessing phase, the many P&G products were aggregated into groups that shared the same technology and could be made at the same plant. The PSH employing the transshipment model was then used by product strategy teams responsible for developing product sourcing options for these product groups. The various plants that could produce the product group were the source nodes, the company's regional distribution centers were the transshipment nodes, and P&G's customer zones were the destinations. Direct shipments to customer zones as well as shipments through distribution centers were employed.

The product strategy teams used the heuristic interactively to explore a variety of questions concerning product sourcing and distribution. For instance, the team might be interested in the impact of closing two of five plants and consolidating production in the three remaining plants. The product sourcing heuristic would then delete the source nodes corresponding to the two closed plants, make any capacity modifications necessary to the sources corresponding to the remaining three plants, and re-solve the transshipment problem. The product strategy team could then examine the new solution, make some more modifications, solve again, and so on.

The Product Sourcing Heuristic was viewed as a valuable decision support system by all who used it. When P&G implemented the results of the study, it realized annual savings in the $200 million range. The PSH proved so successful in North America that P&G used it in other markets around the world.

*Based on information provided by Franz Dill and Tom Chorman of Procter & Gamble.

10.2 # Assignment Problem

The **assignment problem** arises in a variety of decision-making situations; typical assignment problems involve assigning jobs to machines, agents to tasks, sales personnel to sales territories, contracts to bidders, and so on. A distinguishing feature of the assignment problem is that *one* agent is assigned to *one and only one* task. Specifically, we look for the set of assignments that will optimize a stated objective, such as minimize cost, minimize time, or maximize profits.

To illustrate the assignment problem, let us consider the case of Fowle Marketing Research, which has just received requests for market research studies from three new clients. The company faces the task of assigning a project leader (agent) to each client (task). Currently, three individuals have no other commitments and are available for the project leader assignments. Fowle's management realizes, however, that the time required to complete each study will depend on the experience and ability of the project leader assigned. The three projects have approximately the same priority, and management wants to assign project leaders to minimize the total number of days required to complete all three projects. If a project leader is to be assigned to one client only, which assignments should be made?

To answer the assignment question, Fowle's management must first consider all possible project leader–client assignments and then estimate the corresponding project completion times. With three project leaders and three clients, nine assignment alternatives are possible. The alternatives and the estimated project completion times in days are summarized in Table 10.5.

*Try Problem 17, part (a), for practice in developing a network model for an assignment problem.*

Figure 10.10 shows the network representation of Fowle's assignment problem. The nodes correspond to the project leaders and clients, and the arcs represent the possible assignments of project leaders to clients. The supply at each origin node and the demand at each destination node are 1; the cost of assigning a project leader to a client is the time it takes that project leader to complete the client's task. Note the similarity between the network models of the assignment problem (Figure 10.10) and the transportation problem (Figure 10.1). The assignment problem is a special case of the transportation problem in which all supply and demand values equal 1, and the amount shipped over each arc is either 0 or 1.

*The assignment problem is a special case of the transportation problem.*

Because the assignment problem is a special case of the transportation problem, a linear programming formulation can be developed. Again, we need a constraint for each node and a variable for each arc. As in the transportation problem, we use double-subscripted decision variables, with $x_{11}$ denoting the assignment of project leader 1 (Terry) to client 1, $x_{12}$

**TABLE 10.5** ESTIMATED PROJECT COMPLETION TIMES (DAYS) FOR THE FOWLE MARKETING RESEARCH ASSIGNMENT PROBLEM

| | Client | | |
|---|---|---|---|
| **Project Leader** | **1** | **2** | **3** |
| 1. Terry | 10 | 15 | 9 |
| 2. Carle | 9 | 18 | 5 |
| 3. McClymonds | 6 | 14 | 3 |

**FIGURE 10.10** A NETWORK MODEL OF THE FOWLE MARKETING RESEARCH ASSIGNMENT PROBLEM

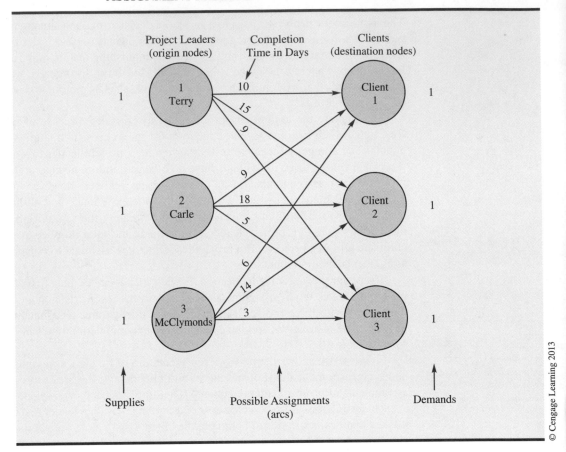

denoting the assignment of project leader 1 (Terry) to client 2, and so on. Thus, we define the decision variables for Fowle's assignment problem as

$$x_{ij} = \begin{cases} 1 & \text{if project leader } i \text{ is assigned to client } j \\ 0 & \text{otherwise} \end{cases}$$

where $i = 1, 2, 3$, and $j = 1, 2, 3$

Using this notation and the completion time data in Table 10.5, we develop completion time expressions:

Days required for Terry's assignment $= 10x_{11} + 15x_{12} + 9x_{13}$

Days required for Carle's assignment $= 9x_{21} + 18x_{22} + 5x_{23}$

Days required for McClymonds's assignment $= 6x_{31} + 14x_{32} + 3x_{33}$

The sum of the completion times for the three project leaders will provide the total days required to complete the three assignments. Thus, the objective function is

Min $10x_{11} + 15x_{12} + 9x_{13} + 9x_{21} + 18x_{22} + 5x_{23} + 6x_{31} + 14x_{32} + 3x_{33}$

*Because the number of project leaders equals the number of clients, all the constraints could be written as equalities. But when the number of project leaders exceeds the number of clients, less-than-or-equal-to constraints must be used for the project leader constraints.*

The constraints for the assignment problem reflect the conditions that each project leader can be assigned to at most one client and that each client must have one assigned project leader. These constraints are written as follows:

$$x_{11} + x_{12} + x_{13} \leq 1 \quad \text{Terry's assignment}$$
$$x_{21} + x_{22} + x_{23} \leq 1 \quad \text{Carle's assignment}$$
$$x_{31} + x_{32} + x_{33} \leq 1 \quad \text{McClymonds's assignment}$$
$$x_{11} + x_{21} + x_{31} = 1 \quad \text{Client 1}$$
$$x_{12} + x_{22} + x_{32} = 1 \quad \text{Client 2}$$
$$x_{13} + x_{23} + x_{33} = 1 \quad \text{Client 3}$$

Note that each node in Figure 10.10 has one constraint.

*Try Problem 17, part (b), for practice in formulating and solving a linear programming model for an assignment problem on the computer.*

Combining the objective function and constraints into one model provides the following nine-variable, six-constraint linear programming model of the Fowle Marketing Research assignment problem:

$$\text{Min} \quad 10x_{11} + 15x_{12} + 9x_{13} + 9x_{21} + 18x_{22} + 5x_{23} + 6x_{31} + 14x_{32} + 3x_{33}$$

s.t.

$$
\begin{array}{llllllll}
x_{11} + & x_{12} + & x_{13} & & & & & \leq 1 \\
& & & x_{21} + & x_{22} + & x_{23} & & \leq 1 \\
& & & & & & x_{31} + x_{32} + x_{33} \leq 1 \\
x_{11} & & & + x_{21} & & & + x_{31} & = 1 \\
& x_{12} & & & + x_{22} & & & + x_{32} = 1 \\
& & x_{13} & & & + x_{23} & & + x_{33} = 1 \\
\end{array}
$$
$$x_{ij} \geq 0 \quad \text{for } i = 1, 2, 3; j = 1, 2, 3$$

Figure 10.11 shows the optimal solution from the answer report for this model. Terry is assigned to client 2 ($x_{12} = 1$), Carle is assigned to client 3 ($x_{23} = 1$), and McClymonds

**FIGURE 10.11**   OPTIMAL SOLUTION FOR THE FOWLE MARKETING RESEARCH ASSIGNMENT PROBLEM

Objective Cell (Min)

| Name | Original Value | Final Value |
|---|---|---|
| Minimize Completion Time | 0.000 | 26.000 |

Variable Cells

| Model Variable | Name | Original Value | Final Value | Integer |
|---|---|---|---|---|
| X11 | Terry to Client 1 | 0.000 | 0.000 | Contin |
| X12 | Terry to Client 2 | 0.000 | 1.000 | Contin |
| X13 | Terry to Client 3 | 0.000 | 0.000 | Contin |
| X21 | Carle to Client 1 | 0.000 | 0.000 | Contin |
| X22 | Carle to Client 2 | 0.000 | 0.000 | Contin |
| X23 | Carle to Client 3 | 0.000 | 1.000 | Contin |
| X31 | McClymonds to Client 1 | 0.000 | 1.000 | Contin |
| X32 | McClymonds to Client 2 | 0.000 | 0.000 | Contin |
| X33 | McClymonds to Client 3 | 0.000 | 0.000 | Contin |

**WEB** file

**Fowle**

© Cengage Learning 2013

**TABLE 10.6**   OPTIMAL PROJECT LEADER ASSIGNMENTS FOR THE FOWLE
MARKETING RESEARCH ASSIGNMENT PROBLEM

| Project Leader | Assigned Client | Days |
|---|---|---|
| Terry | 2 | 15 |
| Carle | 3 | 5 |
| McClymonds | 1 | 6 |
| | Total | 26 |

© Cengage Learning 2013

is assigned to client 1 ($x_{31} = 1$). The total completion time required is 26 days. This solution is summarized in Table 10.6.

## Problem Variations

Because the assignment problem can be viewed as a special case of the transportation problem, the problem variations that may arise in an assignment problem parallel those for the transportation problem. Specifically, we can handle

1. Total number of agents (supply) not equal to the total number of tasks (demand)
2. A maximization objective function
3. Unacceptable assignments

The situation in which the number of agents does not equal the number of tasks is analogous to total supply not equaling total demand in a transportation problem. If the number of agents exceeds the number of tasks, the extra agents simply remain unassigned in the linear programming solution. If the number of tasks exceeds the number of agents, the linear programming model will not have a feasible solution. In this situation, a simple modification is to add enough dummy agents to equalize the number of agents and the number of tasks. For instance, in the Fowle problem we might have had five clients (tasks) and only three project leaders (agents). By adding two dummy project leaders, we can create a new assignment problem with the number of project leaders equal to the number of clients. The objective function coefficients for the assignment of dummy project leaders would be zero so that the value of the optimal solution would represent the total number of days required by the assignments actually made (no assignments will actually be made to the clients receiving dummy project leaders).

If the assignment alternatives are evaluated in terms of revenue or profit rather than time or cost, the linear programming formulation can be solved as a maximization rather than a minimization problem. In addition, if one or more assignments are unacceptable, the corresponding decision variable can be removed from the linear programming formulation. This situation could happen, for example, if an agent did not have the experience necessary for one or more of the tasks.

## A General Linear Programming Model

To show the general linear programming model for an assignment problem with $m$ agents and $n$ tasks, we use the following notation:

$$x_{ij} = \begin{cases} 1 & \text{if agent } i \text{ is assigned to task } j \\ 0 & \text{otherwise} \end{cases}$$

$$c_{ij} = \text{the cost of assigning agent } i \text{ to task } j$$

The general linear programming model is as follows:

$$\text{Min} \quad \sum_{i=1}^{m} \sum_{j=1}^{n} c_{ij} x_{ij}$$

s.t.

$$\sum_{j=1}^{n} x_{ij} \leq 1 \qquad i = 1, 2, \ldots, m \quad \text{Agents}$$

$$\sum_{i=1}^{m} x_{ij} = 1 \qquad j = 1, 2, \ldots, n \quad \text{Tasks}$$

$$x_{ij} \geq 0 \qquad \text{for all } i \text{ and } j$$

At the beginning of this section, we indicated that a distinguishing feature of the assignment problem is that *one* agent is assigned to *one and only one* task. In generalizations of the assignment problem where one agent can be assigned to two or more tasks, the linear programming formulation of the problem can be easily modified. For example, let us assume that in the Fowle Marketing Research problem Terry could be assigned up to two clients; in this case, the constraint representing Terry's assignment would be $x_{11} + x_{12} + x_{13} \leq 2$. In general, if $a_i$ denotes the upper limit for the number of tasks to which agent $i$ can be assigned, we write the agent constraints as

$$\sum_{j=1}^{n} x_{ij} \leq a_i \qquad i = 1, 2, \ldots, m$$

If some tasks require more than one agent, the linear programming formulation can also accommodate the situation. Use the number of agents required as the right-hand side of the appropriate task constraint.

## NOTES AND COMMENTS

1. As noted, the assignment model is a special case of the transportation model. We stated in the Notes and Comments at the end of the preceding section that the optimal solution to the transportation problem will consist of integer values for the decision variables as long as the supplies and demands are integers. For the assignment problem, all supplies and demands equal 1; thus, the optimal solution must be integer valued and the integer values must be 0 or 1.

2. Combining the method for handling multiple assignments with the notion of a dummy agent provides another means of dealing with situations when the number of tasks exceeds the number of agents. That is, we add one dummy agent but provide the dummy agent with the capability to handle multiple tasks. The number of tasks the dummy agent can handle is equal to the difference between the number of tasks and the number of agents.

3. The Q.M. in Action, Assigning Project Managers at Heery International, describes how managers are assigned to construction projects. The application involves multiple assignments.

---

**Q.M.** *in* ACTION

*ASSIGNING PROJECT MANAGERS AT HEERY INTERNATIONAL\**

Heery International contracts with the State of Tennessee and others for a variety of construction projects, including higher education facilities, hotels, and park facilities.

\*Based on Larry J. LeBlanc, Dale Randels, Jr., and T. K. Swann, "Heery International's Spreadsheet Optimization Model for Assigning Managers to Construction Projects," *Interfaces* (November/December 2000): 95–106.

At any particular time, Heery typically has more than 100 ongoing projects. Each of these projects must be assigned a single manager. With seven managers available, more than $700 = 7(100)$ assignments are possible. Assisted by an outside consultant, Heery International

*(continued)*

developed a mathematical model for assigning construction managers to projects.

The assignment problem developed by Heery uses 0–1 decision variables for each manager/project pair, just as in the assignment problem discussed previously. The goal in assigning managers is to balance the workload among managers and, at the same time, to minimize travel cost from the manager's home to the construction site. Thus, an objective function coefficient for each possible assignment was developed that combined project intensity (a function of the size of the project budget) with the travel distance from the manager's home to the construction site. The objective function calls for minimizing the sum over all possible assignments of the product of these coefficients with the assignment variables.

With more construction projects than managers, it was necessary to consider a variation of the standard assignment problem involving multiple assignments. Of the two sets of constraints, one set enforces the requirement that each project receive one and only one manager. The other set of constraints limits the number of assignments each manager can accept by placing an upper bound on the total intensity that is acceptable over all projects assigned.

Heery International implemented this assignment model with considerable success. According to Emory F. Redden, a Heery vice president, "The optimization model . . . has been very helpful for assigning managers to projects. . . . We have been satisfied with the assignments chosen at the Nashville office. . . . We look forward to using the model in our Atlanta office and elsewhere in the Heery organization."

#  Shortest–Route Problem

In this section we consider a problem in which the objective is to determine the **shortest route**, or *path*, between two nodes in a network. We will demonstrate the shortest-route problem by considering the situation facing the Gorman Construction Company. Gorman has several construction sites located throughout a three-county area. With multiple daily trips carrying personnel, equipment, and supplies from Gorman's office to the construction sites, the costs associated with transportation activities are substantial. The travel alternatives between Gorman's office and each construction site can be described by the road network shown in Figure 10.12. The road distances in miles between the nodes are shown above the corresponding arcs. In this application, Gorman would like to determine the route that will minimize the total travel distance between Gorman's office (located at node 1) and the construction site located at node 6.

A key to developing a model for the shortest-route problem is to understand that the problem is a special case of the transshipment problem. Specifically, the Gorman shortest-route problem can be viewed as a transshipment problem with one origin node (node 1), one destination node (node 6), and four transshipment nodes (nodes 2, 3, 4 and 5). The transshipment network for the Gorman shortest-route problem is shown in Figure 10.13. Arrows added to the arcs show the direction of flow, which is always *out* of the origin node and *into* the destination node. Note also that two directed arcs are shown between the pairs of transshipment nodes. For example, one arc going from node 2 to node 3 indicates that the shortest route may go from node 2 to node 3, and one arc going from node 3 to node 2 indicates that the shortest route may go from node 3 to node 2. The distance between two transshipment nodes is the same in either direction.

To find the shortest route between node 1 and node 6, think of node 1 as having a supply of 1 unit and node 6 as having a demand of 1 unit. Let $x_{ij}$ denote the number of units that flow or are shipped from node $i$ to node $j$. Because only 1 unit will be shipped from node 1 to node 6, the value of $x_{ij}$ will be either 1 or 0. Thus, if $x_{ij} = 1$, the arc from node $i$ to node $j$

**FIGURE 10.12**  ROAD NETWORK FOR THE GORMAN COMPANY SHORTEST-ROUTE PROBLEM

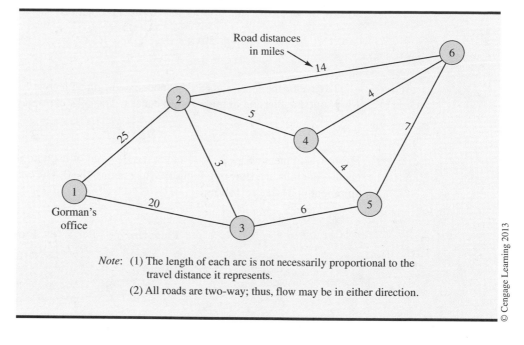

*Note*:  (1) The length of each arc is not necessarily proportional to the travel distance it represents.

(2) All roads are two-way; thus, flow may be in either direction.

**FIGURE 10.13**  TRANSSHIPMENT NETWORK FOR THE GORMAN SHORTEST-ROUTE PROBLEM

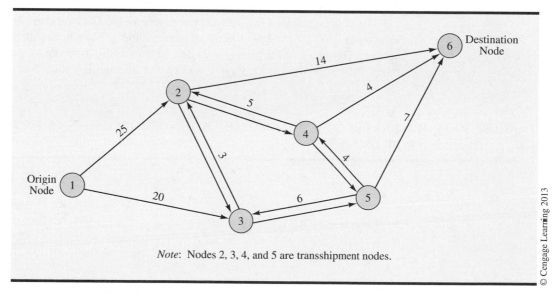

*Note*:  Nodes 2, 3, 4, and 5 are transshipment nodes.

is on the shortest route from node 1 to node 6; if $x_{ij} = 0$, the arc from node $i$ to node $j$ is not on the shortest route. Because we are looking for the shortest route between node 1 and node 6, the objective function for the Gorman problem is

$$\begin{aligned}\text{Min} \quad & 25x_{12} + 20x_{13} + 3x_{23} + 3x_{32} + 5x_{24} + 5x_{42} + 14x_{26} + 6x_{35} + 6x_{53} \\ & + 4x_{45} + 4x_{54} + 4x_{46} + 7x_{56}\end{aligned}$$

To develop the constraints for the model, we begin with node 1. Because the supply at node 1 is 1 unit, the flow out of node 1 must equal 1. Thus, the constraint for node 1 is written

$$x_{12} + x_{13} = 1$$

For transshipment nodes 2, 3, 4, and 5, the flow out of each node must equal the flow into each node; thus, the flow out minus the flow in must be 0. The constraints for the four transshipment nodes are as follows:

| | Flow Out | Flow In |
|---|---|---|
| Node 2 | $x_{23} + x_{24} + x_{26}$ | $-x_{12} - x_{32} - x_{42} = 0$ |
| Node 3 | $x_{32} + x_{35}$ | $-x_{13} - x_{23} - x_{53} = 0$ |
| Node 4 | $x_{42} + x_{45} + x_{46}$ | $-x_{24} - x_{54} = 0$ |
| Node 5 | $x_{53} + x_{54} + x_{56}$ | $-x_{35} - x_{45} = 0$ |

Because node 6 is the destination node with a demand of 1 unit, the flow into node 6 must equal 1. Thus, the constraint for node 6 is written as

$$x_{26} + x_{46} + x_{56} = 1$$

Including the negative constraints $x_{ij} \geq 0$ for all $i$ and $j$, the linear programming model for the Gorman shortest-route problem is shown in Figure 10.14.

The optimal solution from the answer report for the Gorman shortest-route problem is shown in Figure 10.15. The objective function value of 32 indicates that the shortest route between Gorman's office located at node 1 to the construction site located at node 6 is 32 miles. With $x_{13} = 1$, $x_{32} = 1$, $x_{24} = 1$, and $x_{46} = 1$, the shortest route from node 1 to node 6

**FIGURE 10.14** LINEAR PROGRAMMING FORMULATION OF THE GORMAN SHORTEST-ROUTE PROBLEM

$$\text{Min } 25x_{12} + 20x_{13} + 3x_{23} + 3x_{32} + 5x_{24} + 5x_{42} + 14x_{26} + 6x_{35} + 6x_{53} + 4x_{45} + 4x_{54} + 4x_{46} + 7x_{56}$$

s.t.

$$\begin{aligned}
x_{12} + x_{13} &= 1 && \text{Origin node} \\
-x_{12} + x_{23} - x_{32} + x_{24} - x_{42} + x_{26} &= 0 && \\
-x_{13} - x_{23} + x_{32} + x_{35} - x_{53} &= 0 && \text{Transshipment nodes} \\
-x_{24} + x_{42} + x_{45} - x_{54} + x_{46} &= 0 && \\
-x_{35} + x_{53} - x_{45} + x_{54} + x_{56} &= 0 && \\
x_{26} + x_{46} + x_{56} &= 1 && \text{Destination node}
\end{aligned}$$

$x_{ij} \geq 0$ for all $i$ and $j$

**FIGURE 10.15**   OPTIMAL SOLUTION FOR THE GORMAN SHORTEST-ROUTE PROBLEM

Objective Cell (Min)

| Name | Original Value | Final Value |
|---|---|---|
| Total Distance | 0.000 | 32.000 |

Variable Cells

| Cell | Name | Original Value | Final Value | Integer |
|---|---|---|---|---|
| X12 | Flow from Node 1 to 2 | 0.000 | 0.000 | Contin |
| X13 | Flow from Node 1 to 3 | 0.000 | 1.000 | Contin |
| X23 | Flow from Node 2 to 3 | 0.000 | 0.000 | Contin |
| X32 | Flow from Node 3 to 2 | 0.000 | 1.000 | Contin |
| X24 | Flow from Node 2 to 4 | 0.000 | 1.000 | Contin |
| X42 | Flow from Node 4 to 2 | 0.000 | 0.000 | Contin |
| X26 | Flow from Node 2 to 6 | 0.000 | 0.000 | Contin |
| X35 | Flow from Node 3 to 5 | 0.000 | 0.000 | Contin |
| X53 | Flow from Node 5 to 3 | 0.000 | 0.000 | Contin |
| X45 | Flow from Node 4 to 5 | 0.000 | 0.000 | Contin |
| X54 | Flow from Node 5 to 4 | 0.000 | 0.000 | Contin |
| X46 | Flow from Node 4 to 6 | 0.000 | 1.000 | Contin |
| X56 | Flow from Node 5 to 6 | 0.000 | 0.000 | Contin |

**WEB** file

Gorman

*Try Problem 23 to practice solving a shortest-route problem.*

is 1–3–2–4–6; in other words, the shortest route takes us from node 1 to node 3; then from node 3 to node 2; then from node 2 to node 4; and finally from node 4 to node 6.

## A General Linear Programming Model

To show the general linear programming model for the shortest-route problem, we use the following notation:

$$x_{ij} = \begin{cases} 1 & \text{if the arc from node } i \text{ to node } j \text{ is on the shortest route} \\ 0 & \text{otherwise} \end{cases}$$

$c_{ij}$ = the distance, time, or cost associated with the arc from node $i$ to node $j$

The general linear programming model for the shortest-route problem is as follows:

$$\text{Min} \quad \sum_{\text{all arcs}} c_{ij} x_{ij}$$

s.t.

$$\sum_{\text{arcs out}} x_{ij} = 1 \quad \text{Origin node } i$$

$$\sum_{\text{arcs out}} x_{ij} - \sum_{\text{arcs in}} x_{ij} = 0 \quad \text{Transshipment nodes}$$

$$\sum_{\text{arcs in}} x_{ij} = 1 \quad \text{Destination node } j$$

1. In the Gorman problem we assumed that all roads in the network are two-way. As a result, the road connecting nodes 2 and 3 in the road network resulted in the creation of two corresponding arcs in the transshipment network. Two decision variables, $x_{23}$ and $x_{32}$, were required to show that the shortest route might go from node 2 to node 3 or from node 3 to node 2. If the road connecting nodes 2 and 3 had been a one-way road allowing flow only from node 2 to node 3, decision variable $x_{32}$ would not have been included in the model.

# 10.4 Maximal Flow Problem

The objective in a **maximal flow** problem is to determine the maximum amount of flow (vehicles, messages, fluid, etc.) that can enter and exit a network system in a given period of time. In this problem, we attempt to transmit flow through all arcs of the network as efficiently as possible. The amount of flow is limited due to capacity restrictions on the various arcs of the network. For example, highway types limit vehicle flow in a transportation system, while pipe sizes limit oil flow in an oil distribution system. The maximum or upper limit on the flow in an arc is referred to as the **flow capacity** of the arc. Even though we do not specify capacities for the nodes, we do assume that the flow out of a node is equal to the flow into the node.

As an example of the maximal flow problem, consider the north–south interstate highway system passing through Cincinnati, Ohio. The north–south vehicle flow reaches a level of 15,000 vehicles per hour at peak times. Due to a summer highway maintenance program, which calls for the temporary closing of lanes and lower speed limits, a network of alternate routes through Cincinnati has been proposed by a transportation planning committee. The alternate routes include other highways as well as city streets. Because of differences in speed limits and traffic patterns, flow capacities vary depending on the particular streets and roads used. The proposed network with arc flow capacities is shown in Figure 10.16.

**FIGURE 10.16** NETWORK OF HIGHWAY SYSTEM AND FLOW CAPACITIES (1000S/HOUR) FOR CINCINNATI

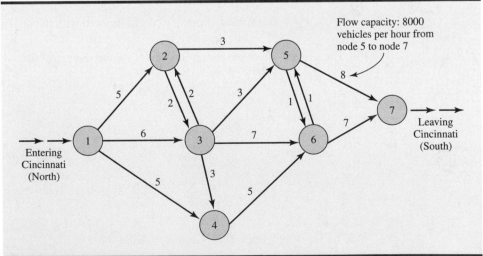

**FIGURE 10.17**   FLOW OVER ARC FROM NODE 7 TO NODE 1 TO REPRESENT
TOTAL FLOW THROUGH THE CINCINNATI HIGHWAY
SYSTEM

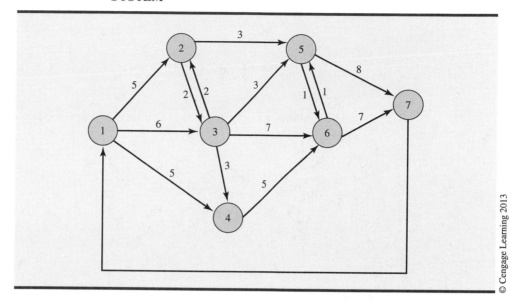

The direction of flow for each arc is indicated, and the arc capacity is shown next to each arc. Note that most of the streets are one-way. However, a two-way street can be found between nodes 2 and 3 and between nodes 5 and 6. In both cases, the capacity is the same in each direction.

We will show how to develop a capacitated transshipment model for the maximal flow problem. First, we will add an arc from node 7 back to node 1 to represent the total flow through the highway system. Figure 10.17 shows the modified network. The newly added arc shows no capacity; indeed, we will want to maximize the flow over that arc. Maximizing the flow over the arc from node 7 to node 1 is equivalent to maximizing the number of cars that can get through the north–south highway system passing through Cincinnati.

The decision variables are as follows:

$$x_{ij} = \text{amount of traffic flow from node } i \text{ to node } j$$

The objective function that maximizes the flow over the highway system is

$$\text{Max } x_{71}$$

As with all transshipment problems, each arc generates a variable and each node generates a constraint. For each node, a conservation of flow constraint represents the requirement that the flow out must equal the flow in. Or, stated another way, the flow out minus the flow in must equal zero. For node 1, the flow out is $x_{12} + x_{13} + x_{14}$, and the flow in is $x_{71}$. Therefore, the constraint for node 1 is

$$x_{12} + x_{13} + x_{14} - x_{71} = 0$$

The conservation of flow constraints for the other six nodes are developed in a similar fashion.

| | **Flow Out** | **Flow In** | |
|---|---|---|---|
| Node 2 | $x_{23} + x_{25}$ | $-x_{12} - x_{32}$ | $= 0$ |
| Node 3 | $x_{32} + x_{34} + x_{35} + x_{36}$ | $-x_{13} - x_{23}$ | $= 0$ |
| Node 4 | $x_{46}$ | $-x_{14} - x_{34}$ | $= 0$ |
| Node 5 | $x_{56} + x_{57}$ | $-x_{25} - x_{35} - x_{65}$ | $= 0$ |
| Node 6 | $x_{65} + x_{67}$ | $-x_{36} - x_{46} - x_{56}$ | $= 0$ |
| Node 7 | $x_{71}$ | $-x_{57} - x_{67}$ | $= 0$ |

Additional constraints are needed to enforce the capacities on the arcs. These 14 simple upper-bound constraints are given.

$$x_{12} \le 5 \quad x_{13} \le 6 \quad x_{14} \le 5$$
$$x_{23} \le 2 \quad x_{25} \le 3$$
$$x_{32} \le 2 \quad x_{34} \le 3 \quad x_{35} \le 5 \quad x_{36} \le 7$$
$$x_{46} \le 5$$
$$x_{56} \le 1 \quad x_{57} \le 8$$
$$x_{65} \le 1 \quad x_{67} \le 7$$

Note that the only arc without a capacity is the one we added from node 7 to node 1.

The optimal solution from the answer report for this 15-variable, 21-constraint linear programming problem is shown in Figure 10.18. We note that the value of the optimal

**FIGURE 10.18**　OPTIMAL SOLUTION FOR THE CINCINNATI HIGHWAY SYSTEM MAXIMAL FLOW PROBLEM

**Cincinnati**

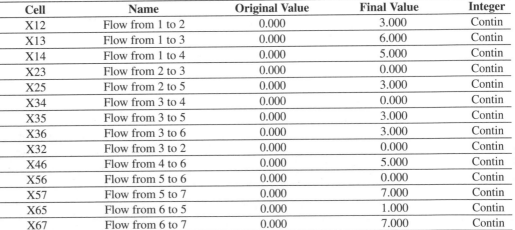

Objective Cell (Max)

| Name | Original Value | Final Value |
|---|---|---|
| Max Flow | 0.000 | 14.000 |

Variable Cells

| Cell | Name | Original Value | Final Value | Integer |
|---|---|---|---|---|
| X12 | Flow from 1 to 2 | 0.000 | 3.000 | Contin |
| X13 | Flow from 1 to 3 | 0.000 | 6.000 | Contin |
| X14 | Flow from 1 to 4 | 0.000 | 5.000 | Contin |
| X23 | Flow from 2 to 3 | 0.000 | 0.000 | Contin |
| X25 | Flow from 2 to 5 | 0.000 | 3.000 | Contin |
| X34 | Flow from 3 to 4 | 0.000 | 0.000 | Contin |
| X35 | Flow from 3 to 5 | 0.000 | 3.000 | Contin |
| X36 | Flow from 3 to 6 | 0.000 | 3.000 | Contin |
| X32 | Flow from 3 to 2 | 0.000 | 0.000 | Contin |
| X46 | Flow from 4 to 6 | 0.000 | 5.000 | Contin |
| X56 | Flow from 5 to 6 | 0.000 | 0.000 | Contin |
| X57 | Flow from 5 to 7 | 0.000 | 7.000 | Contin |
| X65 | Flow from 6 to 5 | 0.000 | 1.000 | Contin |
| X67 | Flow from 6 to 7 | 0.000 | 7.000 | Contin |
| X71 | Flow from 7 to 1 | 0.000 | 14.000 | Contin |

**FIGURE 10.19**   MAXIMAL FLOW PATTERN FOR THE CINCINNATI HIGHWAY
                     SYSTEM NETWORK

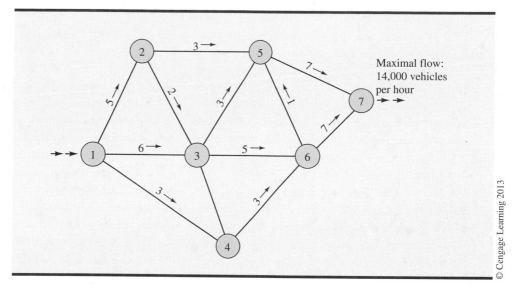

*Try Problem 29 for practice
in solving a maximal flow
problem.*

solution is 14. This result implies that the maximal flow over the highway system is 14,000
vehicles. Figure 10.19 shows how the vehicle flow is routed through the original highway
network. We note, for instance, that 3000 vehicles per hour are routed between nodes 1 and
2, 6000 vehicles per hour are routed between nodes 1 and 3, 0 vehicles are routed between
nodes 2 and 3, and so on.

   The results of the maximal flow analysis indicate that the planned highway network
system will not handle the peak flow of 15,000 vehicles per hour. The transportation
planners will have to expand the highway network, increase current arc flow capacities, or
be prepared for serious traffic problems. If the network is extended or modified, another
maximal flow analysis will determine the extent of any improved flow. The Q.M. in Action,
Optimizing Restoration Capacity at AT&T, notes that AT&T solved shortest-route and
maximal flow problems in designing a transmission network.

## NOTES AND COMMENTS

**1.** The maximal flow problem of this section can
also be solved with a slightly different formulation if the extra arc between nodes 7 and 1 is not
used. The alternate approach is to maximize the
flow into node 7 ($x_{57} + x_{67}$) and drop the conservation of flow constraints for nodes 1 and 7.
However, the formulation used in this section is
most common in practice.

**2.** Network models can be used to describe a variety of management science problems. Unfortunately, no one network solution algorithm can
be used to solve every network problem. It is
important to recognize the specific type of problem being modeled in order to select the correct
specialized solution algorithm.

*OPTIMIZING RESTORATION CAPACITY AT AT&T\**

AT&T is a global telecommunications company that provides long-distance voice and data, video, wireless, satellite, and Internet services. The company uses state-of-the-art switching and transmission equipment to provide service to more than 80 million customers. In the continental United States, AT&T's transmission network consists of more than 40,000 miles of fiber-optic cable. On peak days AT&T handles as many as 290 million calls of various types.

Power outages, natural disasters, cable cuts, and other events can disable a portion of the transmission network. When such events occur, spare capacity comprising the restoration network must be immediately employed so that service is not disrupted. Critical issues

with respect to the restoration network are as follows: How much capacity is necessary? and Where should it be located? In 1997, AT&T assembled a RestNet team to address these issues.

To optimize restoration capacity, the RestNet team developed a large-scale linear programming model. One subproblem in the model involves determining the shortest route connecting an origin and destination whenever a failure occurs in a span of the transmission network. Another subproblem solves a maximal flow problem to find the best restoration paths from each switch to a disaster recovery switch.

The RestNet team was successful, and its work is an example of how valuable management science methodology is to companies. According to C. Michael Armstrong, chair and CEO, "Last year the work of the RestNet team allowed us to reduce capital spending by tens of millions of dollars."

*\*Based on Ken Ambs, Sebastian Cwilich, Mei Deng, David J. Houck, David F. Lynch, and Dicky Yan, "Optimizing Restoration Capacity in the AT&T Network," Interfaces (January/February 2000): 26–44.*

 # 10.5 A Production and Inventory Application

The introduction to supply chain models in Section 10.1 involved applications for the shipment of goods from several supply locations or origins to several demand sites or destinations. Although the shipment of goods is the subject of many supply chain problems, supply chain models can be developed for applications that have nothing to do with the physical shipment of goods from origins to destinations. In this section we show how to use a transshipment model to solve a production and inventory problem.

Contois Carpets is a small manufacturer of carpeting for home and office installations. Production capacity, demand, production cost per square yard, and inventory holding cost per square yard for the next four quarters are shown in Table 10.7. Note that production capacity, demand, and production costs vary by quarter, whereas the cost of carrying inventory from one quarter to the next is constant at $0.25 per yard. Contois wants to

**TABLE 10.7** PRODUCTION, DEMAND, AND COST ESTIMATES FOR CONTOIS CARPETS

| Quarter | Production Capacity (square yards) | Demand (square yards) | Production Cost ($/square yard) | Inventory Cost ($/square yard) |
|---------|------------------------------------|------------------------|----------------------------------|---------------------------------|
| 1 | 600 | 400 | 2 | 0.25 |
| 2 | 300 | 500 | 5 | 0.25 |
| 3 | 500 | 400 | 3 | 0.25 |
| 4 | 400 | 400 | 3 | 0.25 |

determine how many yards of carpeting to manufacture each quarter to minimize the total production and inventory cost for the four-quarter period.

*The network flows into and out of demand nodes are what make the model a transshipment model.*

We begin by developing a network representation of the problem. First, we create four nodes corresponding to the production in each quarter and four nodes corresponding to the demand in each quarter. Each production node is connected by an outgoing arc to the demand node for the same period. The flow on the arc represents the number of square yards of carpet manufactured for the period. For each demand node, an outgoing arc represents the amount of inventory (square yards of carpet) carried over to the demand node for the next period. Figure 10.20 shows the network model. Note that nodes 1–4 represent the production for each quarter and that nodes 5–8 represent the demand for each quarter. The quarterly production capacities are shown in the left margin, and the quarterly demands are shown in the right margin.

**FIGURE 10.20**   NETWORK REPRESENTATION OF THE CONTOIS CARPETS PROBLEM

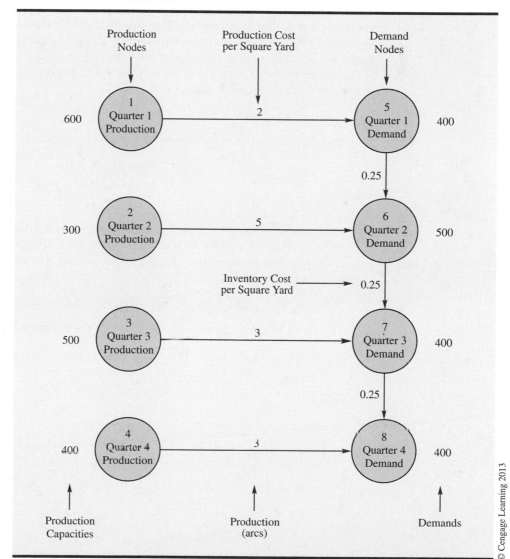

© Cengage Learning 2013

The objective is to determine a production scheduling and inventory policy that will minimize the total production and inventory cost for the four quarters. Constraints involve production capacity and demand in each quarter. As usual, a linear programming model can be developed from the network by establishing a constraint for each node and a variable for each arc.

Let $x_{15}$ denote the number of square yards of carpet manufactured in quarter 1. The capacity of the facility is 600 square yards in quarter 1, so the production capacity constraint is

$$x_{15} \leq 300$$

Using similar decision variables, we obtain the production capacities for quarters 2–4:

$$x_{26} \leq 300$$
$$x_{37} \leq 500$$
$$x_{48} \leq 400$$

We now consider the development of the constraints for each of the demand nodes. For node 5, one arc enters the node, which represents the number of square yards of carpet produced in quarter 1, and one arc leaves the node, which represents the number of square yards of carpet that will not be sold in quarter 1 and will be carried over for possible sale in quarter 2. In general, for each quarter the beginning inventory plus the production minus the ending inventory must equal demand. However, because quarter 1 has no beginning inventory, the constraint for node 5 is

$$x_{15} - x_{56} = 400$$

The constraints associated with the demand nodes in quarters 2, 3, and 4 are

$$x_{56} + x_{26} - x_{67} = 500$$
$$x_{67} + x_{37} - x_{78} = 400$$
$$x_{78} + x_{48} = 400$$

Note that the constraint for node 8 (fourth-quarter demand) involves only two variables because no provision is made for holding inventory for a fifth quarter.

The objective is to minimize total production and inventory cost, so we write the objective function as

$$\text{Min} \quad 2x_{15} + 5x_{26} + 3x_{37} + 3x_{48} + 0.25x_{56} + 0.25x_{67} + 0.25x_{78}$$

The complete linear programming formulation of the Contois Carpets problem is

$$\text{Min} \quad 2x_{15} + 5x_{26} + 3x_{37} + 3x_{48} + 0.25x_{56} + 0.25x_{67} + 0.25x_{78}$$

s.t.

$$
\begin{aligned}
x_{15} & & & & & & & & & & \leq 600 \\
& x_{26} & & & & & & & & & \leq 300 \\
& & x_{37} & & & & & & & & \leq 500 \\
& & & x_{48} & & & & & & & \leq 400 \\
x_{15} & & & & - & x_{56} & & & & & = 400 \\
& x_{26} & & & + & x_{56} & - & x_{67} & & & = 500 \\
& & x_{37} & & & & + & x_{67} & - & x_{78} & = 400 \\
& & & x_{48} & & & & & + & x_{78} & = 400 \\
\end{aligned}
$$

$$x_{ij} \geq 0 \quad \text{for all } i \text{ and } j$$

**FIGURE 10.21**   OPTIMAL SOLUTION FOR THE CONTOIS CARPETS PROBLEM

Objective Cell (Min)

| Name | Original Value | Final Value |
|------|---------------|-------------|
| Total Cost | 0.000 | 5150.000 |

**Contois**

Variable Cells

| Model Variable | Name | Original Value | Final Value | Integer |
|---------------|------|---------------|-------------|---------|
| X15 | Flow from Node 1 to 5 | 0.000 | 600.000 | Contin |
| X26 | Flow from Node 2 to 6 | 0.000 | 300.000 | Contin |
| X37 | Flow from Node 3 to 7 | 0.000 | 400.000 | Contin |
| X48 | Flow from Node 4 to 8 | 0.000 | 400.000 | Contin |
| X56 | Flow from Node 5 to 6 | 0.000 | 200.000 | Contin |
| X67 | Flow from Node 6 to 7 | 0.000 | 0.000 | Contin |
| X78 | Flow from Node 7 to 8 | 0.000 | 0.000 | Contin |

© Cengage Learning 2013

Figure 10.21 shows the optimal solution from the answer report for this problem. Contois Carpets should manufacture 600 square yards of carpet in quarter 1, 300 square yards in quarter 2, 400 square yards in quarter 3, and 400 square yards in quarter 4. Note also that 200 square yards will be carried over from quarter 1 to quarter 2. The total production and inventory cost is $5150.

## NOTES AND COMMENTS

**1.** For the network models presented in this chapter, the amount leaving the starting node for an arc is always equal to the amount entering the ending node for that arc. An extension of such a network model is the case where a gain or a loss occurs as an arc is traversed. The amount entering the destination node may be greater or smaller than the amount leaving the origin node. For instance, if cash is the commodity flowing across an arc, the cash earns interest from one period to the next. Thus, the amount of cash entering the next period is greater than the amount leaving the previous period by the amount of interest earned. Networks with gains or losses are treated in more advanced texts on network flow programming.

## Summary

In this chapter we introduced models related to supply chain problems—specifically, transportation and transshipment problems—as well as assignment, shortest-route, and maximal flow problems. All of these types of problems belong to the special category of linear programs called *network flow problems*. In general, the network model for these problems consists of nodes representing origins, destinations, and, if necessary, transshipment points in the network system. Arcs are used to represent the routes for shipment, travel, or flow between the various nodes.

Transportation problems and transshipment problems are commonly encountered when dealing with supply chains. The general transportation problem has *m* origins and *n* destinations. Given the supply at each origin, the demand at each destination, and unit shipping cost between each origin and each destination, the transportation model determines the optimal amounts to ship from each origin to each destination. The transshipment problem is an extension of the transportation problem involving transfer points referred to as transshipment nodes. In this more general model, we allow arcs between any pair of nodes in the network.

The assignment problem is a special case of the transportation problem in which all supply and all demand values are 1. We represent each agent as an origin node and each task as a destination node. The assignment model determines the minimum cost or maximum profit assignment of agents to tasks.

The shortest-route problem finds the shortest route or path between two nodes of a network. Distance, time, and cost are often the criteria used for this model. The shortest-route problem can be expressed as a transshipment problem with one origin and one destination. By shipping one unit from the origin to the destination, the solution will determine the shortest route through the network.

The maximal flow problem can be used to allocate flow to the arcs of the network so that flow through the network system is maximized. Arc capacities determine the maximum amount of flow for each arc. With these flow capacity constraints, the maximal flow problem is expressed as a capacitated transshipment problem.

In the last section of the chapter, we showed how a variation of the transshipment problem could be used to solve a production and inventory problem. In the chapter appendix we show how to use Excel to solve three of the distribution and network problems presented in the chapter.

## Glossary

**Supply chain**  The set of all interconnected resources involved in producing and distributing a product.

**Transportation problem**  A network flow problem that often involves minimizing the cost of shipping goods from a set of origins to a set of destinations; it can be formulated and solved as a linear program by including a variable for each arc and a constraint for each node.

**Network**  A graphical representation of a problem consisting of numbered circles (nodes) interconnected by a series of lines (arcs); arrowheads on the arcs show the direction of flow. Transportation, assignment, and transshipment problems are network flow problems.

**Nodes**  The intersection or junction points of a network.

**Arcs**  The lines connecting the nodes in a network.

**Dummy origin**  An origin added to a transportation problem to make the total supply equal to the total demand. The supply assigned to the dummy origin is the difference between the total demand and the total supply.

**Capacitated transportation problem**  A variation of the basic transportation problem in which some or all of the arcs are subject to capacity restrictions.

**Transshipment problem**  An extension of the transportation problem to distribution problems involving transfer points and possible shipments between any pair of nodes.

**Capacitated transshipment problem**  A variation of the transshipment problem in which some or all of the arcs are subject to capacity restrictions.

**Assignment problem**  A network flow problem that often involves the assignment of agents to tasks; it can be formulated as a linear program and is a special case of the transportation problem.

**Shortest route**  Shortest path between two nodes in a network.

**Maximal flow**  The maximum amount of flow that can enter and exit a network system during a given period of time.

**Flow capacity**  The maximum flow for an arc of the network. The flow capacity in one direction may not equal the flow capacity in the reverse direction.

## Problems

1. A company imports goods at two ports: Philadelphia and New Orleans. Shipments of one product are made to customers in Atlanta, Dallas, Columbus, and Boston. For the next planning period, the supplies at each port, customer demands, and shipping costs per case from each port to each customer are as follows:

| Port | Atlanta | Customers Dallas | Columbus | Boston | Port Supply |
|---|---|---|---|---|---|
| Philadelphia | 2 | 6 | 6 | 2 | 5000 |
| New Orleans | 1 | 2 | 5 | 7 | 3000 |
| Demand | 1400 | 3200 | 2000 | 1400 | |

Develop a network representation of the distribution system (transportation problem).

2. Consider the following network representation of a transportation problem:

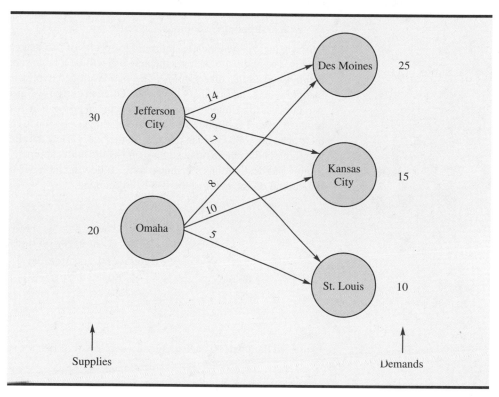

The supplies, demands, and transportation costs per unit are shown on the network.

a. Develop a linear programming model for this problem; be sure to define the variables in your model.

b. Solve the linear program to determine the optimal solution.

3. Tri-County Utilities, Inc., supplies natural gas to customers in a three-county area. The company purchases natural gas from two companies: Southern Gas and Northwest Gas. Demand forecasts for the coming winter season are as follows: Hamilton County, 400 units; Butler County, 200 units; and Clermont County, 300 units. Contracts to provide the following quantities have been written: Southern Gas, 500 units; and Northwest Gas, 400 units. Distribution costs for the counties vary, depending upon the location of the suppliers. The distribution costs per unit (in thousands of dollars) are as follows:

| | | To | |
| --- | --- | --- | --- |
| **From** | **Hamilton** | **Butler** | **Clermont** |
| Southern Gas | 10 | 20 | 15 |
| Northwest Gas | 12 | 15 | 18 |

a. Develop a network representation of this problem.
b. Develop a linear programming model that can be used to determine the plan that will minimize total distribution costs.
c. Describe the distribution plan and show the total distribution cost.
d. Recent residential and industrial growth in Butler County has the potential for increasing demand by as much as 100 units. Which supplier should Tri-County contract with to supply the additional capacity?

4. GloFish, Inc. has genetically engineered a species of fish that glows in normal lighting conditions. The company believes the new fish will be a huge success as a new pet option for children and adults alike. GloFish, Inc. has developed two varieties of its glowing fish: one that glows red and one that glows blue. GloFish currently "grows" its fish at two different fish farms in the United States: one in Michigan and one in Texas. The Michigan farm can produce up to 1 million red and 1 million blue GloFish per year; the Texas farm can produce up to 600,000 GloFish, but only in the blue variety. GloFish ships its fish between the fish farms and its three retail stores using a third-party shipper. The shipment rates between origins and destinations are shown in the following table. These costs are per fish and do not depend on the color of the fish being shipped.

| | Cost of Shipping GloFish | | |
| --- | --- | --- | --- |
| | **Retailer 1** | **Retailer 2** | **Retailer 3** |
| Michigan | $1.00 | $2.50 | $0.50 |
| Texas | $2.00 | $1.50 | $2.80 |

Estimated demands by each retailer for each color of fish are shown in the following table.

| | Demand for GloFish | | |
| --- | --- | --- | --- |
| | **Retailer 1** | **Retailer 2** | **Retailer 3** |
| Red | 320,000 | 300,000 | 160,000 |
| Blue | 380,000 | 450,000 | 290,000 |

a. What is the optimal policy for the fish farms? How many red and blue fish should be produced in Michigan and shipped to each retailer? How many blue fish should be produced in Texas and shipped to each retailer?

b. What is the minimum shipping cost that can be incurred and still meet demand requirements at retailers 1, 2, and 3?

c. How much should GloFish be willing to invest to enable the Texas farm to produce both red and blue GloFish while maintaining the maximum of 600,000 total fish produced at the Texas farm?

5. Premier Consulting's two consultants, Avery and Baker, can be scheduled to work for clients up to a maximum of 160 hours each over the next four weeks. A third consultant, Campbell, has some administrative assignments already planned and is available for clients up to a maximum of 140 hours over the next four weeks. The company has four clients with projects in process. The estimated hourly requirements for each of the clients over the four-week period are as follows:

| Client | Hours |
|--------|-------|
| A | 180 |
| B | 75 |
| C | 100 |
| D | 85 |

Hourly rates vary for the consultant–client combination and are based on several factors, including project type and the consultant's experience. The rates (dollars per hour) for each consultant–client combination are as follows:

| | Client | | | |
|------------|-----|-----|-----|-----|
| Consultant | A | B | C | D |
| Avery | 100 | 125 | 115 | 100 |
| Baker | 120 | 135 | 115 | 120 |
| Campbell | 155 | 150 | 140 | 130 |

a. Develop a network representation of the problem.

b. Formulate the problem as a linear program, with the optimal solution providing the hours each consultant should be scheduled for each client to maximize the consulting firm's billings. What is the schedule and what is the total billing?

c. New information shows that Avery doesn't have the experience to be scheduled for client B. If this consulting assignment is not permitted, what impact does it have on total billings? What is the revised schedule?

6. Klein Chemicals, Inc., produces a special oil-based material that is currently in short supply. Four of Klein's customers have already placed orders that together exceed the combined capacity of Klein's two plants. Klein's management faces the problem of deciding how many units it should supply to each customer. Because the four customers are in different industries, different prices can be charged because of the various industry pricing structures. However, slightly different production costs at the two plants and varying transportation costs between the plants and customers make a "sell to the highest bidder"

strategy unacceptable. After considering price, production costs, and transportation costs, Klein established the following profit per unit for each plant–customer alternative:

| Plant | Customer | | | |
|---|---|---|---|---|
| | $D_1$ | $D_2$ | $D_3$ | $D_4$ |
| Clifton Springs | $32 | $34 | $32 | $40 |
| Danville | $34 | $30 | $28 | $38 |

The plant capacities and customer orders are as follows:

| Plant | Capacity (units) | Distributor Orders (units) |
|---|---|---|
| Clifton Springs | 5000 | $D_1$ 2000 |
| | | $D_2$ 5000 |
| Danville | 3000 | $D_3$ 3000 |
| | | $D_4$ 2000 |

How many units should each plant produce for each customer to maximize profits? Which customer demands will not be met? Show your network model and linear programming formulation.

7. Aggie Power Generation supplies electrical power to residential customers for many U.S. cities. Its main power generation plants are located in Los Angeles, Tulsa, and Seattle. The following table shows Aggie Power Generation's major residential markets, the annual demand in each market (in megawatts or MWs), and the cost to supply electricity to each market from each power generation plant (prices are in $/MW).

| City | Distribution Costs | | | |
|---|---|---|---|---|
| | Los Angeles | Tulsa | Seattle | Demand (MWs) |
| Seattle | $356.25 | $593.75 | $59.38 | 950.00 |
| Portland | $356.25 | $593.75 | $178.13 | 831.25 |
| San Francisco | $178.13 | $475.00 | $296.88 | 2375.00 |
| Boise | $356.25 | $475.00 | $296.88 | 593.75 |
| Reno | $237.50 | $475.00 | $356.25 | 950.00 |
| Bozeman | $415.63 | $415.63 | $296.88 | 593.75 |
| Laramie | $356.25 | $415.63 | $356.25 | 1187.50 |
| Park City | $356.25 | $356.25 | $475.00 | 712.50 |
| Flagstaff | $178.13 | $475.00 | $593.75 | 1187.50 |
| Durango | $356.25 | $296.88 | $593.75 | 1543.75 |

a. If there are no restrictions on the amount of power that can be supplied by any of the power plants, what is the optimal solution to this problem? Which cities should be supplied by which power plants? What is the total annual power distribution cost for this solution?

b. If at most 4000 MWs of power can be supplied by any one of the power plants, what is the optimal solution? What is the annual increase in power distribution cost that results from adding these constraints to the original formulation?

8. Forbelt Corporation has a one-year contract to supply motors for all refrigerators produced by the Ice Age Corporation. Ice Age manufactures the refrigerators at four locations around the country: Boston, Dallas, Los Angeles, and St. Paul. Plans call for the following number (in thousands) of refrigerators to be produced at each location:

| | |
|---|---|
| Boston | 50 |
| Dallas | 70 |
| Los Angeles | 60 |
| St. Paul | 80 |

Forbelt's three plants are capable of producing the motors. The plants and production capacities (in thousands) are as follows:

| | |
|---|---|
| Denver | 100 |
| Atlanta | 100 |
| Chicago | 150 |

Because of varying production and transportation costs, the profit that Forbelt earns on each lot of 1000 units depends on which plant produced the lot and which destination it was shipped to. The following table gives the accounting department estimates of the profit per unit (shipments will be made in lots of 1000 units):

| | Shipped To | | | |
|---|---|---|---|---|
| **Produced At** | **Boston** | **Dallas** | **Los Angeles** | **St. Paul** |
| Denver | 7 | 11 | 8 | 13 |
| Atlanta | 20 | 17 | 12 | 10 |
| Chicago | 8 | 18 | 13 | 16 |

With profit maximization as a criterion, Forbelt's management wants to determine how many motors should be produced at each plant and how many motors should be shipped from each plant to each destination.
   a. Develop a network representation of this problem.
   b. Find the optimal solution.

9. The Ace Manufacturing Company has orders for three similar products:

| Product | Orders (units) |
|---|---|
| A | 2000 |
| B | 500 |
| C | 1200 |

Three machines are available for the manufacturing operations. All three machines can produce all the products at the same production rate. However, due to varying defect percentages of each product on each machine, the unit costs of the products vary depending on the machine used. Machine capacities for the next week and the unit costs are as follows:

| Machine | Capacity (units) |
|---------|------------------|
| 1 | 1500 |
| 2 | 1500 |
| 3 | 1000 |

| Machine | Product A | B | C |
|---------|-----------|-----|-----|
| 1 | $1.00 | $1.20 | $0.90 |
| 2 | $1.30 | $1.40 | $1.20 |
| 3 | $1.10 | $1.00 | $1.20 |

Use the transportation model to develop the minimum cost production schedule for the products and machines. Show the linear programming formulation.

10. Hatcher Enterprises uses a chemical called Rbase in production operations at five divisions. Only six suppliers of Rbase meet Hatcher's quality control standards. All six suppliers can produce Rbase in sufficient quantities to accommodate the needs of each division. The quantity of Rbase needed by each Hatcher division and the price per gallon charged by each supplier are as follows:

| Division | Demand (1000s of gallons) |
|----------|---------------------------|
| 1 | 40 |
| 2 | 45 |
| 3 | 50 |
| 4 | 35 |
| 5 | 45 |

| Supplier | Price per gallon ($) |
|----------|----------------------|
| 1 | 12.60 |
| 2 | 14.00 |
| 3 | 10.20 |
| 4 | 14.20 |
| 5 | 12.00 |
| 6 | 13.00 |

The cost per gallon ($) for shipping from each supplier to each division is provided in the following table:

| Division | Supplier 1 | 2 | 3 | 4 | 5 | 6 |
|----------|-----------|------|------|------|------|------|
| 1 | 2.75 | 2.50 | 3.15 | 2.80 | 2.75 | 2.75 |
| 2 | 0.80 | 0.20 | 5.40 | 1.20 | 3.40 | 1.00 |
| 3 | 4.70 | 2.60 | 5.30 | 2.80 | 6.00 | 5.60 |
| 4 | 2.60 | 1.80 | 4.40 | 2.40 | 5.00 | 2.80 |
| 5 | 3.40 | 0.40 | 5.00 | 1.20 | 2.60 | 3.60 |

Hatcher believes in spreading its business among suppliers so that the company will be less affected by supplier problems (e.g., labor strikes or resource availability). Company policy requires that each division have a separate supplier.

a. For each supplier–division combination, compute the total cost of supplying the division's demand.

b. Determine the optimal assignment of suppliers to divisions.

11. The distribution system for the Herman Company consists of three plants, two warehouses, and four customers. Plant capacities and shipping costs per unit (in $) from each plant to each warehouse are as follows:

| | **Warehouse** | | |
|---|---|---|---|
| **Plant** | **1** | **2** | **Capacity** |
| 1 | 4 | 7 | 450 |
| 2 | 8 | 5 | 600 |
| 3 | 5 | 6 | 380 |

Customer demand and shipping costs per unit (in $) from each warehouse to each customer are as follows:
a. Develop a network representation of this problem.
b. Formulate a linear programming model of the problem.
c. Solve the linear program to determine the optimal shipping plan.

| | **Customer** | | | |
|---|---|---|---|---|
| **Warehouse** | **1** | **2** | **3** | **4** |
| 1 | 6 | 4 | 8 | 4 |
| 2 | 3 | 6 | 7 | 7 |
| Demand | 300 | 300 | 300 | 400 |

12. Refer to Problem 11. Suppose that shipments between the two warehouses are permitted at $2 per unit and that direct shipments can be made from plant 3 to customer 4 at a cost of $7 per unit.
a. Develop a network representation of this problem.
b. Formulate a linear programming model of this problem.
c. Solve the linear program to determine the optimal shipping plan.

13. Sports of All Sorts produces, distributes, and sells high-quality skateboards. Its supply chain consists of three factories (located in Detroit, Los Angeles, and Austin) that produce skateboards. The Detroit and Los Angeles facilities can produce 350 skateboards per week, but the Austin plant is larger and can produce up to 700 skateboards per week. Skateboards must be shipped from the factories to one of four distribution centers, or DCs (located in Iowa, Maryland, Idaho, and Arkansas). Each distribution center can process (repackage, mark for sale, and ship) at most 500 skateboards per week.

Skateboards are then shipped from the distribution centers to retailers. Sports of All Sorts supplies three major U.S. retailers: Just Sports, Sports 'N Stuff, and The Sports Dude. The weekly demands are 200 skateboards at Just Sports, 500 skateboards at Sports 'N Stuff, and 650 skateboards at The Sports Dude. The following tables display the per-unit costs for shipping skateboards between the factories and DCs and for shipping between the DCs and the retailers.

| | | Shipping Costs ($ per skateboard) | | |
|---|---|---|---|---|
| **Factory/DCs** | **Iowa** | **Maryland** | **Idaho** | **Arkansas** |
| Detroit | $25.00 | $25.00 | $35.00 | $40.00 |
| Los Angeles | $35.00 | $45.00 | $35.00 | $42.50 |
| Austin | $40.00 | $40.00 | $42.50 | $32.50 |

| **Retailers/DCs** | **Iowa** | **Maryland** | **Idaho** | **Arkansas** |
|---|---|---|---|---|
| Just Sports | $30.00 | $20.00 | $35.00 | $27.50 |
| Sports 'N Stuff | $27.50 | $32.50 | $40.00 | $25.00 |
| The Sports Dude | $30.00 | $40.00 | $32.50 | $42.50 |

a. Draw the network representation for this problem.

b. Build a model to minimize the transportation cost of a logistics system that will deliver skateboards from the factories to the distribution centers and from the distribution centers to the retailers. What is the optimal production strategy and shipping pattern for Sports of All Sorts? What is the minimum attainable transportation cost?

c. Sports of All Sorts is considering expansion of the Iowa DC capacity to 800 units per week. The annual amortized cost of expansion is $40,000. Should the company expand the Iowa DC capacity so that it can process 800 skateboards per week? (Assume 50 operating weeks per year.)

14. The Moore & Harman Company is in the business of buying and selling grain. An important aspect of the company's business is arranging for the purchased grain to be shipped to customers. If the company can keep freight costs low, profitability will improve.

The company recently purchased three rail cars of grain at Muncie, Indiana; six rail cars at Brazil, Indiana; and five rail cars at Xenia, Ohio. Twelve carloads of grain have been sold. The locations and the amount sold at each location are as follows:

| Location | Number of Rail Car Loads |
|---|---|
| Macon, GA | 2 |
| Greenwood, SC | 4 |
| Concord, SC | 3 |
| Chatham, NC | 3 |

All shipments must be routed through either Louisville or Cincinnati. Shown are the shipping costs per bushel (in cents) from the origins to Louisville and Cincinnati and the costs per bushel to ship from Louisville and Cincinnati to the destinations.

| | To | |
|---|---|---|
| **From** | **Louisville** | **Cincinnati** |
| Muncie | 8 | 6 ← Cost per bushel |
| Brazil | 3 | 8    from Muncie to |
| Xenia | 9 | 3    Cincinnati is 6¢ |

|   | | To | | |
|---|---|---|---|---|
| **From** | **Macon** | **Greenwood** | **Concord** | **Chatham** |
| Louisville | 44 | 34 | 34 | 32 |
| Cincinnati | 57 | 35 | 28 | 24 |

Cost per bushel from
Cincinnati to Greenwood is 35¢

Determine a shipping schedule that will minimize the freight costs necessary to satisfy demand. Which (if any) rail cars of grain must be held at the origin until buyers can be found?

15. The following linear programming formulation is for a transshipment problem:

$$\text{Min} \quad 11x_{13} + 12x_{14} + 10x_{21} + 8x_{34} + 10x_{35} + 11x_{42} + 9x_{45} + 12x_{52}$$

s.t.

$$
\begin{aligned}
x_{13} + x_{14} - x_{21} &\le 5 \\
x_{21} - x_{42} - x_{52} &\le 3 \\
x_{13} - x_{34} - x_{35} &= 6 \\
-x_{14} - x_{34} + x_{42} + x_{45} &\le 2 \\
x_{35} + x_{45} - x_{52} &= 4
\end{aligned}
$$

$$x_{ij} \ge 0 \quad \text{for all } i, j$$

Show the network representation of this problem.

16. A rental car company has an imbalance of cars at seven of its locations. The following network shows the locations of concern (the nodes) and the cost to move a car between locations. A positive number by a node indicates an excess supply at the node, and a negative number indicates an excess demand.

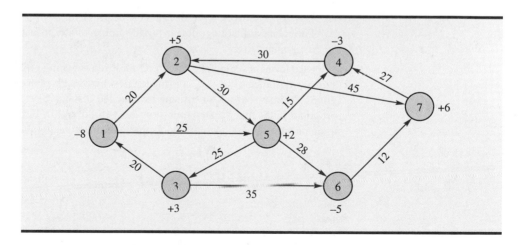

a. Develop a linear programming model of this problem.
b. Solve the model formulated in part (a) to determine how the cars should be redistributed among the locations.

17. Scott and Associates, Inc., is an accounting firm that has three new clients. Project leaders will be assigned to the three clients. Based on the different backgrounds and experiences of the leaders, the various leader–client assignments differ in terms of projected completion times. The possible assignments and the estimated completion times in days are as follows:

|  | Client | | |
| --- | --- | --- | --- |
| **Project Leader** | **1** | **2** | **3** |
| Jackson | 10 | 16 | 32 |
| Ellis | 14 | 22 | 40 |
| Smith | 22 | 24 | 34 |

a. Develop a network representation of this problem.
b. Formulate the problem as a linear program, and solve. What is the total time required?

18. CarpetPlus sells and installs floor covering for commercial buildings. Brad Sweeney, a CarpetPlus account executive, was just awarded the contract for five jobs. Brad must now assign a CarpetPlus installation crew to each of the five jobs. Because the commission Brad will earn depends on the profit CarpetPlus makes, Brad would like to determine an assignment that will minimize total installation costs. Currently, five installation crews are available for assignment. Each crew is identified by a color code, which aids in tracking of job progress on a large white board. The following table shows the costs (in hundreds of dollars) for each crew to complete each of the five jobs:

|  | Job | | | | |
| --- | --- | --- | --- | --- | --- |
| **Crew** | **1** | **2** | **3** | **4** | **5** |
| Red | 30 | 44 | 38 | 47 | 31 |
| White | 25 | 32 | 45 | 44 | 25 |
| Blue | 23 | 40 | 37 | 39 | 29 |
| Green | 26 | 38 | 37 | 45 | 28 |
| Brown | 26 | 34 | 44 | 43 | 28 |

a. Develop a network representation of the problem.
b. Formulate and solve a linear programming model to determine the minimum cost assignment.

19. A local television station plans to drop four Friday evening programs at the end of the season. Steve Botuchis, the station manager, developed a list of six potential replacement programs. Estimates of the advertising revenue ($) that can be expected for each of the new programs in the four vacated time slots are as follows. Mr. Botuchis asked you to find the assignment of programs to time slots that will maximize total advertising revenue.

|  | 5:00–5:30 P.M. | 5:30–6:00 P.M. | 7:00–7:30 P.M. | 8:00–8:30 P.M. |
| --- | --- | --- | --- | --- |
| *Home Improvement* | 5000 | 3000 | 6000 | 4000 |
| *World News* | 7500 | 8000 | 7000 | 5500 |
| *NASCAR Live* | 8500 | 5000 | 6500 | 8000 |
| *Wall Street Today* | 7000 | 6000 | 6500 | 5000 |
| *Hollywood Briefings* | 7000 | 8000 | 3000 | 6000 |
| *Ramundo & Son* | 6000 | 4000 | 4500 | 7000 |

20. The U.S. Cable Company uses a distribution system with five distribution centers and eight customer zones. Each customer zone is assigned a sole source supplier; each customer zone receives all of its cable products from the same distribution center. In an effort to balance demand and workload at the distribution centers, the company's vice president of logistics specified that distribution centers may not be assigned more than three customer zones. The following table shows the five distribution centers and cost of supplying each customer zone (in thousands of dollars):

| Distribution Centers | Los Angeles | Chicago | Columbus | Atlanta | Newark | Kansas City | Denver | Dallas |
|---|---|---|---|---|---|---|---|---|
| Plano | 70 | 47 | 22 | 53 | 98 | 21 | 27 | 13 |
| Nashville | 75 | 38 | 19 | 58 | 90 | 34 | 40 | 26 |
| Flagstaff | 15 | 78 | 37 | 82 | 111 | 40 | 29 | 32 |
| Springfield | 60 | 23 | 8 | 39 | 82 | 36 | 32 | 45 |
| Boulder | 45 | 40 | 29 | 75 | 86 | 25 | 11 | 37 |

Customer Zones (header spanning Los Angeles through Dallas)

   a. Determine the assignment of customer zones to distribution centers that will minimize cost.
   b. Which distribution centers, if any, are not used?
   c. Suppose that each distribution center is limited to a maximum of two customer zones. How does this constraint change the assignment and the cost of supplying customer zones?

21. United Express Service (UES) uses large quantities of packaging materials at its four distribution hubs. After screening potential suppliers, UES identified six vendors that can provide packaging materials that will satisfy its quality standards. UES asked each of the six vendors to submit bids to satisfy annual demand at each of its four distribution hubs over the next year. The following table lists the bids received (in thousands of dollars). UES wants to ensure that each of the distribution hubs is serviced by a different vendor. Which bids should UES accept, and which vendors should UES select to supply each distribution hub?

| Bidder | Distribution Hub 1 | 2 | 3 | 4 |
|---|---|---|---|---|
| Martin Products | 190 | 175 | 125 | 230 |
| Schmidt Materials | 150 | 235 | 155 | 220 |
| Miller Containers | 210 | 225 | 135 | 260 |
| D&J Burns | 170 | 185 | 190 | 280 |
| Larbes Furnishings | 220 | 190 | 140 | 240 |
| Lawler Depot | 270 | 200 | 130 | 260 |

22. The quantitative methods department head at a major midwestern university will be scheduling faculty to teach courses during the coming autumn term. Four core courses need to be covered. The four courses are at the undergraduate (UG), master of business administration (MBA), master of science (MS), and doctor of philosophy (Ph.D.) levels. Four professors will be assigned to the courses, with each professor receiving one of the courses. Student evaluations of professors are available from previous terms. Based on a rating scale of 4 (excellent), 3 (very good), 2 (average), 1 (fair), and 0 (poor), the average student evaluations for each professor are shown. Professor D does not have a Ph.D. and cannot

be assigned to teach the Ph.D. level course. If the department head makes teaching assignments based on maximizing the student evaluation ratings over all four courses, what staffing assignments should be made?

| | | Course | | |
|---|---|---|---|---|
| Professor | UG | MBA | MS | Ph.D. |
| A | 2.8 | 2.2 | 3.3 | 3.0 |
| B | 3.2 | 3.0 | 3.6 | 3.6 |
| C | 3.3 | 3.2 | 3.5 | 3.5 |
| D | 3.2 | 2.8 | 2.5 | — |

23.  Find the shortest route from node 1 to node 7 in the network shown.

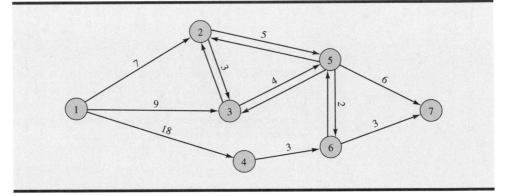

24.  In the original Gorman Construction Company problem, we found the shortest distance from the office (node 1) to the construction site located at node 6. Because some of the roads are highways and others are city streets, the shortest-distance routes between the office and the construction site may not necessarily provide the quickest or shortest-time route. Shown here is the Gorman road network with travel time rather than distance. Find the shortest route from Gorman's office to the construction site at node 6 if the objective is to minimize travel time rather than distance.

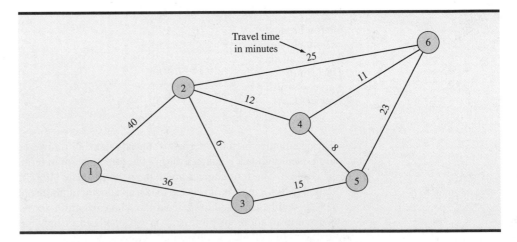

25.  Cleveland Area Rapid Delivery (CARD) operates a delivery service in the Cleveland metropolitan area. Most of CARD's business involves rapid delivery of documents and parcels

between offices during the business day. CARD promotes its ability to make fast and on-time deliveries anywhere in the metropolitan area. When a customer calls with a delivery request, CARD quotes a guaranteed delivery time. The following network shows the street routes available. The numbers above each arc indicate the travel time in minutes between the two locations.

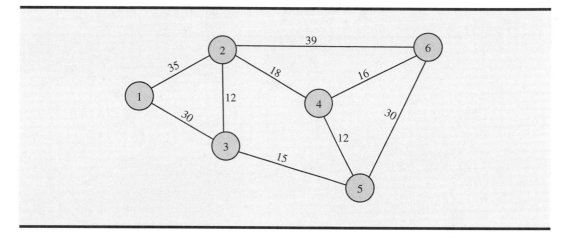

a. Develop a linear programming model that can be used to find the minimum time required to make a delivery from location 1 to location 6.
b. How long does it take to make a delivery from location 1 to location 6?
c. Assume that it is now 1:00 P.M. and that CARD just received a request for a pickup at location 1. The closest CARD courier is 8 minutes away from location 1. If CARD provides a 20% safety margin in guaranteeing a delivery time, what is the guaranteed delivery time if the package picked up at location 1 is to be delivered to location 6?

26. Morgan Trucking Company operates a special pickup and delivery service between Chicago and six other cities located in a four-state area. When Morgan receives a request for service, it dispatches a truck from Chicago to the city requesting service as soon as possible. With both fast service and minimum travel costs as objectives for Morgan, it is important that the dispatched truck take the shortest route from Chicago to the specified city. Assume that the following network (not drawn to scale) with distances given in miles represents the highway network for this problem. Find the shortest-route distances from Chicago to node 6.

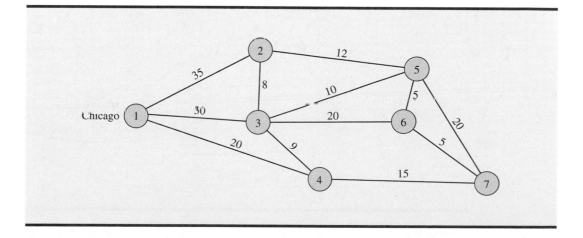

27. City Cab Company identified 10 primary pickup and drop locations for cab riders in New York City. In an effort to minimize travel time and improve customer service and the utilization of the company's fleet of cabs, management would like the cab drivers to take the shortest route between locations whenever possible. Using the following network of roads and streets, what is the route a driver beginning at location 1 should take to reach location 10? The travel times in minutes are shown on the arcs of the network. Note that there are two one-way streets and that the direction is shown by the arrows.

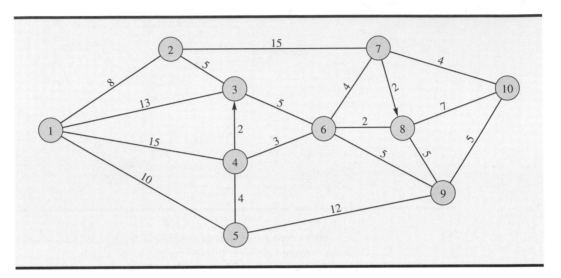

28. The five nodes in the following network represent points one year apart over a four-year period. Each node indicates a time when a decision is made to keep or replace a firm's computer equipment. If a decision is made to replace the equipment, a decision must also be made as to how long the new equipment will be used. The arc from node 0 to node 1 represents the decision to keep the current equipment one year and replace it at the end of the year. The arc from node 0 to node 2 represents the decision to keep the current equipment two years and replace it at the end of year 2. The numbers above the arcs indicate the total cost associated with the equipment replacement decisions. These costs include discounted purchase price, trade-in value, operating costs, and maintenance costs. Use a shortest-route model to determine the minimum cost equipment replacement policy for the four-year period.

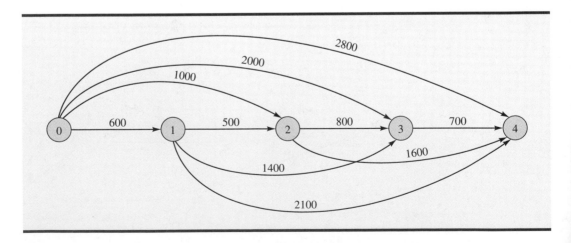

29. The north–south highway system passing through Albany, New York, can accommodate the capacities shown.

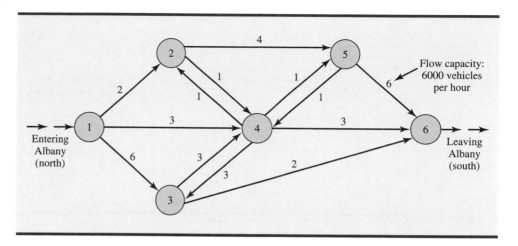

Can the highway system accommodate a north–south flow of 10,000 vehicles per hour?

30. If the Albany highway system described in Problem 29 has revised flow capacities as shown in the following network, what is the maximal flow in vehicles per hour through the system? How many vehicles per hour must travel over each road (arc) to obtain this maximal flow?

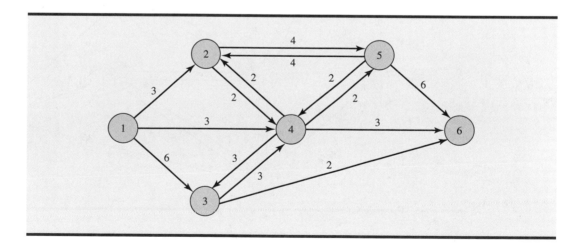

31. A long-distance telephone company uses a fiber-optic network to transmit phone calls and other information between locations. Calls are carried through cable lines and switching nodes. A portion of the company's transmission network is shown here. The numbers above each arc show the capacity in thousands of messages that can be transmitted over that branch of the network.

　　To keep up with the volume of information transmitted between origin and destination points, use the network to determine the maximum number of messages that may be sent from a city located at node 1 to a city located at node 7.

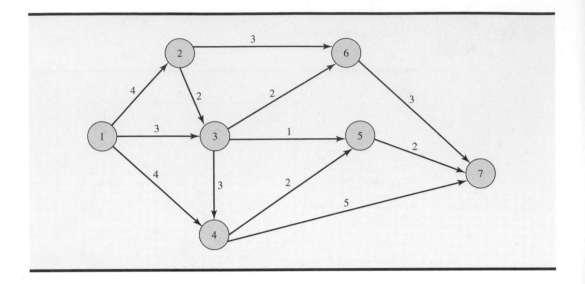

32. The High-Price Oil Company owns a pipeline network that is used to convey oil from its source to several storage locations. A portion of the network is as follows:

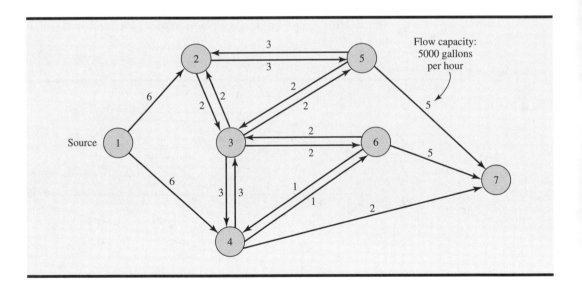

Due to the varying pipe sizes, the flow capacities vary. By selectively opening and closing sections of the pipeline network, the firm can supply any of the storage locations.

a. If the firm wants to fully utilize the system capacity to supply storage location 7, how long will it take to satisfy a location 7 demand of 100,000 gallons? What is the maximal flow for this pipeline system?

b. If a break occurs on line 2–3 and that line is closed down, what is the maximal flow for the system? How long will it take to transmit 100,000 gallons to location 7?

33. For the following highway network system, determine the maximal flow in vehicles per hour:

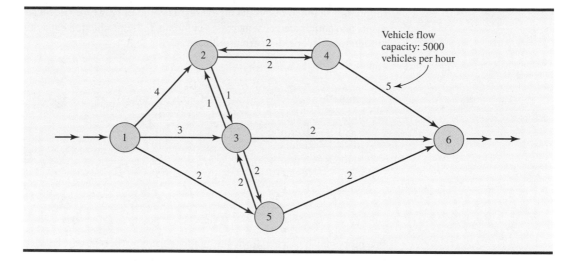

The highway commission is considering adding highway section 3–4 to permit a flow of 2000 vehicles per hour or, at an additional cost, a flow of 3000 vehicles per hour. What is your recommendation for the 3–4 arc of the network?

34. A chemical processing plant has a network of pipes that are used to transfer liquid chemical products from one part of the plant to another. The following pipe network has pipe flow capacities in gallons per minute as shown. What is the maximum flow capacity for the system if the company wishes to transfer as much liquid chemical as possible from location 1 to location 9? How much of the chemical will flow through the section of pipe from node 3 to node 5?

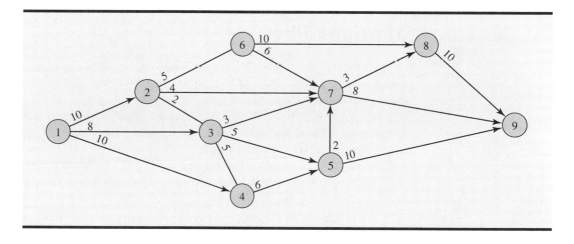

35. Refer to the Contois Carpets problem, for which the network representation is shown in Figure 10.20. Suppose that Contois has a beginning inventory of 50 yards of carpet and requires an inventory of 100 yards at the end of quarter 4.
   a. Develop a network representation of this modified problem.
   b. Develop a linear programming model and solve for the optimal solution.

36. Sanders Fishing Supply of Naples, Florida, manufactures a variety of fishing equipment that it sells throughout the United States. For the next three months, Sanders estimates demand for a particular product at 150, 250, and 300 units, respectively. Sanders can

supply this demand by producing on regular time or overtime. Because of other commitments and anticipated cost increases in month 3, the production capacities in units and the production costs per unit are as follows:

| Production | Capacity (units) | Cost per Unit |
|---|---|---|
| Month 1—Regular | 275 | $ 50 |
| Month 1—Overtime | 100 | $ 80 |
| Month 2—Regular | 200 | $ 50 |
| Month 2—Overtime | 50 | $ 80 |
| Month 3—Regular | 100 | $ 60 |
| Month 3—Overtime | 50 | $100 |

Inventory may be carried from one month to the next, but the cost is $20 per unit per month. For example, regular production from month 1 used to meet demand in month 2 would cost Sanders $50 + $20 = $70 per unit. This same month 1 production used to meet demand in month 3 would cost Sanders $50 + 2($20) = $90 per unit.

a.  Develop a network representation of this production scheduling problem as a transportation problem. (*Hint*: Use six origin nodes; the supply for origin node 1 is the maximum that can be produced in month 1 on regular time, and so on.)

b.  Develop a linear programming model that can be used to schedule regular and overtime production for each of the three months.

c.  What is the production schedule, how many units are carried in inventory each month, and what is the total cost?

d.  Is there any unused production capacity? If so, where?

## Case Problem 1    Solutions Plus

Solutions Plus is an industrial chemicals company that produces specialized cleaning fluids and solvents for a wide variety of applications. Solutions Plus just received an invitation to submit a bid to supply Great North American railroad with a cleaning fluid for locomotives. Great North American needs the cleaning fluid at 11 locations (railway stations); it provided the following information to Solutions Plus regarding the number of gallons of cleaning fluid required at each location (see Table 10.8).

Solutions Plus can produce the cleaning fluid at its Cincinnati plant for $1.20 per gallon. Even though the Cincinnati location is its only plant, Solutions Plus has negotiated with

**TABLE 10.8**    GALLONS OF CLEANING FLUID REQUIRED AT EACH LOCATION

| Location | Gallons Required | Location | Gallons Required |
|---|---|---|---|
| Santa Ana | 22,418 | Glendale | 33,689 |
| El Paso | 6,800 | Jacksonville | 68,486 |
| Pendleton | 80,290 | Little Rock | 148,586 |
| Houston | 100,447 | Bridgeport | 111,475 |
| Kansas City | 241,570 | Sacramento | 112,000 |
| Los Angeles | 64,761 | | |

**TABLE 10.9**    FREIGHT COST ($ PER GALLON)

|             | Cincinnati | Oakland |
|-------------|------------|---------|
| Santa Ana   | —          | 0.22    |
| El Paso     | 0.84       | 0.74    |
| Pendleton   | 0.83       | 0.49    |
| Houston     | 0.45       | —       |
| Kansas City | 0.36       | —       |
| Los Angeles | —          | 0.22    |
| Glendale    | —          | 0.22    |
| Jacksonville| 0.34       | —       |
| Little Rock | 0.34       | —       |
| Bridgeport  | 0.34       | —       |
| Sacramento  | —          | 0.15    |

© Cengage Learning 2013

an industrial chemicals company located in Oakland, California, to produce and ship up to 500,000 gallons of the locomotive cleaning fluid to selected Solutions Plus customer locations. The Oakland company will charge Solutions Plus $1.65 per gallon to produce the cleaning fluid, but Solutions Plus thinks that the lower shipping costs from Oakland to some customer locations may offset the added cost to produce the product.

The president of Solutions Plus, Charlie Weaver, contacted several trucking companies to negotiate shipping rates between the two production facilities (Cincinnati and Oakland) and the locations where the railroad locomotives are cleaned. Table 10.9 shows the quotes received in terms of dollars per gallon. The "—" entries in Table 10.9 identify shipping routes that will not be considered because of the large distances involved. These quotes for shipping rates are guaranteed for one year.

To submit a bid to the railroad company, Solutions Plus must determine the price per gallon it will charge. Solutions Plus usually sells its cleaning fluids for 15% more than its cost to produce and deliver the product. For this big contract, however, Fred Roedel, the director of marketing, suggested that maybe the company should consider a smaller profit margin. In addition, to ensure that if Solutions Plus wins the bid, it will have adequate capacity to satisfy existing orders as well as accept orders for other new business, the management team decided to limit the number of gallons of the locomotive cleaning fluid produced in the Cincinnati plant to 500,000 gallons at most.

## Managerial Report

You are asked to make recommendations that will help Solutions Plus prepare a bid. Your report should address, but not be limited to, the following issues:

1. If Solutions Plus wins the bid, which production facility (Cincinnati or Oakland) should supply the cleaning fluid to the locations where the railroad locomotives are cleaned? How much should be shipped from each facility to each location?
2. What is the breakeven point for Solutions Plus? That is, how low can the company go on its bid without losing money?
3. If Solutions Plus wants to use its standard 15% markup, how much should it bid?
4. Freight costs are significantly affected by the price of oil. The contract on which Solutions Plus is bidding is for two years. Discuss how fluctuation in freight costs might affect the bid Solutions Plus submits.

## Case Problem 2    Supply Chain Design

The Darby Company manufactures and distributes meters used to measure electric power consumption. The company started with a small production plant in El Paso and gradually built a customer base throughout Texas. A distribution center was established in Fort Worth, Texas, and later, as business expanded, a second distribution center was established in Santa Fe, New Mexico.

The El Paso plant was expanded when the company began marketing its meters in Arizona, California, Nevada, and Utah. With the growth of the West Coast business, the Darby Company opened a third distribution center in Las Vegas and just two years ago opened a second production plant in San Bernardino, California.

Manufacturing costs differ between the company's production plants. The cost of each meter produced at the El Paso plant is $10.50. The San Bernardino plant utilizes newer and more efficient equipment; as a result, manufacturing costs are $0.50 per meter less than at the El Paso plant.

Due to the company's rapid growth, not much attention had been paid to the efficiency of its supply chain, but Darby's management decided that it is time to address this issue. The cost of shipping a meter from each of the two plants to each of the three distribution centers is shown in Table 10.10.

The quarterly production capacity is 30,000 meters at the older El Paso plant and 20,000 meters at the San Bernardino plant. Note that no shipments are allowed from the San Bernardino plant to the Fort Worth distribution center.

The company serves nine customer zones from the three distribution centers. The forecast of the number of meters needed in each customer zone for the next quarter is shown in Table 10.11.

**TABLE 10.10**   SHIPPING COST PER UNIT FROM PRODUCTION PLANTS TO DISTRIBUTION CENTERS (IN $)

| Plant | Distribution Center | | |
| | Fort Worth | Santa Fe | Las Vegas |
|---|---|---|---|
| El Paso | 3.20 | 2.20 | 4.20 |
| San Bernardino | — | 3.90 | 1.20 |

**TABLE 10.11**   QUARTERLY DEMAND FORECAST

| Customer Zone | Demand (meters) |
|---|---|
| Dallas | 6300 |
| San Antonio | 4880 |
| Wichita | 2130 |
| Kansas City | 1210 |
| Denver | 6120 |
| Salt Lake City | 4830 |
| Phoenix | 2750 |
| Los Angeles | 8580 |
| San Diego | 4460 |

**TABLE 10.12**   SHIPPING COST FROM THE DISTRIBUTION CENTERS TO THE CUSTOMER ZONES

| Distribution Center | | | | Customer Zone | | | | | |
|---|---|---|---|---|---|---|---|---|---|
| | Dallas | San Antonio | Wichita | Kansas City | Denver | Salt Lake City | Phoenix | Los Angeles | San Diego |
| Fort Worth | 0.3 | 2.1 | 3.1 | 4.4 | 6.0 | — | — | — | — |
| Santa Fe | 5.2 | 5.4 | 4.5 | 6.0 | 2.7 | 4.7 | 3.4 | 3.3 | 2.7 |
| Las Vegas | — | — | — | — | 5.4 | 3.3 | 2.4 | 2.1 | 2.5 |

The cost per unit of shipping from each distribution center to each customer zone is given in Table 10.12; note that some distribution centers cannot serve certain customer zones. These are indicated by a dash, "—".

In its current supply chain, demand at the Dallas, San Antonio, Wichita, and Kansas City customer zones is satisfied by shipments from the Fort Worth distribution center. In a similar manner, the Denver, Salt Lake City, and Phoenix customer zones are served by the Santa Fe distribution center, and the Los Angeles and San Diego customer zones are served by the Las Vegas distribution center. To determine how many units to ship from each plant, the quarterly customer demand forecasts are aggregated at the distribution centers, and a transportation model is used to minimize the cost of shipping from the production plants to the distribution centers.

## Managerial Report

You are asked to make recommendations for improving Darby Company's supply chain. Your report should address, but not be limited to, the following issues:

1. If the company does not change its current supply chain, what will its distribution costs be for the following quarter?
2. Suppose that the company is willing to consider dropping the distribution center limitations; that is, customers could be served by any of the distribution centers for which costs are available. Can costs be reduced? If so, by how much?
3. The company wants to explore the possibility of satisfying some of the customer demand directly from the production plants. In particular, the shipping cost is $0.30 per unit from San Bernardino to Los Angeles and $0.70 from San Bernardino to San Diego. The cost for direct shipments from El Paso to San Antonio is $3.50 per unit. Can distribution costs be further reduced by considering these direct plant-to-customer shipments?
4. Over the next five years, Darby is anticipating moderate growth (5000 meters) to the north and west. Would you recommend that Darby consider plant expansion at this time?

## Appendix 10.1   Excel Solution of Transportation, Transshipment, and Assignment Problems

In this appendix we will use an Excel worksheet to solve transportation, transshipment, and assignment problems. We start with the Foster Generators transportation problem (see Section 10.1).

## Transportation Problem

The first step is to enter the data for the transportation costs, the origin supplies, and the destination demands in the top portion of the worksheet. Then the linear programming model is developed in the bottom portion of the worksheet. As with all linear programs, the worksheet model has four key elements: the decision variables, the objective function, the constraint left-hand sides, and the constraint right-hand sides. For a transportation problem, the decision variables are the amounts shipped from each origin to each destination; the objective function is the total transportation cost; the left-hand sides are the number of units shipped from each origin and the number of units shipped into each destination; and the right-hand sides are the origin supplies and the destination demands.

The formulation and solution of the Foster Generators problem are shown in Figure 10.22. The data are in the top portion of the worksheet. The model appears in the bottom portion of the worksheet.

**FIGURE 10.22**    EXCEL SOLUTION OF THE FOSTER GENERATORS PROBLEM

Foster

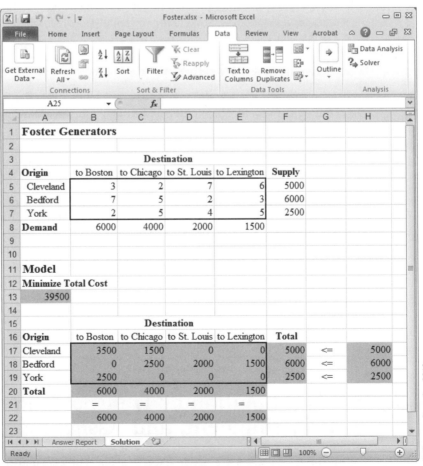

## Formulation

The data and descriptive labels are contained in cells A1:F8. The transportation costs are in cells B5:E7. The origin supplies are in cells F5:F7, and the destination demands are in cells B8:E8. The key elements of the model required by the Excel Solver are the decision variables, the objective function, the constraint left-hand sides, and the constraint right-hand sides.

|  |  |
|---|---|
| **Decision Variables** | Cells B17:E19 are reserved for the decision variables. The optimal values are shown to be $x_{11} = 3500$, $x_{12} = 1500$, $x_{22} = 2500$, $x_{23} = 2000$, $x_{24} = 1500$, and $x_{41} = 2500$. All other decision variables equal zero, indicating that nothing will be shipped over the corresponding routes. |
| **Objective Function** | The formula SUMPRODUCT(B5:E7,B17:E19) has been placed into cell A13 to compute the cost of the solution. The minimum cost solution is shown to have a value of $39,500. |
| **Left-Hand Sides** | Cells F17:F19 contain the left-hand sides for the supply constraints, and cells B20:E20 contain the left-hand sides for the demand constraints.<br><br>    Cell F17 = SUM(B17:E17) (Copy to F18:F19)<br>    Cell B20 = SUM(B17:B19) (Copy to C20:E20) |
| **Right-Hand Sides** | Cells H17:H19 contain the right-hand sides for the supply constraints, and cells B22:E22 contain the right-hand sides for the demand constraints.<br><br>    Cell H17 = F5 (Copy to H18:H19)<br>    Cell B22 = B8 (Copy to C22:E22) |

## Excel Solution

The solution shown in Figure 10.22 can be obtained by selecting **Solver** from the **Analysis Group** in the **Data Ribbon**. The Data Ribbon is displayed at the top of the worksheet in Figure 10.22. When the **Solver Parameters** dialog box appears, enter the proper values for the constraints and the objective function, select **Simplex LP,** and click the checkbox for **Make Unconstrained Variables Non-negative.** Then click **Solve.** The information entered into the **Solver Parameters** dialog box is shown in Figure 10.23.

## Transshipment Problem

The worksheet model we present for the transshipment problem can be used for all the network flow problems (transportation, transshipment, and assignment) in this chapter. We organize the worksheet into two sections: an arc section and a node section. Let us illustrate by showing the worksheet formulation and solution of the Ryan Electronics transshipment problem. Refer to Figure 10.24 as we describe the steps involved.

## Formulation

The arc section uses cells A4:C16. Each arc is identified in cells A5:A16. The arc costs are identified in cells B5:B16, and cells C5:C16 are reserved for the values of the decision variables (the amount shipped over the arcs).

**FIGURE 10.23**    EXCEL SOLVER PARAMETERS DIALOG BOX FOR THE FOSTER
GENERATORS PROBLEM

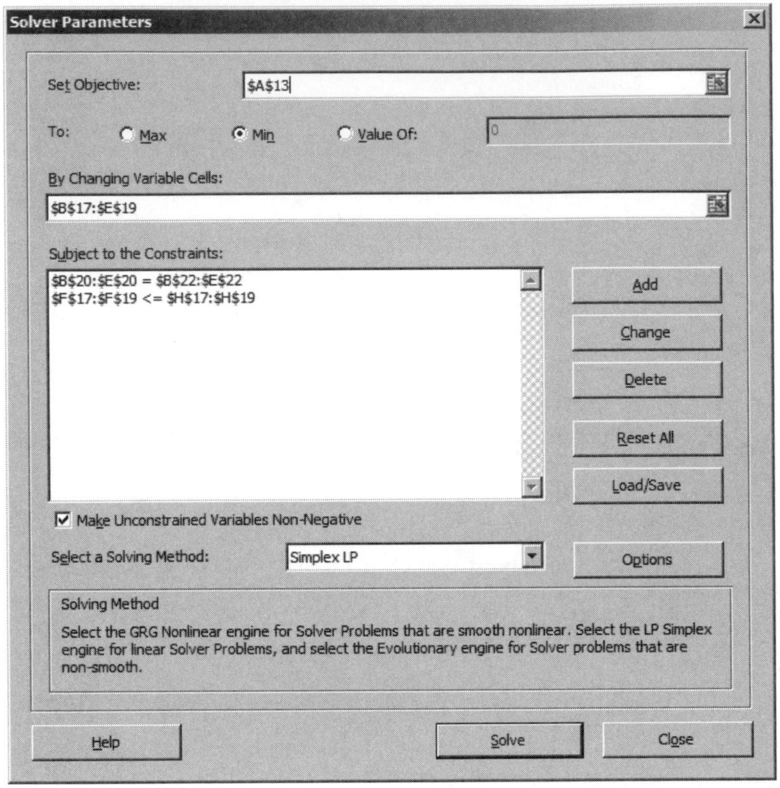

The node section uses cells F5:K14. Each of the nodes is identified in cells F7:F14. The following formulas are entered into cells G7:H14 to represent the flow out and the flow in for each node:

| Units shipped in: | Cell G9 | = C5+C7 |
|---|---|---|
| | Cell G10 | = C6+C8 |
| | Cell G11 | = C9+C13 |
| | Cell G12 | = C10+C14 |
| | Cell G13 | = C11+C15 |
| | Cell G14 | = C12+C16 |

| Units shipped out: | Cell H7 | = SUM(C5:C6) |
|---|---|---|
| | Cell H8 | = SUM(C7:C8) |
| | Cell H9 | = SUM(C9:C12) |
| | Cell H10 | = SUM(C13:C16) |

The net shipments in cells I7:I14 are the flows out minus the flows in for each node. For supply nodes, the flow out will exceed the flow in, resulting in positive net shipments. For demand nodes, the flow out will be less than the flow in, resulting in negative net

**FIGURE 10.24**  EXCEL SOLUTION FOR THE RYAN ELECTRONICS PROBLEM

Ryan

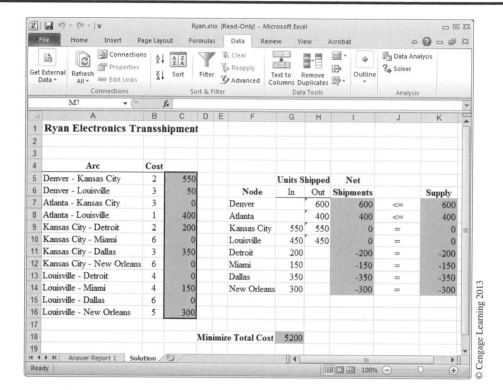

shipments. The "net" supply appears in cells K7:K14. Note that the net supply is negative for demand nodes.

| | |
|---|---|
| Decision Variables | Cells C5:C16 are reserved for the decision variables. The optimal number of units to ship over each arc is shown. |
| Objective Function | The formula =SUMPRODUCT(B5:B16,C5:C16) is placed into cell G18 to show the total cost associated with the solution. As shown, the minimum total cost is $5200. |
| Left-Hand Sides | The left-hand sides of the constraints represent the net shipments for each node. Cells I7:I14 are reserved for these constraints.<br>  Cell I7 = H7-G7 (Copy to I8:I14) |
| Right-Hand Sides | The right-hand sides of the constraints represent the supply at each node. Cells K7:K14 are reserved for these values. (Note the negative supply at the four demand nodes.) |

## Excel Solution

The solution can be obtained by selecting **Solver** from the **Analysis Group** in the **Data Ribbon**. The Data Ribbon is displayed at the top of the worksheet in Figure 10.24. When

**FIGURE 10.25**    EXCEL SOLVER PARAMETERS DIALOG BOX FOR THE RYAN
ELECTRONICS PROBLEM

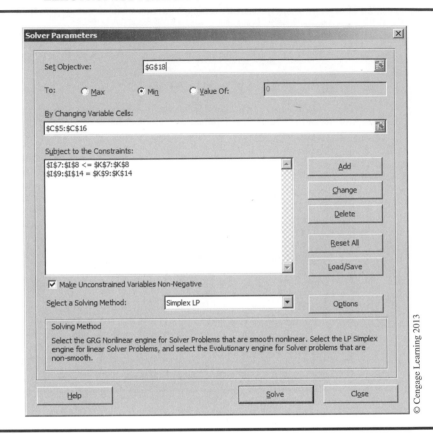

the **Solver Parameters** dialog box appears, enter the proper values for the constraints
and the objective function, select **Simplex LP**, and click the checkbox for **Make
Unconstrained Variables Non-negative.** Then click **Solve.** The information entered into
the **Solver Parameters** dialog box is shown in Figure 10.25.

## Assignment Problem

The first step is to enter the data for the assignment costs in the top portion of the worksheet. Even though the assignment model is a special case of the transportation model, it is
not necessary to enter values for origin supplies and destination demands because they are
always equal to 1.

The linear programming model is developed in the bottom portion of the worksheet. As
with all linear programs, the model has four key elements: the decision variables, the objective function, the constraint left-hand sides, and the constraint right-hand sides. For an assignment problem the decision variables indicate whether an agent is assigned to a task (with
a 1 for yes or 0 for no); the objective function is the total cost of all assignments; the constraint
left-hand sides are the number of tasks that are assigned to each agent and the number of
agents that are assigned to each task; and the right-hand sides are the number of tasks each
agent can handle (1) and the number of agents each task requires (1). The worksheet formulation and solution for the Fowle marketing research problem are shown in Figure 10.26.

**FIGURE 10.26**    EXCEL SOLUTION OF THE FOWLE MARKETING RESEARCH
PROBLEM

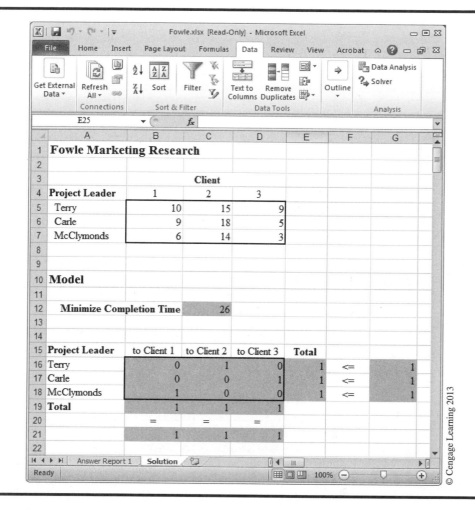

WEB file

Fowle

## Formulation

The data and descriptive labels are contained in cells A3:D7. Note that we have not inserted
supply and demand values because they are always equal to 1 in an assignment problem.
The model appears in the bottom portion of the worksheet.

| | |
|---|---|
| Decision Variables | Cells B16:D18 are reserved for the decision variables. The optimal values are shown to be $x_{12} = 1$, $x_{23} = 1$, and $x_{31} = 1$, with all other variables $= 0$. |
| Objective Function | The formula =SUMPRODUCT(B5:D7,B16:D18) has been placed into cell C12 to compute the number of days required to complete all the jobs. The minimum time solution has a value of 26 days. |
| Left-Hand Sides | Cells E16:E18 contain the left-hand sides of the constraints for the number of clients each project leader can handle. Cells |

B19:D19 contain the left-hand sides of the constraints requiring that each client must be assigned a project leader.

Cell E16 = SUM(B16:D16) (Copy to E17:E18)

Cell B19 = SUM(B16:B18) (Copy to C19:D19)

**Right-Hand Sides**  Cells G16:G18 contain the right-hand sides for the project leader constraints, and cells B21:D21 contain the right-hand sides for the client constraints. All right-hand-side cell values are 1.

## Excel Solution

The solution shown in Figure 10.26 can be obtained by selecting **Solver** from the **Analysis Group** in the **Data Ribbon**. The Data Ribbon is displayed at the top of the worksheet in Figure 10.26. When the **Solver Parameters** dialog box appears, enter the proper values for the constraints and the objective function, select **Simplex LP,** and click the checkbox for **Make Unconstrained Variables Non-negative.** Then click **Solve.** The information entered into the **Solver Parameters** dialog box is shown in Figure 10.27.

**FIGURE 10.27**    EXCEL SOLVER PARAMETERS DIALOG BOX FOR THE FOWLE MARKETING RESEARCH PROBLEM

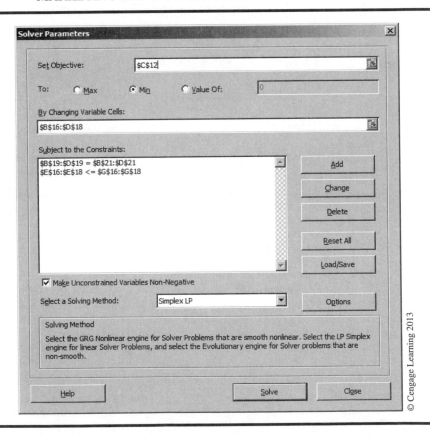

© Cengage Learning 2013

# CHAPTER 13

# Project Scheduling: PERT/CPM

## CONTENTS

In many situations managers are responsible for planning, scheduling, and controlling projects that consist of numerous separate jobs or tasks performed by a variety of departments and individuals. Often these projects are so large or complex that the manager cannot possibly remember all the information pertaining to the plan, schedule, and progress of the project. In these situations the **program evaluation and review technique (PERT)** and the **critical path method (CPM)** have proven to be extremely valuable.

PERT and CPM can be used to plan, schedule, and control a wide variety of projects:

1. Research and development of new products and processes
2. Construction of plants, buildings, and highways
3. Maintenance of large and complex equipment
4. Design and installation of new systems

*Henry L. Gantt developed the Gantt Chart as a graphical aid to scheduling jobs on machines in 1918. This application was the first of what has become known as project scheduling techniques.*

In these types of projects, project managers must schedule and coordinate the various jobs or **activities** so that the entire project is completed on time. A complicating factor in carrying out this task is the interdependence of the activities; for example, some activities depend on the completion of other activities before they can be started. Because projects may have as many as several thousand activities, project managers look for procedures that will help them answer questions such as the following:

1. What is the total time to complete the project?
2. What are the scheduled start and finish dates for each specific activity?
3. Which activities are "critical" and must be completed *exactly* as scheduled to keep the project on schedule?
4. How long can "noncritical" activities be delayed before they cause an increase in the total project completion time?

PERT and CPM can help answer these questions.

Although PERT and CPM have the same general purpose and utilize much of the same terminology, the techniques were developed independently. PERT was developed in the late 1950s by the Navy specifically for the Polaris missile project. Many activities associated with this project had never been attempted previously, so PERT was developed to handle uncertain activity times. CPM was developed originally by DuPont and Remington Rand primarily for industrial projects for which activity times were certain and variability was not a concern. CPM offered the option of reducing activity times by adding more workers and/or resources, usually at an increased cost. Thus, a distinguishing feature of CPM was that it identified trade-offs between time and cost for various project activities.

Today's computerized versions of PERT and CPM combine the best features of both approaches. Thus, the distinction between the two techniques is no longer necessary. As a result, we refer to the project scheduling procedures covered in this chapter as PERT/CPM. We begin the discussion of PERT/CPM by considering a project for the expansion of the Western Hills Shopping Center. At the end of the section, we describe how the investment securities firm of Seasongood & Mayer used PERT/CPM to schedule a $31 million hospital revenue bond project.

## 13.1   Project Scheduling Based on Expected Activity Times

The owner of the Western Hills Shopping Center plans to modernize and expand the current 32-business shopping center complex. The project is expected to provide room for 8 to 10 new businesses. Financing has been arranged through a private investor. All that remains

**TABLE 13.1**    LIST OF ACTIVITIES FOR THE WESTERN HILLS SHOPPING CENTER PROJECT

| Activity | Activity Description | Immediate Predecessor | Expected Activity Time |
|---|---|---|---|
| A | Prepare architectural drawings | — | 5 |
| B | Identify potential new tenants | — | 6 |
| C | Develop prospectus for tenants | A | 4 |
| D | Select contractor | A | 3 |
| E | Prepare building permits | A | 1 |
| F | Obtain approval for building permits | E | 4 |
| G | Perform construction | D, F | 14 |
| H | Finalize contracts with tenants | B, C | 12 |
| I | Tenants move in | G, H | 2 |
| | | Total | 51 |

is for the owner of the shopping center to plan, schedule, and complete the expansion project. Let us show how PERT/CPM can help.

The first step in the PERT/CPM scheduling process is to develop a list of the activities that make up the project. Table 13.1 shows the list of activities for the Western Hills Shopping Center expansion project. Nine activities are described and denoted A through I for later reference. Table 13.1 also shows the immediate predecessor(s) and the activity time (in weeks) for each activity. For a given activity, the **immediate predecessor** column identifies the activities that must be completed *immediately prior* to the start of that activity. Activities A and B do not have immediate predecessors and can be started as soon as the project begins; thus, a dash is written in the immediate predecessor column for these activities. The other entries in the immediate predecessor column show that activities C, D, and E cannot be started until activity A has been completed; activity F cannot be started until activity E has been completed; activity G cannot be started until both activities D and F have been completed; activity H cannot be started until both activities B and C have been completed; and, finally, activity I cannot be started until both activities G and H have been completed. The project is finished when activity I is completed.

The last column in Table 13.1 shows the expected number of weeks required to complete each activity. For example, activity A is expected to take 5 weeks, activity B is expected to take 6 weeks, and so on. The sum of expected activity times is 51. As a result, you may think that the total time required to complete the project is 51 weeks. However, as we show, two or more activities often may be scheduled concurrently (assuming sufficient availability of other required resources, such as labor and equipment), thus shortening the completion time for the project. Ultimately, PERT/CPM will provide a detailed activity schedule for completing the project in the shortest time possible.

Using the immediate predecessor information in Table 13.1, we can construct a graphical representation of the project, or the **project network**. Figure 13.1 depicts the project network for Western Hills Shopping Center. The activities correspond to the *nodes* of the network (drawn as rectangles), and the *arcs* (the lines with arrows) show the precedence relationships among the activities. In addition, nodes have been added to the network to denote the start and the finish of the project. A project network will help a manager visualize the activity relationships and provide a basis for carrying out the PERT/CPM computations.

*The effort that goes into identifying activities, determining interrelationships among activities, and estimating activity times is crucial to the success of PERT/CPM. A significant amount of time may be needed to complete this initial phase of the project scheduling process.*

*Immediate predecessor information determines whether activities can be completed in parallel (worked on simultaneously) or in series (one completed before another begins). Generally, the more series relationships present in a project, the more time will be required to complete the project.*

*A project network is extremely helpful in visualizing the interrelationships among the activities. No rules guide the conversion of a list of activities and immediate predecessor information into a project network. The process of constructing a project network generally improves with practice and experience.*

**FIGURE 13.1**   PROJECT NETWORK FOR THE WESTERN HILLS SHOPPING CENTER

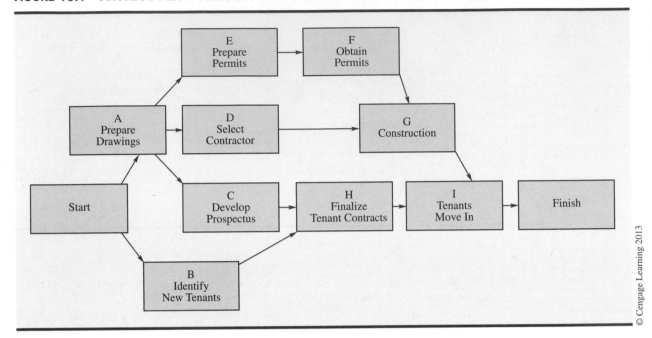

**FIGURE 13.2**   WESTERN HILLS SHOPPING CENTER PROJECT NETWORK WITH ACTIVITY TIMES

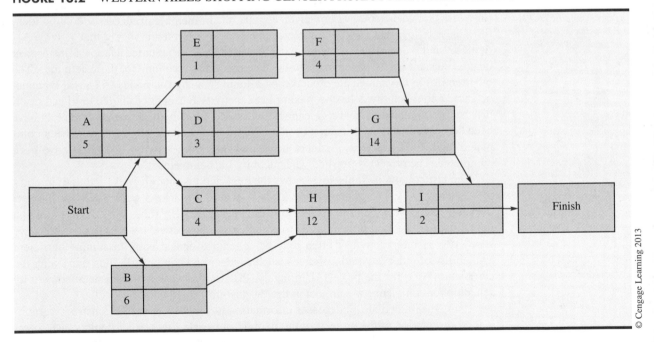

## The Concept of a Critical Path

To facilitate the PERT/CPM computations, we modified the project network as shown in Figure 13.2. Note that the upper left-hand corner of each node contains the corresponding activity letter. The activity time appears immediately below the letter.

*Problem 3 provides the immediate predecessor information for a project with seven activities and asks you to develop the project network.*

*For convenience, we use the convention of referencing activities with letters. Generally, we assign the letters in approximate order as we move from left to right through the project network.*

To determine the project completion time, we have to analyze the network and identify what is called the **critical path** for the network. However, before doing so, we need to define the concept of a path through the network. A **path** is a sequence of connected nodes that leads from the Start node to the Finish node. For instance, one path for the network in Figure 13.2 is defined by the sequence of nodes A-E-F-G-I. By inspection, we see that other paths are possible, such as A-D-G-I, A-C-H-I, and B-H-I. All paths in the network must be traversed in order to complete the project, so we will look for the path that requires the most time. Because all other paths are shorter in duration, this *longest* path determines the total time required to complete the project. If activities on the longest path are delayed, the entire project will be delayed. Thus, the longest path is the *critical path*. Activities on the critical path are referred to as the **critical activities** for the project. The following discussion presents a step-by-step algorithm for finding the critical path in a project network.

## Determining the Critical Path

We begin by finding the **earliest start time** and a **latest start time** for all activities in the network. Let

$$ES = \text{earliest start time for an activity}$$
$$EF = \text{earliest finish time for an activity}$$
$$t = \text{expected activity time}$$

The **earliest finish time** for any activity is

$$EF = ES + t \qquad \textbf{(13.1)}$$

Activity A can start as soon as the project starts, so we set the earliest start time for activity A equal to 0. With an expected activity time of 5 weeks, the earliest finish time for activity A is $EF = ES + t = 0 + 5 = 5$.

We will write the earliest start and earliest finish times in the node to the right of the activity letter. Using activity A as an example, we have

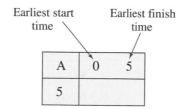

Because an activity cannot be started until *all* immediately preceding activities have been finished, the following rule can be used to determine the earliest start time for each activity:

> The earliest start time for an activity is equal to the *largest* (i.e., *latest*) of the earliest finish times for all its immediate predecessors.

Let us apply the earliest start time rule to the portion of the network involving nodes A, B, C, and H, as shown in Figure 13.3. With an earliest start time of 0 and an activity time of 6 for activity B, we show $ES = 0$ and $EF = ES + t = 0 + 6 = 6$ in the node for

**FIGURE 13.3**    A PORTION OF THE WESTERN HILLS SHOPPING CENTER PROJECT
NETWORK, SHOWING ACTIVITIES A, B, C, AND H

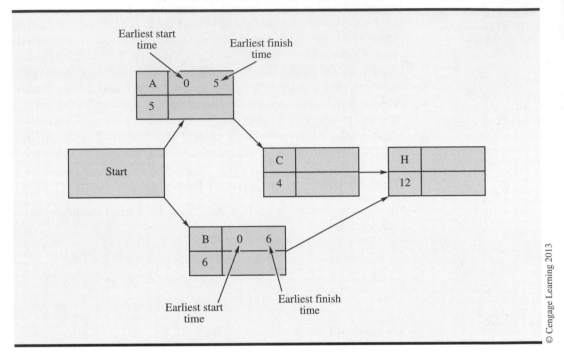

**FIGURE 13.4**    DETERMINING THE EARLIEST START TIME FOR ACTIVITY H

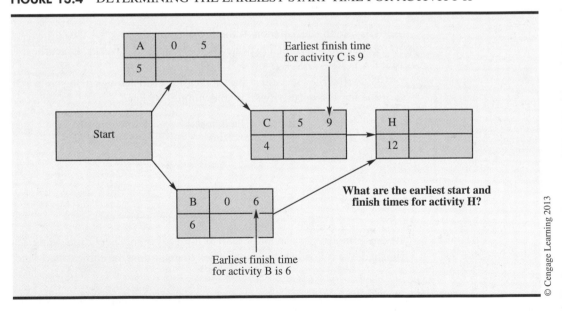

activity B. Looking at node C, we note that activity A is the only immediate predecessor
for activity C. The earliest finish time for activity A is 5, so the earliest start time for activity C must be $ES = 5$. Thus, with an activity time of 4, the earliest finish time for
activity C is $EF = ES + t = 5 + 4 = 9$. Both the earliest start time and the earliest finish
time can be shown in the node for activity C (see Figure 13.4).

*Determining the expected completion time of a project via critical path calculations implicitly assumes there is availability of sufficient resources (labor, equipment, supplies, etc.) to execute activities in parallel. If there is insufficient availability of resources to support the schedule generated by PERT/CPM, then more advanced techniques such as an integer linear programming model (Chapter 11) can be applied.*

Continuing with Figure 13.4, we move on to activity H and apply the earliest start time rule for this activity. With both activities B and C as immediate predecessors, the earliest start time for activity H must be equal to the largest of the earliest finish times for activities B and C. Thus, with $EF = 6$ for activity B and $EF = 9$ for activity C, we select the largest value, 9, as the earliest start time for activity H ($ES = 9$). With an activity time of 12 as shown in the node for activity H, the earliest finish time is $EF = ES + t = 9 + 12 = 21$. The $ES = 9$ and $EF = 21$ values can now be entered in the node for activity H in Figure 13.4.

Continuing with this **forward pass** through the network, we can establish the earliest start times and the earliest finish times for each activity in the network. Figure 13.5 shows the Western Hills Shopping Center project network with the $ES$ and $EF$ values for each activity. Note that the earliest finish time for activity I, the last activity in the project, is 26 weeks. Therefore, we now know that the expected completion time for the entire project is 26 weeks.

We now continue the algorithm for finding the critical path by making a **backward pass** through the network. Because the expected completion time for the entire project is 26 weeks, we begin the backward pass with a **latest finish time** of 26 for activity I. Once the latest finish time for an activity is known, the *latest start time* for an activity can be computed as follows. Let

$$LS = \text{latest start time for an activity}$$

$$LF = \text{latest finish time for an activity}$$

Then

$$LS = LF - t \qquad \textbf{(13.2)}$$

Beginning the backward pass with activity I, we know that the latest finish time is $LF = 26$ and that the activity time is $t = 2$. Thus, the latest start time for activity I is

**FIGURE 13.5**   WESTERN HILLS SHOPPING CENTER PROJECT NETWORK WITH EARLIEST START AND EARLIEST FINISH TIMES SHOWN FOR ALL ACTIVITIES

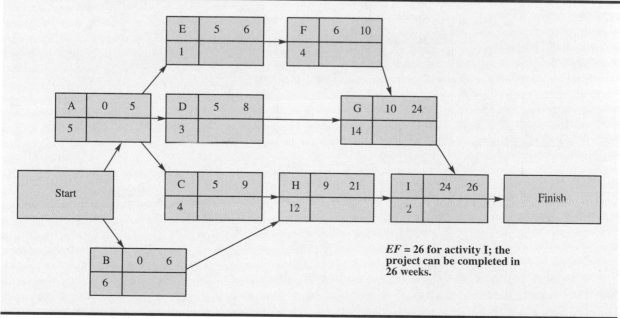

EF = 26 for activity I; the project can be completed in 26 weeks.

© Cengage Learning 2013

$LS = LF - t = 26 - 2 = 24$. We will write the $LS$ and $LF$ values in the node directly below the earliest start ($ES$) and earliest finish ($EF$) times. Thus, for node I, we have

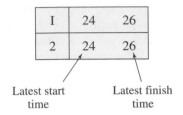

Latest start          Latest finish
time                    time

The following rule can be used to determine the latest finish time for each activity in the network:

> The latest finish time for an activity is the smallest of the latest start times for all activities that immediately follow the activity.

Logically, this rule states that the latest time an activity can be finished equals the earliest (smallest) value for the latest start time of following activities. Figure 13.6 shows the complete project network with the $LS$ and $LF$ backward pass results. We can use the latest finish time rule to verify the $LS$ and $LF$ values shown for activity H. The latest finish time for activity H must be the latest start time for activity I. Thus, we set $LF = 24$ for activity H. Using equation (13.2), we find that $LS = LF - t = 24 - 12 = 12$ as the latest start time for activity H. These values are shown in the node for activity H in Figure 13.6.

**FIGURE 13.6**   WESTERN HILLS SHOPPING CENTER PROJECT NETWORK WITH LATEST START AND LATEST FINISH TIMES SHOWN IN EACH NODE

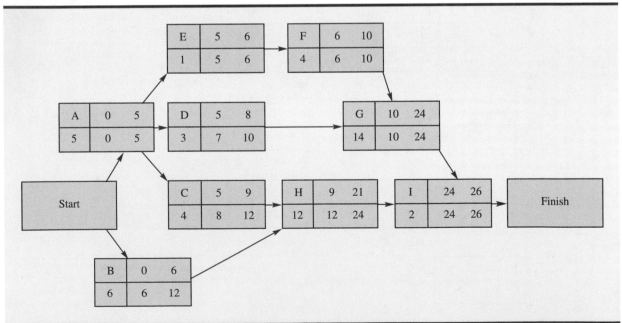

Activity A requires a more involved application of the latest start time rule. First, note that three activities (C, D, and E) immediately follow activity A. Figure 13.6 shows that the latest start times for activities C, D, and E are $LS = 8$, $LS = 7$, and $LS = 5$, respectively. The latest finish time rule for activity A states that the $LF$ for activity A is the smallest of the latest start times for activities C, D, and E. With the smallest value being 5 for activity E, we set the latest finish time for activity A to $LF = 5$. Verify this result and the other latest start times and latest finish times shown in the nodes in Figure 13.6.

*The slack for each activity indicates the length of time the activity can be delayed without increasing the project completion time.*

After we complete the forward and backward passes, we can determine the amount of slack associated with each activity. **Slack** is the length of time an activity can be delayed without increasing the project completion time. The amount of slack for an activity is computed as follows:

$$\text{Slack} = LS - ES = LF - EF \qquad \textbf{(13.3)}$$

*One of the primary contributions of PERT/CPM is the identification of the critical activities. The project manager will want to monitor critical activities closely because a delay in any one of these activities will lengthen the project completion time.*

For example, the slack associated with activity C is $LS - ES = 8 - 5 = 3$ weeks. Hence, activity C can be delayed up to 3 weeks, and the entire project can still be completed in 26 weeks. In this sense, activity C is not critical to the completion of the entire project in 26 weeks. Next, we consider activity E. Using the information in Figure 13.6, we find that the slack is $LS - ES = 5 - 5 = 0$. Thus, activity E has zero, or no, slack. Consequently, this activity cannot be delayed without increasing the completion time for the entire project. In other words, completing activity E exactly as scheduled is critical in terms of keeping the project on schedule, and so activity E is a critical activity. In general, the *critical activities* are the activities with zero slack.

*The critical path algorithm is essentially a longest path algorithm. From the start node to the finish node, the critical path identifies the path that requires the most time.*

The start and finish times shown in Figure 13.6 can be used to develop a detailed start time and finish time schedule for all activities. Putting this information in tabular form provides the activity schedule shown in Table 13.2. Note that the slack column shows that activities A, E, F, G, and I have zero slack. Hence, these activities are the critical activities for the project. The path formed by nodes A-E-F-G-I is the *critical path* in the Western Hills Shopping Center project network. The detailed schedule shown in Table 13.2 indicates the slack or delay that can be tolerated for the noncritical activities before these activities will increase project completion time.

**TABLE 13.2**   ACTIVITY SCHEDULE FOR THE WESTERN HILLS SHOPPING
CENTER PROJECT

| Activity | Earliest Start (ES) | Latest Start (LS) | Earliest Finish (EF) | Latest Finish (LF) | Slack (LS − ES) | Critical Path? |
|---|---|---|---|---|---|---|
| A | 0 | 0 | 5 | 5 | 0 | Yes |
| B | 0 | 6 | 6 | 12 | 6 | |
| C | 5 | 8 | 9 | 12 | 3 | |
| D | 5 | 7 | 8 | 10 | 2 | |
| E | 5 | 5 | 6 | 6 | 0 | Yes |
| F | 6 | 6 | 10 | 10 | 0 | Yes |
| G | 10 | 10 | 24 | 24 | 0 | Yes |
| H | 9 | 12 | 21 | 24 | 3 | |
| I | 24 | 24 | 26 | 26 | 0 | Yes |

## Contributions of PERT/CPM

*If the expected time required to complete the project is too long, judgment about where and how to shorten the time of critical activities must be exercised. If any activity times are altered, the critical path calculations should be repeated to determine the impact on the activity schedule and the impact on the expected project completion time. In Section 13.3 we show how to use linear programming to find the least-cost way to shorten the project completion time.*

We previously stated that project managers look for procedures that will help answer important questions regarding the planning, scheduling, and controlling of projects. Let us reconsider these questions in light of the information that the critical path calculations have given us.

1. How long will the project take to complete?
   *Answer:* The project can be completed in 26 weeks if each activity is completed on schedule.
2. What are the scheduled start and completion times for each activity?
   *Answer:* The activity schedule (see Table 13.2) shows the earliest start, latest start, earliest finish, and latest finish times for each activity.
3. Which activities are critical and must be completed *exactly* as scheduled to keep the project on schedule?
   *Answer:* A, E, F, G, and I are the critical activities.
4. How long can noncritical activities be delayed before they cause an increase in the completion time for the project?
   *Answer:* The activity schedule (see Table 13.2) shows the slack associated with each activity.

*Software packages such as Microsoft Project perform the critical path calculations quickly and efficiently. Program inputs include the activities, their immediate predecessors, and expected activity times. The project manager can modify any aspect of the project and quickly determine how the modification affects the activity schedule and the expected time required to complete the project.*

Such information is valuable in managing any project. Although the effort required to develop the immediate predecessor relationships and the activity time estimates generally increases with the size of the project, the procedure and contribution of PERT/CPM to larger projects are identical to those shown for the shopping center expansion project. The Q.M. in Action, Hospital Revenue Bond at Seasongood & Mayer, describes a 23-activity project that introduced a $31 million hospital revenue bond. PERT/CPM identified the critical activities, the expected project completion time of 29 weeks, and the activity start times and finish times necessary to keep the entire project on schedule.

## Summary of the PERT/CPM Critical Path Procedure

Before leaving this section, let us summarize the PERT/CPM critical path procedure.

**Step 1.** Develop a list of the activities that make up the project.
**Step 2.** Determine the immediate predecessor(s) for each activity in the project.
**Step 3.** Estimate the expected completion time for each activity.
**Step 4.** Draw a project network depicting the activities and immediate predecessors listed in steps 1 and 2.
**Step 5.** Use the project network and the activity time estimates to determine the earliest start and the earliest finish time for each activity by making a forward pass through the network. The earliest finish time for the last activity in the project identifies the expected time required to complete the entire project.
**Step 6.** Use the expected project completion time identified in step 5 as the latest finish time for the last activity and make a backward pass through the network to identify the latest start and latest finish time for each activity.
**Step 7.** Use the difference between the latest start time and the earliest start time for each activity to determine the slack for each activity.
**Step 8.** Find the activities with zero slack; these are the critical activities.
**Step 9.** Use the information from steps 5 and 6 to develop the activity schedule for the project.

### HOSPITAL REVENUE BOND AT SEASONGOOD & MAYER

Seasongood & Mayer is an investment securities firm located in Cincinnati, Ohio. The firm engages in municipal financing, including the underwriting of new issues of municipal bonds, acting as a market maker for previously issued bonds, and performing other investment banking services.

Seasongood & Mayer provided the underwriting for a $31 million issue of hospital facilities revenue bonds for Providence Hospital in Hamilton County, Ohio. The project of underwriting this municipal bond issue began with activities such as drafting the legal documents, drafting a description of the existing hospital facilities, and completing a feasibility study. A total of 23 activities defined the project that would be completed when the hospital

signed the construction contract and then made the bond proceeds available. The immediate predecessor relationships for the activities and the activity times were developed by a project management team.

PERT/CPM analysis of the project network identified the 10 critical path activities. The analysis also provided the expected completion time of 29 weeks, or approximately seven months. The activity schedule showed the start time and finish time for each activity and provided the information necessary to monitor the project and keep it on schedule. PERT/CPM was instrumental in helping Seasongood & Mayer obtain the financing for the project within the time specified in the construction bid.

## NOTES AND COMMENTS

1. Suppose that, after analyzing a PERT/CPM network, the project manager finds that the project completion time is unacceptable (i.e., the project is going to take too long). In this case, the manager must take one or both of the following steps. First, review the original PERT/CPM network to see whether any immediate prede-

cessor relationships can be modified so that at least some of the critical path activities can be done simultaneously. Second, consider adding resources to critical path activities in an attempt to shorten the critical path; we discuss this alternative, referred to as *crashing,* in Section 13.3.

## Project Scheduling Considering Uncertain Activity Times

In this section we consider the details of project scheduling for a problem involving new-product research and development. Because many of the activities in such a project have never been attempted, the project manager wants to account for uncertainties in the activity times. Let us show how project scheduling can be conducted with uncertain activity times.

### The Daugherty Porta-Vac Project

The H. S. Daugherty Company has manufactured industrial vacuum cleaning systems for many years. Recently, a member of the company's new-product research team submitted a report suggesting that the company consider manufacturing a cordless vacuum cleaner. The new product, referred to as Porta-Vac, could contribute to Daugherty's expansion into the household market. Management hopes that it can be manufactured at a reasonable cost and that its portability and no-cord convenience will make it extremely attractive.

*Accurate activity time estimates are important in the development of an activity schedule. When activity times are uncertain, the three time estimates— optimistic, most probable, and pessimistic—allow the project manager to take uncertainty into consideration in determining the critical path and the activity schedule. This approach was developed by the designers of PERT.*

Daugherty's management wants to study the feasibility of manufacturing the Porta-Vac product. The feasibility study will provide a recommendation on the action to be taken. To complete this study, information must be obtained from the firm's research and development (R&D), product testing, manufacturing, cost estimating, and market research groups. How long will it take to complete this feasibility study? In the following discussion, we show how to answer this question and provide an activity schedule for the project.

Again, the first step in the project scheduling process is to identify all activities that make up the project and then determine the immediate predecessor(s) for each activity. Table 13.3 shows these data for the Porta-Vac project.

The Porta-Vac project network is shown in Figure 13.7. Verify that the network does in fact maintain the immediate predecessor relationships shown in Table 13.3.

**TABLE 13.3**   ACTIVITY LIST FOR THE PORTA-VAC PROJECT

| Activity | Description | Immediate Predecessor |
|---|---|---|
| A | Develop product design | — |
| B | Plan market research | — |
| C | Prepare routing (manufacturing engineering) | A |
| D | Build prototype model | A |
| E | Prepare marketing brochure | A |
| F | Prepare cost estimates (industrial engineering) | C |
| G | Do preliminary product testing | D |
| H | Complete market survey | B, E |
| I | Prepare pricing and forecast report | H |
| J | Prepare final report | F, G, I |

© Cengage Learning 2013

**FIGURE 13.7**   PORTA-VAC CORDLESS VACUUM CLEANER PROJECT NETWORK

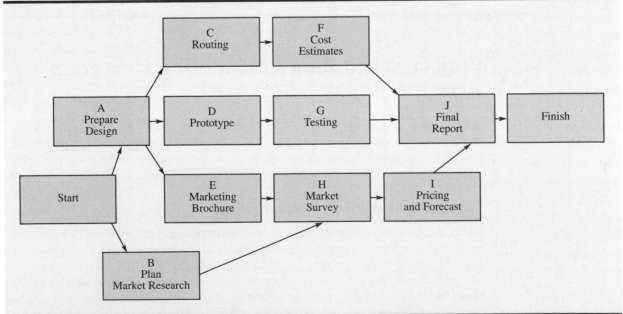

© Cengage Learning 2013

## Uncertain Activity Times

Once we develop the project network, we will need information on the time required to complete each activity. This information is used in the calculating the total time required to complete the project and in the scheduling of specific activities. For repeat projects, such as construction and maintenance projects, managers may have the experience and historical data necessary to provide accurate activity time estimates. However, for new or unique projects, estimating the time for each activity may be quite difficult. In fact, in many cases activity times are uncertain and are best described by a range of possible values rather than by one specific time estimate. In these instances, the uncertain activity times are treated as random variables with associated probability distributions. As a result, probability statements will be provided about the ability to meet a specific project completion date.

To incorporate uncertain activity times into the analysis, we need to obtain three time estimates for each activity:

**Optimistic time** $a$ = the minimum activity time if everything progresses ideally

**Most probable time** $m$ = the most probable activity time under normal conditions

**Pessimistic time** $b$ = the maximum activity time if significant delays are encountered

To illustrate the PERT/CPM procedure with uncertain activity times, let us consider the optimistic, most probable, and pessimistic time estimates for the Porta-Vac activities as presented in Table 13.4. Using activity A as an example, we see that the most probable time is 5 weeks, with a range from 4 weeks (optimistic) to 12 weeks (pessimistic). If the activity could be repeated a large number of times, what is the average time for the activity? This average or **expected time** ($t$) is as follows:

$$t = \frac{a + 4m + b}{6}$$
(13.4)

For activity A we have an average or expected time of

$$t_A = \frac{4 + 4(5) + 12}{6} = \frac{36}{6} = 6 \text{ weeks}$$

**TABLE 13.4**   OPTIMISTIC, MOST PROBABLE, AND PESSIMISTIC ACTIVITY TIME ESTIMATES (IN WEEKS) FOR THE PORTA-VAC PROJECT

| Activity | Optimistic (a) | Most Probable (m) | Pessimistic (b) |
|---|---|---|---|
| A | 4 | 5 | 12 |
| B | 1 | 1.5 | 5 |
| C | 2 | 3 | 4 |
| D | 3 | 4 | 11 |
| E | 2 | 3 | 4 |
| F | 1.5 | 2 | 2.5 |
| G | 1.5 | 3 | 4.5 |
| H | 2.5 | 3.5 | 7.5 |
| I | 1.5 | 2 | 2.5 |
| J | 1 | 2 | 3 |

With uncertain activity times, we can use the *variance* to describe the dispersion or variation in the activity time values. The variance of the activity time is given by the formula[1]

$$\sigma^2 = \left(\frac{b-a}{6}\right)^2 \qquad\qquad \textbf{(13.5)}$$

The difference between the pessimistic (*b*) and optimistic (*a*) time estimates greatly affects the value of the variance. Large differences in these two values reflect a high degree of uncertainty in the activity time. Using equation (13.5), we obtain the measure of uncertainty—that is, the variance—of activity A, denoted $\sigma^2_A$:

$$\sigma^2_A = \left(\frac{12-4}{6}\right)^2 = \left(\frac{8}{6}\right)^2 = 1.78$$

Equations (13.4) and (13.5) are based on the assumption that the activity time distribution can be described by a **beta probability distribution**.[2] With this assumption, the probability distribution for the time to complete activity A is as shown in Figure 13.8. Using equations (13.4) and (13.5) and the data in Table 13.4, we calculated the expected times and variances for all Porta-Vac activities; the results are summarized in Table 13.5. The Porta-Vac project network with expected activity times is shown in Figure 13.9.

**FIGURE 13.8**    ACTIVITY TIME DISTRIBUTION FOR PRODUCT DESIGN (ACTIVITY A) FOR THE PORTA-VAC PROJECT

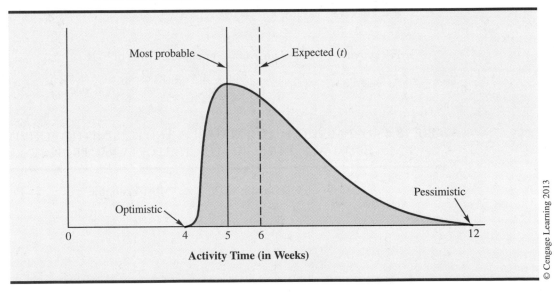

© Cengage Learning 2013

---

[1]The variance equation is based on the notion that a standard deviation is approximately $\frac{1}{6}$ of the difference between the extreme values of the distribution: $(b-a)/6$. The variance is the square of the standard deviation.

[2]The equations for $t$ and $\sigma^2$ require additional assumptions about the parameters of the beta probability distribution. However, even when these additional assumptions are not made, the equations still provide good approximations of $t$ and $\sigma^2$.

**TABLE 13.5** EXPECTED TIMES AND VARIANCES FOR THE PORTA-VAC PROJECT ACTIVITIES

| Activity | Expected Time (weeks) | Variance |
|----------|----------------------|----------|
| A | 6 | 1.78 |
| B | 2 | 0.44 |
| C | 3 | 0.11 |
| D | 5 | 1.78 |
| E | 3 | 0.11 |
| F | 2 | 0.03 |
| G | 3 | 0.25 |
| H | 4 | 0.69 |
| I | 2 | 0.03 |
| J | 2 | 0.11 |
| Total | 32 | |

© Cengage Learning 2013

**FIGURE 13.9** PORTA-VAC PROJECT NETWORK WITH EXPECTED ACTIVITY TIMES

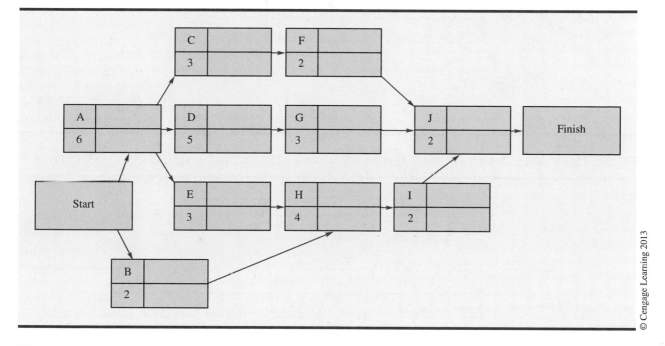

© Cengage Learning 2013

*When uncertain activity times are considered, the actual time required to complete the project may differ from the expected time to complete the project provided by the critical path calculations. However, for planning purposes, the expected time should be valuable information for the project manager.*

## The Critical Path

When we have the project network and the expected activity times, we are ready to proceed with the critical path calculations necessary to determine the expected time required to complete the project and determine the activity schedule. In these calculations, we find the critical path for the Porta-Vac project by applying the critical path procedure introduced in Section 13.1 to the expected activity times (Table 13.5). After the critical activities and the expected time to complete the project have been determined, we analyze the effect of the activity time variability.

Proceeding with a forward pass through the network shown in Figure 13.9, we can establish the earliest start (*ES*) and earliest finish (*EF*) times for each activity. Figure 13.10 shows the project network with the *ES* and *EF* values. Note that the earliest finish time for activity J, the last activity, is 17 weeks. Thus, the expected completion time for the project is 17 weeks. Next, we make a backward pass through the network. The backward pass provides the latest start (*LS*) and latest finish (*LF*) times shown in Figure 13.11.

**FIGURE 13.10**   PORTA-VAC PROJECT NETWORK WITH EARLIEST START AND EARLIEST FINISH TIMES

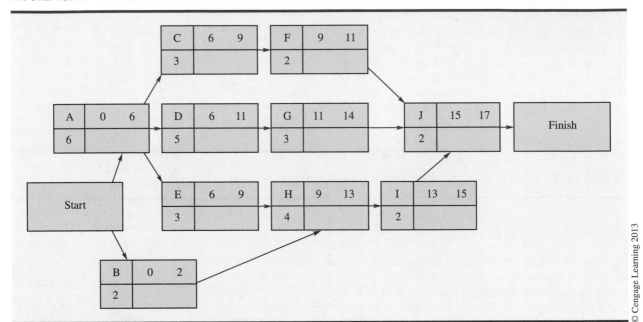

**FIGURE 13.11**   PORTA-VAC PROJECT NETWORK WITH LATEST START AND LATEST FINISH TIMES

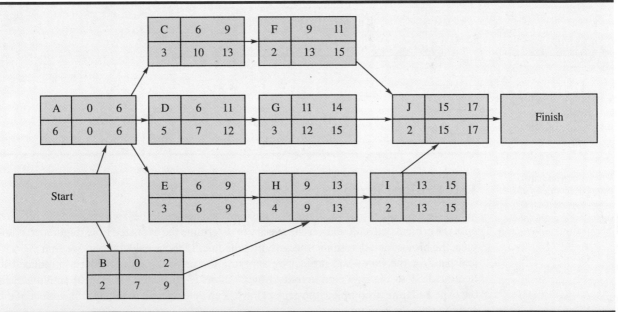

**TABLE 13.6**    ACTIVITY SCHEDULE FOR THE PORTA-VAC PROJECT

| Activity | Earliest Start (ES) | Latest Start (LS) | Earliest Finish (EF) | Latest Finish (LF) | Slack (LS − ES) | Critical Path? |
|---|---|---|---|---|---|---|
| A | 0 | 0 | 6 | 6 | 0 | Yes |
| B | 0 | 7 | 2 | 9 | 7 | |
| C | 6 | 10 | 9 | 13 | 4 | |
| D | 6 | 7 | 11 | 12 | 1 | |
| E | 6 | 6 | 9 | 9 | 0 | Yes |
| F | 9 | 13 | 11 | 15 | 4 | |
| G | 11 | 12 | 14 | 15 | 1 | |
| H | 9 | 9 | 13 | 13 | 0 | Yes |
| I | 13 | 13 | 15 | 15 | 0 | Yes |
| J | 15 | 15 | 17 | 17 | 0 | Yes |

© Cengage Learning 2013

The activity schedule for the Porta-Vac project is shown in Table 13.6. Note that the slack time ($LS - ES$) is also shown for each activity. The activities with zero slack (A, E, H, I, and J) form the critical path for the Porta-Vac project network.

## Variability in Project Completion Time

*Activities that have larger variances exhibit a greater degree of uncertainty. The project manager should monitor the progress of any activity with a large variance even if the expected time does not identify the activity as a critical activity.*

We know that for the Porta-Vac project the critical path of A-E-H-I-J resulted in an expected total project completion time of 17 weeks. However, variation in critical activities can cause variation in the project completion time. Variation in noncritical activities ordinarily has no effect on the project completion time because of the slack time associated with these activities. However, if a noncritical activity is delayed long enough to expend its slack time, it becomes part of a new critical path and may affect the project completion time. Variability leading to a longer-than-expected total time for the critical activities will always extend the project completion time, and, conversely, variability that results in a shorter-than-expected total time for the critical activities will reduce the project completion time, unless other activities become critical. Let us now use the variance in the critical activities to determine the variance in the project completion time.

Let $T$ denote the total time required to complete the project. The expected value of $T$, which is the sum of the expected times for the critical activities, is

$$E(T) = t_A + t_E + t_H + t_I + t_J$$
$$= 6 + 3 + 4 + 2 + 2 = 17 \text{ weeks}$$

*Problem 10 involves a project with uncertain activity times and asks you to compute the expected completion time and the variance for the project.*

The variance in the project completion time is the sum of the variances of the critical path activities. Thus, the variance for the Porta-Vac project completion time is

$$\sigma^2 = \sigma_A^2 + \sigma_E^2 + \sigma_H^2 + \sigma_I^2 + \sigma_J^2$$
$$= 1.78 + 0.11 + 0.69 + 0.03 + 0.11 = 2.72$$

where $\sigma_A^2$, $\sigma_E^2$, $\sigma_H^2$, $\sigma_I^2$, and $\sigma_J^2$ are the variances of the critical activities.

The formula for $\sigma^2$ is based on the assumption that the activity times are independent. If two or more activities are dependent, the formula provides only an approximation of the variance of the project completion time. The closer the activities are to being independent, the better the approximation.

Knowing that the standard deviation is the square root of the variance, we compute the standard deviation $\sigma$ for the Porta-Vac project completion time as

$$\sigma = \sqrt{\sigma^2} = \sqrt{2.72} = 1.65$$

*The normal distribution tends to be a better approximation of the distribution of total time for larger projects, where the critical path has many activities.*

Assuming that the distribution of the project completion time $T$ follows a normal or bell-shaped distribution[3] allows us to draw the distribution shown in Figure 13.12. With this distribution, we can compute the probability of meeting a specified project completion date. For example, suppose that management allotted 20 weeks for the Porta-Vac project. What is the probability that we will meet the 20-week deadline? Using the normal probability distribution shown in Figure 13.13, we are asking for the probability that $T \leq 20$; this

**FIGURE 13.12**    NORMAL DISTRIBUTION OF THE PROJECT COMPLETION TIME
FOR THE PORTA-VAC PROJECT

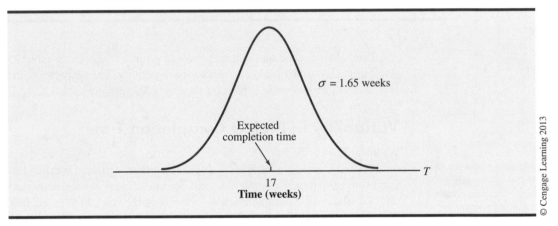

**FIGURE 13.13**    PROBABILITY THE PORTA-VAC PROJECT WILL MEET THE 20-WEEK
DEADLINE

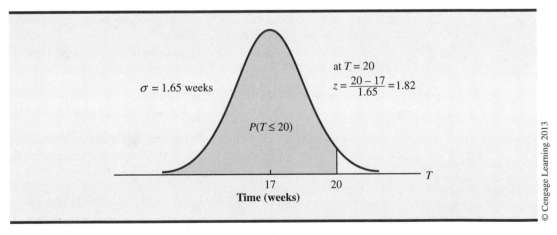

---

[3]Use of the normal distribution as an approximation is based on the central limit theorem, which indicates that the sum of independent random variables (activity times) follows a normal distribution as the number of random variables becomes large.

probability is shown graphically as the shaded area in the figure. The $z$ value for the normal probability distribution at $T = 20$ is

$$z = \frac{20 - 17}{1.65} = 1.82$$

Using $z = 1.82$ and the table for the normal distribution (see Appendix D), we find that the probability of the project meeting the 20-week deadline is 0.9656. Of course, this result also implies the probability we will not meet the 20-week deadline is $1 - 0.9656 = 0.0344$. Thus, even though activity time variability may cause the completion time to exceed 17 weeks, calculations indicate an excellent chance that the project will be completed before the 20-week deadline. Similar probability calculations can be made for other project deadline alternatives.

## NOTES AND COMMENTS

1. For projects involving uncertain activity times, the probability that the project can be completed within a specified amount of time is helpful managerial information. However, remember that this probability estimate is based only on the critical activities. When uncertain activity times exist, longer-than-expected completion times for one or more noncritical activities may cause an original noncritical activity to become critical and hence increase the time required to complete the project. By frequently monitoring the progress of the project to make sure all activities are on schedule, the project manager will be better prepared to take corrective action if a noncritical activity begins to lengthen the duration of the project. The Q.M. in Action, Project Management Helps the U.S. Air Force Reduce Maintenance Time, describes how closely managing the progress of individual activities as well as the assignment of resources led to dramatic improvements in the maintenance of military aircraft.

2. Statistical packages such as Minitab and SAS, as well as Excel, have routines to calculate cumulative probabilities for normally distributed random variables.

## Q.M. *in* ACTION

### PROJECT MANAGEMENT HELPS THE U.S. AIR FORCE REDUCE MAINTENANCE TIME*

Warner Robins Air Logistics Center (WR-ALC) provides maintenance and repair services for U.S. Air Force aircraft and ground equipment. To support combat zone efforts, the U.S. Air Force requested that WR-ALC reduce the amount of time it took to complete maintenance service on its C-5 transporter aircraft.

To identify ways to improve the management of its repair and overhaul process, WR-ALC adopted the method of critical chain project management (CCPM) by viewing each aircraft at its facility as a project with a series of tasks, precedence dependencies between these tasks, and resource requirements. Identifying tasks at a level of detail that allowed supervisors to clearly assign mechanics, maintenance tools, and facilities resulted in a project network of approximately 450 activities.

By explicitly accounting for each task's resource requirements (mechanics, aircraft parts, maintenance tools, etc.), CCPM identifies a "critical chain" of activities. Efforts to reduce the critical chain led to the insight that a task should not be started until all resources needed to complete the task are available. While this approach, called "pipelining," often results in an initial delay to the start of a task, it allows for the quicker completion of the task by eliminating delays after the task's launch and by reducing efficiency-robbing multitasking (across tasks) by the mechanics.

*M. M. Srinivasan, W. D. Best, and S. Chandrasekaran, "Warner Robins Air Logistics Center Streamlines Aircraft Repair and Overhaul," *Interfaces* 37, no. 1 (2007), pp. 7–21.

## (13.3) Considering Time–Cost Trade-Offs

*Using more resources to reduce activity times was proposed by the developers of CPM. The shortening of activity times is referred to as crashing.*

When determining the time estimates for activities in a project, the project manager bases these estimates on the amount of resources (workers, equipment, etc.) that will be assigned to an activity. The original developers of CPM provided the project manager with the option of adding resources to selected activities to reduce project completion time. Added resources (such as more workers, overtime, and so on) generally increase project costs, so the decision to reduce activity times must take into consideration the additional cost involved. In effect, the project manager must make a decision that involves trading reduced activity time for additional project cost.

Table 13.7 defines a two-machine maintenance project consisting of five activities. Management has substantial experience with similar projects and the times for maintenance activities have very little variability; hence, a single time estimate is given for each activity. The project network is shown in Figure 13.14.

The procedure for making critical path calculations for the maintenance project network is the same one used to find the critical path in the networks for both the Western Hills Shopping Center expansion project and the Porta-Vac project. Making the forward pass and backward pass calculations for the network in Figure 13.14, we obtained the activity schedule shown in Table 13.8. The zero slack times, and thus the critical path, are associated with activities A-B-E. The length of the critical path, and thus the total time required to complete the project, is 12 days.

**TABLE 13.7** ACTIVITY LIST FOR THE TWO-MACHINE MAINTENANCE PROJECT

| Activity | Description | Immediate Predecessor | Expected Time (days) |
|----------|-------------|-----------------------|----------------------|
| A | Overhaul machine I | — | 7 |
| B | Adjust machine I | A | 3 |
| C | Overhaul machine II | — | 6 |
| D | Adjust machine II | C | 3 |
| E | Test system | B, D | 2 |

© Cengage Learning 2013

**FIGURE 13.14** TWO-MACHINE MAINTENANCE PROJECT NETWORK

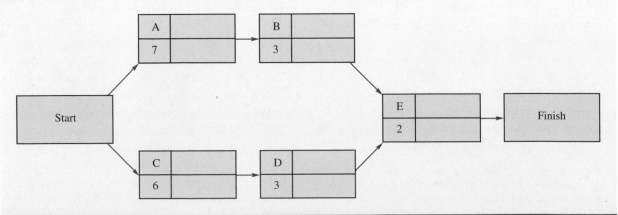

© Cengage Learning 2013

**TABLE 13.8**   ACTIVITY SCHEDULE FOR THE TWO-MACHINE MAINTENANCE PROJECT

| Activity | Earliest Start ($ES$) | Latest Start ($LS$) | Earliest Finish ($EF$) | Latest Finish ($LF$) | Slack ($LS - ES$) | Critical Path? |
|---|---|---|---|---|---|---|
| A | 0 | 0 | 7 | 7 | 0 | Yes |
| B | 7 | 7 | 10 | 10 | 0 | Yes |
| C | 0 | 1 | 6 | 7 | 1 | |
| D | 6 | 7 | 9 | 10 | 1 | |
| E | 10 | 10 | 12 | 12 | 0 | Yes |

© Cengage Learning 2013

## Crashing Activity Times

Now suppose that current production levels make completing the maintenance project within 10 days imperative. By looking at the length of the critical path of the network (12 days), we realize that meeting the desired project completion time is impossible unless we can shorten selected activity times. This shortening of activity times, which usually can be achieved by adding resources, is referred to as **crashing**. Because the added resources associated with crashing activity times usually result in added project costs, we will want to identify the activities that cost the least to crash and then crash those activities only the amount necessary to meet the desired project completion time.

To determine just where and how much to crash activity times, we need information on how much each activity can be crashed and how much the crashing process costs. Hence, we must ask for the following information:

1. Activity cost under the normal or expected activity time
2. Time to complete the activity under maximum crashing (i.e., the shortest possible activity time)
3. Activity cost under maximum crashing

Let

$$\tau_i = \text{expected time for activity } i$$
$$\tau'_i = \text{time for activity } i \text{ under maximum crashing}$$
$$M_i = \text{maximum possible reduction in time for activity } i \text{ due to crashing}$$

Given $\tau_i$ and $\tau'_i$, we can compute $M_i$:

$$M_i = \tau_i - \tau'_i \tag{13.6}$$

Next, let $C_i$ denote the cost for activity $i$ under the normal or expected activity time and let $C'_i$ denote the cost for activity $i$ under maximum crashing. Thus, per unit of time (e.g., per day), the crashing cost $K_i$ for each activity is given by

$$K_i = \frac{C'_i - C_i}{M_i} \tag{13.7}$$

For example, if the normal or expected time for activity A is 7 days at a cost of $C_A = \$500$ and the time under maximum crashing is 4 days at a cost of $C_A = \$800$, equations (13.6) and (13.7) show that the maximum possible reduction in time for activity A is

$$M_A = 7 - 4 = 3 \text{ days}$$

with a crashing cost of

$$K_A = \frac{C_A' - C_A}{M_A} = \frac{800 - 500}{3} = \frac{300}{3} = \$100 \text{ per day}$$

We make the assumption that any portion or fraction of the activity crash time can be achieved for a corresponding portion of the activity crashing cost. For example, if we decided to crash activity A by only $1\frac{1}{2}$ days, the added cost would be $1\frac{1}{2}(\$100) = \$150$, which results in a total activity cost of $\$500 + \$150 = \$650$. Figure 13.15 shows the graph of the time–cost relationship for activity A. The complete normal and crash activity data for the two-machine maintenance project are given in Table 13.9.

**FIGURE 13.15**    TIME-COST RELATIONSHIP FOR ACTIVITY A

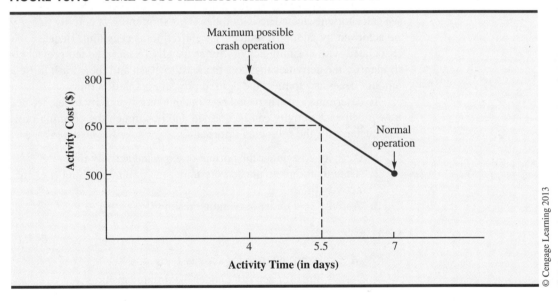

**TABLE 13.9**    NORMAL AND CRASH ACTIVITY DATA FOR THE TWO-MACHINE MAINTENANCE PROJECT

| Activity | Time (days) Normal | Time (days) Crash | Total Cost Normal ($C_i$) | Total Cost Crash ($C_i'$) | Maximum Reduction in Time ($M_i$) | Crash Cost per Day $\left(K_i = \dfrac{C_i' - C_i}{M_i}\right)$ |
|---|---|---|---|---|---|---|
| A | 7 | 4 | $ 500 | $ 800 | 3 | $100 |
| B | 3 | 2 | 200 | 350 | 1 | 150 |
| C | 6 | 4 | 500 | 900 | 2 | 200 |
| D | 3 | 1 | 200 | 500 | 2 | 150 |
| E | 2 | 1 | 300 | 550 | 1 | 250 |
|  |  |  | $1700 | $3100 |  |  |

Which activities should be crashed—and by how much—to meet the 10-day project completion deadline at minimum cost? Your first reaction to this question may be to consider crashing the critical activities—A, B, or E. Activity A has the lowest crashing cost per day of the three, and crashing this activity by 2 days will reduce the A-B-E path to the desired 10 days. Keep in mind, however, that as you crash the current critical activities, other paths may become critical. Thus, you will need to check the critical path in the revised network and perhaps either identify additional activities to crash or modify your initial crashing decision. For a small network, this trial-and-error approach can be used to make crashing decisions; in larger networks, however, a mathematical procedure is required to determine the optimal crashing decisions.

## Linear Programming Model for Crashing

Let us describe how linear programming can be used to solve the network crashing problem. With PERT/CPM, we know that when an activity starts at its earliest start time, then

$$\text{Finish time} = \text{Earliest start time} + \text{Activity time}$$

However, if slack time is associated with an activity, then the activity need not start at its earliest start time. In this case, we may have

$$\text{Finish time} > \text{Earliest start time} + \text{Activity time}$$

Because we do not know ahead of time whether an activity will start at its earliest start time, we use the following inequality to show the general relationship among finish time, earliest start time, and activity time for each activity:

$$\text{Finish time} \geq \text{Earliest start time} + \text{Activity time}$$

Consider activity A, which has an expected time of 7 days. Let $x_A$ = finish time for activity A, and $y_A$ = amount of time activity A is crashed. If we assume that the project begins at time 0, the earliest start time for activity A is 0. Because the time for activity A is reduced by the amount of time that activity A is crashed, the finish time for activity A must satisfy the relationship

$$x_A \geq 0 + (7 - y_A)$$

Moving $y_A$ to the left side,

$$x_A + y_A \geq 7$$

In general, let

$$x_i = \text{the finish time for activity } i \qquad i = \text{A, B, C, D, E}$$
$$y_i = \text{the amount of time activity } i \text{ is crashed} \quad i = \text{A, B, C, D, E}$$

If we follow the same approach that we used for activity A, the constraint corresponding to the finish time for activity C (expected time = 6 days) is

$$x_C \geq 0 + (6 - y_C) \quad \text{or} \quad x_C + y_C \geq 6$$

Continuing with the forward pass of the PERT/CPM procedure, we see that the earliest start time for activity B is $x_A$, the finish time for activity A. Thus, the constraint corresponding to the finish time for activity B is

$$x_B \geq x_A + (3 - y_B) \quad \text{or} \quad x_B + y_B - x_A \geq 3$$

Similarly, we obtain the constraint for the finish time for activity D:

$$x_D \geq x_C + (3 - y_D) \quad \text{or} \quad x_D + y_D - x_C \geq 3$$

Finally, we consider activity E. The earliest start time for activity E equals the *largest* of the finish times for activities B and D. Because the finish times for both activities B and D will be determined by the crashing procedure, we must write two constraints for activity E, one based on the finish time for activity B and one based on the finish time for activity D:

$$x_E + y_E - x_B \geq 2 \quad \text{and} \quad x_E + y_E - x_D \geq 2$$

Recall that current production levels made completing the maintenance project within 10 days imperative. Thus, the constraint for the finish time for activity E is

$$x_E \leq 10$$

In addition, we must add the following five constraints corresponding to the maximum allowable crashing time for each activity:

$$y_A \leq 3, \quad y_B \leq 1, \quad y_C \leq 2, \quad y_D \leq 2, \quad \text{and} \quad y_E \leq 1$$

As with all linear programs, we add the usual nonnegativity requirements for the decision variables.

All that remains is to develop an objective function for the model. Because the total project cost for a normal completion time is fixed at $1700 (see Table 13.9), we can minimize the total project cost (normal cost plus crashing cost) by minimizing the total crashing costs. Thus, the linear programming objective function becomes

$$\text{Min } 100y_A + 150y_B + 200y_C + 150y_D + 250y_E$$

Thus, to determine the optimal crashing for each of the activities, we must solve a 10-variable, 12-constraint linear programming model. Optimization software, such as Excel Solver, provides the optimal solution of crashing activity A by 1 day and activity E by 1 day, with a total crashing cost of $100 + $250 = $350. With the minimum cost crashing solution, the activity times are as follows:

| Activity | Time in Days | |
|----------|--------------|---|
| A | 6 | (Crash 1 day) |
| B | 3 | |
| C | 6 | |
| D | 3 | |
| E | 1 | (Crash 1 day) |

The linear programming solution provided the revised activity times, but not the revised earliest start time, latest start time, and slack information. The revised activity times and the usual PERT/CPM procedure must be used to develop the activity schedule for the project.

## NOTES AND COMMENTS

1. Note that the two-machine maintenance project network for the crashing illustration (see Figure 13.14) has only one activity, activity E, leading directly to the Finish node. As a result, the project completion time is equal to the completion time for activity E. Thus, the linear programming constraint requiring the project completion in 10 days or less could be written $x_E \leq 10$.

If two or more activities lead directly to the Finish node of a project network, a slight modification is required in the linear programming model for crashing. Consider the portion of the project network shown here. In this case, we suggest creating an additional variable, $x_{FIN}$, which indicates the finish or completion time for the entire project. The fact that the project cannot be finished until both activities E and G are completed can be modeled by the two constraints

$$x_{FIN} \geq x_E \quad \text{or} \quad x_{FIN} - x_E \geq 0$$
$$x_{FIN} \geq x_G \quad \text{or} \quad x_{FIN} - x_G \geq 0$$

The constraint that the project must be finished by time $T$ can be added as $x_{FIN} \leq T$.

Problem 22 gives you practice with this type of project network.

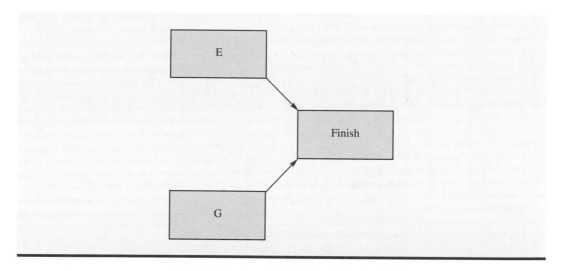

## Summary

In this chapter we showed how PERT/CPM can be used to plan, schedule, and control a wide variety of projects. The key to this approach to project scheduling is the development of a PERT/CPM project network that depicts the activities and their precedence relationships. From this project network and activity time estimates, the critical path for the network and the associated critical activities can be identified. In the process, an activity schedule showing the earliest start and earliest finish times, the latest start and latest finish times, and the slack for each activity can be identified.

We showed how we can include capabilities for handling variable or uncertain activity times and how to use this information to provide a probability statement about the chances the project can be completed in a specified period of time. We introduced crashing as a procedure for reducing activity times to meet project completion deadlines, and we showed how a linear programming model can be used to determine the crashing decisions that will minimize the cost of reducing the project completion time.

## Glossary

**Program evaluation and review technique (PERT)** A network-based project scheduling procedure.

**Critical path method (CPM)** A network-based project scheduling procedure.

**Activities** Specific jobs or tasks that are components of a project. Activities are represented by nodes in a project network.

**Immediate predecessors** The activities that must be completed immediately prior to the start of a given activity.

**Project network** A graphical representation of a project that depicts the activities and shows the predecessor relationships among the activities.

**Critical path** The longest path in a project network.

**Path** A sequence of connected nodes that leads from the Start node to the Finish node.

**Critical activities**  The activities on the critical path.

**Earliest start time**  The earliest time an activity may begin.

**Latest start time**  The latest time an activity may begin without increasing the project completion time.

**Earliest finish time**  The earliest time an activity may be completed.

**Forward pass**  Part of the PERT/CPM procedure that involves moving forward through the project network to determine the earliest start and earliest finish times for each activity.

**Backward pass**  Part of the PERT/CPM procedure that involves moving backward through the network to determine the latest start and latest finish times for each activity.

**Latest finish time**  The latest time an activity may be completed without increasing the project completion time.

**Slack**  The length of time an activity can be delayed without affecting the project completion time.

**Optimistic time**  The minimum activity time if everything progresses ideally.

**Most probable time**  The most probable activity time under normal conditions.

**Pessimistic time**  The maximum activity time if significant delays are encountered.

**Expected time**  The average activity time.

**Beta probability distribution**  A probability distribution used to describe activity times.

**Crashing**  The shortening of activity times by adding resources and hence usually increasing cost.

## Problems

1. The Mohawk Discount Store is designing a management training program for individuals at its corporate headquarters. The company wants to design the program so that trainees can complete it as quickly as possible. Important precedence relationships must be maintained between assignments or activities in the program. For example, a trainee cannot serve as an assistant to the store manager until the trainee has obtained experience in the credit department and at least one sales department. The following activities are the assignments that must be completed by each trainee in the program. Construct a project network for this problem. Do not perform any further analysis.

| Activity | A | B | C | D | E | F | G | H |
|---|---|---|---|---|---|---|---|---|
| Immediate Predecessor | — | — | A | A, B | A, B | C | D, F | E, G |

2. Bridge City Developers is coordinating the construction of an office complex. As part of the planning process, the company generated the following activity list. Draw a project network that can be used to assist in the scheduling of the project activities.

| Activity | A | B | C | D | E | F | G | H | I | J |
|---|---|---|---|---|---|---|---|---|---|---|
| Immediate Predecessor | — | — | — | A, B | A, B | D | E | C | C | F, G, H, I |

3. Construct a project network for the following project. The project is completed when activities F and G are both complete.

| Activity | A | B | C | D | E | F | G |
|---|---|---|---|---|---|---|---|
| Immediate Predecessor | — | — | A | A | C, B | C, B | D, E |

4. Assume that the project in Problem 3 has the following activity times (in months):

| Activity | A | B | C | D | E | F | G |
|---|---|---|---|---|---|---|---|
| Time | 4 | 6 | 2 | 6 | 3 | 3 | 5 |

a.   Find the critical path.

b.   The project must be completed in $1\frac{1}{2}$ years. Do you anticipate difficulty in meeting the deadline? Explain.

5.   Consider the Western Hills Shopping Center Project summarized by Figure 13.6 and Table 13.2. Suppose the project has been underway for seven weeks. Activities A and E have been completed. Activity F has commenced but has three weeks remaining. Activities C and D have not started yet. Activity B has one week remaining (it was not started until week 2). Update the activity schedule for the project. In particular, how has the slack for each activity changed?

6.   Consider the following project network and activity times (in weeks):

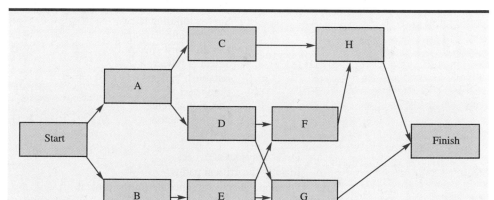

| Activity | A | B | C | D | E | F | G | H |
|----------|---|---|---|---|---|---|----|---|
| Time | 5 | 3 | 7 | 6 | 7 | 3 | 10 | 8 |

a.   Identify the critical path.

b.   How much time will be needed to complete this project?

c.   Can activity D be delayed without delaying the entire project? If so, by how many weeks?

d.   Can activity C be delayed without delaying the entire project? If so, by how many weeks?

e.   What is the schedule for activity E?

7.   Embassy Club Condominium, located on the west coast of Florida, is undertaking a summer renovation of its main building. The project is scheduled to begin May 1, and a September 1 (17-week) completion date is desired. The condominium manager identified the following renovation activities and their estimated times:

| Activity | Immediate Predecessor | Time |
|----------|----------------------|------|
| A | — | 3 |
| B | — | 1 |
| C | — | 2 |
| D | A, B, C | 4 |
| E | C, D | 5 |
| F | A | 3 |
| G | D, F | 6 |
| H | E | 4 |

a.  Draw a project network.
b.  What are the critical activities?
c.  What activity has the most slack time?
d.  Will the project be completed by September 1?

8.  Colonial State College is considering building a new multipurpose athletic complex on campus. The complex would provide a new gymnasium for intercollegiate basketball games, expanded office space, classrooms, and intramural facilities. The following activities would have to be undertaken before construction can begin:

| Activity | Description | Immediate Predecessor | Time (weeks) |
|---|---|---|---|
| A | Survey building site | — | 6 |
| B | Develop initial design | — | 8 |
| C | Obtain board approval | A, B | 12 |
| D | Select architect | C | 4 |
| E | Establish budget | C | 6 |
| F | Finalize design | D, E | 15 |
| G | Obtain financing | E | 12 |
| H | Hire contractor | F, G | 8 |

a.  Draw a project network.
b.  Identify the critical path.
c.  Develop the activity schedule for the project.
d.  Does it appear reasonable that construction of the athletic complex could begin one year after the decision to begin the project with the site survey and initial design plans? What is the expected completion time for the project?

9.  At a local university, the Student Commission on Programming and Entertainment (SCOPE) is preparing to host its first rock concert of the school year. To successfully produce this rock concert, SCOPE has listed the requisite activities and related information in the following table (duration estimates measured in days).

| Activity | Immediate Predecessor(s) | Optimistic | Most Probable | Pessimistic |
|---|---|---|---|---|
| A: Negotiate contract with selected musicians | — | 8 | 10 | 15 |
| B: Reserve site | — | 7 | 8 | 9 |
| C: Manage travel logistics for music group | A | 5 | 6 | 10 |
| D: Screen & hire security personnel | B | 3 | 3 | 3 |
| E: Arrange advertising & ticketing | B, C | 1 | 5 | 9 |
| F: Hire parking staff | D | 4 | 7 | 10 |
| G: Arrange concession sales | E | 3 | 8 | 10 |

a.  Draw the project network.
b.  Compute the expected duration and variance of each activity.
c.  Determine the critical path in the project network.
d.  What is the expected duration and variance of the critical path?
e.  What is the likelihood that the project will be completed within 30 days?
f.  If activity B is delayed by six days beyond its early start time, how does this affect the expected project duration?

10. The following estimates of activity times (in days) are available for a small project:

| Activity | Optimistic | Most Probable | Pessimistic |
|----------|------------|---------------|-------------|
| A | 4 | 5.0 | 6 |
| B | 8 | 9.0 | 10 |
| C | 7 | 7.5 | 11 |
| D | 7 | 9.0 | 10 |
| E | 6 | 7.0 | 9 |
| F | 5 | 6.0 | 7 |

    a. Compute the expected activity completion times and the variance for each activity.
    b. An analyst determined that the critical path consists of activities B-D-F. Compute the expected project completion time and the variance of this path.

11. Building a backyard swimming pool consists of nine major activities. The activities and their immediate predecessors are shown. Develop the project network.

| Activity | A | B | C | D | E | F | G | H | I |
|----------|---|---|---|---|---|---|---|---|---|
| Immediate Predecessor | — | — | A, B | A, B | B | C | D | D, F | E, G, H |

12. Assume that the activity time estimates (in days) for the swimming pool construction project in Problem 11 are as follows:

| Activity | Optimistic | Most Probable | Pessimistic |
|----------|------------|---------------|-------------|
| A | 3 | 5 | 6 |
| B | 2 | 4 | 6 |
| C | 5 | 6 | 7 |
| D | 7 | 9 | 10 |
| E | 2 | 4 | 6 |
| F | 1 | 2 | 3 |
| G | 5 | 8 | 10 |
| H | 6 | 8 | 10 |
| I | 3 | 4 | 5 |

    a. What are the critical activities?
    b. What is the expected time to complete the project?
    c. What is the probability that the project can be completed in 25 or fewer days?

13. Suppose that the following estimates of activity times (in weeks) were provided for the network shown in Problem 6:

| Activity | Optimistic | Most Probable | Pessimistic |
|----------|------------|---------------|-------------|
| A | 4.0 | 5.0 | 6.0 |
| B | 2.5 | 3.0 | 3.5 |
| C | 6.0 | 7.0 | 8.0 |
| D | 5.0 | 5.5 | 9.0 |
| E | 5.0 | 7.0 | 9.0 |
| F | 2.0 | 3.0 | 4.0 |
| G | 8.0 | 10.0 | 12.0 |
| H | 6.0 | 7.0 | 14.0 |

What is the probability that the project will be completed
a.   Within 21 weeks?
b.   Within 22 weeks?
c.   Within 25 weeks?

14.   Davison Construction Company is building a luxury lakefront home in the Finger Lakes region of New York. Coordination of the architect and subcontractors will require a major effort to meet the 44-week (approximately 10-month) completion date requested by the owner. The Davison project manager prepared the following project network:

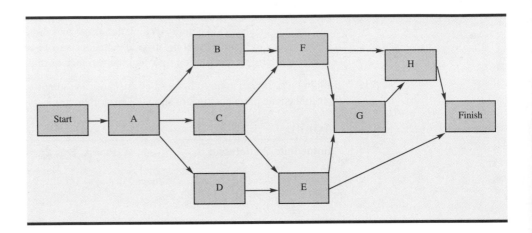

Estimates of the optimistic, most probable, and pessimistic times (in weeks) for the activities are as follows:

| Activity | Optimistic | Most Probable | Pessimistic |
|---|---|---|---|
| A | 4 | 8 | 12 |
| B | 6 | 7 | 8 |
| C | 6 | 12 | 18 |
| D | 3 | 5 | 7 |
| E | 6 | 9 | 18 |
| F | 5 | 8 | 17 |
| G | 10 | 15 | 20 |
| H | 5 | 6 | 13 |

a.   Find the critical path.
b.   What is the expected project completion time?
c.   What is the probability the project can be completed in the 44 weeks as requested by the owner?
d.   What is the probability the building project could run more than 3 months late? Use 57 weeks for this calculation.
e.   What should the construction company tell the owner?

15.   Doug Casey is in charge of planning and coordinating next spring's sales management training program for his company. Doug listed the following activity information for this project:

| Activity | Description | Immediate Predecessor | Optimistic | Most Probable | Pessimistic |
|---|---|---|---|---|---|
| | | | | Time (weeks) | |
| A | Plan topic | — | 1.5 | 2.0 | 2.5 |
| B | Obtain speakers | A | 2.0 | 2.5 | 6.0 |
| C | List meeting locations | — | 1.0 | 2.0 | 3.0 |
| D | Select location | C | 1.5 | 2.0 | 2.5 |
| E | Finalize speaker travel plans | B, D | 0.5 | 1.0 | 1.5 |
| F | Make final check with speakers | E | 1.0 | 2.0 | 3.0 |
| G | Prepare and mail brochure | B, D | 3.0 | 3.5 | 7.0 |
| H | Take reservations | G | 3.0 | 4.0 | 5.0 |
| I | Handle last-minute details | F, H | 1.5 | 2.0 | 2.5 |

   a.   Draw a project network.
   b.   Prepare an activity schedule.
   c.   What are the critical activities and what is the expected project completion time?
   d.   If Doug wants a 0.99 probability of completing the project on time, how far ahead of the scheduled meeting date should he begin working on the project?

16.   The Daugherty Porta-Vac project discussed in Section 13.2 has an expected project completion time of 17 weeks. The probability that the project could be completed in 20 weeks or less is 0.9656. The noncritical paths in the Porta-Vac project network are

$$A\text{-}D\text{-}G\text{-}J$$
$$A\text{-}C\text{-}F\text{-}J$$
$$B\text{-}H\text{-}I\text{-}J$$

   a.   Use the information in Table 13.5 to compute the expected time and variance for each path shown.
   b.   Compute the probability that each path will be completed in the desired 20-week period.
   c.   Why is the computation of the probability of completing a project on time based on the analysis of the critical path? In what case, if any, would making the probability computation for a noncritical path be desirable?

17.   The Porsche Shop, founded in 1985 by Dale Jensen, specializes in the restoration of vintage Porsche automobiles. One of Jensen's regular customers asked him to prepare an estimate for the restoration of a 1964 model 356SC Porsche. To estimate the time and cost to perform such a restoration, Jensen broke the restoration process into four separate activities: disassembly and initial preparation work (A), body restoration (B), engine restoration (C), and final assembly (D). Once activity A has been completed, activities B and C can be performed independently of each other; however, activity D can be started only if both activities B and C have been completed. Based on his inspection of the car, Jensen believes that the following time estimates (in days) are applicable:

| Activity | Optimistic | Most Probable | Pessimistic |
|---|---|---|---|
| A | 3 | 4 | 8 |
| B | 5 | 8 | 11 |
| C | 2 | 4 | 6 |
| D | 4 | 5 | 12 |

Jensen estimates that the parts needed to restore the body will cost $3000 and that the parts needed to restore the engine will cost $5000. His current labor costs are $400 a day.
   a.   Develop a project network.
   b.   What is the expected project completion time?

c.  Jensen's business philosophy is based on making decisions using a best- and worst-case scenario. Develop cost estimates for completing the restoration based on both a best- and worst-case analysis. Assume that the total restoration cost is the sum of the labor cost plus the material cost.

d.  If Jensen obtains the job with a bid that is based on the costs associated with an expected completion time, what is the probability that he will lose money on the job?

e.  If Jensen obtains the job based on a bid of $16,800, what is the probability that he will lose money on the job?

18. The manager of the Oak Hills Swimming Club is planning the club's swimming team program. The first team practice is scheduled for May 1. The activities, their immediate predecessors, and the activity time estimates (in weeks) are as follows:

| Activity | Description | Immediate Predecessor | Time (weeks) | | |
|---|---|---|---|---|---|
| | | | Optimistic | Most Probable | Pessimistic |
| A | Meet with board | — | 1 | 1 | 2 |
| B | Hire coaches | A | 4 | 6 | 8 |
| C | Reserve pool | A | 2 | 4 | 6 |
| D | Announce program | B, C | 1 | 2 | 3 |
| E | Meet with coaches | B | 2 | 3 | 4 |
| F | Order team suits | A | 1 | 2 | 3 |
| G | Register swimmers | D | 1 | 2 | 3 |
| H | Collect fees | G | 1 | 2 | 3 |
| I | Plan first practice | E, H, F | 1 | 1 | 1 |

a.  Draw a project network.
b.  Develop an activity schedule.
c.  What are the critical activities, and what is the expected project completion time?
d.  If the club manager plans to start the project on February 1, what is the probability the swimming program will be ready by the scheduled May 1 date (13 weeks)? Should the manager begin planning the swimming program before February 1?

19. The product development group at Landon Corporation has been working on a new computer software product that has the potential to capture a large market share. Through outside sources, Landon's management learned that a competitor is working to introduce a similar product. As a result, Landon's top management increased its pressure on the product development group. The group's leader turned to PERT/CPM as an aid to scheduling the activities remaining before the new product can be brought to the market. The project network is as follows:

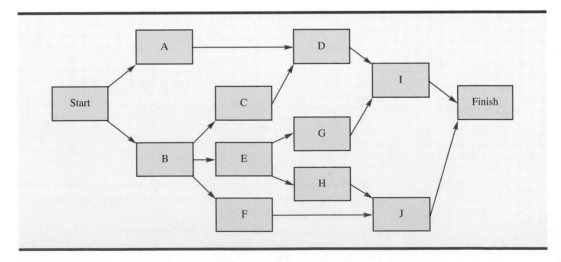

The activity time estimates (in weeks) are as follows:

| Activity | Optimistic | Most Probable | Pessimistic |
|---|---|---|---|
| A | 3.0 | 4.0 | 5.0 |
| B | 3.0 | 3.5 | 7.0 |
| C | 4.0 | 5.0 | 6.0 |
| D | 2.0 | 3.0 | 4.0 |
| E | 6.0 | 10.0 | 14.0 |
| F | 7.5 | 8.5 | 12.5 |
| G | 4.5 | 6.0 | 7.5 |
| H | 5.0 | 6.0 | 13.0 |
| I | 2.0 | 2.5 | 6.0 |
| J | 4.0 | 5.0 | 6.0 |

a. Develop an activity schedule for this project and identify the critical path activities.
b. What is the probability that the project will be completed so that Landon Corporation may introduce the new product within 25 weeks? Within 30 weeks?

20. Norton Industries is installing a new computer system. The activities, the activity times, and the project network are as follows:

| Activity | Time | Activity | Time |
|---|---|---|---|
| A | 3 | E | 4 |
| B | 6 | F | 3 |
| C | 2 | G | 9 |
| D | 5 | H | 3 |

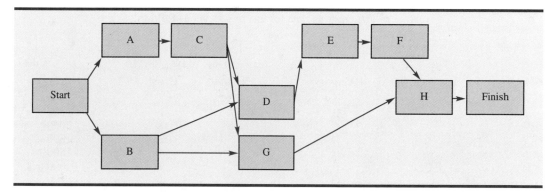

The critical path calculation shows B-D-E-F-H is the critical path, and the expected project completion time is 21 weeks. After viewing this information, management requested overtime be used to complete the project in 16 weeks. Thus, crashing of the project is necessary. The following information is relevant:

| Activity | Time (weeks) | | Cost ($) | |
|---|---|---|---|---|
| | Normal | Crash | Normal | Crash |
| A | 3 | 1 | 900 | 1700 |
| B | 6 | 3 | 2000 | 4000 |
| C | 2 | 1 | 500 | 1000 |
| D | 5 | 3 | 1800 | 2400 |
| E | 4 | 3 | 1500 | 1850 |
| F | 3 | 1 | 3000 | 3900 |
| G | 9 | 4 | 8000 | 9800 |
| H | 3 | 2 | 1000 | 2000 |

a. Formulate a linear programming model that can be used to make the crashing decisions for this project.
b. Solve the linear programming model and make the minimum cost crashing decisions. What is the added cost of meeting the 16-week completion time?
c. Develop a complete activity schedule based on the crashed activity times.

21. Consider the following project network and activity times (in days):

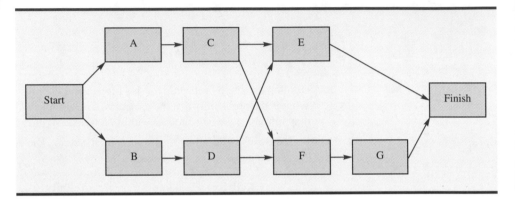

| Activity | A | B | C | D | E | F | G |
|----------|---|---|---|---|---|---|---|
| Time     | 3 | 2 | 5 | 5 | 6 | 2 | 2 |

The crashing data for this project are as follows:

| Activity | Time (days) Normal | Crash | Cost ($) Normal | Crash |
|----------|--------------------|-------|-----------------|-------|
| A | 3 | 2 | 800 | 1400 |
| B | 2 | 1 | 1200 | 1900 |
| C | 5 | 3 | 2000 | 2800 |
| D | 5 | 3 | 1500 | 2300 |
| E | 6 | 4 | 1800 | 2800 |
| F | 2 | 1 | 600 | 1000 |
| G | 2 | 1 | 500 | 1000 |

a. Find the critical path and the expected project completion time.
b. What is the total project cost using the normal times?

22. Refer to Problem 21. Assume that management desires a 12-day project completion time.
a. Formulate a linear programming model that can be used to assist with the crashing decisions.
b. What activities should be crashed?
c. What is the total project cost for the 12-day completion time?

23. Consider the following project network. Note that the normal or expected activity times are denoted $\tau_i$, $i$ = A, B, . . . , I. Let $x_i$ = the earliest finish time for activity $i$. Formulate a linear programming model that can be used to determine the length of the critical path.

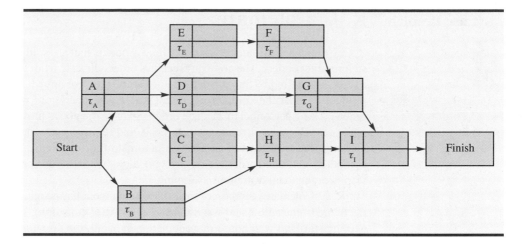

24. Office Automation, Inc., developed a proposal for introducing a new computerized office system that will standardize the electronic archiving of invoices for a particular company. Contained in the proposal is a list of activities that must be accomplished to complete the new office system project. Use the following relevant information about the activities:

| Activity | Description | Immediate Predecessor | Time (weeks) | | Cost ($1000s) | |
|---|---|---|---|---|---|---|
| | | | Normal | Crash | Normal | Crash |
| A | Plan needs | — | 10 | 8 | 30 | 70 |
| B | Order equipment | A | 8 | 6 | 120 | 150 |
| C | Install equipment | B | 10 | 7 | 100 | 160 |
| D | Set up training lab | A | 7 | 6 | 40 | 50 |
| E | Conduct training course | D | 10 | 8 | 50 | 75 |
| F | Test system | C, E | 3 | 3 | 60 | — |

    a. Develop a project network.

    b. Develop an activity schedule.

    c. What are the critical activities, and what is the expected project completion time?

    d. Assume that the company wants to complete the project in six months or 26 weeks. What crashing decisions do you recommend to meet the desired completion time at the least possible cost? Work through the network and attempt to make the crashing decisions by inspection.

    e. Develop an activity schedule for the crashed project.

    f. What added project cost is required to meet the six-month completion time?

25. Because Landon Corporation (see Problem 19) is being pressured to complete the product development project at the earliest possible date, the project leader requested that the possibility of crashing the project be evaluated.

    a. Formulate a linear programming model that could be used in making the crashing decisions.

    b. What information would have to be provided before the linear programming model could be implemented?

**Case Problem**

# R. C. Coleman

R. C. Coleman distributes a variety of food products that are sold through grocery store and supermarket outlets. The company receives orders directly from the individual outlets, with a typical order requesting the delivery of several cases of anywhere from 20 to 50 different products. Under the company's current warehouse operation, warehouse clerks dispatch order-picking personnel to fill each order and have the goods moved to the warehouse shipping area. Because of the high labor costs and relatively low productivity of hand order-picking, management has decided to automate the warehouse operation by installing a computer-controlled order-picking system, along with a conveyor system for moving goods from storage to the warehouse shipping area.

R. C. Coleman's director of material management has been named the project manager in charge of the automated warehouse system. After consulting with members of the engineering staff and warehouse management personnel, the director compiled a list of activities associated with the project. The optimistic, most probable, and pessimistic times (in weeks) have also been provided for each activity.

| Activity | Description | Immediate Predecessor |
|---|---|---|
| A | Determine equipment needs | — |
| B | Obtain vendor proposals | — |
| C | Select vendor | A, B |
| D | Order system | C |
| E | Design new warehouse layout | C |
| F | Design warehouse | E |
| G | Design computer interface | C |
| H | Interface computer | D, F, G |
| I | Install system | D, F |
| J | Train system operators | H |
| K | Test system | I, J |

| | Time (weeks) | | |
|---|---|---|---|
| Activity | Optimistic | Most Probable | Pessimistic |
| A | 4 | 6 | 8 |
| B | 6 | 8 | 16 |
| C | 2 | 4 | 6 |
| D | 8 | 10 | 24 |
| E | 7 | 10 | 13 |
| F | 4 | 6 | 8 |
| G | 4 | 6 | 20 |
| H | 4 | 6 | 8 |
| I | 4 | 6 | 14 |
| J | 3 | 4 | 5 |
| K | 2 | 4 | 6 |

## Managerial Report

Develop a report that presents the activity schedule and expected project completion time for the warehouse expansion project. Include a project network in the report. In addition, take into consideration the following issues:

1. R. C. Coleman's top management established a required 40-week completion time for the project. Can this completion time be achieved? Include probability information in your discussion. What recommendations do you have if the 40-week completion time is required?

2. Suppose that management requests that activity times be shortened to provide an 80% chance of meeting the 40-week completion time. If the variance in the project completion time is the same as you found in part (1), how much should the expected project completion time be shortened to achieve the goal of an 80% chance of completion within 40 weeks?

3. Using the expected activity times as the normal times and the following crashing information, determine the activity crashing decisions and revised activity schedule for the warehouse expansion project:

| Activity | Crashed Activity Time (weeks) | Cost ($) Normal | Cost ($) Crashed |
|:---:|:---:|:---:|:---:|
| A | 4 | 1,000 | 1,900 |
| B | 7 | 1,000 | 1,800 |
| C | 2 | 1,500 | 2,700 |
| D | 8 | 2,000 | 3,200 |
| E | 7 | 5,000 | 8,000 |
| F | 4 | 3,000 | 4,100 |
| G | 5 | 8,000 | 10,250 |
| H | 4 | 5,000 | 6,400 |
| I | 4 | 10,000 | 12,400 |
| J | 3 | 4,000 | 4,400 |
| K | 3 | 5,000 | 5,500 |

## Appendix 13.1 Finding Cumulative Probabilities for Normally Distributed Random Variables

Excel can be used to find the probability a project with uncertain activity times will be completed in some given completion time (assuming the project completion time is normally distributed). We demonstrate this on the Porta-Vac Project we considered in Section 13.2. Recall that management allotted 20 days to complete the project. We have found the $z$ value that corresponds to $T = 20$:

$$z = \frac{20 - 17}{1.65} = 1.82$$

*The Excel function NORM.S.DIST is only recognized by Excel 2010. Earlier versions of Excel use the function name NORMSDIST to compute the same value.*

Now we will make use the Excel function

$$=\text{NORM.S.DIST}(z, \text{TRUE})$$

by substituting the value of $z$ we have found into the function (entering "TRUE" for the second argument signifies that we desire the cumulative probability associated with $z$). Enter the following function into any empty cell in an Excel worksheet:

$$=\text{NORM.S.DIST}(1.82, \text{TRUE})$$

The resulting value is 0.96562, which is the probability that the completion time for the Porta-Vac project will be no more than 20 days.

# CHAPTER 16

# Simulation

## CONTENTS

**Simulation** is one of the most widely used quantitative approaches to decision making. It is a method for learning about a real system by experimenting with a model that represents the system. The simulation model contains the mathematical expressions and logical relationships that describe how to compute the value of the outputs given the values of the inputs. Any simulation model has two inputs: controllable inputs and probabilistic inputs. Figure 16.1 shows a conceptual diagram of a simulation model.

In conducting a **simulation experiment**, an analyst selects the value, or values, for the **controllable inputs**. Then values for the **probabilistic inputs** are randomly generated. The simulation model uses the values of the controllable inputs and the values of the probabilistic inputs to compute the value, or values, of the output. By conducting a series of experiments using a variety of values for the controllable inputs, the analyst learns how values of the controllable inputs affect or change the output of the simulation model. After reviewing the simulation results, the analyst is often able to make decision recommendations for the controllable inputs that will provide the desired output for the real system.

Simulation has been successfully applied in a variety of applications. The following examples are typical:

1. *New Product Development* The objective of this simulation is to determine the probability that a new product will be profitable. A model is developed that relates profit (the output measure) to various probabilistic inputs such as demand, parts cost, and labor cost. The only controllable input is whether to introduce the product. A variety of possible values will be generated for the probabilistic inputs, and the resulting profit will be computed. We develop a simulation model for this type of application in Section 16.1.

2. *Airline Overbooking* The objective of this simulation is to determine the number of reservations an airline should accept for a particular flight. A simulation model is developed that relates profit for the flight to a probabilistic input, the number of passengers with a reservation who show up and use their reservation, and a controllable input, the number of reservations accepted for the flight. For each selected value for the controllable input, a variety of possible values will be generated for the number of passengers who show up, and the resulting profit can be computed. Similar simulation models are applicable for hotel and car rental reservation systems.

3. *Inventory Policy* The objective of this simulation is to choose an inventory policy that will provide good customer service at a reasonable cost. A model is developed that relates two output measures, total inventory cost and the service level, to probabilistic inputs, such as product demand and delivery lead time from vendors, and controllable inputs, such as the order quantity and the reorder point. For each setting of the controllable inputs, a variety of possible values would be

**FIGURE 16.1**   DIAGRAM OF A SIMULATION MODEL

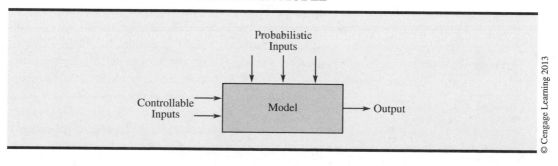

© Cengage Learning 2013

generated for the probabilistic inputs, and the resulting cost and service levels would be computed.

4. *Traffic Flow* The objective of this simulation is to determine how installing a left turn signal will affect the flow of traffic through a busy intersection. A model is developed that relates waiting time for vehicles to get through the intersection to probabilistic inputs, such as the number of vehicle arrivals and the fraction that want to make a left turn, and controllable inputs, such as the length of time the left turn signal is on. For each setting of the controllable inputs, values would be generated for the probabilistic inputs, and the resulting vehicle waiting times would be computed.

5. *Waiting Lines* The objective of this simulation is to determine the waiting times for customers requesting service from a facility, such as customers phoning a call center. A model is developed that relates customer waiting times to probabilistic inputs, such as customer arrivals and service times, and a controllable input, such as the number of servers (e.g., call center agents). For each value of the controllable input (call center agents), a variety of values would be generated for the probabilistic inputs and the customer waiting times would be computed. The Q.M. in Action, Call Center Design, describes how simulation of a waiting line system at a call center helped the company balance the service to its customers with the cost of agents providing the service.

## Q.M. *in* ACTION

### CALL CENTER DESIGN*

A call center is a place where large volumes of calls are made to or received from current or potential customers. More than 60,000 call centers operate in the United States. Saltzman and Mehrotra describe how a simulation model helped make a strategic change in the design of the technical support call center for a major software company. The application used a waiting line simulation model to balance the service to customers calling for assistance with the cost of agents providing the service.

Historically, the software company provided free phone-in technical support, but over time service requests grew to the point where 80% of the callers were waiting between 5 and 10 minutes and abandonment rates were too high. On some days 40% of the callers hung up before receiving service. This service level was unacceptable. As a result, management considered instituting a Rapid Program in which customers would pay a fee for service but would be guaranteed to receive service within one minute, or the service would be free. Nonpaying customers would

continue receiving service but without a guarantee of short waiting times.

A simulation model was developed to help understand the impact of this new program on the waiting line characteristics of the call center. Data available were used to develop the arrival distribution, the service time distribution, and the probability distribution for abandonment. The key design variables considered were the number of agents (servers) and the percentage of callers subscribing to the Rapid Program. The model was developed using the Arena simulation package.

The simulation results helped the company decide to implement the Rapid Program. Under most of the scenarios considered, the simulation model showed that 95% of the callers in the Rapid Program would receive service within one minute and that free service to the remaining customers could be maintained within acceptable limits. Within nine months, 10% of the software company's customers subscribed to the Rapid Program, generating $2 million in incremental revenue. The company viewed the simulation model as a vehicle for mitigating risk. The model helped evaluate the likely impact of the Rapid Program without experimenting with actual customers.

---

*Based on R. M. Saltzman and V. Mehrotra, "A Call Center Uses Simulation to Drive Strategic Change," *Interfaces* (May/June 2001): 87–101.

Simulation is not an optimization technique. It is a method that can be used to describe or predict how a system will operate given certain choices for the controllable inputs and randomly generated values for the probabilistic inputs. Analysts often use simulation to determine values for the controllable inputs that are likely to lead to desirable system outputs. In this sense, simulation can be an effective tool in designing a system to provide good performance.

In this chapter we begin by showing how simulation can be used to study the financial risks associated with the development of a new product. We continue with illustrations showing how simulation can be used to establish an effective inventory policy and how it can be used to design waiting line systems. We conclude with a discussion of other issues, such as verifying the simulation program, validating the model, and selecting a simulation software package.

 # Risk Analysis

**Risk analysis** is the process of predicting the outcome of a decision in the face of uncertainty. In this section we describe a problem that involves considerable uncertainty: the development of a new product. We first show how risk analysis can be conducted without using simulation; we then show how a more comprehensive risk analysis can be conducted with the aid of simulation.

## PortaCom Project

PortaCom manufactures notebook computers and related equipment. PortaCom's product design group developed a prototype for a new high-quality portable printer. The new printer features an innovative design and has the potential to capture a significant share of the portable printer market. Preliminary marketing and financial analyses provided the following selling price, first-year administrative cost, and first-year advertising cost:

$$\text{Selling price} = \$249 \text{ per unit}$$
$$\text{Administrative cost} = \$400,000$$
$$\text{Advertising cost} = \$600,000$$

In the simulation model for the PortaCom problem, the preceding values are constants and are referred to as **parameters** of the model.

The cost of direct labor, the cost of parts, and the first-year demand for the printer are not known with certainty and are considered probabilistic inputs. At this stage of the planning process, PortaCom's best estimates of these inputs are $45 per unit for the direct labor cost, $90 per unit for the parts cost, and 15,000 units for the first-year demand. PortaCom would like an analysis of the first-year profit potential for the printer. Because of PortaCom's tight cash flow situation, management is particularly concerned about the potential for a loss.

## What-If Analysis

One approach to risk analysis is called **what-if analysis**. A what-if analysis involves generating values for the probabilistic inputs (direct labor cost, parts cost, and first-year demand) and computing the resulting value for the output (profit). With a selling price of $249 per unit and administrative plus advertising costs equal to $400,000 + $600,000 = $1,000,000, the PortaCom profit model is

$$\text{Profit} = (\$249 - \text{Direct labor cost per unit} - \text{Parts cost per unit})(\text{Demand}) - \$1,000,000$$

**FIGURE 16.2**    PORTACOM PROFIT MODEL

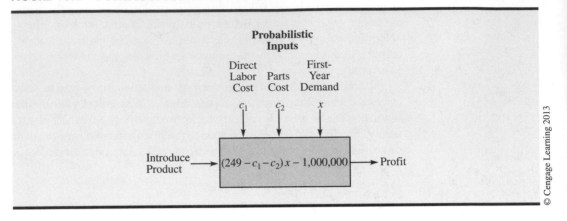

Letting

$$c_1 = \text{direct labor cost per unit}$$
$$c_2 = \text{parts cost per unit}$$
$$x = \text{first-year demand}$$

the profit model for the first year can be written as follows:

$$\text{Profit} = (249 - c_1 - c_2)x - 1{,}000{,}000 \qquad \textbf{(16.1)}$$

The PortaCom profit model can be depicted as shown in Figure 16.2.

Recall that PortaCom's best estimates of the direct labor cost per unit, the parts cost per unit, and first-year demand are $45, $90, and 15,000 units, respectively. These values constitute the **base-case scenario** for PortaCom. Substituting these values into equation (16.1) yields the following profit projection:

$$\text{Profit} = (249 - 45 - 90)(15{,}000) - 1{,}000{,}000 = 710{,}000$$

Thus, the base-case scenario leads to an anticipated profit of $710,000.

In risk analysis we are concerned with both the probability of a loss and the magnitude of a loss. Although the base-case scenario looks appealing, PortaCom might be interested in what happens if the estimates of the direct labor cost per unit, parts cost per unit, and first-year demand do not turn out to be as expected under the base-case scenario. For instance, suppose that PortaCom believes that direct labor costs could range from $43 to $47 per unit, parts cost could range from $80 to $100 per unit, and first-year demand could range from 1500 to 28,500 units. Using these ranges, what-if analysis can be used to evaluate a **worst-case scenario** and a **best-case scenario**.

The worst-case value for the direct labor cost is $47 (the highest value), the worst-case value for the parts cost is $100 (the highest value), and the worst-case value for demand is 1500 units (the lowest value). Thus, in the worst-case scenario, $c_1 = 47$, $c_2 = 100$, and $x = 1500$. Substituting these values into equation (16.1) leads to the following profit projection:

$$\text{Profit} = (249 - 47 - 100)(1500) - 1{,}000{,}000 = -847{,}000$$

So the worst-case scenario leads to a projected loss of $847,000.

The best-case value for the direct labor cost is $43 (the lowest value), the best-case value for the parts cost is $80 (the lowest value), and the best-case value for demand is

28,500 units (the highest value). Substituting these values into equation (16.1) leads to the following profit projection:

$$\text{Profit} = (249 - 43 - 80)(28{,}500) - 1{,}000{,}000 = 2{,}591{,}000$$

So the best-case scenario leads to a projected profit of $2,591,000.

*Problem 2 will give you practice using what-if analysis.*

At this point the what-if analysis provides the conclusion that profits can range from a loss of $847,000 to a profit of $2,591,000 with a base-case profit of $710,000. Although the base-case profit of $710,000 is possible, the what-if analysis indicates that either a substantial loss or a substantial profit is possible. Other scenarios that PortaCom might want to consider can also be evaluated. However, the difficulty with what-if analysis is that it does not indicate the likelihood of the various profit or loss values. In particular, we do not know anything about the *probability* of a loss.

## Simulation

Using simulation to perform risk analysis for the PortaCom problem is like playing out many what-if scenarios by randomly generating values for the probabilistic inputs. The advantage of simulation is that it allows us to assess the probability of a profit and the probability of a loss.

Using the what-if approach to risk analysis, we selected values for the probabilistic inputs [direct labor cost per unit ($c_1$), parts cost per unit ($c_2$), and first-year demand ($x$)], and then computed the resulting profit. Applying simulation to the PortaCom problem requires generating values for the probabilistic inputs that are representative of what we might observe in practice. To generate such values, we must know the probability distribution for each probabilistic input. Further analysis by PortaCom led to the following probability distributions for the direct labor cost per unit, the parts cost per unit, and first-year demand:

*One advantage of simulation is the ability to use probability distributions that are unique to the system being studied.*

**Direct Labor Cost**  PortaCom believes that the direct labor cost will range from $43 to $47 per unit and is described by the discrete probability distribution shown in Table 16.1. Thus, we see a 0.1 probability that the direct labor cost will be $43 per unit, a 0.2 probability that the direct labor cost will be $44 per unit, and so on. The highest probability of 0.4 is associated with a direct labor cost of $45 per unit.

**Parts Cost**  This cost depends upon the general economy, the overall demand for parts, and the pricing policy of PortaCom's parts suppliers. PortaCom believes that the parts cost will range from $80 to $100 per unit and is described by the uniform probability distribution shown in Figure 16.3. Costs per unit between $80 and $100 are equally likely.

**First-Year Demand**  PortaCom believes that first-year demand is described by the normal probability distribution shown in Figure 16.4. The mean or expected value of first-year

**TABLE 16.1**  PROBABILITY DISTRIBUTION FOR DIRECT LABOR COST PER UNIT

| Direct Labor Cost per Unit | Probability |
|---|---|
| $43 | 0.1 |
| $44 | 0.2 |
| $45 | 0.4 |
| $46 | 0.2 |
| $47 | 0.1 |

**FIGURE 16.3**    UNIFORM PROBABILITY DISTRIBUTION FOR THE PARTS COST PER UNIT

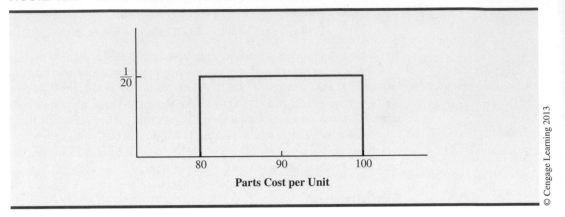

**FIGURE 16.4**    NORMAL PROBABILITY DISTRIBUTION OF FIRST-YEAR DEMAND

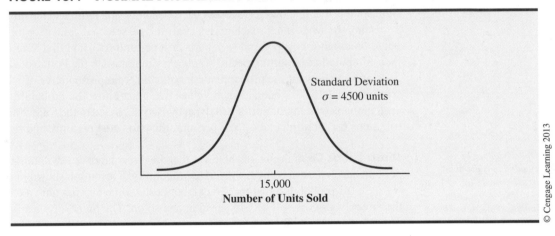

demand is 15,000 units. The standard deviation of 4500 units describes the variability in the first-year demand.

To simulate the PortaCom problem, we must generate values for the three probabilistic inputs and compute the resulting profit. Then we generate another set of values for the probabilistic inputs, compute a second value for profit, and so on. We continue this process until we are satisfied that enough trials have been conducted to describe the probability distribution for profit. This process of generating probabilistic inputs and computing the value of the output is called *simulation*. The sequence of logical and mathematical operations required to conduct a simulation can be depicted with a flowchart. A flowchart for the PortaCom simulation is shown in Figure 16.5.

*A flowchart provides a graphical representation that helps describe the logic of the simulation model.*

Following the logic described by the flowchart, we see that the model parameters—selling price, administrative cost, and advertising cost—are $249, $400,000, and $600,000, respectively. These values will remain fixed throughout the simulation.

The next three blocks depict the generation of values for the probabilistic inputs. First, a value for the direct labor cost ($c_1$) is generated. Then a value for the parts cost ($c_2$) is generated, followed by a value for the first-year demand ($x$). These probabilistic input values are combined using the profit model given by equation (16.1).

$$\text{Profit} = (249 - c_1 - c_2)x - 1{,}000{,}000$$

**FIGURE 16.5**   FLOWCHART FOR THE PORTACOM SIMULATION

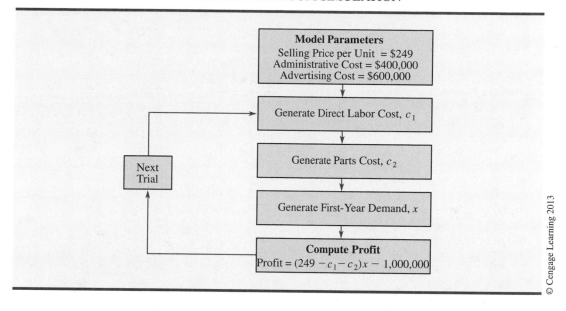

The computation of profit completes one trial of the simulation. We then return to the block where we generated the direct labor cost and begin another trial. This process is repeated until a satisfactory number of trials has been generated.

At the end of the simulation, output measures of interest can be developed. For example, we will be interested in computing the average profit and the probability of a loss. For the output measures to be meaningful, the values of the probabilistic inputs must be representative of what is likely to happen when the PortaCom printer is introduced into the market. An essential part of the simulation procedure is the ability to generate representative values for the probabilistic inputs. We now discuss how to generate these values.

**Random Numbers and Generating Probabilistic Input Values**   In the PortaCom simulation, representative values must be generated for the direct labor cost per unit $(c_1)$, the parts cost per unit $(c_2)$, and the first-year demand $(x)$. Random numbers and the probability distributions associated with each probabilistic input are used to generate representative values. To illustrate how to generate these values, we need to introduce the concept of computer-generated random numbers.

*Because random numbers are equally likely, quantitative analysts can assign ranges of random numbers to corresponding values of probabilistic inputs so that the probability of any input value to the simulation model is identical to the probability of its occurrence in the real system.*

Computer-generated random numbers[1] are randomly selected numbers from 0 up to, but not including, 1. All values of the computer-generated random numbers are equally likely and so are uniformly distributed over the interval from 0 to 1. Computer-generated random numbers can be obtained using built-in functions available in computer simulation packages and spreadsheets. For instance, placing =RAND() in a cell of an Excel worksheet will result in a random number between 0 and 1 being placed into that cell.

Table 16.2 contains 500 random numbers generated using Excel. These numbers can be viewed as a random sample of 500 values from a uniform probability distribution over the

---

[1]Computer-generated random numbers are called pseudorandom numbers. Because they are generated through the use of mathematical formulas, they are not technically random. The difference between random numbers and pseudorandom numbers is primarily philosophical, and we use the term *random numbers* regardless of whether they are generated by a computer.

**TABLE 16.2**    500 COMPUTER-GENERATED RANDOM NUMBERS

| | | | | | | | | | |
|---|---|---|---|---|---|---|---|---|---|
| 0.6953 | 0.5247 | 0.1368 | 0.9850 | 0.7467 | 0.3813 | 0.5827 | 0.7893 | 0.7169 | 0.8166 |
| 0.0082 | 0.9925 | 0.6874 | 0.2122 | 0.6885 | 0.2159 | 0.4299 | 0.3467 | 0.2186 | 0.1033 |
| 0.6799 | 0.1241 | 0.3056 | 0.5590 | 0.0423 | 0.6515 | 0.2750 | 0.8156 | 0.2871 | 0.4680 |
| 0.8898 | 0.1514 | 0.1826 | 0.0004 | 0.5259 | 0.2425 | 0.8421 | 0.9248 | 0.9155 | 0.9518 |
| 0.6515 | 0.5027 | 0.9290 | 0.5177 | 0.3134 | 0.9177 | 0.2605 | 0.6668 | 0.1167 | 0.7870 |
| 0.3976 | 0.7790 | 0.0035 | 0.0064 | 0.0441 | 0.3437 | 0.1248 | 0.5442 | 0.9800 | 0.1857 |
| 0.0642 | 0.4086 | 0.6078 | 0.2044 | 0.0484 | 0.4691 | 0.7058 | 0.8552 | 0.5029 | 0.3288 |
| 0.0377 | 0.5250 | 0.7774 | 0.2390 | 0.9121 | 0.5345 | 0.8178 | 0.8443 | 0.4154 | 0.2526 |
| 0.5739 | 0.5181 | 0.0234 | 0.7305 | 0.0376 | 0.5169 | 0.5679 | 0.5495 | 0.7872 | 0.5321 |
| 0.5827 | 0.0341 | 0.7482 | 0.6351 | 0.9146 | 0.4700 | 0.7869 | 0.1337 | 0.0702 | 0.4219 |
| 0.0508 | 0.7905 | 0.2932 | 0.4971 | 0.0225 | 0.4466 | 0.5118 | 0.1200 | 0.0200 | 0.5445 |
| 0.4757 | 0.1399 | 0.5668 | 0.9569 | 0.7255 | 0.4650 | 0.4084 | 0.3701 | 0.9446 | 0.8064 |
| 0.6805 | 0.9931 | 0.4166 | 0.1091 | 0.7730 | 0.0691 | 0.9411 | 0.3468 | 0.0014 | 0.7379 |
| 0.2603 | 0.7507 | 0.6414 | 0.9907 | 0.2699 | 0.4571 | 0.9254 | 0.2371 | 0.8664 | 0.9553 |
| 0.8143 | 0.7625 | 0.1708 | 0.1900 | 0.2781 | 0.2830 | 0.6877 | 0.0488 | 0.8635 | 0.3155 |
| 0.5681 | 0.7854 | 0.5016 | 0.9403 | 0.1078 | 0.5255 | 0.8727 | 0.3815 | 0.5541 | 0.9833 |
| 0.1501 | 0.9363 | 0.3858 | 0.3545 | 0.5448 | 0.0643 | 0.3167 | 0.6732 | 0.6283 | 0.2631 |
| 0.8806 | 0.7989 | 0.7484 | 0.8083 | 0.2701 | 0.5039 | 0.9439 | 0.1027 | 0.9677 | 0.4597 |
| 0.4582 | 0.7590 | 0.4393 | 0.4704 | 0.6903 | 0.3732 | 0.6587 | 0.8675 | 0.2905 | 0.3058 |
| 0.0785 | 0.1467 | 0.3880 | 0.5274 | 0.8723 | 0.7517 | 0.9905 | 0.8904 | 0.8177 | 0.6660 |
| 0.1158 | 0.6635 | 0.4992 | 0.9070 | 0.2975 | 0.5686 | 0.8495 | 0.1652 | 0.2039 | 0.2553 |
| 0.2762 | 0.7018 | 0.6782 | 0.4013 | 0.2224 | 0.4672 | 0.5753 | 0.6219 | 0.6871 | 0.9255 |
| 0.9382 | 0.6411 | 0.7984 | 0.0608 | 0.5945 | 0.3977 | 0.4570 | 0.9924 | 0.8398 | 0.8361 |
| 0.5102 | 0.7021 | 0.4353 | 0.3398 | 0.8038 | 0.2260 | 0.1250 | 0.1884 | 0.3432 | 0.1192 |
| 0.2354 | 0.7410 | 0.7089 | 0.2579 | 0.1358 | 0.8446 | 0.1648 | 0.3889 | 0.5620 | 0.6555 |
| 0.9082 | 0.7906 | 0.7589 | 0.8870 | 0.1189 | 0.7125 | 0.6324 | 0.1096 | 0.5155 | 0.3449 |
| 0.6936 | 0.0702 | 0.9716 | 0.0374 | 0.0683 | 0.2397 | 0.7753 | 0.2029 | 0.1464 | 0.8000 |
| 0.4042 | 0.8158 | 0.3623 | 0.6614 | 0.7954 | 0.7516 | 0.6518 | 0.3638 | 0.3107 | 0.2718 |
| 0.9410 | 0.2201 | 0.6348 | 0.0367 | 0.0311 | 0.0688 | 0.2346 | 0.3927 | 0.7327 | 0.9994 |
| 0.0917 | 0.2504 | 0.2878 | 0.1735 | 0.3872 | 0.6816 | 0.2731 | 0.3846 | 0.6621 | 0.8983 |
| 0.8532 | 0.4869 | 0.2685 | 0.6349 | 0.9364 | 0.3451 | 0.4998 | 0.2842 | 0.0643 | 0.6656 |
| 0.8980 | 0.0455 | 0.8314 | 0.8189 | 0.6783 | 0.8086 | 0.1386 | 0.4442 | 0.9941 | 0.6812 |
| 0.8412 | 0.8792 | 0.2025 | 0.9320 | 0.7656 | 0.3815 | 0.5302 | 0.8744 | 0.4584 | 0.3585 |
| 0.5688 | 0.8633 | 0.5818 | 0.0692 | 0.2543 | 0.5453 | 0.9955 | 0.1237 | 0.7535 | 0.5993 |
| 0.5006 | 0.1215 | 0.8102 | 0.1026 | 0.9251 | 0.6851 | 0.1559 | 0.1214 | 0.2628 | 0.9374 |
| 0.5748 | 0.4164 | 0.3427 | 0.2809 | 0.8064 | 0.5855 | 0.2229 | 0.2805 | 0.9139 | 0.9013 |
| 0.1100 | 0.0873 | 0.9407 | 0.8747 | 0.0496 | 0.4380 | 0.5847 | 0.4183 | 0.5929 | 0.4863 |
| 0.5802 | 0.7747 | 0.1285 | 0.0074 | 0.6252 | 0.7747 | 0.0112 | 0.3958 | 0.3285 | 0.5389 |
| 0.1019 | 0.6628 | 0.8998 | 0.1334 | 0.2798 | 0.7351 | 0.7330 | 0.6723 | 0.6924 | 0.3963 |
| 0.9909 | 0.8991 | 0.2298 | 0.2603 | 0.6921 | 0.5573 | 0.8191 | 0.0384 | 0.2954 | 0.0636 |
| 0.6292 | 0.4923 | 0.0276 | 0.6734 | 0.6562 | 0.4231 | 0.1980 | 0.6551 | 0.3716 | 0.0507 |
| 0.9430 | 0.2579 | 0.7933 | 0.0945 | 0.3192 | 0.3195 | 0.7772 | 0.4672 | 0.7070 | 0.5925 |
| 0.9938 | 0.7098 | 0.7964 | 0.7952 | 0.8947 | 0.1214 | 0.8454 | 0.8294 | 0.5394 | 0.9413 |
| 0.4690 | 0.1395 | 0.0930 | 0.3189 | 0.6972 | 0.7291 | 0.8513 | 0.9256 | 0.7478 | 0.8124 |
| 0.2028 | 0.3774 | 0.0485 | 0.7718 | 0.9656 | 0.2444 | 0.0304 | 0.1395 | 0.1577 | 0.8625 |
| 0.6141 | 0.4131 | 0.2006 | 0.2329 | 0.6182 | 0.5151 | 0.6300 | 0.9311 | 0.3837 | 0.7828 |
| 0.2757 | 0.8479 | 0.7880 | 0.8492 | 0.6859 | 0.8947 | 0.6246 | 0.1574 | 0.4936 | 0.8077 |
| 0.0561 | 0.0126 | 0.6531 | 0.0378 | 0.4975 | 0.1133 | 0.3572 | 0.0071 | 0.4555 | 0.7563 |
| 0.1419 | 0.4308 | 0.8073 | 0.4681 | 0.0481 | 0.2918 | 0.2975 | 0.0685 | 0.6384 | 0.0812 |
| 0.3125 | 0.0053 | 0.9209 | 0.9768 | 0.3584 | 0.0390 | 0.2161 | 0.6333 | 0.4391 | 0.6991 |

**TABLE 16.3** RANDOM NUMBER INTERVALS FOR GENERATING VALUES OF DIRECT LABOR COST PER UNIT

| Direct Labor Cost per Unit | Probability | Interval of Random Numbers |
|:---:|:---:|:---:|
| $43 | 0.1 | 0.0 but less than 0.1 |
| $44 | 0.2 | 0.1 but less than 0.3 |
| $45 | 0.4 | 0.3 but less than 0.7 |
| $46 | 0.2 | 0.7 but less than 0.9 |
| $47 | 0.1 | 0.9 but less than 1.0 |

© Cengage Learning 2013

interval from 0 to 1. Let us show how random numbers can be used to generate values for the PortaCom probability distributions. We begin by showing how to generate a value for the direct labor cost per unit. The approach described is applicable for generating values from any discrete probability distribution.

An interval of random numbers is assigned to each possible value of the direct labor cost in such a fashion that the probability of generating a random number in the interval is equal to the probability of the corresponding direct labor cost. Table 16.3 shows how this process is done. The interval of random numbers from 0 up to but not including 0.1 is associated with a direct labor cost of $43, the interval of random numbers from 0.1 up to but not including 0.3 is associated with a direct labor cost of $44, and so on. With this assignment of random number intervals to the possible values of the direct labor cost, the probability of generating a random number in any interval is equal to the probability of obtaining the corresponding value for the direct labor cost. Thus, to select a value for the direct labor cost, we generate a random number between 0 and 1. If the random number is at least 0.0 but less than 0.1, we set the direct labor cost equal to $43. If the random number is at least 0.1 but less than 0.3, we set the direct labor cost equal to $44, and so on.

*Try Problem 5 for an opportunity to establish intervals of random numbers and simulate demand from a discrete probability distribution.*

Each trial of the simulation requires a value for the direct labor cost. Suppose that on the first trial the random number is 0.9109. From Table 16.3, the simulated value for the direct labor cost is $47 per unit. Suppose that on the second trial the random number is 0.2841. From Table 16.3, the simulated value for the direct labor cost is $44 per unit. Table 16.4 shows the results obtained for the first 10 simulation trials.

**TABLE 16.4** RANDOM GENERATION OF 10 VALUES FOR THE DIRECT LABOR COST PER UNIT

| Trial | Random Number | Direct Labor Cost ($) |
|:---:|:---:|:---:|
| 1 | 0.9109 | 47 |
| 2 | 0.2841 | 44 |
| 3 | 0.6531 | 45 |
| 4 | 0.0367 | 43 |
| 5 | 0.3451 | 45 |
| 6 | 0.2757 | 44 |
| 7 | 0.6859 | 45 |
| 8 | 0.6246 | 45 |
| 9 | 0.4936 | 45 |
| 10 | 0.8077 | 46 |

© Cengage Learning 2013

Each trial in the simulation also requires a value of the parts cost and first-year demand. Let us now turn to the issue of generating values for the parts cost. The probability distribution for the parts cost per unit is the uniform distribution shown in Figure 16.3. Because this random variable has a different probability distribution than direct labor cost, we use random numbers in a slightly different way to generate values for parts cost. With a uniform probability distribution, the following relationship between the random number and the associated value of the parts cost is used:

$$\text{Parts cost} = a + r(b - a) \tag{16.2}$$

where

$$r = \text{random number between 0 and 1}$$
$$a = \text{smallest value for parts cost}$$
$$b = \text{largest value for parts cost}$$

For PortaCom, the smallest value for the parts cost is \$80 and the largest value is \$100. Applying equation (16.2) with $a = 80$ and $b = 100$ leads to the following formula for generating the parts cost given a random number, $r$:

$$\text{Parts cost} = 80 + r(100 - 80) = 80 + r20 \tag{16.3}$$

Equation (16.3) generates a value for the parts cost. Suppose that a random number of 0.2680 is obtained. The value for the parts cost is

$$\text{Parts cost} = 80 + 0.2680(20) = 85.36 \text{ per unit}$$

Suppose that a random number of 0.5842 is generated on the next trial. The value for the parts cost is

$$\text{Parts cost} = 80 + 0.5842(20) = 91.68 \text{ per unit}$$

With appropriate choices of $a$ and $b$, equation (16.2) can be used to generate values for any uniform probability distribution. Table 16.5 shows the generation of 10 values for the parts cost per unit.

Finally, we need a random number procedure for generating the first-year demand. Because first-year demand is normally distributed with a mean of 15,000 units and a standard deviation of 4500 units (see Figure 16.4), we need a procedure for generating random values from this normal probability distribution. Once again we will use a random number

**TABLE 16.5**    RANDOM GENERATION OF 10 VALUES FOR THE PARTS COST PER UNIT

| Trial | Random Number | Parts Cost (\$) |
|:---:|:---:|:---:|
| 1 | 0.2680 | 85.36 |
| 2 | 0.5842 | 91.68 |
| 3 | 0.6675 | 93.35 |
| 4 | 0.9280 | 98.56 |
| 5 | 0.4180 | 88.36 |
| 6 | 0.7342 | 94.68 |
| 7 | 0.4325 | 88.65 |
| 8 | 0.1186 | 82.37 |
| 9 | 0.6944 | 93.89 |
| 10 | 0.7869 | 95.74 |

between 0 and 1 for this simulation. Suppose that the random number of 0.6026 is obtained. Using 0.6026 as the cumulative normal probability and the standard normal distribution table in Appendix D, this cumulative probability occurs at $z = 0.26$ standard deviations above the mean. Because demand is normally distributed with a mean $\mu = 15,000$ and a standard deviation $\sigma = 4500$, the simulated first-year demand is $\mu + z\sigma = 15,000 + 0.26(4500) = 16,170$ units. Note that random numbers less than 0.5 generate first-year demand values below the mean (since the corresponding z values are negative) and that random numbers greater than 0.5 generate first-year demand values greater than the mean (since the corresponding z values are positive).

In practice, Excel and simulation software programs provide built-in functions that can be used to generate values from a specified probability distribution, such as a normal probability distribution, quickly and easily. The user only needs to provide the mean and standard deviation to obtain a simulated value from the specified normal distribution. For example, the following Excel function can be placed into a worksheet cell to obtain a simulated value from a normal distribution:

*The Excel function NORM.INV is only recognized by Excel 2010. Earlier versions of Excel use the function name NORMINV to compute the same value.*

$$=\text{NORM.INV(RAND(), Mean, Standard Deviation)}. \qquad \textbf{(16.4)}$$

The RAND() function provides the random number between 0 and 1, which is used as the cumulative normal probability. Using the PortaCom normal distribution with mean $\mu = 15,000$ and a standard deviation $\sigma = 4500$, the Excel function =NORM.INV(RAND(), 15000, 4500) will provide a normally distributed value for first-year demand. Table 16.6 shows the results for 10 randomly generated values from RAND() and the corresponding normally distributed demand values. Note that random numbers less than 0.5 generate first-year demand values below the mean and that random numbers greater than 0.5 generate first-year demand values greater than the mean. See Appendix 16.1 for more details on implementing a simulation model in Excel.

**Running the Simulation Model** Running the simulation model means implementing the sequence of logical and mathematical operations described in the flowchart in Figure 16.5. The model parameters are $249 per unit for the selling price, $400,000 for the administrative cost, and $600,000 for the advertising cost. Each trial in the simulation involves randomly generating values for the probabilistic inputs (direct labor cost, parts cost, and first-year demand) and computing profit. The simulation is complete when a satisfactory number of trials have been conducted.

**TABLE 16.6**  RANDOM GENERATION OF 10 VALUES FOR FIRST-YEAR DEMAND

| Trial | Random Number | Demand |
|---|---|---|
| 1 | 0.7005 | 17,366 |
| 2 | 0.3204 | 12,900 |
| 3 | 0.8968 | 20,686 |
| 4 | 0.1804 | 10,888 |
| 5 | 0.4346 | 14,259 |
| 6 | 0.9605 | 22,904 |
| 7 | 0.5646 | 15,732 |
| 8 | 0.7334 | 17,804 |
| 9 | 0.0216 | 5,902 |
| 10 | 0.3218 | 12,918 |

© Cengage Learning 2013

**TABLE 16.7**   PORTACOM SIMULATION RESULTS FOR 10 TRIALS

| Trial | Direct Labor Cost per Unit ($) | Parts Cost per Unit ($) | Units Sold | Profit ($) |
|-------|-------------------------------|-------------------------|------------|------------|
| 1 | 47 | 85.36 | 17,366 | 1,025,570 |
| 2 | 44 | 91.68 | 12,900 | 461,828 |
| 3 | 45 | 93.35 | 20,686 | 1,288,906 |
| 4 | 43 | 98.56 | 10,888 | 169,807 |
| 5 | 45 | 88.36 | 14,259 | 648,911 |
| 6 | 44 | 94.68 | 22,904 | 1,526,769 |
| 7 | 45 | 88.65 | 15,732 | 814,686 |
| 8 | 45 | 82.37 | 17,804 | 1,165,501 |
| 9 | 45 | 93.89 | 5,902 | −350,131 |
| 10 | 46 | 95.74 | 12,918 | 385,585 |
| Total | 449 | 912.64 | 151,359 | 7,137,432 |
| Average | $44.90 | $91.26 | 15,136 | $713,743 |

Let us compute the profit for the first trial assuming the following probabilistic inputs:

$$\text{Direct labor cost:} \quad c_1 = 47$$
$$\text{Parts cost:} \quad c_2 = 85.36$$
$$\text{First-year demand:} \quad x = 17,366$$

Referring to the flowchart in Figure 16.5, we see that the profit obtained is

$$\text{Profit} = (249 - c_1 - c_2)x - 1,000,000$$
$$= (249 - 47 - 85.36)17,366 - 1,000,000 = 1,025,570$$

The first row of Table 16.7 shows the result of this trial of the PortaCom simulation.

If the direct labor cost is $47 per unit, the parts cost is $85.36 per unit, and first-year demand is 17,366 units, the simulated profit for the PortaCom printer is $1,025,570. Of course, one simulation trial does not provide a complete understanding of the possible profit and loss. Because other values are possible for the probabilistic inputs, we can benefit from additional simulation trials.

Suppose that on a second simulation trial, random numbers of 0.2841, 0.5842, and 0.3204 are generated for the direct labor cost, the parts cost, and first-year demand, respectively. These random numbers will provide the probabilistic inputs of $44 for the direct labor cost, $91.68 for the parts cost, and 12,900 for first-year demand. These values provide a simulated profit of $461,828 on the second simulation trial (see the second row of Table 16.7).

Repetition of the simulation process with different values for the probabilistic inputs is an essential part of any simulation. Through the repeated trials, management will begin to understand what might happen when the product is introduced into the real world. We have shown the results of 10 simulation trials in Table 16.7. For these 10 simulated cases, we find extremes of $1,526,769 in profit for the sixth trial and a loss of $350,131 for the ninth trial. Thus, we see both the possibility of a profit and a loss. Averages for the ten trials are presented at the bottom of the table. We see that the average profit for the 10 trials is $713,743. The probability of a loss is 0.10, because one of the 10 trials (the ninth) resulted in a loss. We note also that the average simulated values for labor cost, parts cost, and first-year demand are fairly close to their means of $45, $90, and 15,000, respectively.

## Simulation of the PortaCom Problem

*Excel worksheets for all simulations presented in this chapter are available at the WEBfile links on the website that accompanies this text.*

Using an Excel worksheet, we simulated the PortaCom project 500 times. The worksheet used to carry out the simulation is shown in Figure 16.6. Note that the simulation results for trials 6 through 495 have been hidden so that the results can be shown in a reasonably sized figure. If desired, the rows for these trials can be shown and the simulation results displayed for all 500 trials. The details of the Excel worksheet that provided the PortaCom simulation are described in Appendix 16.1.

*Simulation studies enable an objective estimate of the probability of a loss, which is an important aspect of risk analysis.*

The simulation summary statistics in Figure 16.6 provide information about the risk associated with PortaCom's new printer. The worst result obtained in a simulation of 500 trials is a loss of $785,234, and the best result is a profit of $2,367,058. The mean profit is $698,457. Fifty-one of the trials resulted in a loss; thus, the estimated probability of a loss is 51/500 = 0.1020.

A histogram of simulated profit values is shown in Figure 16.7. We note that the distribution of profit values is fairly symmetric, with a large number of values in the range of $250,000 to $1,250,000. The probability of a large loss or a large gain is small. Only three trials resulted in a loss of more than $500,000, and only three trials resulted in a profit greater than $2,000,000. However, the probability of a loss is substantial. Forty-eight of the 500 trials resulted in a loss in the $0 to $500,000 range—almost 10%. The modal category, the one with the largest number of values, is the range of profits between $750,000 and $1,000,000.

**FIGURE 16.6**   EXCEL WORKSHEET FOR THE PORTACOM PROBLEM

**WEB**file

**PortaCom**

| | A | B | C | D | E | F |
|---|---|---|---|---|---|---|
| 1 | **PortaCom Risk Analysis** | | | | | |
| 2 | | | | | | |
| 3 | Selling Price per Unit | | $249 | | | |
| 4 | Administrative Cost | | $400,000 | | | |
| 5 | Advertising Cost | | $600,000 | | | |
| 6 | | | | | | |
| 7 | **Direct Labor Cost** | | | **Parts Cost (Uniform Distribution)** | | |
| 8 | Lower | Upper | | Smallest Value | $80 | |
| 9 | Random No. | Random No. | Cost per Unit | Largest Value | $100 | |
| 10 | 0.0 | 0.1 | $43 | | | |
| 11 | 0.1 | 0.3 | $44 | | | |
| 12 | 0.3 | 0.7 | $45 | **Demand (Normal Distribution)** | | |
| 13 | 0.7 | 0.9 | $46 | Mean | 15000 | |
| 14 | 0.9 | 1.0 | $47 | Standard Dev | 4500 | |
| 15 | | | | | | |
| 16 | | | | | | |
| 17 | **Simulation Trials** | | | | | |
| 18 | | | | | | |
| 19 | | Direct Labor | Parts | First-Year | | |
| 20 | Trial | Cost Per Unit | Cost Per Unit | Demand | Profit | |
| 21 | 1 | 47 | $85.36 | 17,366 | $1,025,570 | |
| 22 | 2 | 44 | $91.68 | 12,900 | $461,828 | |
| 23 | 3 | 45 | $93.35 | 20,686 | $1,288,906 | |
| 24 | 4 | 43 | $98.56 | 10,888 | $169,807 | |
| 25 | 5 | 45 | $88.36 | 14,259 | $648,911 | |
| 516 | 496 | 44 | $98.67 | 8,730 | ($71,739) | |
| 517 | 497 | 45 | $94.38 | 19,257 | $1,110,952 | |
| 518 | 498 | 44 | $90.85 | 14,920 | $703,118 | |
| 519 | 499 | 43 | $90.37 | 13,471 | $557,652 | |
| 520 | 500 | 46 | $92.50 | 18,614 | $1,056,847 | |
| 521 | | | | | | |
| 522 | | | **Summary Statistics** | | | |
| 523 | | | Mean Profit | | $698,457 | |
| 524 | | | Standard Deviation | | $520,485 | |
| 525 | | | Minimum Profit | | ($785,234) | |
| 526 | | | Maximum Profit | | $2,367,058 | |
| 527 | | | Number of Losses | | 51 | |
| 528 | | | Probability of Loss | | 0.1020 | |
| 529 | | | | | | |

© Cengage Learning 2013

**FIGURE 16.7**    HISTOGRAM OF SIMULATED PROFIT FOR 500 TRIALS
OF THE PORTACOM SIMULATION

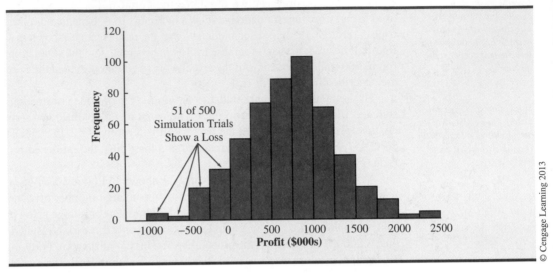

*For practice working
through a simulation
problem, try Problems 9
and 14.*

In comparing the simulation approach, risk analysis, and the what-if approach, we see that much more information is obtained by using simulation. With the what-if analysis, we learned that the base-case scenario projected a profit of $710,000. The worst-case scenario projected a loss of $847,000, and the best-case scenario projected a profit of $2,591,000. From the 500 trials of the simulation run, we see that the worst- and best-case scenarios, although possible, are unlikely. None of the 500 trials provided a loss as low as the worst case or a profit as high as the best case. Indeed, the advantage of simulation for risk analysis is the information it provides on the likely values of the output. We now know the probability of a loss, how the profit values are distributed over their range, and what profit values are most likely.

The simulation results help PortaCom's management better understand the profit/loss potential of the PortaCom portable printer. The 0.1020 probability of a loss may be acceptable to management given a probability of almost 0.80 (see Figure 16.7) that profit will exceed $250,000. On the other hand, PortaCom might want to conduct further market research before deciding whether to introduce the product. In any case, the simulation results should be helpful in reaching an appropriate decision. The Q.M. in Action, Meeting Demand Levels at Pfizer, describes how a simulation model helped find ways to meet increasing demand for a product.

## Q.M. *in* ACTION

### MEETING DEMAND LEVELS AT PFIZER*

Pharmacia & Upjohn's merger with Pfizer created one of the world's largest pharmaceutical firms. Demand for one of Pharmacia & Upjohn's long-standing products remained stable for several years at a level easily satisfied by the company's manufacturing facility. However, changes in market conditions caused an increase in demand to a level beyond the current capacity. A simulation model of the production process was developed to explore ways to increase production to meet the new level of demand in a cost-effective manner.

Simulation results were used to help answer the following questions:

• What is the maximum throughput of the existing facility?

*Based on information provided by D. B. Magerlein, J. M. Magerlein, and M. J. Goodrich.

(*continued*)

- How can the existing production process be modified to increase throughput?
- How much equipment must be added to the existing facility to meet the increased demand?
- What is the desired size and configuration of the new production process?

The simulation model was able to demonstrate that the existing facilities, with some operating policy improvements, were large enough to satisfy the increased demand for the next several years. Expansion to a new production facility was not necessary. The simulation model also helped determine the number of operators required as the production level increased in the future. This result helped ensure that the proper number of operators would be trained by the time they were needed. The simulation model also provided a way reprocessed material could be used to replace fresh raw materials, resulting in a savings of approximately $3 million per year.

## NOTES AND COMMENTS

1. The PortaCom simulation model is based on independent trials in which the results for one trial do not affect what happens in subsequent trials. This independence is maintained in the model through the selection of separate random numbers for each of the probabilistic inputs. Historically, this type of simulation study was referred to as a *Monte Carlo simulation.* The term *Monte Carlo simulation* was used because early practitioners of simulation saw similarities between the models they were developing and the gambling games played in the casinos of Monte Carlo. Today, many individuals interpret the term *Monte Carlo simulation* more broadly to mean any simulation that involves randomly generating values for the probabilistic inputs.

2. The probability distribution used to generate values for probabilistic inputs in a simulation model is often developed using historical data. For instance, suppose that an analysis of daily sales at a new car dealership for the past 50 days showed that on 2 days no cars were sold, on 5 days one car was sold, on 9 days two cars were sold, on 24 days three cars were sold, on 7 days four cars were sold, and on 3 days five cars were sold. We can estimate the probability distribution of daily demand using the relative frequencies for the observed data. An estimate of the probability that no cars are sold on a given day is $2/50 = 0.04$, an estimate of the probability that one car is sold is $5/50 = 0.10$, and so on. The estimated probability distribution of daily demand is shown in the following table.

| **Daily Sales** | 0 | 1 | 2 | 3 | 4 | 5 |
|---|---|---|---|---|---|---|
| **Probability** | 0.04 | 0.10 | 0.18 | 0.48 | 0.14 | 0.06 |

3. Spreadsheet add-in packages such as @RISK®, Risk Solver Platform©, and Crystal Ball® have been developed to make spreadsheet simulation easier. For instance, using Crystal Ball we could simulate the PortaCom new product introduction by first entering the formulas describing the relationships between the probabilistic inputs and the output measure (profit). Then a probability distribution type is selected for each probabilistic input from a menu of choices. Crystal Ball will generate random values for each probabilistic input, compute output values (e.g., profit), and repeat the simulation for as many trials as specified. Graphical displays and a variety of descriptive statistics can easily be obtained.

 **Inventory Simulation**

In this section we describe how simulation can be used to establish an inventory policy for a product that has an uncertain demand. The product is a home ventilation fan distributed by the Butler Electrical Supply Company. Each fan costs Butler $75 and sells for $125. Thus Butler realizes a gross profit of $125 − $75 = $50 for each fan sold. Monthly demand for the fan is described by a normal probability distribution with a mean of 100 units and a standard deviation of 20 units.

Butler receives monthly deliveries from its supplier and replenishes its inventory to a level of $Q$ at the beginning of each month. This beginning inventory level is referred to as the re-plenishment level. If monthly demand is less than the replenishment level, an inventory hold-ing cost of $15 is charged for each unit that is not sold. However, if monthly demand is greater than the replenishment level, a stock-out occurs and a shortage cost is incurred. Because Butler assigns a goodwill cost of $30 for each customer turned away, a shortage cost of $30 is charged for each unit of demand that cannot be satisfied. Management would like to use a simulation model to determine the average monthly net profit resulting from using a particu-lar replenishment level. Management would also like information on the percentage of total demand that will be satisfied. This percentage is referred to as the *service level*.

The controllable input to the Butler simulation model is the replenishment level, $Q$. The probabilistic input is the monthly demand, $D$. The two output measures are the average monthly net profit and the service level. Computation of the service level requires that we keep track of the number of fans sold each month and the total demand for fans for each month. The service level will be computed at the end of the simulation run as the ratio of total units sold to total demand. A diagram of the relationship between the inputs and the outputs is shown in Figure 16.8.

When demand is less than or equal to the replenishment level ($D \leq Q$), $D$ units are sold, and an inventory holding cost of $15 is incurred for each of the $Q - D$ units that remain in inventory. Net profit for this case is computed as follows:

**Case 1: $D \leq Q$**

$$\text{Gross profit} = \$50D$$
$$\text{Holding cost} = \$15(Q - D) \tag{16.5}$$
$$\text{Net profit} = \text{Gross profit} - \text{Holding cost} = \$50D - \$15(Q - D)$$

When demand is greater than the replenishment level ($D > Q$), $Q$ fans are sold, and a short-age cost of $30 is imposed for each of the $D - Q$ units of demand not satisfied. Net profit for this case is computed as follows:

**Case 2: $D > Q$**

$$\text{Gross profit} = \$50Q$$
$$\text{Holding cost} = \$30(D - Q) \tag{16.6}$$
$$\text{Net profit} = \text{Gross profit} - \text{Holding cost} = \$50Q - \$30(D - Q)$$

**FIGURE 16.8**   BUTLER INVENTORY SIMULATION MODEL

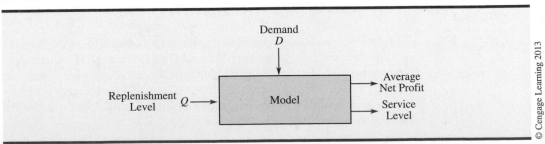

© Cengage Learning 2013

Figure 16.9 shows a flowchart that defines the sequence of logical and mathematical operations required to simulate the Butler inventory system. Each trial in the simulation represents one month of operation. The simulation is run for 300 months using a given replenishment level, $Q$. Then the average profit and service level output measures are computed. Let us describe the steps involved in the simulation by illustrating the results for the first two months of a simulation run using a replenishment level of $Q = 100$.

The first block of the flowchart in Figure 16.9 sets the values of the model parameters: gross profit = \$50 per unit, holding cost = \$15 per unit, and shortage cost = \$30 per unit. The next block shows that a replenishment level of $Q$ is selected; in our illustration, $Q = 100$. A value for monthly demand is then generated from a normal distribution with a mean of 100 units and

**FIGURE 16.9**  FLOWCHART FOR THE BUTLER INVENTORY SIMULATION

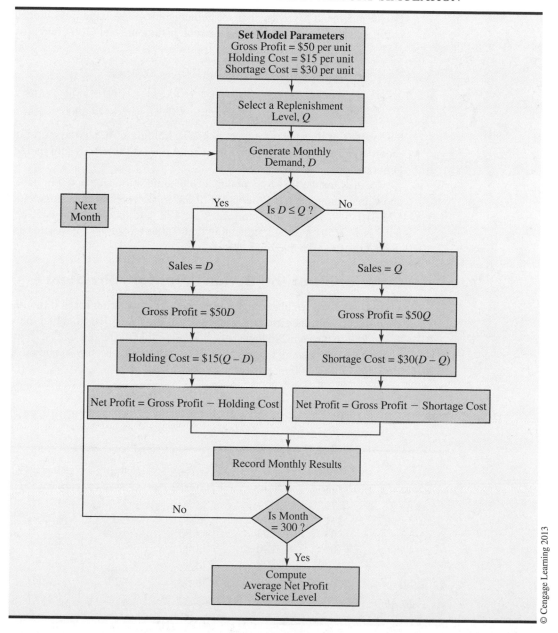

a standard devision of 20 units; this can be done in Excel using equation (16.4). Suppose that a value of $D = 79$ is generated on the first trial. This value of demand is then compared with the replenishment level, $Q$. With the replenishment level set at $Q = 100$, demand is less than the replenishment level, and the left branch of the flowchart is followed. Sales are set equal to demand (79), and gross profit, holding cost, and net profit are computed as follows:

$$\text{Gross profit} = 50D = 50(79) = 3950$$
$$\text{Holding cost} = 15(Q - D) = 15(100 - 79) = 315$$
$$\text{Net profit} = \text{Gross profit} - \text{Holding cost} = 3950 - 315 = 3635$$

The values of demand, sales, gross profit, holding cost, and net profit are recorded for the first month. The first row of Table 16.8 summarizes the information for this first trial.

For the second month, suppose that a value of 111 is generated for monthly demand. Because demand is greater than the replenishment level, the right branch of the flowchart is followed. Sales are set equal to the replenishment level (100), and gross profit, shortage cost, and net profit are computed as follows:

$$\text{Gross profit} = 50Q = 50(100) = 5000$$
$$\text{Shortage cost} = 30(D - Q) = 30(111 - 100) = 330$$
$$\text{Net profit} = \text{Gross profit} - \text{Shortage cost} = 5000 - 330 = 4670$$

The values of demand, sales, gross profit, holding cost, shortage cost, and net profit are recorded for the second month. The second row of Table 16.8 summarizes the information generated in the second trial.

Results for the first five months of the simulation are shown in Table 16.8. The totals show an accumulated total net profit of $22,310, which is an average monthly net profit of $22,310/5 = $4462. Total unit sales are 472, and total demand is 501. Thus, the service level is 472/501 = 0.942, indicating that Butler has been able to satisfy 94.2% of demand during the five-month period.

## Simulation of the Butler Inventory Problem

Using Excel, we simulated the Butler inventory operation for 300 months. The worksheet used to carry out the simulation is shown in Figure 16.10. Note that the simulation results for months 6 through 295 have been hidden so that the results can be shown in a reasonably sized figure. If desired, the rows for these months can be shown and the simulation results displayed for all 300 months.

**TABLE 16.8**    BUTLER INVENTORY SIMULATION RESULTS FOR FIVE TRIALS WITH $Q = 100$

| Month | Demand | Sales | Gross Profit ($) | Holding Cost ($) | Shortage Cost ($) | Net Profit ($) |
|---|---|---|---|---|---|---|
| 1 | 79 | 79 | 3,950 | 315 | 0 | 3,635 |
| 2 | 111 | 100 | 5,000 | 0 | 330 | 4,670 |
| 3 | 93 | 93 | 4,650 | 105 | 0 | 4,545 |
| 4 | 100 | 100 | 5,000 | 0 | 0 | 5,000 |
| 5 | 118 | 100 | 5,000 | 0 | 540 | 4,460 |
| Totals | 501 | 472 | 23,600 | 420 | 870 | 22,310 |
| Average | 100 | 94 | $4,720 | $84 | $174 | $4,462 |

**FIGURE 16.10**   EXCEL WORKSHEET FOR THE BUTLER INVENTORY PROBLEM

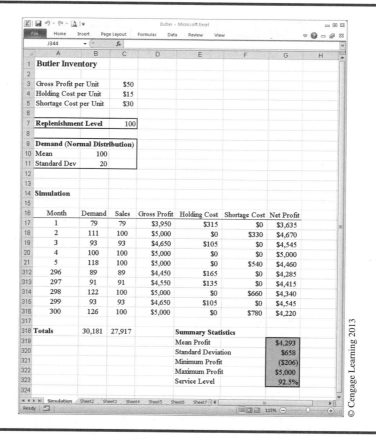

WEB**file**

**Butler**

*Simulation allows the user to consider different operating policies and changes to model parameters and then observe the impact of the changes on output measures such as profit or service level.*

The summary statistics in Figure 16.10 show what can be anticipated over 300 months if Butler operates its inventory system using a replenishment level of 100. The average net profit is $4293 per month. Because 27,917 units of the total demand of 30,181 units were satisfied, the service level is 27,917/30,181 = 92.5%. We are now ready to use the simulation model to consider other replenishment levels that may improve the net profit and the service level.

At this point we have conducted a series of simulation experiments by repeating the Butler inventory simulation with replenishment levels of 110, 120, 130, and 140 units. The average monthly net profits and the service levels are shown in Table 16.9. The highest

**TABLE 16.9**   BUTLER INVENTORY SIMULATION RESULTS FOR 300 TRIALS

| Replenishment Level | Average Net Profit ($) | Service Level (%) |
|---|---|---|
| 100 | 4293 | 92.5 |
| 110 | 4524 | 96.5 |
| 120 | 4575 | 98.6 |
| 130 | 4519 | 99.6 |
| 140 | 4399 | 99.9 |

monthly net profit of $4575 occurs with a replenishment level of $Q = 120$. The associated service level is 98.6%. On the basis of these results, Butler selected a replenishment level of $Q = 120$.

Experimental simulation studies, such as this one for Butler's inventory policy, can help identify good operating policies and decisions. Butler's management used simulation to choose a replenishment level of 120 for its home ventilation fan. With the simulation model in place, management can also explore the sensitivity of this decision to some of the model parameters. For instance, we assigned a shortage cost of $30 for any customer demand not met. With this shortage cost, the replenishment level was $Q = 120$ and the service level was 98.6%. If management felt a more appropriate shortage cost was $10 per unit, running the simulation again using $10 as the shortage cost would be a simple matter.

Earlier we mentioned that simulation is not an optimization technique. Even though we used simulation to choose a replenishment level, it does not guarantee that this choice is optimal. All possible replenishment levels were not tested. Perhaps a manager would like to consider additional simulation runs with replenishment levels of $Q = 115$ and $Q = 125$ to search for a superior inventory policy. We also have no guarantee that the replenishment level with the highest profit would be the same for another set of 300 randomly generated demand values. However, with a large number of simulation trials, we should find a near-optimal solution. The Q.M. in Action, Reducing Patient Infections in the ICU, describes a simulation application designed to assess the reduction of infections resulting from the creation of a new isolation ward in the intensive-care unit and from stricter adherence to hand-hygiene protocols at Cook County Hospital in Chicago.

*Problem 18 gives you a chance to develop a different simulation model.*

## Q.M. in ACTION

### REDUCING PATIENT INFECTIONS IN THE ICU*

Approximately two million patients acquire an infection after being admitted to the hospital in the United States each year. More than 100,000 of these patients die as a result of their hospital-acquired infections. This problem is expected to worsen as pathogens continue to develop greater resistance to antibiotics.

Two methods of decreasing the rate of hospital-acquired infections are (1) patient isolation and (2) greater adherence to hand-washing hygiene. If infected patients can be identified quickly, they can be quarantined to prevent greater outbreaks. Furthermore, proper hand washing can greatly reduce the number of pathogens present on the skin and thereby also lead to fewer infections. Yet previous studies have found that less than half of all health workers completely and correctly follow hand-hygiene protocols.

A group of researchers used data from the intensive-care unit (ICU) at Cook County Hospital in Chicago, Illinois, to create a simulation model of the movements of patients, health care workers, hospital visitors, and actual pathogens that lead to infections. The researchers were able to simulate both the creation of a new isolation ward in the ICU and model better hand-hygiene habits. The simulation estimated rates of infection and impacts on hospital costs in each scenario.

The simulation showed that both patient isolation and better hand-hygiene can greatly reduce infection rates. Improving hand-hygiene is considerably cheaper than building and maintaining additional quarantine facilities, but the researchers point out that even the best simulations do not consider psychological responses of health care workers. The simulation cannot detect why hand-hygiene compliance is currently low, so improving adherence in practice could be challenging.

*From R. Hagtvedt, P. Griffin, P. Keskinocak, and R. Roberts, "A Simulation Model to Compare Strategies for the Reduction of Health-Care-Associated Infections," *Interfaces* 39, no. 3 (May–June), 2009.

# Waiting Line Simulation

The simulation models discussed thus far have been based on independent trials in which the results for one trial do not affect what happens in subsequent trials. In this sense, the system being modeled does not change or evolve over time. Simulation models such as these are referred to as **static simulation models**. In this section we develop a simulation model of a waiting line system where the state of the system, including the number of customers in the waiting line and whether the service facility is busy or idle, changes or evolves over time. To incorporate time into the simulation model, we use a simulation clock to record the time that each customer arrives for service as well as the time that each customer completes service. Simulation models that must take into account how the system changes or evolves over time are referred to as **dynamic simulation models**. In situations where the arrivals and departures of customers are **events** that occur at *discrete* points in time, the simulation model is also referred to as a **discrete-event simulation model**.

In Chapter 15 we presented formulas that could be used to compute the steady-state operating characteristics of a waiting line, including the average waiting time, the average number of units in the waiting line, the probability of waiting, and so on. In most cases, the waiting line formulas were based on specific assumptions about the probability distribution for arrivals, the probability distribution for service times, the queue discipline, and so on. Simulation, as an alternative for studying waiting lines, is more flexible. In applications where the assumptions required by the waiting line formulas are not reasonable, simulation may be the only feasible approach to studying the waiting line system. In this section we discuss the simulation of the waiting line at the quality inspection department for Black Sheep Scarves.

## Black Sheep Scarves

Black Sheep Scarves will open several new production facilities during the coming year. Each new production facility is designed to have one quality inspector who checks the knitting of the wool scarves before they are shipped to retailers. The arrival of hand-knit wool scarves to the quality inspection department is variable over the 24-hour workday (three 8-hour shifts). A concern is that during busy periods, the shipment of scarves to retailers may be delayed as they wait to be inspected. This concern prompted Black Sheep Scarves to undertake a study of the flow of scarves into the quality inspection department as a waiting line. Black Sheep Scarves' vice president wants to determine whether one quality inspector per shift at each facility will be sufficient. Black Sheep Scarves established service guidelines stating that the average delay waiting for quality inspection should be no more than one minute. Let us show how a simulation model can be used to study the quality inspection for a particular production facility. Note that each scarf can be viewed as a customer in this example since scarves are the flow unit passing through the system.

## Customer (Scarf) Arrival Times

One probabilistic input to the Black Sheep Scarves simulation model is the arrival times of scarves to the quality inspection department. In waiting line simulations, arrival times are determined by randomly generating the time between successive arrivals, referred to as the *interarrival time*. For the quality inspection department being studied, the scarf interarrival times are assumed to be uniformly distributed between 0 and 5 minutes, as shown in Figure 16.11. With *r* denoting a random number between 0 and 1, an interarrival

**FIGURE 16.11**    UNIFORM PROBABILITY DISTRIBUTION OF INTERARRIVAL TIMES
FOR THE BLACK SHEEP SCARVES PROBLEM

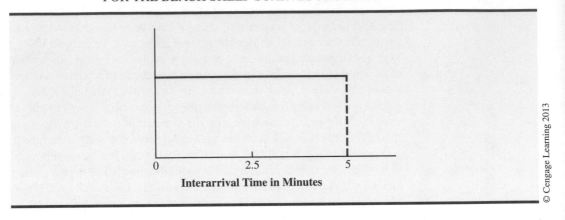

time for two successive scarves can be simulated by using the formula for generating values from a uniform probability distribution.

$$\text{Interarrival time} = a + r(b - a) \tag{16.7}$$

where

$$r = \text{random number between 0 and 1}$$
$$a = \text{minimum interarrival time}$$
$$b = \text{maximum interarrival time}$$

*A uniform probability distribution of interarrival times is used here to illustrate the simulation computations. Actually, any interarrival time probability distribution can be assumed, and the fundamental logic of the waiting line simulation model will not change.*

For the Black Sheep system, the minimum interarrival time is $a = 0$ minutes, and the maximum interarrival time is $b = 5$ minutes; therefore, the formula for generating an interarrival time is

$$\text{Interarrival time} = 0 + r(5 - 0) = 5r \tag{16.8}$$

Assume that the simulation run begins at time $= 0$. A random number of $r = 0.2804$ generates an interarrival time of $5(0.2804) = 1.4$ minutes for scarf 1. Thus, scarf 1 arrives 1.4 minutes after the simulation run begins. A second random number of $r = 0.2598$ generates an interarrival time of $5(0.2598) = 1.3$ minutes, indicating that scarf 2 arrives 1.3 minutes after scarf 1. Thus, scarf 2 arrives $1.4 + 1.3 = 2.7$ minutes after the simulation begins. Continuing, a third random number of $r = 0.9802$ indicates that scarf 3 arrives 4.9 minutes after scarf 2, which is 7.6 minutes after the simulation begins.

## Customer (Scarf) Service Times

Another probabilistic input in the Black Sheep Scarves simulation model is service time, which is the time it takes a quality inspector to check a scarf. Past data from similar quality inspection departments indicate that a normal probability distribution with a mean of 2 minutes and a standard deviation of 0.5 minutes, as shown in Figure 16.12, can be used to describe service (inspection) times. As discussed in Section 16.1, values from a normal probability distribution with mean 2 and standard deviation 0.5 can be generated in Excel using equation (16.4). For example, the random number of 0.7257 generates a scarf service time of 2.3 minutes.

**FIGURE 16.12** NORMAL PROBABILITY DISTRIBUTION OF SERVICE TIMES FOR THE BLACK SHEEP SCARVES PROBLEM

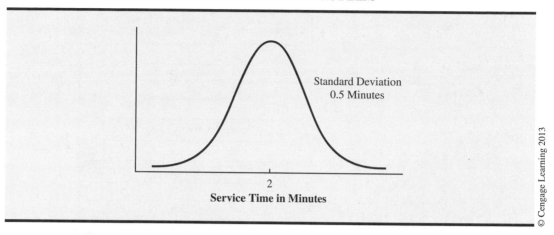

Standard Deviation 0.5 Minutes

2

**Service Time in Minutes**

© Cengage Learning 2013

## Simulation Model

The probabilistic inputs to the Black Sheep Scarves simulation model are the interarrival time and the service time. The controllable input is the number of quality inspectors. The output will consist of various operating characteristics, such as the probability of waiting, the average waiting time, the maximum waiting time, and so on. We show a diagram of the Black Sheep simulation model in Figure 16.13.

Figure 16.14 shows a flowchart that defines the sequence of logical and mathematical operations required to simulate the Black Sheep Scarves system. The flowchart uses the following notation:

$$IAT = \text{Interarrival time generated}$$
$$\text{Arrival time } (i) = \text{Time at which scarf } i \text{ arrives}$$
$$\text{Start time } (i) = \text{Time at which scarf } i \text{ starts service}$$
$$\text{Wait time } (i) = \text{Waiting time for scarf } i$$
$$ST = \text{Service time generated}$$
$$\text{Completion time } (i) = \text{Time at which scarf } i \text{ completes service}$$
$$\text{System time } (i) = \text{System time for scarf } i \text{ (completion time} - \text{arrival time)}$$

Referring to Figure 16.14, we see that the simulation is initialized in the first block of the flowchart. A new scarf is then created. An interarrival time is generated to determine

**FIGURE 16.13** BLACK SHEEP SCARVES SIMULATION MODEL

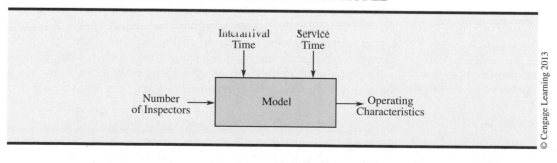

Interarrival Time    Service Time

Number of Inspectors → Model → Operating Characteristics

© Cengage Learning 2013

**FIGURE 16.14**    FLOWCHART OF THE BLACK SHEEP SCARVES SIMULATION

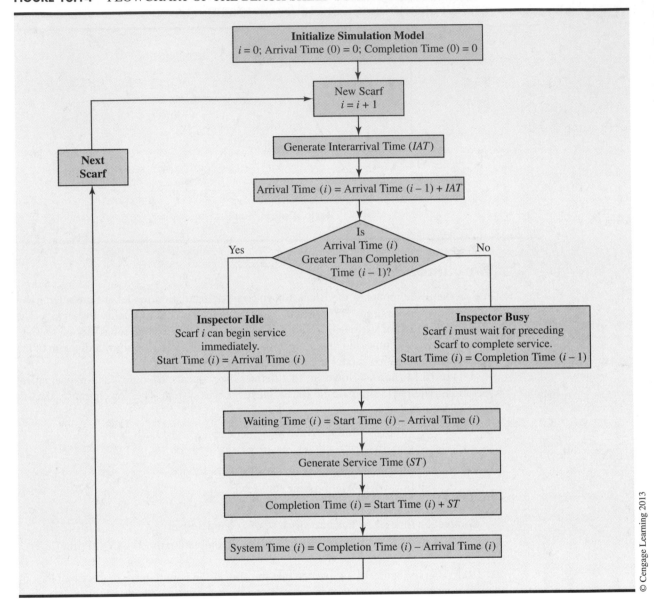

*The decision rule for deciding whether the server (the quality inspector in the Black Sheep Scarves example) is idle or busy is the most difficult aspect of the logic in a waiting line simulation model.*

the time that has passed since the preceding scarf arrived.[2] The arrival time for the new scarf is then computed by adding the interarrival time to the arrival time of the preceding scarf.

The arrival time for the new scarf must be compared to the completion time of the preceding scarf to determine whether the quality inspector is idle or busy. If the arrival time of the new scarf is greater than the completion time of the preceding scarf, the preceding scarf will have finished service (been inspected) prior to the arrival of the new scarf. In this case, the quality inspector will be idle, and the new scarf can begin service immediately. In such

---

[2]For the first scarf, the interarrival time determines the time since the simulation started. Thus, the first interarrival time determines the time the first scarf arrives.

cases the service start time for the new scarf is equal to the arrival time of the new scarf. However, if the arrival time for the new scarf is not greater than the completion time of the preceding scarf, the new scarf arrived before the preceding scarf finished service. In this case, the quality inspector is busy, and inspection of the new scarf cannot begin until the quality inspector completes the inspection of the preceding scarf. The service start time for the new scarf is equal to the completion time of the preceding scarf.

Note that the time the new scarf has to wait to use the quality inspector is the difference between the scarf's service start time and the scarf's arrival time. At this point, the scarf is ready to use the quality inspector, and the simulation run continues with the generation of the scarf's service time. The time at which the scarf begins service plus the service time generated determine the scarf's completion time, which then becomes the earliest start time for inspection of the next scarf that arrives. Finally, the total time the scarf spends in the system is the difference between the scarf's service completion time and the scarf's arrival time. At this point, the computations are complete for the current scarf, and the simulation continues with the next scarf. The simulation is continued until a specified number of scarves have been served by the quality inspector.

Simulation results for the first ten scarves are shown in Table 16.10. We discuss the computations for the first three scarves to illustrate the logic of the simulation model and to show how the information in Table 16.10 was developed.

### Scarf 1

- An interarrival time of $IAT = 1.4$ minutes is generated.
- Because the simulation run begins at time 0, the arrival time for scarf 1 is $0 + 1.4 = 1.4$ minutes.
- Scarf 1 may begin service immediately with a start time of 1.4 minutes.
- The waiting time for scarf 1 is the start time minus the arrival time: $1.4 - 1.4 = 0$ minutes.
- A service time of $ST = 2.3$ minutes is generated for scarf 1.
- The completion time for scarf 1 is the start time plus the service time: $1.4 + 2.3 = 3.7$ minutes.
- The time in the system for scarf 1 is the completion time minus the arrival time: $3.7 - 1.4 = 2.3$ minutes.

**TABLE 16.10** SIMULATION RESULTS FOR 10 SCARVES

| Scarf | Interarrival Time | Arrival Time | Service Start Time | Waiting Time | Service Time | Completion Time | Time in System |
|-------|-------------------|--------------|--------------------|--------------|--------------|-----------------|----------------|
| 1 | 1.4 | 1.4 | 1.4 | 0.0 | 2.3 | 3.7 | 2.3 |
| 2 | 1.3 | 2.7 | 3.7 | 1.0 | 1.5 | 5.2 | 2.5 |
| 3 | 4.9 | 7.6 | 7.6 | 0.0 | 2.2 | 9.8 | 2.2 |
| 4 | 3.5 | 11.1 | 11.1 | 0.0 | 2.5 | 13.6 | 2.5 |
| 5 | 0.7 | 11.8 | 13.6 | 1.8 | 1.8 | 15.4 | 3.6 |
| 6 | 2.8 | 14.6 | 15.4 | 0.8 | 2.4 | 17.8 | 3.2 |
| 7 | 2.1 | 16.7 | 17.8 | 1.1 | 2.1 | 19.9 | 3.2 |
| 8 | 0.6 | 17.3 | 19.9 | 2.6 | 1.8 | 21.7 | 4.4 |
| 9 | 2.5 | 19.8 | 21.7 | 1.9 | 2.0 | 23.7 | 3.9 |
| 10 | 1.9 | 21.7 | 23.7 | 2.0 | 2.3 | 26.0 | 4.3 |
| Totals | 21.7 | | | 11.2 | 20.9 | | 32.1 |
| Averages | 2.17 | | | 1.12 | 2.09 | | 3.21 |

### Scarf 2

- An interarrival time of $IAT = 1.3$ minutes is generated.
- Because the arrival time of scarf 1 is 1.4, the arrival time for scarf 2 is $1.4 + 1.3 = 2.7$ minutes.
- Because the completion time of scarf 1 is 3.7 minutes, the arrival time of scarf 2 is not greater than the completion time of scarf 1; thus, the quality inspector is busy when scarf 2 arrives.
- Scarf 2 must wait for scarf 1 to complete service before beginning service. Scarf 1 completes service at 3.7 minutes, which becomes the start time for scarf 2.
- The waiting time for scarf 2 is the start time minus the arrival time: $3.7 - 2.7 = 1$ minute.
- A service time of $ST = 1.5$ minutes is generated for scarf 2.
- The completion time for scarf 2 is the start time plus the service time: $3.7 + 1.5 = 5.2$ minutes.
- The time in the system for scarf 2 is the completion time minus the arrival time: $5.2 - 2.7 = 2.5$ minutes.

### Scarf 3

- An interarrival time of $IAT = 4.9$ minutes is generated.
- Because the arrival time of scarf 2 was 2.7 minutes, the arrival time for scarf 3 is $2.7 + 4.9 = 7.6$ minutes.
- The completion time of scarf 2 is 5.2 minutes, so the arrival time for scarf 3 is greater than the completion time of scarf 2. Thus, the quality inspector is idle when scarf 3 arrives.
- Scarf 3 begins service immediately with a start time of 7.6 minutes.
- The waiting time for scarf 3 is the start time minus the arrival time: $7.6 - 7.6 = 0$ minutes.
- A service time of $ST = 2.2$ minutes is generated for scarf 3.
- The completion time for scarf 3 is the start time plus the service time: $7.6 + 2.2 = 9.8$ minutes.
- The time in the system for scarf 3 is the completion time minus the arrival time: $9.8 - 7.6 = 2.2$ minutes.

Using the totals in Table 16.10, we can compute an average waiting time for the 10 scarves of $11.2/10 = 1.12$ minutes, and an average time in the system of $32.1/10 = 3.21$ minutes. Table 16.10 shows that 7 of the 10 scarves had to wait. The total time for the 10-scarf simulation is given by the completion time of the 10th scarf: 26.0 minutes. However, at this point, we realize that a simulation for 10 scarves is much too short a period to draw any firm conclusions about the operation of the waiting line.

## Simulation of Black Sheep Scarves

Using an Excel worksheet, we simulated the operation of the waiting line for the Black Sheep Scarves' quality inspection of 1000 scarves. The worksheet used to carry out the simulation is shown in Figure 16.15. Note that the simulation results for scarves 6 through 995 have been hidden so that the results can be shown in a reasonably sized figure. If desired, the rows for these scarves can be shown and the simulation results displayed for all 1000 scarves.

Summary statistics will ultimately be collected in order to describe the results of 1000 scarves. Before collecting the summary statistics, let us point out that many simulation

**FIGURE 16.15**  EXCEL WORKSHEET FOR BLACK SHEEP SCARVES WITH ONE QUALITY INSPECTOR

**WEB** file

Black Sheep 1

| Customer | Interarrival Time | Arrival Time | Service Start Time | Waiting Time | Service Time | Completion Time | Time in System |
|---|---|---|---|---|---|---|---|
| 1 | 1.4 | 1.4 | 1.4 | 0.0 | 2.3 | 3.7 | 2.3 |
| 2 | 1.3 | 2.7 | 3.7 | 1.0 | 1.5 | 5.2 | 2.5 |
| 3 | 4.9 | 7.6 | 7.6 | 0.0 | 2.2 | 9.8 | 2.2 |
| 4 | 3.5 | 11.1 | 11.1 | 0.0 | 2.5 | 13.6 | 2.5 |
| 5 | 0.7 | 11.8 | 13.6 | 1.8 | 1.8 | 15.4 | 3.6 |
| 996 | 0.5 | 2496.8 | 2498.1 | 1.3 | 0.6 | 2498.7 | 1.9 |
| 997 | 0.2 | 2497.0 | 2498.7 | 1.7 | 2.0 | 2500.7 | 3.7 |
| 998 | 2.7 | 2499.7 | 2500.7 | 1.0 | 1.8 | 2502.5 | 2.8 |
| 999 | 3.7 | 2503.4 | 2503.4 | 0.0 | 2.4 | 2505.8 | 2.4 |
| 1000 | 4.0 | 2507.4 | 2507.4 | 0.0 | 1.9 | 2509.3 | 1.9 |

Summary Statistics

| | |
|---|---|
| Number Waiting | 549 |
| Probability of Waiting | 0.6100 |
| Average Waiting Time | 1.59 |
| Maximum Waiting Time | 13.5 |
| Utilization of Quality Inspector | 0.7860 |
| Number Waiting > 1 Min | 393 |
| Probability of Waiting > 1 Min | 0.4367 |

© Cengage Learning 2013

studies of dynamic systems focus on the operation of the system during its long-run or steady-state operation. To ensure that the effects of startup conditions are not included in the steady-state calculations, a dynamic simulation model is usually run for a specified period without collecting any data about the operation of the system. The length of the startup period can vary depending on the application but can be determined by experimenting with the simulation model. Since the Black Sheep Scarves' production facility operates 24 hours per day, we want to avoid the transient effects by treating the results for the first 100 scarves as the startup period. Thus, the summary statistics shown in Figure 16.15 are for the 900 scarves arriving during the steady-state period.

The summary statistics show that 549 of the 900 scarves had to wait. This result provides a $549/900 = 0.61$ probability that a scarf will have to wait for service. In other words, approximately 61% of the scarves will have to wait because the quality inspector is in use. The average waiting time is 1.59 minutes per scarf, with at least one scarf waiting a maximum time of 13.5 minutes. The utilization rate of 0.786 indicates that the quality inspector is in use 78.6% of the time. Finally, 393 of the 900 scarves had to wait more than 1 minute (43.67% of all scarves). A histogram of waiting times for the 900 scarves is shown in Figure 16.16. This figure shows that 45 scarves (5%) had a waiting time greater than 6 minutes. Note that if we had used all 1000 simulated arrivals, these estimates could have

**FIGURE 16.16**   HISTOGRAM SHOWING THE WAITING TIME FOR 900 SCARVES

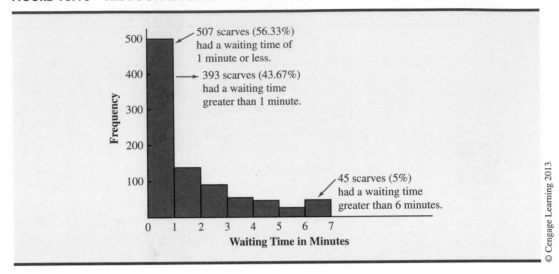

been substantially different because the scarves that arrived early in the simulation had to wait less often.

The simulation supports the conclusion that the production facility will have a busy quality inspection department. With an average scarf wait time of 1.59 minutes, the system does not satisfy Black Sheep's service guideline. This production facility is a good candidate for a second quality inspector or a more efficient inspection process.

## Simulation with Two Quality Inspectors

We extended the simulation model to the case of two quality inspectors. For the second quality inspector we also assume that the service time is normally distributed with a mean of 2 minutes and a standard deviation of 0.5 minutes. Table 16.11 shows the simulation

**TABLE 16.11**   SIMULATION RESULTS FOR 10 SCARVES FOR A TWO-QUALITY-INSPECTOR SYSTEM

| Scaarf | Interarrival Time | Arrival Time | Service Start Time | Waiting Time | Service Time | Completion Time | Time in System | Time Available QI 1 | QI 2 |
|---|---|---|---|---|---|---|---|---|---|
| 1 | 1.7 | 1.7 | 1.7 | 0.0 | 2.1 | 3.8 | 2.1 | 3.8 | 0.0 |
| 2 | 0.7 | 2.4 | 2.4 | 0.0 | 2.0 | 4.4 | 2.0 | 3.8 | 4.4 |
| 3 | 2.0 | 4.4 | 4.4 | 0.0 | 1.4 | 5.8 | 1.4 | 5.8 | 4.4 |
| 4 | 0.1 | 4.5 | 4.5 | 0.0 | 0.9 | 5.4 | 0.9 | 5.8 | 5.4 |
| 5 | 4.6 | 9.1 | 9.1 | 0.0 | 2.2 | 11.3 | 2.2 | 5.8 | 11.3 |
| 6 | 1.3 | 10.4 | 10.4 | 0.0 | 1.6 | 12.0 | 1.6 | 12.0 | 11.3 |
| 7 | 0.6 | 11.0 | 11.3 | 0.3 | 1.7 | 13.0 | 2.0 | 12.0 | 13.0 |
| 8 | 0.3 | 11.3 | 12.0 | 0.7 | 2.2 | 14.2 | 2.9 | 14.2 | 13.0 |
| 9 | 3.4 | 14.7 | 14.7 | 0.0 | 2.9 | 17.6 | 2.9 | 14.2 | 17.6 |
| 10 | 0.1 | 14.8 | 14.8 | 0.0 | 2.8 | 17.6 | 2.8 | 17.6 | 17.6 |
| Totals | 14.8 | | | 1.0 | 19.8 | | 20.8 | | |
| Averages | 1.48 | | | 0.1 | 1.98 | | 2.08 | | |

results for the first ten scarves. In comparing the two-quality-inspector system results in Table 16.11 with the single-quality-inspector simulation results shown in Table 16.10, we see that two additional columns are needed. These two columns show when each quality inspector becomes available for scarf service. We assume that, when a new scarf arrives, the scarf will be served by the quality inspector who is available first. When the simulation begins, the first scarf is arbitrarily assigned to quality inspector 1.

Table 16.11 shows that scarf 7 is the first scarf that has to wait to use an quality inspector. We describe how scarves 6, 7, and 8 are processed to show how the logic of the simulation run for two quality inspectors differs from that with a single quality inspector.

### Scarf 6

- An interarrival time of 1.3 minutes is generated, and scarf 6 arrives 9.1 + 1.3 = 10.4 minutes into the simulation.
- From the scarf 5 row, we see that quality inspector 1 frees up at 5.8 minutes, and quality inspector 2 will free up at 11.3 minutes into the simulation. Because quality inspector 1 is free, scarf 6 does not wait and begins service on quality inspector 1 at the arrival time of 10.4 minutes.
- A service time of 1.6 minutes is generated for scarf 6. So scarf 6 has a completion time of 10.4 + 1.6 = 12.0 minutes.
- The time quality inspector 1 will next become available is set at 12.0 minutes; the time available for quality inspector 2 remains 11.3 minutes.

### Scarf 7

- An interarrival time of 0.6 minutes is generated, and scarf 7 arrives 10.4 + 0.6 = 11.0 minutes into the simulation.
- From the previous row, we see that quality inspector 1 will not be available until 12.0 minutes, and quality inspector 2 will not be available until 11.3 minutes. So scarf 7 must wait to use an quality inspector. Because quality inspector 2 will free up first, scarf 7 begins service on that machine at a start time of 11.3 minutes. With an arrival time of 11.0 and a service start time of 11.3, scarf 7 experiences a waiting time of 11.3 − 11.0 = 0.3 minutes.
- A service time of 1.7 minutes is generated, leading to a completion time of 11.3 + 1.7 = 13.0 minutes.
- The time available for quality inspector 2 is updated to 13.0 minutes, and the time available for quality inspector 1 remains at 12.0 minutes.

### Scarf 8

- An interarrival time of 0.3 minutes is generated, and scarf 8 arrives 11.0 + 0.3 = 11.3 minutes into the simulation.
- From the previous row, we see that quality inspector 1 will be the first available. Thus, scarf 8 starts service on quality inspector 1 at 12.0 minutes, resulting in a waiting time of 12.0 − 11.3 = 0.7 minutes.
- A service time of 2.2 minutes is generated, resulting in a completion time of 12.0 + 2.2 = 14.2 minutes and a system time of 0.7 + 2.2 = 2.9 minutes.
- The time available for quality inspector 1 is updated to 14.2 minutes, and the time available for quality inspector 2 remains at 13.0 minutes.

From the totals in Table 16.11, we see that the average waiting time for these 10 scarves is only 1.0/10 = 0.1 minutes. Of course, a much longer simulation will be necessary before any reliable conclusions can be drawn.

## Simulation Results with Two Quality Inspectors

*Worksheets for the Black Sheep Scarves one-quality-inspector and two-quality-inspector systems are available at the WEBfile links on the website that accompanies this text.*

The Excel worksheet that we used to conduct a simulation for 1000 scarves using two quality inspectors is shown in Figure 16.17. Results for the first 100 scarves were discarded to account for the startup period. With two quality inspectors, the number of scarves that had to wait was reduced from 549 to 78. This reduction provides a $78/900 = 0.0867$ probability that a scarf will have to wait for service when two quality inspectors are used. The two-quality-inspector system also reduced the average waiting time to 0.07 minutes (4.2 seconds) per scarf. The maximum waiting time was reduced from 13.5 to 2.9 minutes, and each quality inspector was in use 40.84% of the time. Finally, only 23 of the 900 scarves had to wait more than 1 minute for an quality inspector to become available. Thus, only 2.56% of scarves had to wait more than 1 minute. The simulation results provide evidence that Black Sheep Scarves should expand to two quality inspectors.

The simulation models that we developed can now be used to study the quality inspection at other production facilities. In each case, assumptions must be made about the appropriate interarrival time and service time probability distributions. However, once appropriate assumptions have been made, the same simulation models can be used to determine the operating characteristics of the quality inspector waiting line system. The Q.M. in Action, Preboard Screening at Vancouver International Airport, describes another use of simulation for a queuing system.

**FIGURE 16.17**  EXCEL WORKSHEET FOR BLACK SHEEP SCARVES WITH TWO QUALITY INSPECTORS

**WEBfile**

**Black Sheep 2**

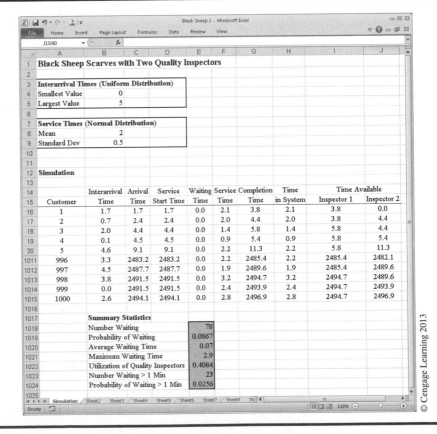

*PREBOARD SCREENING AT VANCOUVER INTERNATIONAL AIRPORT\**

Following the September 11, 2001, terrorist attacks in the United States, long lines at airport security checkpoints became commonplace. In order to reduce passenger waiting time, the Vancouver International Airport Authority teamed up with students and faculty at the University of British Columbia's Centre for Operations Excellence (COE) to build a simulation model of the airport's preboard screening security checkpoints. The goal was to use the simulation model to help achieve acceptable service standards.

Prior to building the simulation model, students from the COE observed the flow of passengers through the screening process and collected data on the service time at each process step. In addition to service time data, passenger demand data provided input to the simulation model. Two triangular probability distributions

were used to simulate passenger arrivals at the preboarding facilities. For flights to Canadian destinations a 90-40-20 triangle was used. This distribution assumes that, for each flight, the first passenger will arrive at the screening checkpoint 90 minutes before departure, the last passenger will arrive 20 minutes before departure, and the most likely arrival time is 40 minutes before departure. For international flights a 150-80-20 triangle was used.

Output statistics from the simulation model provided information concerning resource utilization, waiting line lengths, and the time passengers spend in the system. The simulation model provided information concerning the number of personnel needed to process 90% of the passengers with a waiting time of 10 minutes or less. Ultimately the airport authority was able to design and staff the preboarding checkpoints so that waiting times for 90% of the passengers were a maximum of 10 minutes.

*\*Based on D. Atkins et al., "Right on Queue," OR/MS Today (April 2003): 26–29.*

## NOTES AND COMMENTS

1. The Black Sheep Scarves waiting line model was based on uniformly distributed interarrival times and normally distributed service times. One advantage of simulation is its flexibility in accommodating a variety of different probability distributions. For instance, if we believe an exponential distribution is more appropriate for interarrival times, this waiting line simulation could easily be repeated by simply changing the way the interarrival times are generated.

2. At the beginning of this section, we defined discrete-event simulation as involving a dynamic system that evolves over time. The simulation computations focus on the sequence of events as they occur at discrete points in time. In the Black Sheep Scarves waiting line example, scarf arrivals and the scarf service completions were the discrete events. Referring to the arrival times and completion times in Table 16.10, we

see that the first five discrete events for this waiting line simulation were as follows:

| Event | Time |
|---|---|
| Scarf 1 arrives | 1.4 |
| Scarf 2 arrives | 2.7 |
| Scarf 1 finished | 3.7 |
| Scarf 2 finished | 5.2 |
| Scarf 3 arrives | 7.6 |

3. We did not keep track of the number of scarves in the quality inspection waiting line as we carried out the quality inspection simulation computations on a scarf-by-scarf basis. However, we can determine the average number of scarves in the waiting line from other information in the simulation output. The following relationship is valid for any waiting line system:

$$\frac{\text{Average number}}{\text{in waiting line}} = \frac{\text{Total waiting time}}{\text{Total time of simulation}}$$

(*continued*)

For the system with one quality inspector, the 100th scarf completed service at 247.8 minutes into the simulation. Thus, the total time of the simulation for the next 900 scarves was $2509.3 - 247.8 = 2261.5$ minutes. The average waiting time was 1.59 minutes. During the simulation, the 900 scarves had a total waiting time of $900(1.59) = 1431$ minutes. Therefore, the average number of scarves in the waiting line is

$$\begin{aligned} \text{Average number} \\ \text{in waiting line} &= 1431/2261.5 \\ &= 0.63 \text{ scarves} \end{aligned}$$

# 16.4  Other Simulation Issues

Because simulation is one of the most widely used quantitative analysis techniques, various software tools have been developed to help analysts implement a simulation model on a computer. In this section we comment on the software available and discuss some issues involved in verifying and validating a simulation model. We close the section with a discussion of some of the advantages and disadvantages of using simulation to study a real system.

## Computer Implementation

The use of spreadsheets for simulation has grown rapidly in recent years, and third-party software vendors have developed spreadsheet add-ins that make building simulation models on a spreadsheet much easier. These add-in packages provide an easy facility for generating random values from a variety of probability distributions and offer a rich array of statistics describing the simulation output. Popular spreadsheet add-ins include Crystal Ball from Oracle Corporation, @RISK from Palisade Corporation, and Risk Solver Platform from Frontline Systems. Although spreadsheets can be a valuable tool for some simulation studies, they are generally limited to smaller, less complex systems.

With the growth of simulation applications, both users of simulation and software developers began to realize that computer simulations have many common features: developing models, generating values from probability distributions, maintaining a record of what happens during the simulation, and recording and summarizing the simulation output. A variety of special-purpose simulation packages are available, including GPSS®, SIMSCRIPT®, SLAM®, and Arena®. These packages have built-in simulation clocks, simplified methods for generating probabilistic inputs, and procedures for collecting and summarizing the simulation output. Special-purpose simulation packages enable quantitative analysts to simplify the process of developing and implementing the simulation model. Indeed, Arena was used to develop the simulation model described in the Q.M. in Action, Preboard Screening at Vancouver International Airport.

Simulation models can also be developed using general-purpose computer programming languages such as BASIC, FORTRAN, PASCAL, C, and C++. The disadvantage of using these languages is that special simulation procedures are not built in. One command in a special-purpose simulation package often performs the computations and record-keeping tasks that would require several BASIC, FORTRAN, PASCAL, C, or C++ statements to duplicate. The advantage of using any of these general-purpose programming languages is that they offer greater flexibility in terms of being able to model more complex systems.

*The computational and record-keeping aspects of simulation models are assisted by specialized simulation software packages. The packages ease the tasks of developing a computer simulation model.*

To decide which software to use, an analyst will have to consider the relative merits of a spreadsheet, a special-purpose simulation package, and a general-purpose computer programming language. The goal is to select the method that is easy to use but provides an adequate representation of the system being studied.

## Verification and Validation

An important aspect of any simulation study involves confirming that the simulation model accurately describes the real system. Inaccurate simulation models cannot be expected to provide worthwhile information. Thus, before using simulation results to draw conclusions about a real system, one must take steps to verify and validate the simulation model.

**Verification** is the process of determining that the computer procedure that performs the simulation calculations is logically correct. Verification is largely a debugging task to make sure that no errors are in the computer procedure that implements the simulation. In some cases, an analyst may compare computer results for a limited number of events with independent hand calculations. In other cases, tests may be performed to verify that the probabilistic inputs are being generated correctly and that the output from the simulation model seems reasonable. The verification step is not complete until the user develops a high degree of confidence that the computer procedure is error free.

**Validation** is the process of ensuring that the simulation model provides an accurate representation of a real system. Validation requires an agreement among analysts and managers that the logic and the assumptions used in the design of the simulation model accurately reflect how the real system operates. The first phase of the validation process is done prior to, or in conjunction with, the development of the computer procedure for the simulation process. Validation continues after the computer program has been developed, with the analyst reviewing the simulation output to see whether the simulation results closely approximate the performance of the real system. If possible, the output of the simulation model is compared to the output of an existing real system to make sure that the simulation output closely approximates the performance of the real system. If this form of validation is not possible, an analyst can experiment with the simulation model and have one or more individuals experienced with the operation of the real system review the simulation output to determine whether it is a reasonable approximation of what would be obtained with the real system under similar conditions.

Verification and validation are not tasks to be taken lightly. They are key steps in any simulation study and are necessary to ensure that decisions and conclusions based on the simulation results are appropriate for the real system.

## Advantages and Disadvantages of Using Simulation

The primary advantages of simulation are that it is easy to understand and that the methodology can be used to model and learn about the behavior of complex systems that would be difficult, if not impossible, to deal with analytically. Simulation models are flexible; they can be used to describe systems without requiring the assumptions that are often required by other mathematical models. In general, the larger the number of probabilistic inputs a system has, the more likely that a simulation model will provide the best approach for studying the system. Another advantage of simulation is that a simulation model provides a convenient experimental laboratory for the real system. Changing assumptions or operating policies in the simulation model and rerunning it can provide results that help predict how such changes will affect the operation of the real system. Experimenting directly with a real system is often not feasible (consider the Q.M. in Action, Reducing Patient Infections in the ICU).

*Using simulation, we can ask what-if questions and project how the real system will behave. Although simulation does not guarantee optimality, it will usually provide near-optimal solutions. In addition, simulation models often warn against poor decision strategies by projecting disastrous outcomes such as system failures, large financial losses, and so on.*

Simulation is not without disadvantages. For complex systems, the process of developing, verifying, and validating a simulation model can be time-consuming and expensive (however, the process of developing the model generally leads to a better understanding of the system, which is an important benefit). In addition, each simulation run provides only a sample of how the real system will operate. As such, the summary of the simulation data provides only estimates or approximations about the real system. Consequently, simulation does not guarantee an optimal solution. Nonetheless, the danger of obtaining poor solutions is slight if the analyst exercises good judgment in developing the simulation model and if the simulation process is run long enough under a wide variety of conditions so that the analyst has sufficient data to predict how the real system will operate.

## Summary

Simulation is a method for learning about a real system by experimenting with a model that represents the system. Some of the reasons simulation is frequently used are as follows:

1. It can be used for a wide variety of practical problems.
2. The simulation approach is relatively easy to explain and understand, which facilitates acceptance and implementation of the results.
3. Spreadsheet packages now provide another alternative for model implementation, and third-party vendors have developed add-ins that expand the capabilities of the spreadsheet packages.
4. Computer software developers have produced simulation packages that make it easier to develop and implement simulation models for more complex problems.

We first showed how simulation can be used for risk analysis by analyzing a situation involving the development of a new product: the PortaCom printer. We then showed how simulation can be used to select an inventory replenishment level that would provide both a good profit and a good customer service level. Finally, we developed a simulation model for the Black Sheep Scarves quality inspection waiting line system. This model is an example of a dynamic simulation model in which the state of the system changes or evolves over time.

Our approach was to develop a simulation model that contained both controllable inputs and probabilistic inputs. Procedures were developed for randomly generating values for the probabilistic inputs, and a flowchart was developed to show the sequence of logical and mathematical operations that describe the steps of the simulation process. Simulation results were obtained by running the simulation for a suitable number of trials or length of time. Simulation results were obtained and conclusions were drawn about the operation of the real system.

The Q.M. in Action, Netherlands Company Improves Warehouse Order-Picking Efficiency, describes how a simulation model determined the warehouse storage location for 18,000 products and the sequence in which products were retrieved by order-picking personnel.

## Q.M. *in* ACTION

### NETHERLANDS COMPANY IMPROVES WAREHOUSE ORDER-PICKING EFFICIENCY*

As a wholesaler of tools, hardware, and garden equipment, Ankor, based in The Netherlands, warehouses more than 18,000 different products for customers who are primarily retail store chains, do-it-yourself businesses, and

garden centers. Warehouse managers store the fastest-moving products on the ends of the aisles on the ground floor, the medium-moving products in the middle section of the aisles on the ground floor, and the slow-moving products on the mezzanine.

When a new order is received, a warehouse order-picker travels to each product location and selects the

*Based on R. Dekker, M. B. M. de Koster, K. J. Roodbergen, and H. van Kalleveen, "Improving Order-Picking Response Time at Ankor's Warehouse," *Interfaces* (July/August 2004): 303–313.

(*continued*)

requested number of units. An average order includes 25 different products, which requires the order-picker to travel to 25 different locations in the warehouse. In order to minimize damage to the products, heavier products are picked first and breakable products are picked last. Order-picking is typically one of the most time-consuming and expensive aspects of operating the warehouse. The company is under continuous pressure to improve the efficiency of this operation.

To increase efficiency, researchers developed a simulation model of the warehouse order-picking system. Using a sequence of 1098 orders received for 27,790 products over a seven-week period, the researchers used the model to simulate the required order-picking times. The researchers, with the help of the model, varied the assignment of products to storage locations and the sequence in which products were retrieved from the storage locations. The model simulated order-picking times for a variety of product storage location alternatives and four different routing policies that determined the sequence in which products were picked.

Analysis of the simulation results provided a new storage assignment policy for the warehouse as well as new routing rules for the sequence in which to retrieve products from storage. Implementation of the new storage and routing procedures reduced the average route length of the order-picking operation by 31%. Due to the increased efficiency of the operation, the number of order-pickers was reduced by more than 25%, saving the company an estimated €140,000 per year.

## Glossary

**Simulation** A method for learning about a real system by experimenting with a model that represents the system.

**Simulation experiment** Generating a sample of values for the probabilistic inputs of a simulation model and computing the resulting values of the model outputs.

**Controllable input** Input to a simulation model that is selected by the decision maker.

**Probabilistic input** Input to a simulation model that is subject to uncertainty. A probabilistic input is described by a probability distribution.

**Risk analysis** The process of predicting the outcome of a decision in the face of uncertainty.

**Parameters** Numeric values that appear in the mathematical relationships of a model. Parameters are considered known and remain constant over all trials of a simulation.

**What-if analysis** A trial-and-error approach to learning about the range of possible outputs for a model. Trial values are chosen for the model inputs (these are the what-ifs) and the value of the output(s) is computed.

**Base-case scenario** Determining the output given the most likely values for the probabilistic inputs of a model.

**Worst-case scenario** Determining the output given the worst values that can be expected for the probabilistic inputs of a model.

**Best-case scenario** Determining the output given the best values that can be expected for the probabilistic inputs of a model.

**Static simulation model** A simulation model used in situations where the state of the system at one point in time does not affect the state of the system at future points in time. Each trial of the simulation is independent.

**Dynamic simulation model** A simulation model used in situations where the state of the system affects how the system changes or evolves over time.

**Event** An instantaneous occurrence that changes the state of the system in a simulation model.

**Discrete-event simulation model**  A simulation model that describes how a system evolves over time by using events that occur at discrete points in time.

**Verification**  The process of determining that a computer program implements a simulation model as it is intended.

**Validation**  The process of determining that a simulation model provides an accurate representation of a real system.

## Problems

*Note:* Problems 1–12 are designed to give you practice in setting up a simulation model and demonstrating how random numbers can be used to generate values for the probabilistic inputs. These problems, which ask you to provide a small number of simulation trials, can be done with hand calculations. This approach should give you a good understanding of the simulation process, but the simulation results will not be sufficient for you to draw final conclusions or make decisions about the situation. Problems 13–25 are more realistic in that they ask you to generate simulation output(s) for a large number of trials and use the results to draw conclusions about the behavior of the system being studied. These problems require the use of a computer to carry out the simulation computations. The ability to use Excel will be necessary when you attempt Problems 13–25.

1.  Consider the PortaCom project discussed in Section 16.1.
    a.  An engineer on the product development team believes that first-year sales for the new printer will be 20,000 units. Using estimates of $45 per unit for the direct labor cost and $90 per unit for the parts cost, what is the first-year profit using the engineer's sales estimate?
    b.  The financial analyst on the product development team is more conservative, indicating that parts cost may well be $100 per unit. In addition, the analyst suggests that a sales volume of 10,000 units is more realistic. Using the most likely value of $45 per unit for the direct labor cost, what is the first-year profit using the financial analyst's estimates?
    c.  Why is the simulation approach to risk analysis preferable to generating a variety of what-if scenarios such as those suggested by the engineer and the financial analyst?

2.  The management of Madeira Manufacturing Company is considering the introduction of a new product. The fixed cost to begin the production of the product is $30,000. The variable cost for the product is expected to be between $16 and $24, with a most likely value of $20 per unit. The product will sell for $50 per unit. Demand for the product is expected to range from 300 to 2100 units, with 1200 units the most likely demand.
    a.  Develop the profit model for this product.
    b.  Provide the base-case, worst-case, and best-case analyses.
    c.  Discuss why simulation would be desirable.

3.  a.  Use the random numbers 0.3753, 0.9218, 0.0336, 0.5145, and 0.7000 to generate five simulated values for the PortaCom direct labor cost per unit.
    b.  Use the random numbers 0.6221, 0.3418, 0.1402, 0.5198, and 0.9375 to generate five simulated values for the PortaCom parts cost.
    c.  Use the random numbers 0.8531, 0.1762, 0.5000, 0.6810, and 0.2879 and the table for the cumulative standard normal distribution in Appendix D to generate five simulated values for the PortaCom first-year demand.

4.  To generate leads for new business, Gustin Investment Services offers free financial planning seminars at major hotels in Southwest Florida. Attendance is limited to 25 individuals per seminar. Each seminar costs Gustin $3500, and the average first-year commission

for each new account opened is $5000. Historical data collected over the past four years show that the number of new accounts opened at a seminar varies from no accounts opened to a maximum of six accounts opened according to the following probability distribution:

| Number of New Accounts Opened | Probability |
|:---:|:---:|
| 0 | 0.01 |
| 1 | 0.04 |
| 2 | 0.10 |
| 3 | 0.25 |
| 4 | 0.40 |
| 5 | 0.15 |

   a.   Set up intervals of random numbers that can be used to simulate the number of new accounts opened at a seminar.

   b.   Using the first 10 random numbers in column 9 of Table 16.2, simulate the number of new accounts opened for 10 seminars.

   c.   Would you recommend that Gustin continue running the seminars?

5.   The price of a share of a particular stock listed on the New York Stock Exchange is currently $39. The following probability distribution shows how the price per share is expected to change over a three-month period:

| Stock Price Change ($) | Probability |
|:---:|:---:|
| −2 | 0.05 |
| −1 | 0.10 |
| 0 | 0.25 |
| +1 | 0.20 |
| +2 | 0.20 |
| +3 | 0.10 |
| +4 | 0.10 |

   a.   Set up intervals of random numbers that can be used to generate the change in stock price over a three-month period.

   b.   With the current price of $39 per share and the random numbers 0.1091, 0.9407, 0.1941, and 0.8083, simulate the price per share for the next four 3-month periods. What is the ending simulated price per share?

6.   The Statewide Auto Insurance Company developed the following probability distribution for automobile collision claims paid during the past year:

| Payment($) | Probability |
|:---:|:---:|
| 0 | 0.83 |
| 500 | 0.06 |
| 1,000 | 0.05 |
| 2,000 | 0.02 |
| 5,000 | 0.02 |
| 8,000 | 0.01 |
| 10,000 | 0.01 |

a. Set up intervals of random numbers that can be used to generate automobile collision claim payments.

b. Using the first 20 random numbers in column 4 of Table 16.2, simulate the payments for 20 policyholders. How many claims are paid and what is the total amount paid to the policyholders?

7. A variety of routine maintenance checks are made on commercial airplanes prior to each takeoff. A particular maintenance check of an airplane's landing gear requires an average of 15 minutes of a maintenance engineer's time. In fact, the exact time required is normally distributed with a mean of 15 minutes and a standard deviation of 3 minutes. As part of a larger simulation model designed to determine total on-ground maintenance time for an airplane, we will need to simulate the actual time required to perform this maintenance check on the airplane's landing gear. Using random numbers of 0.1562, 0.9821, 0.3409, 0.5594, and 0.7758, compute the time required for each of five simulated maintenance checks of the airplane's landing gear.

8. Major League Baseball's World Series is a maximum of seven games, with the winner being the first team to win four games. Assume that the Atlanta Braves are in the World Series and that the first two games are to be played in Atlanta, the next three games at the opponent's ballpark, and the last two games, if necessary, back in Atlanta. Taking into account the projected starting pitchers for each game and the home field advantage, the probabilities of Atlanta winning each game are as follows:

| Game | 1 | 2 | 3 | 4 | 5 | 6 | 7 |
|---|---|---|---|---|---|---|---|
| **Probability of Win** | 0.60 | 0.55 | 0.48 | 0.45 | 0.48 | 0.55 | 0.50 |

a. Set up random number intervals that can be used to determine the winner of each game. Let the smaller random numbers indicate that Atlanta wins the game. For example, the random number interval "0.00 but less than 0.60" corresponds to Atlanta winning game 1.

b. Use the random numbers in column 6 of Table 16.2 beginning with 0.3813 to simulate the playing of the World Series. Do the Atlanta Braves win the series? How many games are played?

c. Discuss how repeated simulation trials could be used to estimate the overall probability of Atlanta winning the series as well as the most likely number of games in the series.

9. A project has four activities (A, B, C, and D) that must be performed sequentially. The probability distributions for the time required to complete each of the activities are as follows:

| Activity | Activity Time (weeks) | Probability |
|---|---|---|
| A | 5 | 0.25 |
|  | 6 | 0.35 |
|  | 7 | 0.25 |
|  | 8 | 0.15 |
| B | 3 | 0.20 |
|  | 5 | 0.55 |
|  | 7 | 0.25 |
| C | 10 | 0.10 |
|  | 12 | 0.25 |
|  | 14 | 0.40 |
|  | 16 | 0.20 |
|  | 18 | 0.05 |
| D | 8 | 0.60 |
|  | 10 | 0.40 |

    a.   Provide the base-case, worst-case, and best-case calculations for the time to complete the project.

    b.   Use the random numbers 0.1778, 0.9617, 0.6849, and 0.4503 to simulate the completion time of the project in weeks.

    c.   Discuss how simulation could be used to estimate the probability that the project can be completed in 35 weeks or less.

10.   Blackjack, or 21, is a popular casino game that begins with each player and the dealer being dealt two cards. The value of each hand is determined by the point total of the cards in the hand. Face cards and 10s count 10 points, aces can be counted as either 1 or 11 points, and all other cards count at their face value. For instance, the value of a hand consisting of a jack and an 8 is 18; the value of a hand consisting of an ace and a 2 is either 3 or 13 depending on whether the ace is counted as 1 or 11 points. The goal is to obtain a hand with a value of 21, or as close to it as possible without exceeding 21. After the initial deal, each player and the dealer may draw additional cards (called "taking a hit") in order to improve their hand. If a player or the dealer takes a hit and the value of his or her hand exceeds 21, that person "goes broke" and loses. The dealer's advantage is that each player must decide whether to take a hit before the dealer. If a player takes a hit and goes over 21, the player loses even if the dealer later takes a hit and goes over 21. For this reason, players will often decide not to take a hit when the value of their hand is 12 or greater.

       The dealer's hand is dealt with one card up and one card down. The player then decides whether to take a hit based on knowledge of the dealer's up card. A gambling professional determined that when the dealer's up card is a 6, the following probabilities describe the ending value of the dealer's hand:

| Value of Hand | 17 | 18 | 19 | 20 | 21 | Broke |
|---|---|---|---|---|---|---|
| Probability | 0.1654 | 0.1063 | 0.1063 | 0.1017 | 0.0972 | 0.4231 |

    a.   Set up intervals of random numbers that can be used to simulate the ending value of the dealer's hand when the dealer has a 6 as the up card.

    b.   Use the random numbers in column 4 of Table 16.2 to simulate the ending value of the dealer's hand for 20 plays of the game.

    c.   Suppose you are playing blackjack and your hand has a value of 16 for the two cards initially dealt. If you decide to take a hit, the following cards will improve your hand: ace, 2, 3, 4, and 5. Any card with a point count greater than 5 will result in you going broke. Suppose you have a hand with a value of 16 and decide to take a hit. The following probabilities describe the ending value of your hand:

| Value of Hand | 17 | 18 | 19 | 20 | 21 | Broke |
|---|---|---|---|---|---|---|
| Probability | 0.0769 | 0.0769 | 0.0769 | 0.0769 | 0.0769 | 0.6155 |

       Use the random numbers in column 5 of Table 16.2 to simulate the ending value of your hand after taking a hit for 20 plays of the game.

    d.   Use the results of parts (b) and (c) to simulate the result of 20 blackjack hands when the dealer has a 6 up and the player chooses to take a hit with a hand that has a value of 16. How many hands result in the dealer winning, a push (a tie), and the player winning?

    e.   If the player has a hand with a value of 16 and doesn't take a hit, the only way the player can win is if the dealer goes broke. How many of the hands in part (b) result in the player winning without taking a hit? On the basis of this result and the results in part (d), would you recommend the player take a hit if the player has a hand with a value of 16 and the dealer has a 6 up?

11.   Over a five-year period, the quarterly change in the price per share of common stock for a major oil company ranged from $-8\%$ to 12%. A financial analyst wants to learn what can

be expected for price appreciation of this stock over the next two years. Using the five-year history as a basis, the analyst is willing to assume that the change in price for each quarter is uniformly distributed between $-8\%$ and $12\%$. Use simulation to provide information about the price per share for the stock over the coming two-year period (eight quarters).

a. Use two-digit random numbers from column 2 of Table 16.2, beginning with 0.52, 0.99, and so on, to simulate the quarterly price change for each of the eight quarters.

b. If the current price per share is $80, what is the simulated price per share at the end of the two-year period?

c. Discuss how risk analysis would be helpful in identifying the risk associated with a two-year investment in this stock.

12. The management of Brinkley Corporation is interested in using simulation to estimate the profit per unit for a new product. Probability distributions for the purchase cost, the labor cost, and the transportation cost are as follows:

| Purchase Cost ($) | Probability | Labor Cost ($) | Probability | Transportation Cost ($) | Probability |
|---|---|---|---|---|---|
| 10 | 0.25 | 20 | 0.10 | 3 | 0.75 |
| 11 | 0.45 | 22 | 0.25 | 5 | 0.25 |
| 12 | 0.30 | 24 | 0.35 | | |
| | | 25 | 0.30 | | |

Assume that these are the only costs and that the selling price for the product will be $45 per unit.

a. Provide the base-case, worst-case, and best-case calculations for the profit per unit.

b. Set up intervals of random numbers that can be used to randomly generate the three cost components.

c. Using the random numbers 0.3726, 0.5839, and 0.8275, calculate the profit per unit.

d. Using the random numbers 0.1862, 0.7466, and 0.6171, calculate the profit per unit.

e. Management believes the project may not be profitable if the profit per unit is less than $5. Explain how simulation can be used to estimate the probability that the profit per unit will be less than $5.

13. Develop your own worksheet for the PortaCom simulation model described in Section 16.1.

a. Compute the mean profit, the minimum profit, and the maximum profit.

b. What is your estimate of the probability of a loss?

14. Develop a worksheet simulation for the following problem. The management of Madeira Manufacturing Company is considering the introduction of a new product. The fixed cost to begin the production of the product is $30,000. The variable cost for the product is uniformly distributed between $16 and $24 per unit. The product will sell for $50 per unit. Demand for the product is best described by a normal probability distribution with a mean of 1200 units and a standard deviation of 300 units. Develop a spreadsheet simulation similar to Figure 16.6. Use 500 simulation trials to answer the following questions:

a. What is the mean profit for the simulation?

b. What is the probability that the project will result in a loss?

c. What is your recommendation concerning the introduction of the product?

15. Use a worksheet to simulate the rolling of dice. Use the VLOOKUP function as described in Appendix 16.1 to select the outcome for each die. Place the number for the first die in column B and the number for the second die in column C. Show the sum in column D. Repeat the simulation for 1000 rolls of the dice. What is your simulation estimate of the probability of rolling a 7?

16. Strassel Investors buys real estate, develops it, and resells it for a profit. A new property is available, and Bud Strassel, the president and owner of Strassel Investors, believes it can be sold for $160,000. The current property owner asked for bids and stated that the property will be sold for the highest bid in excess of $100,000. Two competitors will be submitting bids for the property. Strassel does not know what the competitors will bid, but he assumes for planning purposes that the amount bid by each competitor will be uniformly distributed between $100,000 and $150,000.

    a. Develop a worksheet that can be used to simulate the bids made by the two competitors. Strassel is considering a bid of $130,000 for the property. Using a simulation of 1000 trials, what is the estimate of the probability that Strassel will be able to obtain the property using a bid of $130,000?

    b. How much does Strassel need to bid to be assured of obtaining the property? What is the profit associated with this bid?

    c. Use the simulation model to compute the profit for each trial of the simulation run. With maximization of profit as Strassel's objective, use simulation to evaluate Strassel's bid alternatives of $130,000, $140,000, or $150,000. What is the recommended bid, and what is the expected profit?

17. Grear Tire Company has produced a new tire with an estimated mean lifetime mileage of 36,500 miles. Management also believes that the standard deviation is 5000 miles and that tire mileage is normally distributed. Use a worksheet to simulate the miles obtained for a sample of 500 tires.

    a. Use the Excel COUNTIF function (see appendix A for a description of the Excel COUNTIF function) to determine the number of tires that last longer than 40,000 miles. What is your estimate of the percentage of tires that will exceed 40,000 miles?

    b. Use COUNTIF to find the number of tires that obtain mileage less than 32,000 miles. Then find the number with less than 30,000 miles and the number with less than 28,000 miles.

    c. If management would like to advertise a tire mileage guarantee such that approximately no more than 10% of the tires would obtain mileage low enough to qualify for the guarantee, what tire mileage considered in part (b) would you recommend for the guarantee?

18. A building contractor is preparing a bid on a new construction project. Two other contractors will be submitting bids for the same project. Based on past bidding practices, bids from the other contractors can be described by the following probability distributions:

| Contractor | Probability Distribution of Bid |
|---|---|
| A | Uniform probability distribution between $600,000 and $800,000 |
| B | Normal probability distribution with a mean bid of $700,000 and a standard deviation of $50,000 |

    a. If the building contractor submits a bid of $750,000, what is the probability that the building contractor will obtain the bid? Use a worksheet to simulate 1000 trials of the contract bidding process.

    b. The building contractor is also considering bids of $775,000 and $785,000. If the building contractor would like to bid such that the probability of winning the bid is about 0.80, what bid would you recommend? Repeat the simulation process with bids of $775,000 and $785,000 to justify your recommendation.

19. Develop your own worksheet for the Butler inventory simulation model shown in Figure 16.10. Suppose that management prefers not to charge for loss of goodwill. Run the Butler

inventory simulation model with replenishment levels of 110, 115, 120, and 125. What is your recommendation?

20. In preparing for the upcoming holiday season, Mandrell Toy Company designed a new doll called Freddy. The fixed cost to produce the doll is $100,000. The variable cost, which includes material, labor, and shipping costs, is $34 per doll. During the holiday selling season, Mandrell will sell the dolls for $42 each. If Mandrell overproduces the dolls, the excess dolls will be sold in January through a distributor who has agreed to pay Mandrell $10 per doll. Demand for new toys during the holiday selling season is extremely uncertain. Forecasts are for expected sales of 60,000 dolls with a standard deviation of 15,000. The normal probability distribution is assumed to be a good description of the demand.

   a. Create a worksheet similar to the inventory worksheet in Figure 16.10. Include columns showing demand, sales, revenue from sales, amount of surplus, revenue from sales of surplus, total cost, and net profit. Use your worksheet to simulate the sales of the Freddy doll using a production quantity of 60,000 units. Using 500 simulation trials, what is the estimate of the mean profit associated with the production quantity of 60,000 dolls?

   b. Before making a final decision on the production quantity, management wants an analysis of a more aggressive 70,000-unit production quantity and a more conservative 50,000-unit production quantity. Run your simulation with these two production quantities. What is the mean profit associated with each? What is your recommendation on the production of the Freddy doll?

   c. Assuming that Mandrell's management adopts your recommendation, what is the probability of a stock-out and a shortage of the Freddy dolls during the holiday season?

21. South Central Airlines operates a commuter flight between Atlanta and Charlotte. The plane holds 30 passengers, and the airline makes a $100 profit on each passenger on the flight. When South Central takes 30 reservations for the flight, experience has shown that, on average, two passengers do not show up. As a result, with 30 reservations, South Central is averaging 28 passengers with a profit of 28(100) = $2800 per flight. The airline operations office has asked for an evaluation of an overbooking strategy in which the airline would accept 32 reservations even though the airplane holds only 30 passengers. The probability distribution for the number of passengers showing up when 32 reservations are accepted is as follows:

| Passengers Showing Up | Probability |
|---|---|
| 28 | 0.05 |
| 29 | 0.25 |
| 30 | 0.50 |
| 31 | 0.15 |
| 32 | 0.05 |

The airline will receive a profit of $100 for each passenger on the flight, up to the capacity of 30 passengers. The airline will also incur a cost for any passenger denied seating on the flight. This cost covers added expenses of rescheduling the passenger as well as loss of goodwill, estimated to be $150 per passenger. Develop a worksheet model that will simulate the performance of the overbooking system. Simulate the number of passengers showing up for each of 500 flights by using the VLOOKUP function as described in Appendix 16.1. Use the results to compute the profit for each flight.

   a. Does your simulation recommend the overbooking strategy? What is the mean profit per flight if overbooking is implemented?

   b. Explain how your simulation model could be used to evaluate other overbooking levels, such as 31, 33, and 34, and for recommending a best overbooking strategy.

22. Develop your own waiting line simulation model for the Black Sheep Scarves problem described in Section 16.3. Assume that a quality inspection department for a new production facility is expected to check scarves with times uniformly distributed between 0 and 4 minutes. The service times of the quality inspection are anticipated to be normal, with a mean of 2 minutes and a standard deviation of 0.5 minutes. Simulate the operation of this system for 1000 scarves using one quality inspector. Discard the first 100 scarves and collect data over the next 900 scarves. What is your assessment of the ability to operate with one quality inspector? What happens to the average waiting time for scarves near the end of the simulation period?

23. The Burger Dome waiting line model in Section 15.1 studies the waiting time of customers at its fast-food restaurant. Burger Dome's single-server waiting line system has an arrival rate of 0.75 customers per minute and a service rate of 1 customer per minute.
    a. Use a worksheet based on Figure 16.15 to simulate the operation of this waiting line. Assuming that customer arrivals follow a Poisson probability distribution, the interarrival times can be simulated with the cell formula $-(1/\lambda)*LN(RAND())$, where $\lambda = 0.75$. Assuming that the service time follows an exponential probability distribution, the service times can be simulated with the cell formula $-\mu*LN(RAND())$, where $\mu = 1$. Run the Burger Dome simulation for 1000 customers. Discard the first 100 customers and collect data over the next 900 customers. The analytical model in Chapter 15 indicates an average waiting time of 3 minutes per customer. What average waiting time does your simulation model show?
    b. One advantage of using simulation is that a simulation model can be altered easily to reflect other assumptions about the probabilistic inputs. Assume that the service time is more accurately described by a normal probability distribution with a mean of 1 minute and a standard deviation of 0.2 minutes. This distribution has less service time variability than the exponential probability distribution used in part (a). What is the impact of this change on the average waiting time?

24. Telephone calls come into an airline reservations office randomly at the mean rate of 15 calls per hour. The time between calls follows an exponential distribution with a mean of 4 minutes. When the two reservation agents are busy, a telephone message tells the caller that the call is important and to please wait on the line until the next reservation agent becomes available. The service time for each reservation agent is normally distributed with a mean of 4 minutes and a standard deviation of 1 minute. Use a two-server waiting line simulation model to evaluate this waiting line system. Use the worksheet design shown in Figure 16.17. The cell formula $=-4*LN(RAND())$ can be used to generate the interarrival times. Simulate the operation of the telephone reservation system for 600 customers. Discard the first 100 customers, and collect data over the next 500 customers.
    a. Compute the mean interarrival time and the mean service time. If your simulation model is operating correctly, both of these should have means of approximately 4 minutes.
    b. What is the mean customer waiting time for this system?
    c. Use the $=COUNTIF$ function to determine the number of customers who have to wait for a reservation agent. What percentage of the customers have to wait?

25. The wedding date for a couple is quickly approaching, and the wedding planner must provide the caterer an estimate of how many people will attend the reception so that the appropriate quantity of food is prepared for the buffet. The following table contains information on the number of RSVP'ed guests for the 225 invitations. Based on her experience, the wedding planner knows it is extremely rare for guests to attend a wedding if they notified that they will not be attending. Therefore, the wedding planner will assume that no one from these 50 invitations will attend. The wedding planner estimates that the each of the 50 guests planning to come solo has a 75% chance of attending alone, a 20% chance of not attending, and a 5% chance of bringing a companion. For each of the 100 RSVPs who plan to bring a companion, there is a 90% chance that she or he will attend with a companion, a 5% chance of attending solo, and a 5% chance of not attending at all. For the 25 people who

have not responded, the wedding planner assumes that there's an 80% chance that each will not attend. If any of these individuals does attend, there is a 75% chance that she or he will attend alone and a 25% chance that she or he will bring a companion.

| Number of Invitations | RSVP'ed Guests |
|:---:|:---:|
| 50 | 0 |
| 50 | 1 |
| 100 | 2 |
| 25 | No response |

a.    Assist the wedding planner by constructing a simulation model to determine the expected number of guests who will attend the reception. Base your estimate on 1000 replications of the wedding reception.

b.    To be accommodating hosts, the couple has instructed the wedding planner to use the simulation model to determine $X$, the minimum number of guests for which the caterer should prepare the meal, so that there is at least a 90% chance that the actual attendance is less than or equal to $X$. Base your estimate on 1000 replications of the wedding reception.

## Case Problem 1    Tri-State Corporation

What will your portfolio be worth in 10 years? In 20 years? When you stop working? The Human Resources Department at Tri-State Corporation was asked to develop a financial planning model that would help employees address these questions. Tom Gifford was asked to lead this effort and decided to begin by developing a financial plan for himself. Tom has a degree in business and, at the age of 25, is making $34,000 per year. After two years of contributions to his company's retirement program and the receipt of a small inheritance, Tom has accumulated a portfolio valued at $14,500. Tom plans to work 30 more years and hopes to accumulate a portfolio valued at $1,000,000. Can he do it?

Tom began with a few assumptions about his future salary, his new investment contributions, and his portfolio growth rate. He assumed 5% annual salary growth rate as reasonable and wanted to make new investment contributions at 4% of his salary. After some research on historical stock market performance, Tom decided that a 10% annual portfolio growth rate was reasonable. Using these assumptions, Tom developed the Excel worksheet shown in Figure 16.18. Tom's specific situation and his assumptions are in the top portion of the worksheet (cells D3:D8). The worksheet provides a financial plan for the next five years. In computing the portfolio earnings for a given year, Tom assumed that his new investment contribution would occur evenly throughout the year, and thus half of the new investment could be included in the computation of the portfolio earnings for the year. Using Figure 16.18, we see that at age 29, Tom is projected to have a portfolio valued at $32,898.

Tom's plan was to use this worksheet as a template to develop financial plans for the company's employees. The assumptions in cells D3:D8 would be different for each employee, and rows would be added to the worksheet to reflect the number of years appropriate for each employee. After adding another 25 rows to the worksheet, Tom found that he could expect to have a portfolio of $627,937 after 30 years. Tom then took his results to show his boss, Kate Riegle.

Although Kate was pleased with Tom's progress, she voiced several criticisms. One of the criticisms was the assumption of a constant annual salary growth rate. She noted that most employees experience some variation in the annual salary growth rate from year to year. In addition, she pointed out that the constant annual portfolio growth rate was unrealistic and

**FIGURE 16.18**   FINANCIAL PLANNING WORKSHEET FOR TOM GIFFORD

Gifford

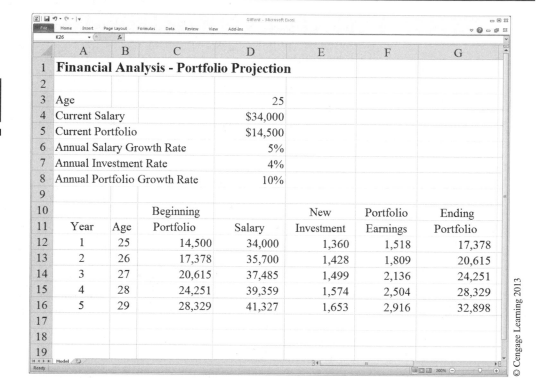

| | Year | Age | Beginning Portfolio | Salary | New Investment | Portfolio Earnings | Ending Portfolio |
|---|---|---|---|---|---|---|---|
| 1 | | | | | | | |
| | | | | | | | |
| 3 | Age | | | 25 | | | |
| 4 | Current Salary | | | $34,000 | | | |
| 5 | Current Portfolio | | | $14,500 | | | |
| 6 | Annual Salary Growth Rate | | | 5% | | | |
| 7 | Annual Investment Rate | | | 4% | | | |
| 8 | Annual Portfolio Growth Rate | | | 10% | | | |
| 12 | 1 | 25 | 14,500 | 34,000 | 1,360 | 1,518 | 17,378 |
| 13 | 2 | 26 | 17,378 | 35,700 | 1,428 | 1,809 | 20,615 |
| 14 | 3 | 27 | 20,615 | 37,485 | 1,499 | 2,136 | 24,251 |
| 15 | 4 | 28 | 24,251 | 39,359 | 1,574 | 2,504 | 28,329 |
| 16 | 5 | 29 | 28,329 | 41,327 | 1,653 | 2,916 | 32,898 |

that the actual growth rate would vary considerably from year to year. She further suggested that a simulation model for the portfolio projection might allow Tom to account for the random variability in the salary growth rate and the portfolio growth rate.

After some research, Tom and Kate decided to assume that the annual salary growth rate would vary from 0% to 10% and that a uniform probability distribution would provide a realistic approximation. Tri-State's accounting firm suggested that the annual portfolio growth rate could be approximated by a normal probability distribution with a mean of 10% and a standard deviation of 5%. With this information, Tom set off to develop a simulation model that could be used by the company's employees for financial planning.

## Managerial Report

Play the role of Tom Gifford and develop a simulation model for financial planning. Write a report for Tom's boss and, at a minimum, include the following:

1. Without considering the random variability in growth rates, extend the worksheet in Figure 16.18 to 30 years. Confirm that by using the constant annual salary growth rate and the constant annual portfolio growth rate, Tom can expect to have a 30-year portfolio of $627,937. What would Tom's annual investment rate have to increase to in order for his portfolio to reach a 30-year, $1,000,000 goal?

2. Incorporate the random variability of the annual salary growth rate and the annual portfolio growth rate into a simulation model. Assume that Tom is willing to use the annual investment rate that predicted a 30-year, $1,000,000 portfolio in part 1. Show how to simulate Tom's 30-year financial plan. Use results from the simulation model

to comment on the uncertainty associated with Tom reaching the 30-year, $1,000,000 goal. Discuss the advantages of repeating the simulation numerous times.

3. What recommendations do you have for employees with a current profile similar to Tom's after seeing the impact of the uncertainty in the annual salary growth rate and the annual portfolio growth rate?

4. Assume that Tom is willing to consider working 35 years instead of 30 years. What is your assessment of this strategy if Tom's goal is to have a portfolio worth $1,000,000?

5. Discuss how the financial planning model developed for Tom Gifford can be used as a template to develop a financial plan for any of the company's employees.

## Case Problem 2   Harbor Dunes Golf Course

Harbor Dunes Golf Course was recently honored as one of the top public golf courses in South Carolina. The course, situated on land that was once a rice plantation, offers some of the best views of saltwater marshes available in the Carolinas. Harbor Dunes targets the upper end of the golf market and, in the peak spring golfing season, charges green fees of $160 per person and golf cart fees of $20 per person.

Harbor Dunes takes reservations for tee times for groups of four players (foursomes) starting at 7:30 each morning. Foursomes start at the same time on both the front nine and the back nine of the course, with a new group teeing off every nine minutes. The process continues, with new foursomes starting play on both the front and back nine at noon. To enable all players to complete 18 holes before darkness, the last two afternoon foursomes start their rounds at 1:21 P.M. Under this plan, Harbor Dunes can sell a maximum of 20 afternoon tee times.

Last year Harbor Dunes was able to sell every morning tee time available for every day of the spring golf season. The same result is anticipated for the coming year. Afternoon tee times, however, are generally more difficult to sell. An analysis of the sales data for last year enabled Harbor Dunes to develop the probability distribution of sales for the afternoon tee times as shown in Table 16.12. For the season, Harbor Dunes averaged selling approximately 14 of the 20 available afternoon tee times. The average income from afternoon green fees and cart fees has been $10,240. However, the average of six unused tee times per day resulted in lost revenue.

**TABLE 16.12**   PROBABILITY DISTRIBUTION OF SALES FOR THE AFTERNOON TEE TIMES

| Number of Tee Times Sold | Probability |
|---|---|
| 8 | 0.01 |
| 9 | 0.04 |
| 10 | 0.06 |
| 11 | 0.08 |
| 12 | 0.10 |
| 13 | 0.11 |
| 14 | 0.12 |
| 15 | 0.15 |
| 16 | 0.10 |
| 17 | 0.09 |
| 18 | 0.07 |
| 19 | 0.05 |
| 20 | 0.02 |

© Cengage Learning 2013

**TABLE 16.13**   PROBABILITY DISTRIBUTIONS FOR THE NUMBER OF GROUPS
REQUESTING A REPLAY

| Option 1: $25 per Person + Cart Fee | | Option 2: $50 per Person + Cart Fee | |
|---|---|---|---|
| **Number of Foursomes Requesting a Replay** | **Probability** | **Number of Foursomes Requesting a Replay** | **Probability** |
| 0 | 0.01 | 0 | 0.06 |
| 1 | 0.03 | 1 | 0.09 |
| 2 | 0.05 | 2 | 0.12 |
| 3 | 0.05 | 3 | 0.17 |
| 4 | 0.11 | 4 | 0.20 |
| 5 | 0.15 | 5 | 0.13 |
| 6 | 0.17 | 6 | 0.11 |
| 7 | 0.15 | 7 | 0.07 |
| 8 | 0.13 | 8 | 0.05 |
| 9 | 0.09 | | |
| 10 | 0.06 | | |

In an effort to increase the sale of afternoon tee times, Harbor Dunes is considering an idea popular at other golf courses. These courses offer foursomes that play in the morning the option to play another round of golf in the afternoon by paying a reduced fee for the afternoon round. Harbor Dunes is considering two replay options: (1) a green fee of $25 per player plus a cart fee of $20 per player; (2) a green fee of $50 per player plus a cart fee of $20 per player. For option 1, each foursome will generate additional revenues of $180; for option 2, each foursome will generate additional revenues of $280. The key in making a decision as to what option is best depends upon the number of groups that find the option attractive enough to take the replay offer. Working with a consultant who has expertise in statistics and the golf industry, Harbor Dunes developed probability distributions for the number of foursomes requesting a replay for each of the two options. These probability distributions are shown in Table 16.13.

In offering these replay options, Harbor Dunes' first priority will be to sell full-price afternoon advance reservations. If the demand for replay tee times exceeds the number of afternoon tee times available, Harbor Dunes will post a notice that the course is full. In this case, any excess replay requests will not be accepted.

## Managerial Report

Develop simulation models for both replay options using Crystal Ball. Run each simulation for 5000 trials. Prepare a report that will help management of Harbor Dunes Golf Course decide which replay option to implement for the upcoming spring golf season. In preparing your report, be sure to include the following:

1. Statistical summaries of the revenue expected under each replay option
2. Your recommendation as to the best replay option
3. Assuming a 90-day spring golf season, an estimate of the added revenue using your recommendation
4. Any other recommendations you have that might improve the income for Harbor Dunes

# Case Problem 3   County Beverage Drive-Thru

County Beverage Drive-Thru, Inc., operates a chain of beverage supply stores in northern Illinois. Each store has a single service lane; cars enter at one end of the store and exit at the other end. Customers pick up soft drinks, beer, snacks, and party supplies without getting out of their cars. When a new customer arrives at the store, the customer waits until the preceding customer's order is complete and then drives up to the store order window for service.

Typically, three employees operate each store during peak periods; one clerk takes orders, another clerk fills orders, and a third clerk serves as cashier and store supervisor. County Beverage is considering a revised store design in which computerized order-taking and payment are integrated with specialized warehousing equipment. Management hopes that the new design will permit operating each store with one clerk. To determine whether the new design is beneficial, management decided to build a new store using the revised design.

County Beverage's new store will be located near a major shopping center. Based on experience at other locations, management believes that during the peak late afternoon and evening hours, the time between arrivals follows an exponential probability distribution with a mean of six minutes. These peak hours are the most critical time period for the company; most of the company's profit is generated during these peak hours.

An extensive study of times required to fill orders with a single clerk led to the following probability distribution of service times:

| Service Time (minutes) | Probability |
|:---:|:---:|
| 2 | 0.24 |
| 3 | 0.20 |
| 4 | 0.15 |
| 5 | 0.14 |
| 6 | 0.12 |
| 7 | 0.08 |
| 8 | 0.05 |
| 9 | 0.02 |
| Total | 1.00 |

In case customer waiting times prove too long with just a single clerk, County Beverage's management is considering two design alternatives: (1) add a second clerk to help with bagging, taking orders, and related tasks (still functioning as a single-server system and serving one car), or (2) enlarge the drive-through area so that two cars can be served at once (operating as a two-server system). With either of these options, two clerks will be needed. With the two-server option, service times are expected to be the same for each clerk (server). With the second clerk teaming with the first clerk in the single server design, service times will be reduced and would be given by the probability distribution in the following table.

| Service Time (minutes) | Probability |
|:---:|:---:|
| 1 | 0.20 |
| 2 | 0.35 |
| 3 | 0.30 |
| 4 | 0.10 |
| 5 | 0.05 |
| Total | 1.00 |

County Beverage's management would like you to develop a spreadsheet simulation model of the new system and use it to compare the operation of the system using the following three designs:

| Design | |
|---|---|
| A | Single-server system operated by one clerk |
| B | Single-server system operated by two clerks |
| C | Two-server system operated by two clerks |

Management is especially concerned with how long customers have to wait for service. Research has shown that 30% of the customers will wait no longer than 6 minutes and that 90% will wait no longer than 10 minutes. As a guideline, management requires the average waiting time to be less than 1.5 minutes.

## Managerial Report

Prepare a report that discusses the general development of the spreadsheet simulation model, and make any recommendations that you have regarding the best store design and staffing plan for County Beverage. One additional consideration is that the design allowing for a two-server system will cost an additional $10,000 to build.

1. List the information the spreadsheet simulation model should generate so that a decision can be made on the store design and the desired number of clerks.
2. Run the simulation for 1000 customers for each alternative considered. You may want to consider making more than one run with each alternative. [*Note:* Values from an exponential probability distribution with mean $\mu$ can be generated in Excel using the following function: $= -\mu*\text{LN(RAND())}$.]
3. Be sure to note the number of customers County Beverage is likely to lose due to long customer waiting times with each design alternative.

## Appendix 16.1    Simulation with Excel

Excel enables small and moderate-sized simulation models to be implemented relatively easily and quickly. In this appendix we show the Excel worksheets for the three simulation models presented in the chapter.

### The PortaCom Simulation Model

We simulated the PortaCom problem 500 times. The worksheet used to carry out the simulation is shown again in Figure 16.19. Note that the simulation results for trials 6 through 495 have been hidden so that the results can be shown in a reasonably sized figure. If desired, the rows for these trials can be shown and the simulation results displayed for all 500 trials. Let us describe the details of the Excel worksheet that provided the PortaCom simulation.

First, the PortaCom data are presented in the first 14 rows of the worksheet. The selling price per unit, administrative cost, and advertising cost parameters are entered directly into cells C3, C4, and C5. The discrete probability distribution for the direct labor cost per unit is shown in a tabular format. Note that the random number intervals are entered first, followed by the corresponding cost per unit. For example, 0.0 in cell A10 and 0.1 in cell B10 show that a cost of $43 per unit will be assigned if the random number is in the interval 0.0 but less than 0.1. Thus, approximately 10% of the simulated direct labor costs will be $43 per unit. The uniform probability distribution with a smallest value of $80 in cell E8 and a

**FIGURE 16.19**   WORKSHEET FOR THE PORTACOM PROBLEM

PortaCom

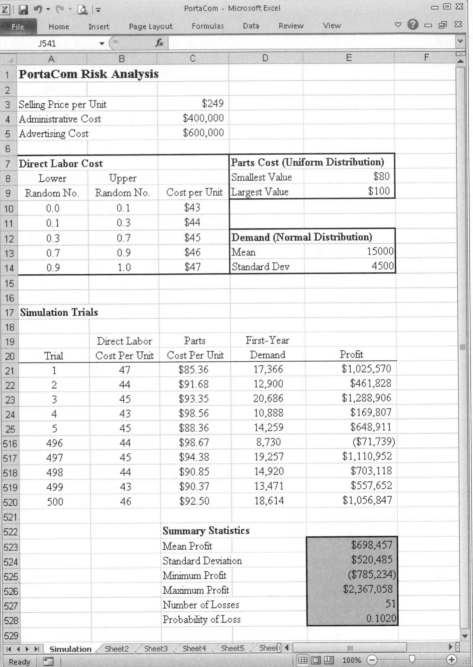

largest value of \$100 in cell E9 describes the parts cost per unit. Finally, a normal probability distribution with a mean of 15,000 units in cell E13 and a standard deviation of 4500 units in cell E14 describes the first-year demand distribution for the product. At this point we are ready to insert the Excel formulas that will carry out each simulation trial.

Simulation information for the first trial appears in row 21 of the worksheet. The cell formulas for row 21 are as follows:

Cell A21    Enter 1 for the first simulation trial

Cell B21    Simulate the direct labor cost per unit[3]
$\qquad$ =VLOOKUP(RAND(), \$A\$10:\$C\$14, 3)

Cell C21    Simulate the parts cost per unit (uniform distribution)
$\qquad$ =\$E\$8+(\$E\$9−\$E\$8)*RAND()

Cell D21    Simulate the first-year demand (normal distribution)
$\qquad$ =NORMINV(RAND(), \$E\$13, \$E\$14)

Cell E21    The profit obtained for the first trial
$\qquad$ =(\$C\$3−B21−C21)*D21−\$C\$4−\$C\$5

Cells A21:E21 can be copied to A520:E520 in order to provide the 500 simulation trials.

Ultimately, summary statistics will be collected in order to describe the results of the 500 simulated trials. Using the standard Excel functions, the following summary statistics are computed for the 500 simulated profits appearing in cells E21 to E520:

Cell E523    The mean profit per trial =AVERAGE(E21:E520)

Cell E524    The standard deviation of profit =STDEV(E21:E520)

Cell E525    The minimum profit =MIN(E21:E520)

Cell E526    The maximum profit =MAX(E21:E520)

Cell E527    The count of the number of trials where a loss occurred (i.e., profit < \$0)
$\qquad$ =COUNTIF(E21:E520, "<0")

Cell E528    The percentage or probability of a loss based on the 500 trials =E527/500

The F9 key can be used to perform another complete simulation of PortaCom. In this case, the entire worksheet will be recalculated and a set of new simulation results will be provided. Any data summaries, measures, or functions that have been built into the worksheet earlier will be updated automatically.

## The Butler Inventory Simulation Model

We simulated the Butler inventory operation for 300 months. The worksheet used to carry out the simulation is shown again in Figure 16.20. Note that the simulation results for months 6 through 295 have been hidden so that the results can be shown in a reasonably sized figure. If desired, the rows for these months can be shown and the simulation results displayed for all 300 months. Let us describe the details of the Excel worksheet that provided the Butler inventory simulation.

First, the Butler inventory data are presented in the first 11 rows of the worksheet. The gross profit per unit, holding cost per unit, and shortage cost per unit data are entered directly into cells C3, C4, and C5. The replenishment level is entered into cell C7, and the mean and standard deviation of the normal probability distribution for demand are entered into cells B10 and B11. At this point we are ready to insert Excel formulas that will carry out each simulation month or trial.

---

[3]See Appendix A for an explanation of the VLOOKUP function.

**FIGURE 16.20**   WORKSHEET FOR THE BUTLER INVENTORY PROBLEM

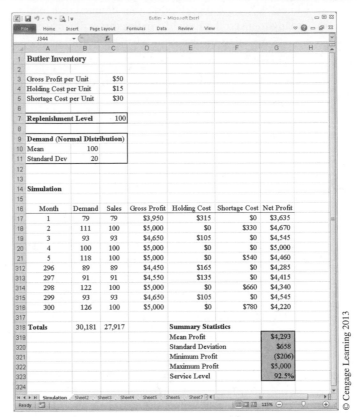

Simulation information for the first month or trial appears in row 17 of the worksheet. The cell formulas for row 17 are as follows:

Cell A17   Enter 1 for the first simulation month

Cell B17   Simulate demand (normal distribution)
          =NORMINV(RAND(), $B$10, $B$11)

Next compute the sales, which is equal to demand (cell B17) if demand is less than or equal to the replenishment level, or is equal to the replenishment level (cell C7) if demand is greater than the replenishment level.

Cell C17   Compute sales =IF(B17<=$C$7, B17, $C$7)

Cell D17   Calculate gross profit =$C$3*C17

Cell E17   Calculate the holding cost if demand is less than or equal to the replenishment level
          =IF(B17<= $C$7, $C$4*($C$7−B17), 0)

Cell F17   Calculate the shortage cost if demand is greater than the replenishment level
          =IF(B17>$C$7, $C$5*(B17−$C$7), 0)

Cell G17   Calculate net profit =D17−E17−F17

Cells A17:G17 can be copied to cells A316:G316 in order to provide the 300 simulation months.

Finally, summary statistics will be collected in order to describe the results of the 300 simulated trials. Using the standard Excel functions, the following totals and summary statistics are computed for the 300 months:

Cell B318   Total demand =SUM(B17:B316)

Cell C319   Total sales =SUM(C17:C316)

Cell G319   The mean profit per month =AVERAGE(G17:G316)

Cell G320   The standard deviation of net profit =STDEV(G17:G316)

Cell G321   The minimum net profit =MIN(G17:G316)

Cell G322   The maximum net profit =MAX(G17:G316)

Cell G323   The service level =C318/B318

## The Black Sheep Scarves Simulation Model

We simulated the operation of the Black Sheep Scarves quality inspection waiting line system for 1000 scarves. The worksheet used to carry out the simulation is shown again in Figure 16.21. Note that the simulation results for scarves 6 through 995 have been hidden

**FIGURE 16.21**   WORKSHEET FOR BLACK SHEEP SCARVES WITH ONE QUALITY INSPECTOR

**Black Sheep 1**

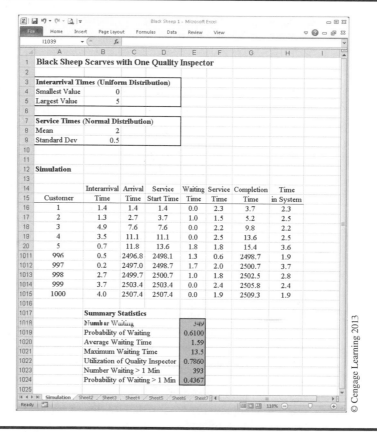

© Cengage Learning 2013

so that the results can be shown in a reasonably sized figure. If desired, the rows for these scarves can be shown and the simulation results displayed for all 1000 scarves. Let us describe the details of the Excel worksheet that provided Black Sheep Scarves simulation.

The data are presented in the first nine rows of the worksheet. The interarrival times are described by a uniform distribution with a smallest time of 0 minutes (cell B4) and a largest time of 5 minutes (cell B5). A normal probability distribution with a mean of 2 minutes (cell B8) and a standard deviation of 0.5 minute (cell B9) describes the service time distribution.

Simulation information for the first scarf appears in row 16 of the worksheet. The cell formulas for row 16 are as follows:

Cell A16    Enter 1 for the first scarf

Cell B16    Simulate the interarrival time for scarf 1 (uniform distribution)
             =$B$4+RAND()*($B$5−$B$4)

Cell C16    Compute the arrival time for scarf 1 =B16

Cell D16    Compute the start time for scarf 1 =C16

Cell E16    Compute the waiting time for scarf 1 =D1−C16

Cell F16    Simulate the service time for scarf 1 (normal distribution)
             =NORMINV(RAND(), $B$8, $B$9)

Cell G16    Compute the completion time for scarf 1 =D16+F16

Cell H16    Compute the time in the system for scarf 1 =G16−C16

Simulation information for the second scarf appears in row 17 of the worksheet. The cell formulas for row 17 are as follows:

Cell A17    Enter 2 for the second scarf

Cell B17    Simulate the interarrival time for scarf 2 (uniform distribution)
             =$B$4+RAND()*($B$5−$B$4)

Cell C17    Compute the arrival time for scarf 2 =C16+B17

Cell D17    Compute the start time for scarf 2 =IF(C17>G16, C17, G16)

Cell E17    Compute the waiting time for scarf 2 =D17−C17

Cell F17    Simulate the service time for scarf 2 (normal distribution)
             =NORMINV(RAND(), $B$8, $B$9)

Cell G17    Compute the completion time for scarf 2 =D17+F17

Cell H17    Compute the time in the system for scarf 2 =G17−C17

Cells A17:H17 can be copied to cells A1015:H1015 in order to provide the 1000-scarf simulation.

Ultimately, summary statistics will be collected in order to describe the results of 1000 scarves. Before collecting the summary statistics, let us point out that most simulation studies of dynamic systems focus on the operation of the system during its long-run or steady-state operation. To ensure that the effects of startup conditions are not included in the steady-state calculations, a dynamic simulation model is usually run for a specified period without collecting any data about the operation of the system. The length of the startup period can vary depending on the application. For the Black Sheep Scarves simulation, we treated the results for the first 100 scarves as the startup period. The simulation information for scarf 100 appears in row 115 of the spreadsheet. Cell G115 shows that the completion time for the 100th scarf is 247.8. Thus, the length of the start-up period is 247.8 minutes.

Summary statistics are collected for the next 900 scarves, corresponding to rows 116 to 1015 of the spreadsheet. The following Excel formulas provided the summary statistics:

Cell E1018    Number of scarves who had to wait (i.e., waiting time > 0)
=COUNTIF(E116:E1015, ">0")

Cell E1019    Probability of waiting =E1018/900

Cell E1020    The average waiting time =AVERAGE(E116:E1015)

Cell E1021    The maximum waiting time =MAX(E116:E1015)

Cell E1022    The utilization of the quality inspector[4] =SUM(F116:F1015)/
(G1015−G115)

Cell E1023    The number of scarves who had to wait more than 1 minute
=COUNTIF(E116:E1015, ">1")

Cell E1024    Probability of waiting more than 1 minute =E1023/900

# Appendix 16.2   Simulation Using Crystal Ball

In Section 16.1 we used simulation to perform risk analysis for the PortaCom problem, and in Appendix 16.1 we showed how to construct the Excel worksheet that provided the simulation results. Developing the worksheet simulation for the PortaCom problem using the basic Excel package was relatively easy. The use of add-ins enables larger and more complex simulation problems to be analyzed easily using spreadsheets. In this appendix we show how Crystal Ball, an add-in package, can be used to perform the PortaCom simulation. We will run the simulation for 1000 trials here. Instructions for installing and starting Crystal Ball are included with the Crystal Ball software.

## Formulating a Crystal Ball Model

We begin by entering the problem data into the top portion of the worksheet. For the PortaCom problem, we must enter the following data: selling price, administrative cost, advertising cost, probability distribution for the direct labor cost per unit, smallest and largest values for the parts cost per unit (uniform distribution), and the mean and standard deviation for first-year demand (normal distribution). These data with appropriate descriptive labels are shown in cells A1:E13 of Figure 16.22.

For the PortaCom problem, the Crystal Ball model contains the following two components: (1) cells for the probabilistic inputs (direct labor cost, parts cost, first-year demand), and (2) a cell containing a formula for computing the value of the simulation model output (profit). In Crystal Ball the cells that contain the values of the probabilistic inputs are called *assumption cells*, and the cells that contain the formulas for the model outputs are referred to as *forecast cells*. The PortaCom problem requires only one output (profit), and thus the Crystal Ball model only contains one forecast cell. In more complex simulation problems, more than one forecast cell may be necessary.

The assumption cells may only contain simple numeric values. In this model-building stage, we entered PortaCom's best estimates of the direct labor cost ($45), the parts cost

---

[4]The proportion of time the quality inspector is in use is equal to the sum of the 900 scarf service times in column F divided by the total elapsed time required for the 900 scarves to complete service. This total elapsed time is the difference between the completion time of scarf 1000 and the completion time of scarf 100.

**FIGURE 16.22**   CRYSTAL BALL WORKSHEET FOR THE PORTACOM PROBLEM

**WEB file**

PortaCom Crystal Ball

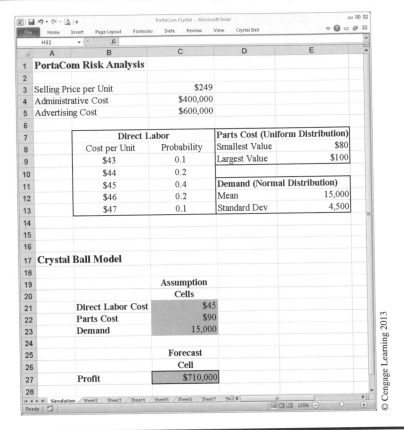

($90), and the first-year demand (15,000) into cells C21:C23, respectively. The forecast cells in a Crystal Ball model contain formulas that refer to one or more of the assumption cells. Because only one forecast cell in the PortaCom problem corresponds to profit, we entered the following formula into cell C27:

$$=(C3-C21-C22)*C23-C4-C5$$

The resulting value of $710,000 is the profit corresponding to the base-case scenario discussed in Section 16.1.

## Defining and Entering Assumptions

We are now ready to define the probability distributions corresponding to each of the assumption cells. We begin by defining the probability distribution for the direct labor cost.

**Step 1.** Select cell C21
**Step 2.** Choose **Define Assumption**
**Step 3.** When the **Distribution Gallery: Cell 21** dialog box appears:
     Choose **Custom**[5]
     Click **OK**

---

[5]You may have to click All and use the scroll bar to see all possible distributions.

**Step 4.** When the **Define Assumption: Cell C21** dialog box appears:

> If the ⊗ button is to the right of the **Name** box, proceed to Step 5
>
> If the ⊗ button is to the right of the **Name** box, click the ⊗ button to
>
> obtain the ⊗ button

**Step 5.** Choose **Load Data**
Enter B9:C13 in the **Location of data** box
Click **Keep Linked to Spreadsheet**
Click **OK** to terminate the data entry process
Click **OK**

The procedure for defining the probability distribution for the parts cost is similar.

**Step 1.** Select cell C22
**Step 2.** Choose **Define Assumption**
**Step 3.** When the **Distribution Gallery: Cell C22** dialog box appears:
Choose **Uniform** (Use the scroll bar to see all possible distributions.)
Click **OK**
**Step 4.** When the **Define Assumption: Cell C22** dialog box appears:
Enter =E8 in the **Minimum** box
Enter =E9 in the **Maximum** box
Click **Enter**
Click **OK**

Finally, we perform the following steps to define the probability distribution for first-year demand:

**Step 1.** Select cell C23
**Step 2.** Choose **Define Assumption**
**Step 3.** When the **Distribution Gallery: Cell 23** dialog box appears:
Choose **Normal**
Click **OK**
**Step 4.** When the **Define Assumption: Cell C23** dialog box appears:
Enter =E12 in the **Mean** box
Enter =E13 in the **Std. Dev.** box
Click **Enter**
Click **OK**

## Defining Forecasts

After defining the assumption cells, we are ready to define the forecast cells. The following steps show this process for cell C27, which is the profit forecast cell for the PortaCom problem:

**Step 1.** Select cell C27
**Step 2.** Choose **Define Forecast**
**Step 3.** When the **Define Forecast: Cell C27** dialog box appears:
Profit will appear in the **Name** box
Click **OK**

## Setting Run Preferences

We must now make the choices that determine how Crystal Ball runs the simulation. For the PortaCom simulation, we only need to specify the number of trials.

**Step 1.** Choose **Run Preferences**
**Step 2.** When the **Run Preferences** dialog box appears:
    Make sure the **Trials** tab has been selected
    Enter 1000 in the **Number of trials to run:** box
    Click **OK**

## Running the Simulation

Crystal Ball repeats three steps on each of the 1000 trials of the PortaCom simulation.

1. Values are generated for the three assumption cells according to the defined probability distributions.
2. A new simulated profit (forecast cell) is computed based on the new values in the three assumption cells.
3. The new simulated profit is recorded.

To begin the simulation, choose **Start.**

When the run is complete, Crystal Ball displays a Forecast: Profit window, which shows a frequency distribution of the simulated profit values obtained during the simulation run (see Figure 16.23). Other types of charts and output can be displayed. For instance, the following steps describe how to display the descriptive statistics for the simulation run:

**Step 1.** Select the **View** menu in the **Forecast: Profit** window
**Step 2.** Choose **Statistics**

**FIGURE 16.23**   CRYSTAL BALL FREQUENCY CHART FOR THE PORTACOM SIMULATION

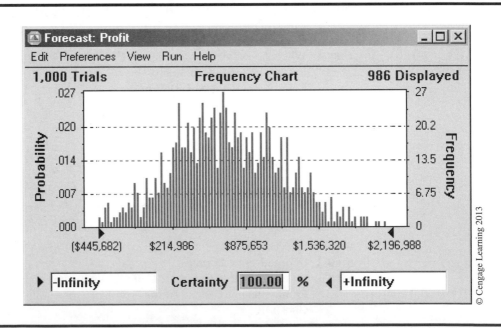

**FIGURE 16.24**   CRYSTAL BALL STATISTICS FOR THE PORTACOM SIMULATION

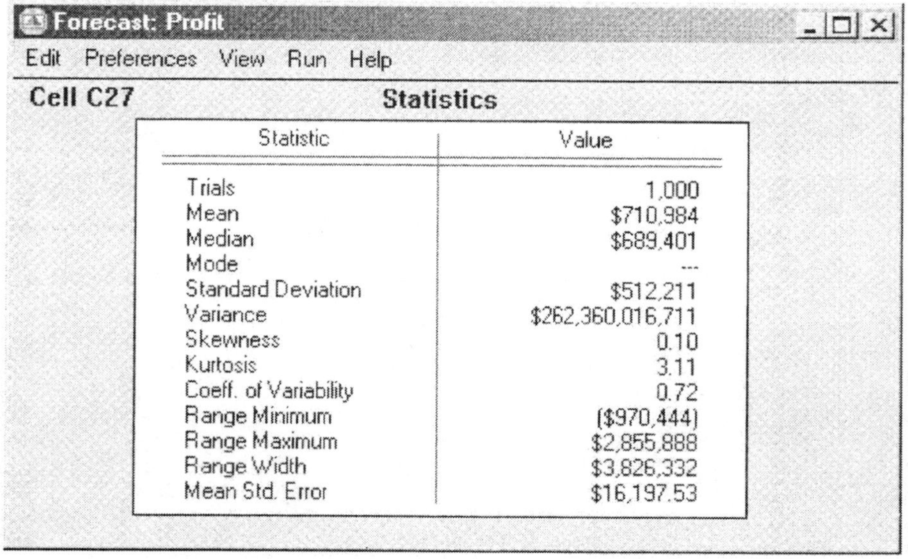

| Statistic | Value |
|---|---|
| Trials | 1,000 |
| Mean | $710,984 |
| Median | $689,401 |
| Mode | --- |
| Standard Deviation | $512,211 |
| Variance | $262,360,016,711 |
| Skewness | 0.10 |
| Kurtosis | 3.11 |
| Coeff. of Variability | 0.72 |
| Range Minimum | ($970,444) |
| Range Maximum | $2,855,888 |
| Range Width | $3,826,332 |
| Mean Std. Error | $16,197.53 |

© Cengage Learning 2013

Figure 16.24 shows the Forecast: Profit window with descriptive statistics. Note that the worst result obtained in this simulation of 1000 trials is a loss of $970,444, and the best result is a profit of $2,855,888. The mean profit is $710,984. These values are similar to the results obtained in Section 16.1. The differences result from the different random numbers used in the two simulations and from the fact that we used 1000 trials with Crystal Ball. If you perform another simulation, your results will differ slightly.

# APPENDIXES

The purpose of this appendix is twofold. First, we provide an overview of Excel and discuss the basic operations needed to work with Excel workbooks and worksheets. Second, we provide an introduction to building mathematical models using Excel, including a discussion of how to find and use particular Excel functions, how to design and build good spreadsheet models, and how to ensure that these models are free of errors.

## Overview of Microsoft Excel

*A workbook is a file containing one or more worksheets.*

When using Excel for modeling, the data and the model are displayed in workbooks, each of which contains a series of worksheets. Figure A.1 shows the layout of the blank workbook created each time Excel is opened. The workbook is named Book1 and consists of three worksheets named Sheet1, Sheet2, and Sheet3. Excel highlights the worksheet currently displayed (Sheet1) by setting the name on the worksheet tab in bold. To select a different worksheet, simply click on the corresponding tab. Note that cell A1 is initially selected.

The wide bar located across the top of the workbook is referred to as the Ribbon. Tabs, located at the top of the Ribbon, provide quick access to groups of related commands. There are eight tabs: Home, Insert, Page Layout, Formulas, Data, Review, View, and Add-Ins. Each tab contains several groups of related commands. Note that the Home tab is selected when Excel is opened. Four of the seven groups are displayed in Figure A.2. Under the Home tab there are seven groups of related commands: Clipboard, Font, Alignment, Number, Styles, Cells, and Editing. Commands are arranged within each group. For example, to change selected text to boldface, click the Home tab and click the Bold button in the Font group.

Figure A.3 illustrates the location of the File tab, the Quick Access Toolbar, and the Formula Bar. When you click the File tab, Excel provides a list of workbook options such as opening, saving, and printing (worksheets). The Quick Access Toolbar allows you to quickly access these workbook options. For instance, the Quick Access Toolbar shown in Figure A.3 includes a Save button 🖫 that can be used to save files without having to first click the File tab. To add or remove features on the Quick Access Toolbar click the Customize Quick Access Toolbar button ⤓ on the Quick Access Toolbar.

The Formula Bar contains a Name box, the Insert Function button $f_x$, and a Formula box. In Figure A.3, "A1" appears in the Name box because cell A1 is selected. You can select any other cell in the worksheet by using the mouse to move the cursor to another cell and clicking or by typing the new cell location in the name box and pressing the Enter key. The Formula box is used to display the formula in the currently selected cell. For instance, if you had entered =A1+A2 into cell A3, whenever you select cell A3, the formula =A1+A2 will be shown in the Formula box. This feature makes it very easy to see and edit a formula in a particular cell. The Insert Function button allows you to quickly access all of the functions available in Excel. Later, we show how to find and use a particular function.

**FIGURE A.1**   BLANK WORKBOOK CREATED WHEN EXCEL IS STARTED

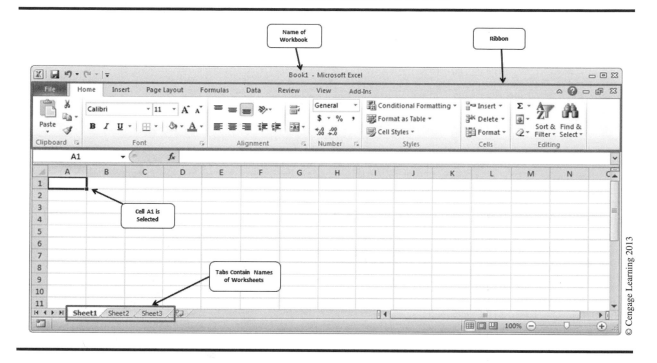

**FIGURE A.2**   PORTION OF THE HOME TAB

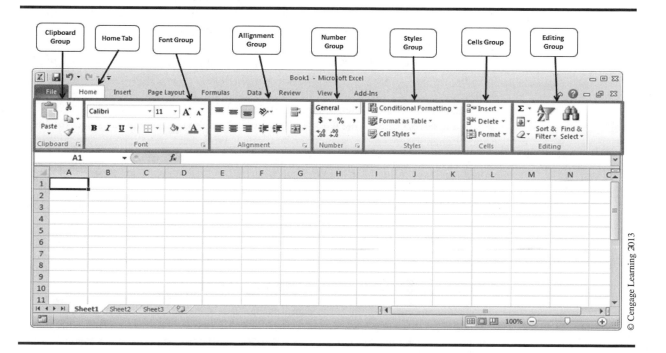

**FIGURE A.3**    EXCEL FILE TAB, QUICK ACCESS TOOLBAR, AND FORMULA BAR

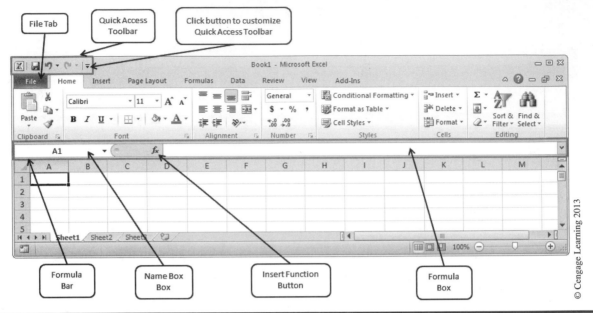

# Basic Workbook Operations

Figure A.4 illustrates the worksheet options that can be performed after right clicking on a worksheet tab. For instance, to change the name of the current worksheet from "Sheet1" to "NowlinModel," right click the worksheet tab named "Sheet1" and select the Rename option. The current worksheet name (Sheet1) will be highlighted. Then, simply type the new name (NowlinModel) and press the Enter key to rename the worksheet.

Suppose that you wanted to create a copy of "Sheet1." After right clicking the tab named "Sheet1," select the Move or Copy option. When the Move or Copy dialog box appears, select Create a Copy and click OK. The name of the copied worksheet will appear as "Sheet1 (2)." You can then rename it, if desired.

To add a worksheet to the workbook, right click any worksheet tab and select the Insert option; when the Insert dialog box appears, select Worksheet and click OK. An additional blank worksheet titled "Sheet4" will appear in the workbook. You can also insert a new worksheet by clicking the Insert Worksheet tab button 🔖 that appears to the right of the last worksheet tab displayed. Worksheets can be deleted by right clicking the worksheet tab and choosing Delete. After clicking Delete, a window will appear warning you that any data appearing in the worksheet will be lost. Click Delete to confirm that you do want to delete the worksheet. Worksheets can also be moved to other workbooks or a different position in the current workbook by using the Move or Copy option.

## Creating, Saving, and Opening Files

As an illustration of manually entering, saving, and opening a file, we will use the Nowlin Plastics production example from Chapter 1. The objective is to compute the breakeven point for a product that has a fixed cost of $3000, a variable cost per unit of $2, and a selling price per unit of $5. We begin by creating a worksheet containing the problem data.

**FIGURE A.4**   WORKSHEET OPTIONS OBTAINED AFTER RIGHT CLICKING ON A
WORKSHEET TAB

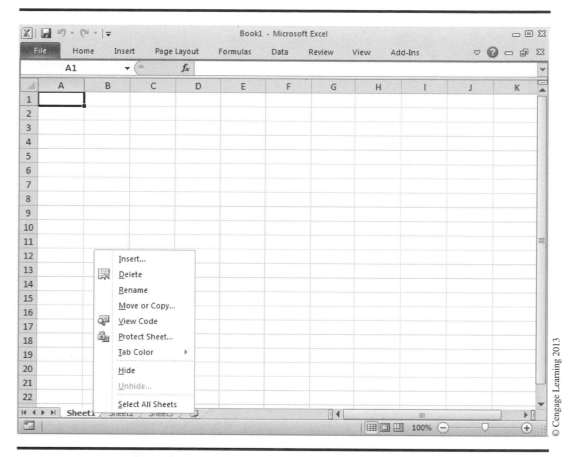

If you have just opened Excel, a blank workbook containing three worksheets will be
displayed. The Nowlin data can now be entered manually by simply typing the fixed cost
of $3000, the variable cost of $2, and the selling price of $5 into one of the worksheets. If
Excel is currently running and no blank workbook is displayed, you can create a new blank
workbook using the following steps:

**Step 1.** Click the **File** tab
**Step 2.** Click **New** in the list of options
**Step 3.** When the New Workbook dialog box appears:
Double click **Blank Workbook**

A new workbook containing three worksheets labeled Sheet1, Sheet2, and Sheet3 will
appear.

We will place the data for the Nowlin example in the top portion of Sheet1 of the new
workbook. First, we enter the label "Nowlin Plastics" into cell A1. To identify each of the
three data values we enter the label "Fixed Cost" into cell A3, the label "Variable Cost Per
Unit" into cell A5, and the label "Selling Price Per Unit" into cell A7. Next, we enter the
actual cost and price data into the corresponding cells in column B: the value of $3000 in
cell B3; the value of $2 in cell B5; and the value of $5 into cell B7. Finally, we will change

**FIGURE A.5**    NOWLIN PLASTICS DATA

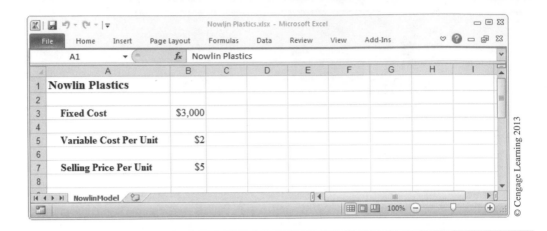

the name of the worksheet from "Sheet1" to "NowlinModel" using the procedure described previously. Figure A.5 shows a portion of the worksheet we have just developed.

Before we begin the development of the model portion of the worksheet, we recommend that you first save the current file; this will prevent you from having to reenter the data in case something happens that causes Excel to close. To save the workbook using the filename "Nowlin," we perform the following steps:

**Step 1.** Click the **File** tab
**Step 2.** Click **Save** in the list of options
**Step 3.** When the **Save As** dialog box appears:
Select the location where you want to save the file
Type the file name "Nowlin" in the **File name** box
Click **Save**

Excel's Save command is designed to save the file as an Excel workbook. As you work with and build models in Excel, you should follow the practice of periodically saving the file so you will not lose any work. Simply follow the procedure described above, using the Save command.

*Keyboard shortcut: To save the file, press **CTRL S**.*

You may want to create a copy of an existing file. For instance, suppose you change one or more of the data values and would like to save the modified file using the filename "NowlinMod." The following steps show how to save the modified workbook using filename "NowlinMod."

**Step 1.** Click the **File** tab
**Step 2.** Position the mouse pointer over **Save As**
**Step 3.** Click **Excel Workbook** from the list of options
**Step 4.** When the **Save As** dialog box appears:
In the **Save in** box select the location where you want to save the file
Type the filename "NowlinMod" in the **File name** box
Click **Save**

Once the *NowlinMod* workbook has been saved, you can continue to work with the file to perform whatever type of analysis is appropriate. When you are finished working with the file, simply click the close window button ☒ located at the top right-hand corner of the Ribbon.

You can easily access a saved file at another point in time. For example, the following steps show how to open the previously saved Nowlin workbook.

**Step 1.** Click the **File** tab
**Step 2.** Click **Open** in the list of options
**Step 3.** When the **Open** dialog box appears:
            Select the location where you previously saved the file
            Type the filename "Nowlin" in the **File name** box
            Click **Open**

The procedures we showed for saving or opening a workbook begin by clicking on the File tab to access the Save and Open commands. Once you have used Excel for a while, you will probably find it more convenient to add these commands to the Quick Access Toolbar.

# Cells, References, and Formulas in Excel

Assume that the Nowlin workbook is open again and that we would like to develop a model that can be used to compute the profit or loss associated with a given production volume. We will use the bottom portion of the worksheet shown in Figure A.5 to develop the model. The model will contain formulas that *refer to the location of the data cells* in the upper section of the worksheet. By putting the location of the data cells in the formula, we will build a model that can be easily updated with new data. This will be discussed in more detail later in this appendix in the section Principles for Building Good Spreadsheet Models.

We enter the label "Model" into cell A10 to provide a visual reminder that the bottom portion of this worksheet will contain the model. Next, we enter the labels "Production Volume" into cell A12, "Total Cost" into cell A14, "Total Revenue" into cell A16, and "Total Profit (Loss)" into cell A18. Cell B12 is used to contain a value for the production volume. We will now enter formulas into cells B14, B16, and B18 that use the production volume in cell B12 to compute the values for total cost, total revenue, and total profit or loss.

Total cost is the sum of the fixed cost (cell B3) and the total variable cost. The total variable cost is the product of the variable cost per unit (cell B5) and production volume (cell B12). Thus, the formula for total variable cost is B5*B12 and to compute the value of total cost, we enter the formula =B3+B5*B12 into cell B14. Next, total revenue is the product of the selling price per unit (cell B7) and the number of units produced (cell B12), which we enter in cell B16 as the formula =B7*B12. Finally, the total profit or loss is the difference between the total revenue (cell B16) and the total cost (cell B14). Thus, in cell B18 we enter the formula =B16−B14. Figure A.6 shows a portion of the worksheet just described.

We can now compute the total profit or loss for a particular production volume by entering a value for the production volume into cell B12. Figure A.7 shows the results after entering a value of 800 into cell B12. We see that a production volume of 800 units results in a total cost of $4600, a total revenue of $4000, and a loss of $600.

**FIGURE A.6**   NOWLIN PLASTICS DATA AND MODEL

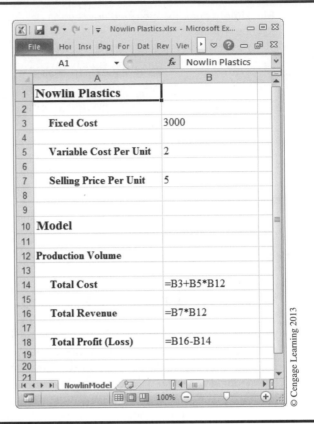

© Cengage Learning 2013

# Using Excel Functions

Excel provides a wealth of built-in formulas or functions for developing mathematical models. If we know which function is needed and how to use it, we can simply enter the function into the appropriate worksheet cell. However, if we are not sure which functions are available to accomplish a task or are not sure how to use a particular function, Excel can provide assistance.

## Finding the Right Excel Function

To identify the functions available in Excel, click the Formulas tab on the Ribbon and then click the Insert Function button in the Function Library group. Alternatively, click the Insert Function button $f_x$ on the formula bar. Either approach provides the Insert Function dialog box shown in Figure A.8.

The Search for a function box at the top of the Insert Function dialog box enables us to type a brief description for what we want to do. After doing so and clicking Go, Excel will search for and display, in the Select a function box, the functions that may accomplish our task. In many situations, however, we may want to browse through an entire category of functions to see what is available. For this task, the Or select a category box is helpful.

**FIGURE A.7**   NOWLIN PLASTICS RESULTS

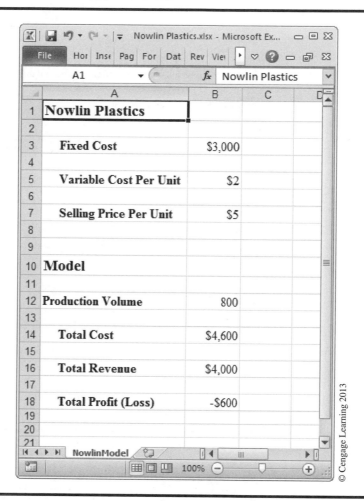

The Or select a category box contains a dropdown list of several categories of functions provided by Excel. Figure A.8 shows that we selected the Math & Trig category. As a result, Excel's Math & Trig functions appear in alphabetical order in the Select a function box. We see the ABS function listed first, followed by the ACOS function, and so on.

## Colon Notation

Although many functions, such as the ABS function, have a single argument, some Excel functions depend on arrays. Colon notation provides an efficient way to convey arrays and matrices of cells to functions. The colon notation may be described as follows: B1:B5 means cell B1 "through" cell B5, namely the array of values stored in the locations (B1,B2,B3,B4,B5). Consider for example the following function =SUM(B1:B5). The sum function adds up the elements contained in the function's argument. Hence, =SUM(B1:B5) evaluates the following formula:

$$=B1+B2+B3+B4+B5$$

**FIGURE A.8**    INSERT FUNCTION DIALOG BOX

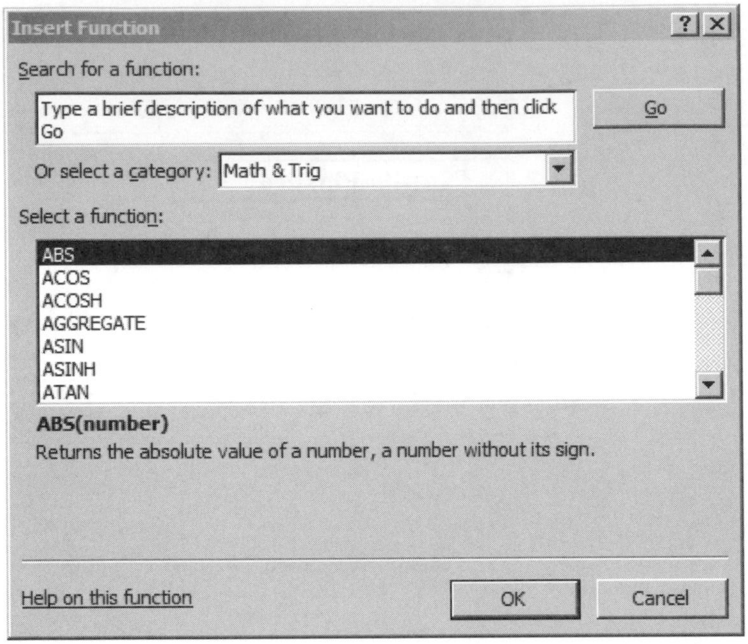

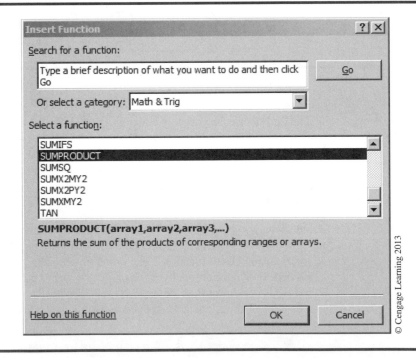

**FIGURE A.9**    DESCRIPTION OF THE SUMPRODUCT FUNCTION IN THE INSERT
FUNCTION DIALOG BOX

## Inserting a Function into a Worksheet Cell

Through the use of an example, we will now show how to use the Insert Function and Function Arguments dialog boxes to select a function, develop its arguments, and insert the function into a worksheet cell. We also illustrate the use of a very useful function, the SUMPRODUCT function, and how to use colon notation in the argument of a function.

The SUMPRODUCT function, as shown in Figure A.9, is used in many of the Solver examples in the textbook. Note that SUMPRODUCT is now highlighted, and that immediately below the Select a function box we see SUMPRODUCT(array1,array2,array3, . . .), which indicates that the SUMPRODUCT function contains the array arguments array1, array2, array3, . . . . In addition, we see that the description of the SUMPRODUCT function is "Returns the sum of the products of corresponding ranges or arrays." For example, the function =SUMPRODUCT(A1:A3,B1:B3) evaluates the formula A1*B1 + A2*B2 + A3*B3. As shown in the following example, this function can be very useful in calculations of cost, profit, and other such functions involving multiple arrays of numbers.

Figure A.10 displays an Excel worksheet for the Foster Generators Problem that appears in Chapter 10. This problem involves the transportation of a product from three plants (Cleveland, Bedford, and York) to four distribution centers (Boston, Chicago, St. Louis, and

**FIGURE A.10**    EXCEL WORKSHEET USED TO CALCULATE TOTAL SHIPPING COSTS FOR THE FOSTER GENERATORS TRANSPORTATION PROBLEM

**WEB file**

**Foster Generators**

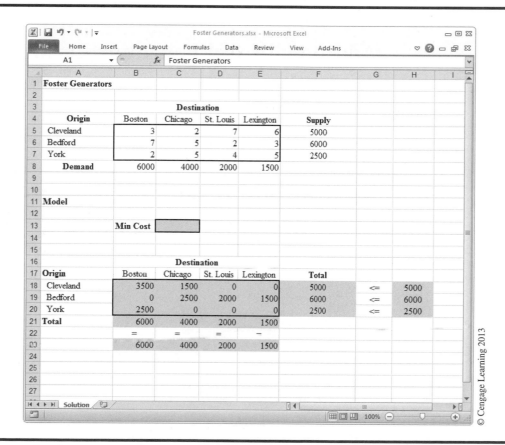

© Cengage Learning 2013

Lexington). The costs for each unit shipped from each plant to each distribution center are shown in cells B5:E7, and the values in cells B18:E20 are the number of units shipped from each plant to each distribution center. Cell C13 will contain the total transportation cost corresponding to the transportation cost values in cells B5:E7.

The following steps show how to use the SUMPRODUCT function to compute the total transportation cost for Foster Generators.

**Step 1.** Select **cell C13**
**Step 2.** Click $f_x$ on the formula bar
**Step 3.** When the **Insert Function** dialog box appears:
Select **Math & Trig** in the **Or select a category** box
Select **SUMPRODUCT** in the **Select a function** box (as shown in Figure A.9)
Click **OK**
**Step 4.** When the **Function Arguments** box appears (see Figure A.11):
Enter B5:E7 in the **Array1** box
Enter B18:E20 in the **Array2** box
Click **OK**

The worksheet then appears as shown in Figure A.12. The value of the total transportation cost in cell C13 is 39,500, or $39,500.

We illustrated the use of Excel's capability to provide assistance in using the SUMPRODUCT function. The procedure is similar for all Excel functions. This capability is especially helpful if you do not know which function to use or forget the proper name and/or syntax for a function.

# Additional Excel Functions for Modeling

In this section we introduce some additional Excel functions that have proven useful in modeling decision problems.

**FIGURE A.11**    COMPLETED FUNCTION ARGUMENTS DIALOG BOX FOR THE SUMPRODUCT FUNCTION

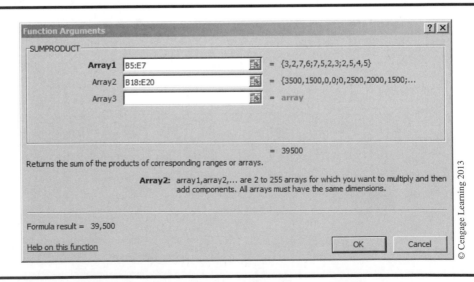

**FIGURE A.12** EXCEL WORKSHEET SHOWING THE USE OF EXCEL'S SUMPRODUCT FUNCTION TO CALCULATE TOTAL SHIPPING COSTS

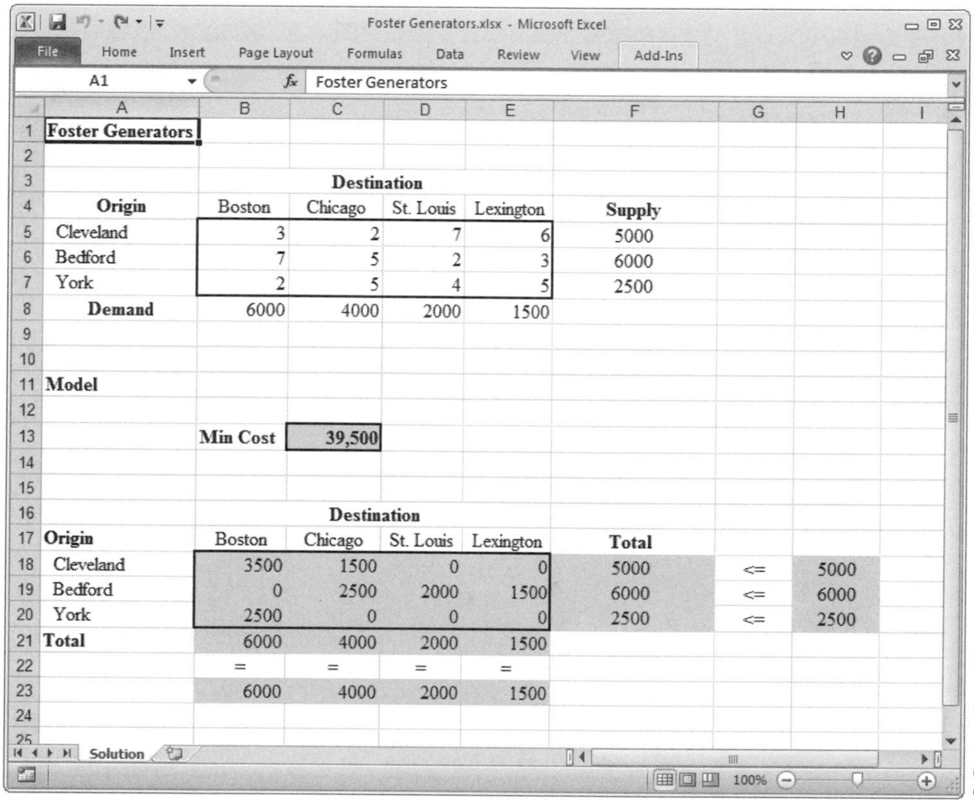


| | A | B | C | D | E | F | G | H |
|---|---|---|---|---|---|---|---|---|
| 1 | Foster Generators | | | | | | | |
| 2 | | | | | | | | |
| 3 | | | Destination | | | | | |
| 4 | Origin | Boston | Chicago | St. Louis | Lexington | Supply | | |
| 5 | Cleveland | 3 | 2 | 7 | 6 | 5000 | | |
| 6 | Bedford | 7 | 5 | 2 | 3 | 6000 | | |
| 7 | York | 2 | 5 | 4 | 5 | 2500 | | |
| 8 | Demand | 6000 | 4000 | 2000 | 1500 | | | |
| 9 | | | | | | | | |
| 10 | | | | | | | | |
| 11 | Model | | | | | | | |
| 12 | | | | | | | | |
| 13 | | Min Cost | 39,500 | | | | | |
| 14 | | | | | | | | |
| 15 | | | | | | | | |
| 16 | | | Destination | | | | | |
| 17 | Origin | Boston | Chicago | St. Louis | Lexington | Total | | |
| 18 | Cleveland | 3500 | 1500 | 0 | 0 | 5000 | <= | 5000 |
| 19 | Bedford | 0 | 2500 | 2000 | 1500 | 6000 | <= | 6000 |
| 20 | York | 2500 | 0 | 0 | 0 | 2500 | <= | 2500 |
| 21 | Total | 6000 | 4000 | 2000 | 1500 | | | |
| 22 | | = | = | = | = | | | |
| 23 | | 6000 | 4000 | 2000 | 1500 | | | |
| 24 | | | | | | | | |



## IF and COUNTIF Functions

Let us consider the case of Gambrell Manufacturing. Gambrell Manufacturing produces car stereos. Stereos are composed of a variety of components that the company must carry in inventory to keep production running smoothly. However, because inventory can be a costly investment, Gambrell generally likes to keep the amount of inventory of the components it uses in manufacturing to a minimum. To help monitor and control its inventory of components, Gambrell uses an inventory policy known as an "order up to" policy. This type of inventory policy and others are discussed in detail in Chapter 14.

The "order up to policy" is as follows. Whenever the inventory on hand drops below a certain level, enough units are ordered to return the inventory to that predetermined level. If the current number of units in inventory, denoted by $H$, drops below $M$ units, we order enough to get the inventory level back up to $M$ units. $M$ is called the Order Up to Point. Stated mathematically, if $Q$ is the amount we order, then

$$Q = M - H$$

An inventory model for Gambrell Manufacturing appears in Figure A.13. In this worksheet, labeled "OrderQuantity" in the upper half of the worksheet, the component ID number, inventory on hand ($H$), order up to point ($M$), and cost per unit are given for each of

**FIGURE A.13**   THE GAMBRELL MANUFACTURING COMPONENT ORDERING MODEL

WEB file

Gambrell

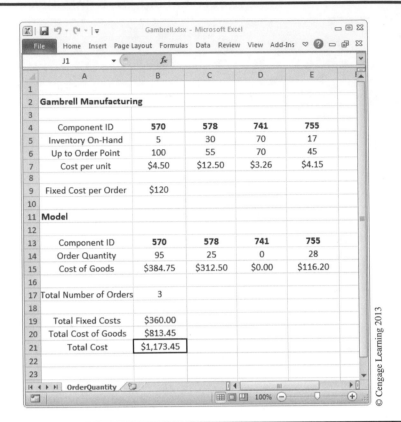

© Cengage Learning 2013

four components. Also given in this sheet is the fixed cost per order. The fixed cost is interpreted as follows: Each time a component is ordered, it costs Gambrell $120 to process the order. The fixed cost of $120 is incurred regardless of how many units are ordered.

The model portion of the worksheet calculates the order quantity for each component. For example, for component 570, $M = 100$ and $H = 5$, so $Q = M - H = 100 - 5 = 95$. For component 741, $M = 70$ and $H = 70$ and no units are ordered because the on-hand inventory of 70 units is equal to the order point of 70. The calculations are similar for the other two components.

Depending on the number of units ordered, Gambrell receives a discount on the cost per unit. If 50 or more units are ordered, there is a quantity discount of 10% on every unit purchased. For example, for component 741, the cost per unit is $4.50 and 95 units are ordered. Because 95 exceeds the 50-unit requirement, there is a 10% discount and the cost per unit is reduced to $4.50 - 0.1($4.50) = $4.50 - $0.45 = $4.05. Not including the fixed cost, the cost of goods purchased is then $4.05(95) = $384.75.

The Excel functions used to perform these calculations are shown in Figure A.14. The IF function is used to calculate the purchase cost of goods for each component in row 15. The general form of the IF function is

=IF(*condition, result if condition is true, result if condition is false*)

For example, in cell B15 we have =IF(B14>=50,0.9*B7,B7)*B14. This statement says if the order quantity (cell B14) is greater than or equal to 50, then the cost per unit is 0.9*B7 (there

**FIGURE A.14**   FORMULAS AND FUNCTIONS FOR GAMBRELL MANUFACTURING

| | A | B | C | D | E |
|---|---|---|---|---|---|
| 1 | | | | | |
| 2 | **Gambrell Manufacturing** | | | | |
| 3 | | | | | |
| 4 | Component ID | 570 | 578 | 741 | 755 |
| 5 | Inventory On-Hand | 5 | 30 | 70 | 17 |
| 6 | Up to Order Point | 100 | 55 | 70 | 45 |
| 7 | Cost per unit | 4.5 | 12.5 | 3.26 | 4.15 |
| 8 | | | | | |
| 9 | Fixed Cost per Order | 120 | | | |
| 10 | | | | | |
| 11 | **Model** | | | | |
| 12 | | | | | |
| 13 | Component ID | =B4 | =C4 | =D4 | =E4 |
| 14 | Order Quantity | =B6-B5 | =C6-C5 | =D6-D5 | =E6-E5 |
| 15 | Cost of Goods | =IF(B14 >= 50, 0.9*B7,B7)*B14 | =IF(C14 >= 50, 0.9*C7,C7)*C14 | =IF(D14 >= 50, 0.9*D7,D7)*D14 | =IF(E14 >= 50, 0.9*E7,E7)*E14 |
| 16 | | | | | |
| 17 | Total Number of Orders | =COUNTIF(B14:E14,">0") | | | |
| 18 | | | | | |
| 19 | Total Fixed Costs | =B17*B9 | | | |
| 20 | Total Cost of Goods | =SUM(B15:E15) | | | |
| 21 | Total Cost | =SUM(B19:B20) | | | |
| 22 | | | | | |
| 23 | | | | | |
| 24 | | | | | |

OrderQuantity

© Cengage Learning 2013

is a 10% discount); otherwise, there is no discount and the cost per unit is the amount given in cell B7. The purchase cost of goods for the other components are computed in a like manner.

The total cost in cell B21 is the sum of the purchase cost of goods ordered in row 15 and the fixed ordering costs. Because we place three orders (one each for components 570, 578, and 755), the fixed cost of the orders is 3*120 = $360.

The COUNTIF function in cell B17 is used to count how many times we order. In particular, it counts the number of components having a positive order quantity. The general form of the COUNTIF function is

$$=COUNTIF(range, condition)$$

The *range* is the range to search for the *condition*. The condition is the test to be counted when satisfied. *Note that quotes are required for the condition with the COUNTIF function.* In the Gambrell model in Figure A.14, cell B17 counts the number of cells that are greater than zero in the range of cells B14:E14. In the model, because only cells B14, C14, and E14 are greater than zero, the COUNTIF function in cell B17 returns 3.

As we have seen, IF and COUNTIF are powerful functions that allow us to make calculations based on a condition holding (or not). There are other such conditional functions available in Excel. In the problems at the end of this appendix, we ask you to investigate one such function, the SUMIF function. Another conditional function that is extremely useful in modeling is the VLOOKUP function. We discuss the VLOOKUP function with an example in the next section.

## VLOOKUP Function

Next, consider the workbook named *OM455* shown in Figure A.15. The worksheet named Grades is shown. This worksheet calculates the course grades for the course OM 455. There are 11 students in the course. Each student has a midterm exam score and a final exam score,

**FIGURE A.15**   OM455 GRADE SPREADSHEET

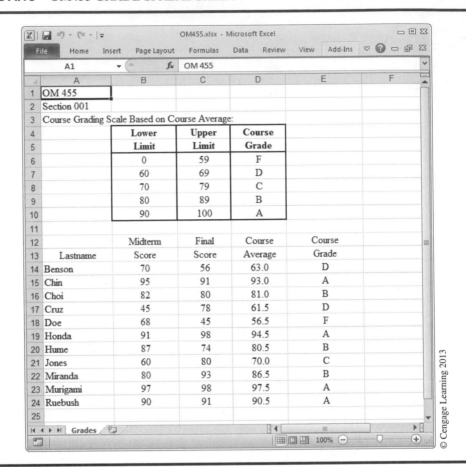

and these are averaged in column D to get the course average. The scale given in the upper portion of the worksheet is used to determine the course grade for each student. Consider, for example, the performance of student Choi in row 16. This student earned an 82 on the midterm, an 80 on the final, and a course average of 81. From the grading scale, this equates to a course grade of B.

The course average is simply the average of the midterm and final scores, but how do we get Excel to look in the grading scale table and automatically assign the correct course letter grade to each student? The VLOOKUP function allows us to do just that. The formulas and functions used in *OM455* are shown in Figure A.16.

The VLOOKUP function allows the user to pull a subset of data from a larger table of data based on some criterion. The general form of the VLOOKUP function is

$$=VLOOKUP(arg1, arg2, arg3, arg4)$$

where *arg1* is the value to search for in the first column of the table, *arg2* is the table location, *arg3* is the column location in the table to be returned, and *arg4* is TRUE if looking for the first partial match of *arg1* and FALSE for looking for an exact match of *arg1*. We will explain the difference between a partial and exact match in a moment. VLOOKUP assumes that the first column of the table is sorted in ascending order.

The VLOOKUP function for student Choi in cell E16 is as follows:

$$=VLOOKUP(D16, B6:D10, 3, TRUE)$$

**FIGURE A.16**    THE FORMULAS AND FUNCTIONS USED IN OM 455

| | A | B | C | D | E |
|---|---|---|---|---|---|
| 1 | OM 455 | | | | |
| 2 | Section 001 | | | | |
| 3 | Course Grading Scale Based on Co | | | | |
| 4 | | Lower | Upper | Course | |
| 5 | | Limit | Limit | Grade | |
| 6 | | 0 | 59 | F | |
| 7 | | 60 | 69 | D | |
| 8 | | 70 | 79 | C | |
| 9 | | 80 | 89 | B | |
| 10 | | 90 | 100 | A | |
| 11 | | | | | |
| 12 | | Midterm | Final | Course | Course |
| 13 | Lastname | Score | Score | Average | Grade |
| 14 | Benson | 70 | 56 | =AVERAGE(B14:C14) | =VLOOKUP(D14,B6:D10,3,TRUE) |
| 15 | Chin | 95 | 91 | =AVERAGE(B15:C15) | =VLOOKUP(D15,B6:D10,3,TRUE) |
| 16 | Choi | 82 | 80 | =AVERAGE(B16:C16) | =VLOOKUP(D16,B6:D10,3,TRUE) |
| 17 | Cruz | 45 | 78 | =AVERAGE(B17:C17) | =VLOOKUP(D17,B6:D10,3,TRUE) |
| 18 | Doe | 68 | 45 | =AVERAGE(B18:C18) | =VLOOKUP(D18,B6:D10,3,TRUE) |
| 19 | Honda | 91 | 98 | =AVERAGE(B19:C19) | =VLOOKUP(D19,B6:D10,3,TRUE) |
| 20 | Hume | 87 | 74 | =AVERAGE(B20:C20) | =VLOOKUP(D20,B6:D10,3,TRUE) |
| 21 | Jones | 60 | 80 | =AVERAGE(B21:C21) | =VLOOKUP(D21,B6:D10,3,TRUE) |
| 22 | Miranda | 80 | 93 | =AVERAGE(B22:C22) | =VLOOKUP(D22,B6:D10,3,TRUE) |
| 23 | Murigami | 97 | 98 | =AVERAGE(B23:C23) | =VLOOKUP(D23,B6:D10,3,TRUE) |
| 24 | Ruebush | 90 | 91 | =AVERAGE(B24:C24) | =VLOOKUP(D24,B6:D10,3,TRUE) |
| 25 | | | | | |

*It is important to remember that VLOOKUP assumes that the column being searched is sorted in ascending order. You can sort values in ascending order by choosing the **Data** tab from the Ribbon, then choosing the **Sort & Filter** group and then choosing **Sort**.*

This function uses the course average from cell D16 and searches the first column of the table defined by B6:D10. In the first column of the table (column B), Excel searches from the top until it finds a number strictly greater than the value of D16 (81). It then backs up one row (to row 9)[1]. That is, it finds the last value in the first column less than or equal to 81. Because there is a 3 in the third argument of the VLOOKUP function, it takes the element in row 9 in the third column of the table, which is the letter "B." In summary, the VLOOKUP takes the first argument and searches the first column of the table for the last row that is less than or equal to the first argument. It then selects from that row the element in the column number of the third argument.

*Note:* If the last element of the VLOOKUP function is "False," the only change is that Excel searches for an exact match of the first argument in the first column of the data. VLOOKUP is very useful when you seek subsets of a table based on a condition.

# Principles for Building Good Spreadsheet Models

We have covered some of the fundamentals of building spreadsheet models. There are some generally accepted guiding principles for how to build a spreadsheet so that it is more easily used by others and so that the risk of error is mitigated. In this section we discuss some of those principles.

---

[1] If the value being searched for in the VLOOKUP function is larger than the largest value in the column being searched, then Excel will return the value from the row of the largest value. If the value being searched for is smaller than the smallest value in the column being searched, Excel will return a "#N/A" error.

## Separate the Data from the Model

One of the first principles of good modeling is to separate the data from the model. This enables the user to update the model parameters without fear of mistakenly typing over a formula or function. For this reason, it is good practice to have a data section at the top of the spreadsheet. A separate model section should contain all calculations and in general should not be updated by a user. For a what-if model or an optimization model, there might also be a separate section for decision cells (values that are not data or calculations, but are the outputs we seek from the model).

The Nowlin model in Figure A.6 is a good example. The data section is in the upper part of the spreadsheet followed by the model section that contains the calculations. The Gambrell model in Figure A.13 does not totally employ the principle of data/model separation. A better model would have the 50-unit hurdle and the 90% cost (10% discount) as data in the upper section. Then the formulas in row 15 would simply refer to the cells in the upper section. This would allow the user to easily change the discount, for example, without having to change all four formulas in row 15.

## Document the Model

A good spreadsheet model is well documented. Clear labels and proper formatting and alignment make the spreadsheet easier to navigate and understand. For example, if the values in a worksheet are cost, currency formatting should be used. No cells should be unlabeled. A new user should be able to easily understand the model and its calculations. Figure A.17 shows a better-documented version of the Foster Generators model previously discussed (Figure A.10). The tables are more explicitly labeled, and shading focuses the user on the objective and the decision cells (amount to ship). The per-unit shipping cost data and total (Min) cost have been properly formatted as currency.

## Use Simple Formulas and Cell Names

Clear formulas can eliminate unnecessary calculations, reduce errors, and make it easier to maintain your spreadsheet. Long and complex calculations should be divided into several cells. This makes the formula easier to understand and easier to edit. Avoid using numbers in a formula. Instead, put the number in a cell in the data section of your worksheet and refer to the cell location of the data in the formula. Building the formula in this manner avoids having to edit the formula for a simple data change.

Using cell names can make a formula much easier to understand. To assign a name to a cell, use the following steps:

**Step 1.** Select the cell or range of cells you would like to name
**Step 2.** Select the **Formulas** tab from the Ribbon
**Step 3.** Choose **Define Name** from the **Defined Names** group
**Step 4.** The **New Name** dialog box will appear, as shown in Figure A.18
Enter the name you would like to use in the **Name:** box and Click **OK**

Following this procedure and naming all cells in the *Nowlin Plastics* spreadsheet model leads to the model shown in Figure A.19. Compare this to Figure A.6 to easily understand the formulas in the model.

**FIGURE A.17**   A BETTER-DOCUMENTED FOSTER GENERATORS MODEL

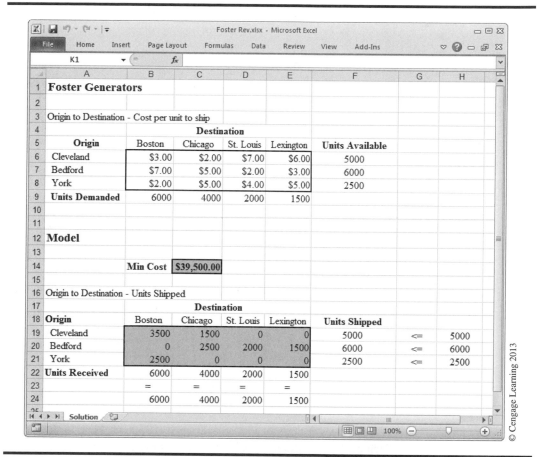

**FIGURE A.18**   THE DEFINE NAME DIALOG BOX

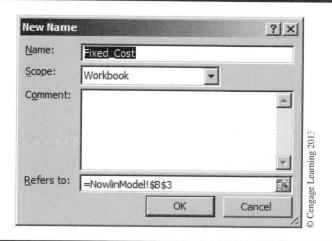

**FIGURE A.19**    THE NOWLIN PLASTICS MODEL FORMULAS WITH NAMED CELLS

**Nowlin Plastics**

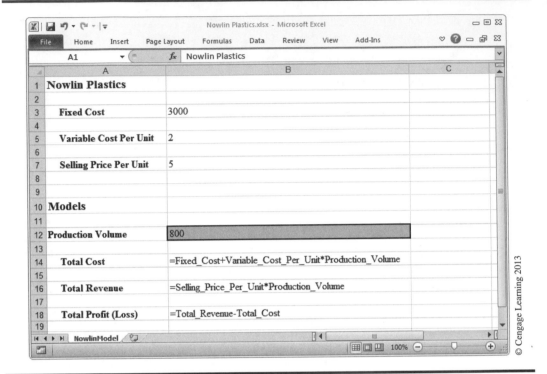

A name is also easily applied to a range as follows. First, highlight the range of interest. Then click on the Name Box in the Formula Bar (refer back to Figure A.3) and type in the desired range name.

## Use of Relative and Absolute Cell References

There are a number of ways to copy a formula from one cell to another in an Excel worksheet. One way to copy the a formula from one cell to another is presented here:

**Step 1.**  Select the cell you would like to copy
**Step 2.**  Right click on the mouse
**Step 3.**  Click **Copy**
**Step 4.**  Select the cell where you would like to put the copy
**Step 5.**  Right click on the mouse
**Step 6.**  Click **Paste**

When copying in Excel, one can use a relative or an absolute address. When copied, a relative address adjusts with the move of the copy, whereas an absolute address stays in its original form. Relative addresses are of the form C7. Absolute addresses have $ in front of the column and/or row, for example, $C$7. How you use relative and absolute addresses can have an impact on the amount of effort it takes to build a model and the opportunity for error in constructing the model.

Let us reconsider the *OM455* grading spreadsheet previously discussed in this appendix and shown in Figure A.16. Recall that we used the VLOOKUP function to retrieve the appropriate letter grade for each student. The following formula is in cell E14:

$$=VLOOKUP(D14,B6:D10,3,TRUE)$$

Note that this formula contains only relative addresses. If we copy this to cell E15, we get the following result:

$$=VLOOKUP(D15,B7:D11,3,TRUE)$$

Although the first argument has correctly changed to D15 (we want to calculate the letter grade for the student in row 15), the table in the function has also shifted to B7:D11. What we desired was for this table location to remain the same. A better approach would have been to use the following formula in cell E14:

$$=VLOOKUP(D14,\$B\$6:\$D\$10,3,TRUE)$$

Copying this formula to cell E15 results in the following formula:

$$=VLOOKUP(D15,\$B\$6:\$D\$10,3,TRUE)$$

This correctly changes the first argument to D15 and keeps the data table intact. Using absolute referencing is extremely useful if you have a function that has a reference that should not change when applied to another cell and you are copying the formula to other locations. In the case of the *OM455* workbook, instead of typing the VLOOKUP for each student, we can use absolute referencing on the table and then copy from row 14 to rows 15 through 24.

In this section we have discussed guidelines for good spreadsheet model building. In the next section we discuss Excel tools available for checking and debugging spreadsheet models.

# Auditing Excel Models

Excel contains a variety of tools to assist you in the development and debugging of spreadsheet models. These tools are found in the Formula Auditing group of the Formulas Tab as shown in Figure A.20. Let us review each of the tools available in this group.

**FIGURE A.20**  THE FORMULA AUDITING GROUP OF THE FORMULAS TAB

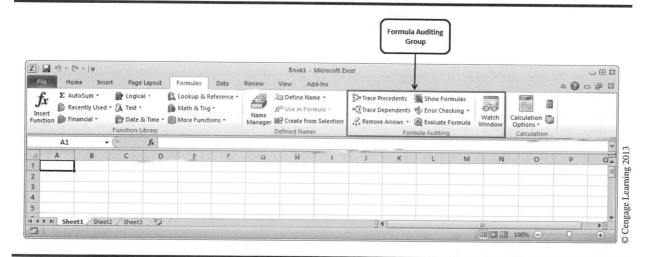

© Cengage Learning 2013

## Trace Precedents and Dependents

The Trace Precedents button, ⊹ Trace Precedents , creates arrows pointing to the selected cell from cells that are part of the formula in that cell. The Trace Dependents button, ⊰ Trace Dependents , on the other hand, shows arrows pointing from the selected cell to cells that depend on the selected cell. Both of the tools are excellent for quickly ascertaining how parts of a model are linked.

An example of Trace Precedents is shown in Figure A.21. Here we have opened the *Foster Rev* worksheet, selected cell C14, and clicked the Trace Precedents button in the Formula Auditing group. Recall that the cost in cell C14 is calculated as the SUMPRODUCT of the per-unit shipping cost and units shipped. In Figure A.21, to show this relationship, arrows are drawn to these respective areas of the spreadsheet to cell C14. These arrows may be removed by clicking on the Remove Arrows button in the Formula Auditing group.

**FIGURE A.21**   TRACE PRECEDENTS FOR CELL C14 (COST) IN THE FOSTER GENERATORS REV MODEL

**Foster Rev**

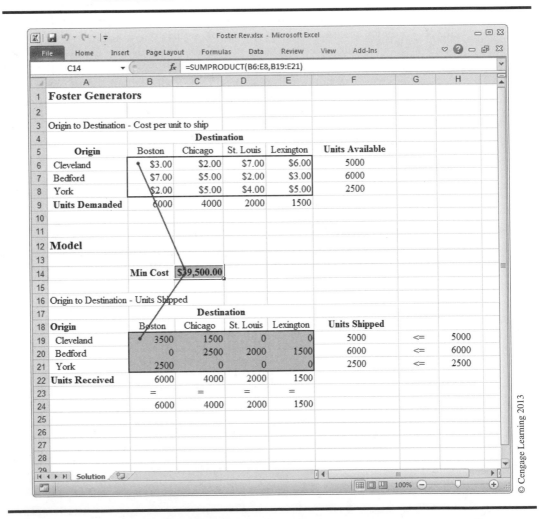

© Cengage Learning 2013

An example of Trace Dependents is shown in Figure A.22. We have selected cell E20, the units shipped from Bedford to Lexington, and clicked on the Trace Dependents button in the Formula Auditing group. As shown in Figure A.22, units shipped from Bedford to Lexington impacts the cost function in cell C14, the total units shipped from Bedford given in cell F20, and the total units shipped to Lexington in cell E22. These arrows may be removed by clicking on the Remove Arrows button in the Formula Auditing group.

Trace Precedents and Trace Dependents can highlight errors in copying and formula construction by showing that incorrect sections of the worksheet are referenced.

## Show Formulas

The Show Formulas button, [Show Formulas] , does exactly that. To see the formulas in a worksheet, simply click on any cell in the worksheet and then click on Show Formulas. You will see the formulas that exist in that worksheet. To go back to hiding the formulas, click

**FIGURE A.22**    TRACE DEPENDENTS FOR CELL E20 (UNITS SHIPPED FROM BEDFORD TO LEXINGTON) IN THE FOSTER GENERATORS REV MODEL

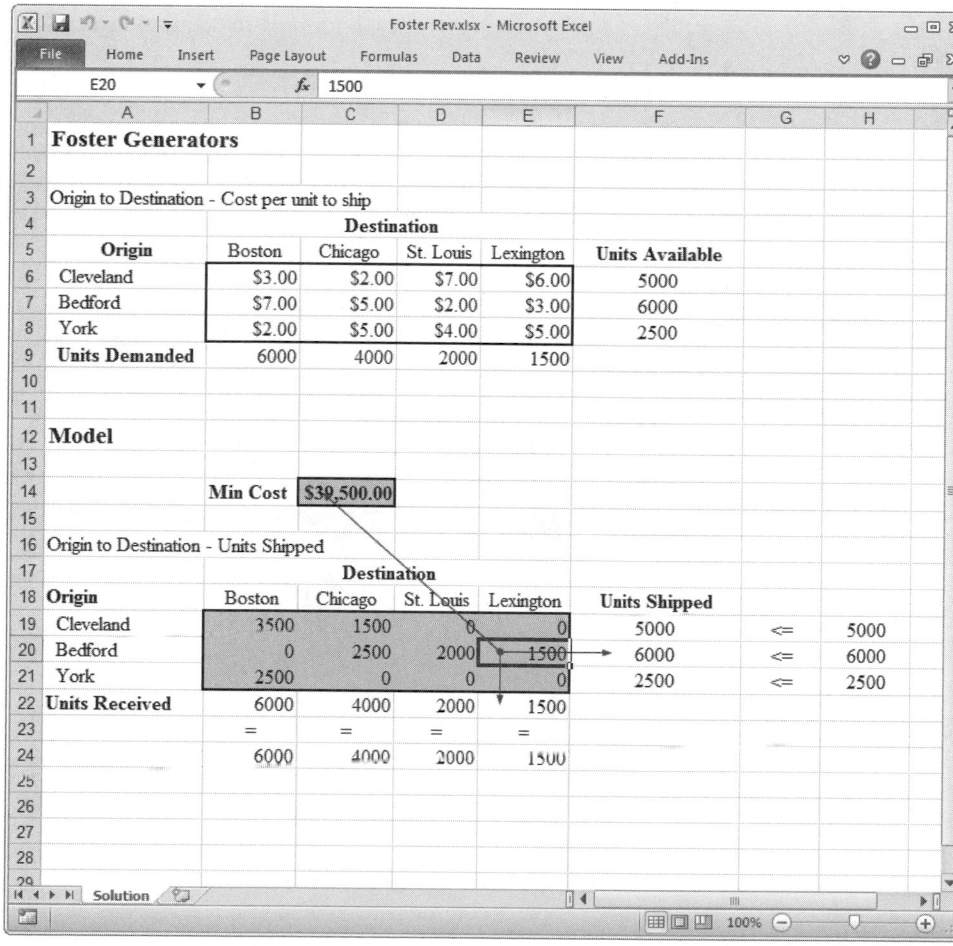

**FIGURE A.23**   THE EVALUATE FORMULA DIALOG BOX

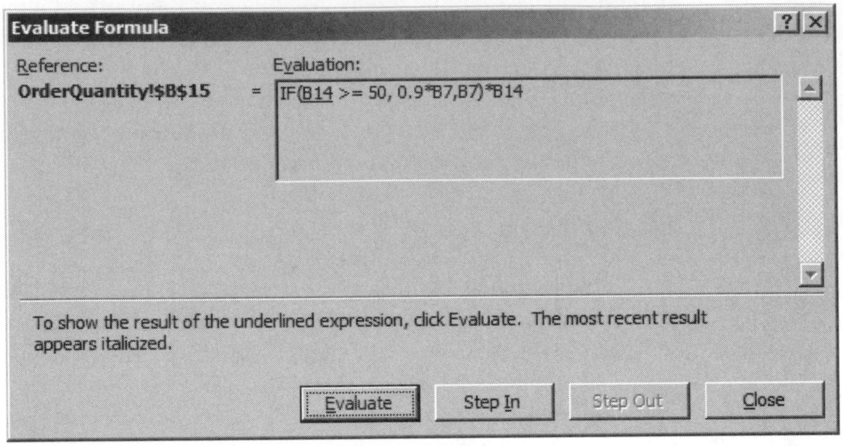

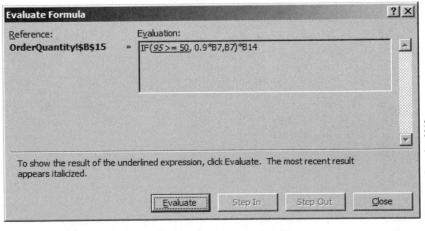

again on the Show Formulas button. Figure A.6 gives an example of the show formulas view. This allows you to inspect each formula in detail in its cell location.

## Evaluate Formulas

The Evaluate Formula button, 🔎 Evaluate Formula , allows you to investigate the calculations of particular cell in great detail. To invoke this tool, we simply select a cell containing a formula and click on the Evaluate Formula button in the Formula Auditing group. As an example, we select cell B15 of the Gambrell Manufacturing model (see Figures A.13 and A.14). Recall we are calculating cost of goods based upon whether or not there is a quantity discount. Clicking on the Evaluate button allows you to evaluate this formula explicitly. The Evaluate Formula dialog box appears in Figure A.23. Figure A.24 shows the result of one

**FIGURE A.24**   THE EVALUATE FORMULA AFTER ONE CLICK OF THE
                  EVALUATE BUTTON

click of the Evaluate button. The B14 has changed to its value of 95. Further clicks would evaluate in order, from left to right, the remaining components of the formula. We ask the reader to further explore this tool in an exercise at the end of this appendix.

The Evaluate Formula tool provides an excellent means of identifying the exact location of an error in a formula.

## Error Checking

The Error Checking button, 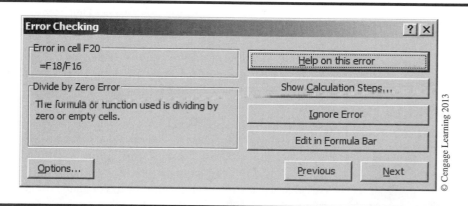, provides an automatic means of checking for mathematical errors within formulas of a worksheet. Clicking on the Error Checking button causes Excel to check every formula in the sheet for calculation errors. If an error is found, the Error Checking dialog box appears. An example for a hypothetical division by zero error is shown in Figure A.25. From this box, the formula can be edited or the calculation steps can be observed (as in the previous section on Evaluate Formulas).

## Watch Window

The Watch Window, located in the Formula Auditing group, allows the user to observe the values of cells included in the Watch Window box list. This is useful for large models when not all the model is observable on the screen or when multiple worksheets are used. The user can monitor how the listed cells change with a change in the model without searching through the worksheet or changing from one worksheet to another.

A Watch Window for the Gambrell Manufacturing model is shown in Figure A.26. The following steps were used from the OrderQuantity worksheet to add cell B15 of the OrderQuantity worksheet to the watch list:

**Step 1.** Select the **Formulas** tab
**Step 2.** Select **Watch Window** from the **Formula Auditing** group
The **Watch Window** will appear
**Step 3.** Select **Add Watch**
**Step 4.** Click on the cell you would like to add to the watch list (in this case **B15**)

As shown in Figure A.26, the list gives the workbook name, worksheet name, cell name (if used), cell location, cell value, and cell formula. To delete a cell from the watch list, select

**FIGURE A.25**    THE ERROR CHECKING DIALOG BOX FOR A DIVISION
BY ZERO ERROR

**FIGURE A.26**    THE WATCH WINDOW FOR THE GAMBRELL MANUFACTURING MODEL

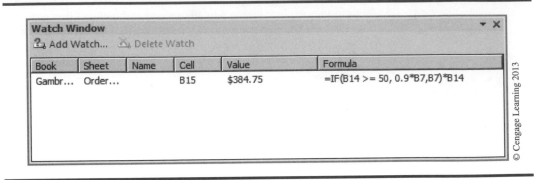

the entry from the list and then click on the Delete Watch button in the upper part of the Watch Window.

The Watch Window, as shown in Figure A.26, allows us to monitor the value of B15 as we make changes elsewhere in the worksheet. Furthermore, if we had other worksheets in this workbook, we could monitor changes to B15 of the OrderQuantity worksheet even from these other worksheets. The Watch Window is observable regardless of where we are in any worksheet of a workbook.

## Summary

In this appendix we have discussed how to build effective spreadsheet models using Excel. We provided an overview on workbooks and worksheets and details on useful Excel functions. We also discussed a set of principles for good modeling and tools for auditing spreadsheet models.

## Problems

**Nowlin Plastics**

1.  Open the file *Nowlin Plastics*. Recall that we have modeled total profit for the product CD-50 in this spreadsheet. Suppose we have a second product called a CD-100, with the following characteristics:

$$\text{Fixed Cost} = \$2500$$
$$\text{Variable Cost per Unit} = \$1.67$$
$$\text{Selling Price per Unit} = \$4.40$$

Extend the model so that the profit is calculated for each product and then totaled to give an overall profit generated for the two products. Use a CD-100 production volume of 1200. Save this file as *Nowlin Plastics2*. *Hint*: Place the data for CD-100 in column C and copy the formulas in rows 14, 16, and 18 to column C.

2.  Assume that in an empty Excel worksheet in cell A1 you enter the formula =B1*$F$3. You now copy this formula into cell E6. What is the modified formula that appears in E6?

**Foster Rev**

3.  Open the file *Foster Rev*. Select cells B6:E8 and name these cells Shipping_Cost. Select cells B19:E21 and name these cells Units_Shipped. Use these names in the SUMPRODUCT function in cell C14 to compute cost and verify that you obtain the same cost ($39,500).

4. Open the file *Nowlin Plastics*. Recall that we have modeled total profit for the product CD-50 in this spreadsheet. Modify the spreadsheet to take into account production capacity and forecasted demand. If forecasted demand is less than or equal to capacity, Nowlin will produce only the forecasted demand; otherwise, they will produce the full capacity. For this example, use forecasted demand of 1200 and capacity of 1500. *Hint*: Enter demand and capacity into the data section of the model. Then use an IF statement to calculate production volume.

5. Cox Electric makes electronic components and has estimated the following for a new design of one of its products:

$$\text{Fixed Cost} = \$10{,}000$$
$$\text{Revenue per unit} = \$0.65$$
$$\text{Material cost per unit} = \$0.15$$
$$\text{Labor cost per unit} = \$0.10$$

These data are given in the spreadsheet *Cox Electric*. Also in the spreadsheet in row 14 is a profit model that gives the profit (or loss) for a specified volume (cell C14).

a. Use the Show Formula button in the Formula Auditing group of the Formulas tab to see the formulas and cell references used in row 14.

b. Use the Trace Precedents tool to see how the formulas are dependent on the elements of the data section.

c. Use trial and error, by trying various values of volume in cell C14, to arrive at a breakeven volume.

6. Return to the *Cox Electric* spreadsheet. Build a table of profits based on different volume levels by doing the following: In cell C15, enter a volume of 20,000. Look at each formula in row 14 and decide which references should be absolute or relative for purposes of copying the formulas to row 15. Make the necessary changes to row 14 (change any references that should be absolute by putting in $). Copy cells D14:I14 to row 15. Continue this with new rows until a positive profit is found. Save your file as *Cox_Breakeven*.

7. Open the workbook *OM455*. Save the file under a new name, *OM455COUNTIF*. Suppose we wish to automatically count the number of each letter grade.

a. Begin by putting the letters A, B, C, D, and F in cells C29:C33. Use the COUNTIF function in cells D29:D33 to count the number of each letter grade. *Hint*: Create the necessary COUNTIF function in cell D29. Use absolute referencing on the range ($E14:$E$24) and then copy the function to cells D30:D33 to count the number of each of the other letter grades.

b. We are considering a different grading scale as follows:

| Lower | Upper | Grade |
|-------|-------|-------|
| 0 | 69 | F |
| 70 | 76 | D |
| 77 | 84 | C |
| 85 | 92 | B |
| 93 | 100 | A |

For the current list of students, use the COUNTIF function to determine the number of A, B, C, D, and F letter grades earned under this new system.

OM455

8. Open the workbook *OM455*. Save the file under a new name, *OM4555Revised*. Suppose we wish to use a more refined grading system, as shown below:

| Lower | Upper | Grade |
|-------|-------|-------|
| 0 | 59 | F |
| 60 | 69 | D |
| 70 | 72 | C− |
| 73 | 76 | C− |
| 77 | 79 | C+ |
| 80 | 82 | B− |
| 83 | 86 | B |
| 87 | 89 | B+ |
| 90 | 92 | A− |
| 93 | 100 | A |

Update the file to use this more refined grading system. How many of each letter grade are awarded under the new system? *Hint*: Build a new grading table and use VLOOKUP and an absolute reference to the table. Then use COUNTIF to count the number of each letter grade.

Newton_data

9. Newton Manufacturing produces scientific calculators. The models are N350, N450, and the N900. Newton has planned its distribution of these products around eight customer zones: Brazil, China, France, Malaysia, U.S. Northeast, U.S. Southeast, U.S. Midwest, and U.S. West. Data for the current quarter (volume to be shipped in thousands of units) for each product and each customer zone are given in the file *Newton_data*.

Newton would like to know the total number of units going to each customer zone and also the total units of each product shipped. There are several ways to get this information from the data set. One way is to use the SUMIF function.

The SUMIF function extends the SUM function by allowing the user to add the values of cells meeting a logical condition. This general form of the function is

$$=\text{SUMIF}(test\ range,\ condition,\ range\ to\ be\ summed)$$

The *test range* is an area to search to test the *condition,* and the *range to be summed* is the position of the data to be summed. So, for example, using the *Newton_data* file, we would use the following function to get the total units sent to Malaysia:

$$=\text{SUMIF}(A3{:}A26,A3,C3{:}C26)$$

Here, A3 is Malaysia, A3:A26 is the range of customer zones, and C3:C26 are the volumes for each product for these customer zones. The SUMIF looks for matches of Malaysia in column A and, if a match is found, adds the volume to the total. Use the SUMIF function to get each total volume by zone and each total volume by product.

Williamson

10. Consider the transportation model given in the Excel file *Williamson*. It is a model that is very similar to the Foster Generators model. Williamson produces a single product and has plants in Atlanta, Lexington, Chicago, and Salt Lake City and warehouses in Portland, St. Paul, Las Vegas, Tuscon, and Cleveland. Each plant has a capacity and each warehouse has a demand. Williamson would like to find a low-cost shipping plan. Mr. Williamson has reviewed the results and notices right away that the total cost is way out of line. Use the Formula Auditing Tools under the Formulas tab in Excel to find any errors in this

model. Correct the errors. *Hint*: There are two errors in this model. Be sure to check every formula.

The following two problems concern constructing well-structured and useful spreadsheet models. Many of the concepts discussed in Appendix A will be useful in doing these problems.

11. Develop a spreadsheet model that could be used to assist a user with retirement planning. Your model should include the following input parameters:

    User's Current Age = 40 years

    User's Current Total Retirement Savings = $250,000

    Annual Rate of Return on Retirement Savings = 5%

    User's Current Annual Salary = $145,000

    Expected Annual Percentage Increase in Salary = 3%

    User's Percentage of Annual Salary Contributed to Retirement = 10%

    Income Tax Rate Pre-Retirement = 28%

    User's Expected Age of Retirement = 65

    User's Expected Annual Expenses after Retirement (current dollars) = $55,000

    Rate of Return on Retirement Savings After Retirement = 3%

    Income Tax Rate Post-Retirement = 15%

    Assume that the user's employer contributes 6% of the user's salary to his/her retirement fund and that the user's annual contributions to his/her retirement are before taxes (tax free) up to a contribution of $16,000.

    Your spreadsheet model should provide the accumulated savings at the onset of retirement as well as the age at which funds will be depleted (given assumptions on the input parameters).

    Perform and report an analysis to demonstrate the sensitivity of the age at which funds will be depleted on the retirement age and the percent of annual salary contributed to retirement.

12. A few years back, Dave and Jana bought a new home. They borrowed $230,415 at a fixed rate of 5.49% (15-year term) with monthly payments of $1,881.46. They just made their twenty-fifth payment and the current balance on the loan is $208,555.87.

    Interest rates are at an all-time low and Dave and Jana are thinking of refinancing to a new 15-year fixed loan. Their bank has made the following offer: 15-year term, 3.8%, plus out-of-pocket costs of $2,937. The out-of-pocket costs must be paid in full at the time of refinancing.

    Build a spreadsheet model to evaluate this offer. The Excel function

$$=PMT(rate, nper, pv, fv, type)$$

calculates the payment for a loan based on constant payments and a constant interest rate. The arguments of this function are

*rate* = the interest rate for the loan

*nper* = the total number of payments

*pv* = present value—the amount borrowed

*fv* = future value—the desired cash balance after the last payment (usually 0)

*type* = payment type (0 = end of period, 1 = beginning of the period)

For example, for the Dave and Jana's original loan there will be 180 payments (12*15 = 180), so we would use =PMT(.0549/12,180,230415,0,0) = $1881.46. For payment calculations, we assume that the payment is made at the end of the month.

The savings from refinancing occur over time and therefore need to be discounted back to today's dollars. The formula for converting $K$ dollars saved $t$ months from now to today's dollars is:

$$\frac{K}{(1 + r)^{t-1}}$$

where $r$ is the monthly inflation rate. Assume $r = .002$.

Use your model to get the savings in today's dollars associated with the refinanced loan versus staying with the original loan.

Entries in the following table give the probability of $x$ successes in $n$ trials of a binomial experiment, where $p$ is the probability of a success on one trial. For example, with $n = 6$ trials and $p = 0.40$, the probability of $x = 2$ successes is 0.3110.

| $n$ | $x$ | 0.05 | 0.10 | 0.15 | 0.20 | 0.25 | 0.30 | 0.35 | 0.40 | 0.45 | 0.50 |
|---|---|---|---|---|---|---|---|---|---|---|---|
| 1 | 0 | 0.9500 | 0.9000 | 0.8500 | 0.8000 | 0.7500 | 0.7000 | 0.6500 | 0.6000 | 0.5500 | 0.5000 |
|   | 1 | 0.0500 | 0.1000 | 0.1500 | 0.2000 | 0.2500 | 0.3000 | 0.3500 | 0.4000 | 0.4500 | 0.5000 |
| 2 | 0 | 0.9025 | 0.8100 | 0.7225 | 0.6400 | 0.5625 | 0.4900 | 0.4225 | 0.3600 | 0.3025 | 0.2500 |
|   | 1 | 0.0950 | 0.1800 | 0.2550 | 0.3200 | 0.3750 | 0.4200 | 0.4550 | 0.4800 | 0.4950 | 0.5000 |
|   | 2 | 0.0025 | 0.0100 | 0.0225 | 0.0400 | 0.0625 | 0.0900 | 0.1225 | 0.1600 | 0.2025 | 0.2500 |
| 3 | 0 | 0.8574 | 0.7290 | 0.6141 | 0.5120 | 0.4219 | 0.3430 | 0.2746 | 0.2160 | 0.1664 | 0.1250 |
|   | 1 | 0.1354 | 0.2430 | 0.3251 | 0.3840 | 0.4219 | 0.4410 | 0.4436 | 0.4320 | 0.4084 | 0.3750 |
|   | 2 | 0.0071 | 0.0270 | 0.0574 | 0.0960 | 0.1406 | 0.1890 | 0.2389 | 0.2880 | 0.3341 | 0.3750 |
|   | 3 | 0.0001 | 0.0010 | 0.0034 | 0.0080 | 0.0156 | 0.0270 | 0.0429 | 0.0640 | 0.0911 | 0.1250 |
| 4 | 0 | 0.8145 | 0.6561 | 0.5220 | 0.4096 | 0.3164 | 0.2401 | 0.1785 | 0.1296 | 0.0915 | 0.0625 |
|   | 1 | 0.1715 | 0.2916 | 0.3685 | 0.4096 | 0.4219 | 0.4116 | 0.3845 | 0.3456 | 0.2995 | 0.2500 |
|   | 2 | 0.0135 | 0.0486 | 0.0975 | 0.1536 | 0.2109 | 0.2646 | 0.3105 | 0.3456 | 0.3675 | 0.3750 |
|   | 3 | 0.0005 | 0.0036 | 0.0115 | 0.0256 | 0.0469 | 0.0756 | 0.1115 | 0.1536 | 0.2005 | 0.2500 |
|   | 4 | 0.0000 | 0.0001 | 0.0005 | 0.0016 | 0.0039 | 0.0081 | 0.0150 | 0.0256 | 0.0410 | 0.0625 |
| 5 | 0 | 0.7738 | 0.5905 | 0.4437 | 0.3277 | 0.2373 | 0.1681 | 0.1160 | 0.0778 | 0.0503 | 0.0312 |
|   | 1 | 0.2036 | 0.3280 | 0.3915 | 0.4096 | 0.3955 | 0.3602 | 0.3124 | 0.2592 | 0.2059 | 0.1562 |
|   | 2 | 0.0214 | 0.0729 | 0.1382 | 0.2048 | 0.2637 | 0.3087 | 0.3364 | 0.3456 | 0.3369 | 0.3125 |
|   | 3 | 0.0011 | 0.0081 | 0.0244 | 0.0512 | 0.0879 | 0.1323 | 0.1811 | 0.2304 | 0.2757 | 0.3125 |
|   | 4 | 0.0000 | 0.0004 | 0.0022 | 0.0064 | 0.0146 | 0.0284 | 0.0488 | 0.0768 | 0.1128 | 0.1562 |
|   | 5 | 0.0000 | 0.0000 | 0.0001 | 0.0003 | 0.0010 | 0.0024 | 0.0053 | 0.0102 | 0.0185 | 0.0312 |
| 6 | 0 | 0.7351 | 0.5314 | 0.3771 | 0.2621 | 0.1780 | 0.1176 | 0.0754 | 0.0467 | 0.0277 | 0.0156 |
|   | 1 | 0.2321 | 0.3543 | 0.3993 | 0.3932 | 0.3560 | 0.3025 | 0.2437 | 0.1866 | 0.1359 | 0.0938 |
|   | 2 | 0.0305 | 0.0984 | 0.1762 | 0.2458 | 0.2966 | 0.3241 | 0.3280 | 0.3110 | 0.2780 | 0.2344 |
|   | 3 | 0.0021 | 0.0146 | 0.0415 | 0.0819 | 0.1318 | 0.1852 | 0.2355 | 0.2765 | 0.3032 | 0.3125 |
|   | 4 | 0.0001 | 0.0012 | 0.0055 | 0.0154 | 0.0330 | 0.0595 | 0.0951 | 0.1382 | 0.1861 | 0.2344 |
|   | 5 | 0.0000 | 0.0001 | 0.0004 | 0.0015 | 0.0044 | 0.0102 | 0.0205 | 0.0369 | 0.0609 | 0.0938 |
|   | 6 | 0.0000 | 0.0000 | 0.0000 | 0.0001 | 0.0002 | 0.0007 | 0.0018 | 0.0041 | 0.0083 | 0.0156 |
| 7 | 0 | 0.6983 | 0.4783 | 0.3206 | 0.2097 | 0.1335 | 0.0824 | 0.0490 | 0.0280 | 0.0152 | 0.0078 |
|   | 1 | 0.2573 | 0.3720 | 0.3960 | 0.3670 | 0.3115 | 0.2471 | 0.1848 | 0.1306 | 0.0872 | 0.0547 |
|   | 2 | 0.0406 | 0.1240 | 0.2097 | 0.2753 | 0.3115 | 0.3177 | 0.2985 | 0.2613 | 0.2140 | 0.1641 |
|   | 3 | 0.0036 | 0.0230 | 0.0617 | 0.1147 | 0.1730 | 0.2269 | 0.2679 | 0.2903 | 0.2918 | 0.2734 |
|   | 4 | 0.0002 | 0.0026 | 0.0109 | 0.0287 | 0.0577 | 0.0972 | 0.1442 | 0.1935 | 0.2388 | 0.2734 |
|   | 5 | 0.0000 | 0.0002 | 0.0012 | 0.0043 | 0.0115 | 0.0250 | 0.0466 | 0.0774 | 0.1172 | 0.1641 |
|   | 6 | 0.0000 | 0.0000 | 0.0001 | 0.0004 | 0.0013 | 0.0036 | 0.0084 | 0.0172 | 0.0320 | 0.0547 |
|   | 7 | 0.0000 | 0.0000 | 0.0000 | 0.0000 | 0.0001 | 0.0002 | 0.0006 | 0.0016 | 0.0037 | 0.0078 |

**Binomial Probabilities** (*Continued*)

| n | x | 0.05 | 0.10 | 0.15 | 0.20 | 0.25 | 0.30 | 0.35 | 0.40 | 0.45 | 0.50 |
|---|---|------|------|------|------|------|------|------|------|------|------|
| 8 | 0 | 0.6634 | 0.4305 | 0.2725 | 0.1678 | 0.1001 | 0.0576 | 0.0319 | 0.0168 | 0.0084 | 0.0039 |
|   | 1 | 0.2793 | 0.3826 | 0.3847 | 0.3355 | 0.2670 | 0.1977 | 0.1373 | 0.0896 | 0.0548 | 0.0312 |
|   | 2 | 0.0515 | 0.1488 | 0.2376 | 0.2936 | 0.3115 | 0.2965 | 0.2587 | 0.2090 | 0.1569 | 0.1094 |
|   | 3 | 0.0054 | 0.0331 | 0.0839 | 0.1468 | 0.2076 | 0.2541 | 0.2786 | 0.2787 | 0.2568 | 0.2188 |
|   | 4 | 0.0004 | 0.0046 | 0.0185 | 0.0459 | 0.0865 | 0.1361 | 0.1875 | 0.2322 | 0.2627 | 0.2734 |
|   | 5 | 0.0000 | 0.0004 | 0.0026 | 0.0092 | 0.0231 | 0.0467 | 0.0808 | 0.1239 | 0.1719 | 0.2188 |
|   | 6 | 0.0000 | 0.0000 | 0.0002 | 0.0011 | 0.0038 | 0.0100 | 0.0217 | 0.0413 | 0.0703 | 0.1094 |
|   | 7 | 0.0000 | 0.0000 | 0.0000 | 0.0001 | 0.0004 | 0.0012 | 0.0033 | 0.0079 | 0.0164 | 0.0312 |
|   | 8 | 0.0000 | 0.0000 | 0.0000 | 0.0000 | 0.0000 | 0.0001 | 0.0002 | 0.0007 | 0.0017 | 0.0039 |
| 9 | 0 | 0.6302 | 0.3874 | 0.2316 | 0.1342 | 0.0751 | 0.0404 | 0.0207 | 0.0101 | 0.0046 | 0.0020 |
|   | 1 | 0.2985 | 0.3874 | 0.3679 | 0.3020 | 0.2253 | 0.1556 | 0.1004 | 0.0605 | 0.0339 | 0.0176 |
|   | 2 | 0.0629 | 0.1722 | 0.2597 | 0.3020 | 0.3003 | 0.2668 | 0.2162 | 0.1612 | 0.1110 | 0.0703 |
|   | 3 | 0.0077 | 0.0446 | 0.1069 | 0.1762 | 0.2336 | 0.2668 | 0.2716 | 0.2508 | 0.2119 | 0.1641 |
|   | 4 | 0.0006 | 0.0074 | 0.0283 | 0.0661 | 0.1168 | 0.1715 | 0.2194 | 0.2508 | 0.2600 | 0.2461 |
|   | 5 | 0.0000 | 0.0008 | 0.0050 | 0.0165 | 0.0389 | 0.0735 | 0.1181 | 0.1672 | 0.2128 | 0.2461 |
|   | 6 | 0.0000 | 0.0001 | 0.0006 | 0.0028 | 0.0087 | 0.0210 | 0.0424 | 0.0743 | 0.1160 | 0.1641 |
|   | 7 | 0.0000 | 0.0000 | 0.0000 | 0.0003 | 0.0012 | 0.0039 | 0.0098 | 0.0212 | 0.0407 | 0.0703 |
|   | 8 | 0.0000 | 0.0000 | 0.0000 | 0.0000 | 0.0001 | 0.0004 | 0.0013 | 0.0035 | 0.0083 | 0.0176 |
|   | 9 | 0.0000 | 0.0000 | 0.0000 | 0.0000 | 0.0000 | 0.0000 | 0.0001 | 0.0003 | 0.0008 | 0.0020 |
| 10 | 0 | 0.5987 | 0.3487 | 0.1969 | 0.1074 | 0.0563 | 0.0282 | 0.0135 | 0.0060 | 0.0025 | 0.0010 |
|   | 1 | 0.3151 | 0.3874 | 0.3474 | 0.2684 | 0.1877 | 0.1211 | 0.0725 | 0.0403 | 0.0207 | 0.0098 |
|   | 2 | 0.0746 | 0.1937 | 0.2759 | 0.3020 | 0.2816 | 0.2335 | 0.1757 | 0.1209 | 0.0763 | 0.0439 |
|   | 3 | 0.0105 | 0.0574 | 0.1298 | 0.2013 | 0.2503 | 0.2668 | 0.2522 | 0.2150 | 0.1665 | 0.1172 |
|   | 4 | 0.0010 | 0.0112 | 0.0401 | 0.0881 | 0.1460 | 0.2001 | 0.2377 | 0.2508 | 0.2384 | 0.2051 |
|   | 5 | 0.0001 | 0.0015 | 0.0085 | 0.0264 | 0.0584 | 0.1029 | 0.1536 | 0.2007 | 0.2340 | 0.2461 |
|   | 6 | 0.0000 | 0.0001 | 0.0012 | 0.0055 | 0.0162 | 0.0368 | 0.0689 | 0.1115 | 0.1596 | 0.2051 |
|   | 7 | 0.0000 | 0.0000 | 0.0001 | 0.0008 | 0.0031 | 0.0090 | 0.0212 | 0.0425 | 0.0746 | 0.1172 |
|   | 8 | 0.0000 | 0.0000 | 0.0000 | 0.0001 | 0.0004 | 0.0014 | 0.0043 | 0.0106 | 0.0229 | 0.0439 |
|   | 9 | 0.0000 | 0.0000 | 0.0000 | 0.0000 | 0.0000 | 0.0001 | 0.0005 | 0.0016 | 0.0042 | 0.0098 |
|   | 10 | 0.0000 | 0.0000 | 0.0000 | 0.0000 | 0.0000 | 0.0000 | 0.0000 | 0.0001 | 0.0003 | 0.0010 |
| 12 | 0 | 0.5404 | 0.2824 | 0.1422 | 0.0687 | 0.0317 | 0.0138 | 0.0057 | 0.0022 | 0.0008 | 0.0002 |
|   | 1 | 0.3413 | 0.3766 | 0.3012 | 0.2062 | 0.1267 | 0.0712 | 0.0368 | 0.0174 | 0.0075 | 0.0029 |
|   | 2 | 0.0988 | 0.2301 | 0.2924 | 0.2835 | 0.2323 | 0.1678 | 0.1088 | 0.0639 | 0.0339 | 0.0161 |
|   | 3 | 0.0173 | 0.0853 | 0.1720 | 0.2362 | 0.2581 | 0.2397 | 0.1954 | 0.1419 | 0.0923 | 0.0537 |
|   | 4 | 0.0021 | 0.0213 | 0.0683 | 0.1329 | 0.1936 | 0.2311 | 0.2367 | 0.2128 | 0.1700 | 0.1208 |
|   | 5 | 0.0002 | 0.0038 | 0.0193 | 0.0532 | 0.1032 | 0.1585 | 0.2039 | 0.2270 | 0.2225 | 0.1934 |
|   | 6 | 0.0000 | 0.0005 | 0.0040 | 0.0155 | 0.0401 | 0.0792 | 0.1281 | 0.1766 | 0.2124 | 0.2256 |
|   | 7 | 0.0000 | 0.0000 | 0.0006 | 0.0033 | 0.0115 | 0.0291 | 0.0591 | 0.1009 | 0.1489 | 0.1934 |
|   | 8 | 0.0000 | 0.0000 | 0.0001 | 0.0005 | 0.0024 | 0.0078 | 0.0199 | 0.0420 | 0.0762 | 0.1208 |
|   | 9 | 0.0000 | 0.0000 | 0.0000 | 0.0001 | 0.0004 | 0.0015 | 0.0048 | 0.0125 | 0.0277 | 0.0537 |
|   | 10 | 0.0000 | 0.0000 | 0.0000 | 0.0000 | 0.0000 | 0.0002 | 0.0008 | 0.0025 | 0.0068 | 0.0161 |
|   | 11 | 0.0000 | 0.0000 | 0.0000 | 0.0000 | 0.0000 | 0.0000 | 0.0001 | 0.0003 | 0.0010 | 0.0029 |
|   | 12 | 0.0000 | 0.0000 | 0.0000 | 0.0000 | 0.0000 | 0.0000 | 0.0000 | 0.0000 | 0.0001 | 0.0002 |
| 15 | 0 | 0.4633 | 0.2059 | 0.0874 | 0.0352 | 0.0134 | 0.0047 | 0.0016 | 0.0005 | 0.0001 | 0.0000 |
|   | 1 | 0.3658 | 0.3432 | 0.2312 | 0.1319 | 0.0668 | 0.0305 | 0.0126 | 0.0047 | 0.0016 | 0.0005 |
|   | 2 | 0.1348 | 0.2669 | 0.2856 | 0.2309 | 0.1559 | 0.0916 | 0.0476 | 0.0219 | 0.0090 | 0.0032 |

**Binomial Probabilities** (*Continued*)

| n | x | 0.05 | 0.10 | 0.15 | 0.20 | 0.25 | 0.30 | 0.35 | 0.40 | 0.45 | 0.50 |
|---|---|------|------|------|------|------|------|------|------|------|------|
|   | 3  | 0.0307 | 0.1285 | 0.2184 | 0.2501 | 0.2252 | 0.1700 | 0.1110 | 0.0634 | 0.0318 | 0.0139 |
|   | 4  | 0.0049 | 0.0428 | 0.1156 | 0.1876 | 0.2252 | 0.2186 | 0.1792 | 0.1268 | 0.0780 | 0.0417 |
|   | 5  | 0.0006 | 0.0105 | 0.0449 | 0.1032 | 0.1651 | 0.2061 | 0.2123 | 0.1859 | 0.1404 | 0.0916 |
|   | 6  | 0.0000 | 0.0019 | 0.0132 | 0.0430 | 0.0917 | 0.1472 | 0.1906 | 0.2066 | 0.1914 | 0.1527 |
|   | 7  | 0.0000 | 0.0003 | 0.0030 | 0.0138 | 0.0393 | 0.0811 | 0.1319 | 0.1771 | 0.2013 | 0.1964 |
|   | 8  | 0.0000 | 0.0000 | 0.0005 | 0.0035 | 0.0131 | 0.0348 | 0.0710 | 0.1181 | 0.1647 | 0.1964 |
|   | 9  | 0.0000 | 0.0000 | 0.0001 | 0.0007 | 0.0034 | 0.0116 | 0.0298 | 0.0612 | 0.1048 | 0.1527 |
|   | 10 | 0.0000 | 0.0000 | 0.0000 | 0.0001 | 0.0007 | 0.0030 | 0.0096 | 0.0245 | 0.0515 | 0.0916 |
|   | 11 | 0.0000 | 0.0000 | 0.0000 | 0.0000 | 0.0001 | 0.0006 | 0.0024 | 0.0074 | 0.0191 | 0.0417 |
|   | 12 | 0.0000 | 0.0000 | 0.0000 | 0.0000 | 0.0000 | 0.0001 | 0.0004 | 0.0016 | 0.0052 | 0.0139 |
|   | 13 | 0.0000 | 0.0000 | 0.0000 | 0.0000 | 0.0000 | 0.0000 | 0.0001 | 0.0003 | 0.0010 | 0.0032 |
|   | 14 | 0.0000 | 0.0000 | 0.0000 | 0.0000 | 0.0000 | 0.0000 | 0.0000 | 0.0000 | 0.0001 | 0.0005 |
|   | 15 | 0.0000 | 0.0000 | 0.0000 | 0.0000 | 0.0000 | 0.0000 | 0.0000 | 0.0000 | 0.0000 | 0.0000 |
| 18 | 0  | 0.3972 | 0.1501 | 0.0536 | 0.0180 | 0.0056 | 0.0016 | 0.0004 | 0.0001 | 0.0000 | 0.0000 |
|   | 1  | 0.3763 | 0.3002 | 0.1704 | 0.0811 | 0.0338 | 0.0126 | 0.0042 | 0.0012 | 0.0003 | 0.0001 |
|   | 2  | 0.1683 | 0.2835 | 0.2556 | 0.1723 | 0.0958 | 0.0458 | 0.0190 | 0.0069 | 0.0022 | 0.0006 |
|   | 3  | 0.0473 | 0.1680 | 0.2406 | 0.2297 | 0.1704 | 0.1046 | 0.0547 | 0.0246 | 0.0095 | 0.0031 |
|   | 4  | 0.0093 | 0.0700 | 0.1592 | 0.2153 | 0.2130 | 0.1681 | 0.1104 | 0.0614 | 0.0291 | 0.0117 |
|   | 5  | 0.0014 | 0.0218 | 0.0787 | 0.1507 | 0.1988 | 0.2017 | 0.1664 | 0.1146 | 0.0666 | 0.0327 |
|   | 6  | 0.0002 | 0.0052 | 0.0301 | 0.0816 | 0.1436 | 0.1873 | 0.1941 | 0.1655 | 0.1181 | 0.0708 |
|   | 7  | 0.0000 | 0.0010 | 0.0091 | 0.0350 | 0.0820 | 0.1376 | 0.1792 | 0.1892 | 0.1657 | 0.1214 |
|   | 8  | 0.0000 | 0.0002 | 0.0022 | 0.0120 | 0.0376 | 0.0811 | 0.1327 | 0.1734 | 0.1864 | 0.1669 |
|   | 9  | 0.0000 | 0.0000 | 0.0004 | 0.0033 | 0.0139 | 0.0386 | 0.0794 | 0.1284 | 0.1694 | 0.1855 |
|   | 10 | 0.0000 | 0.0000 | 0.0001 | 0.0008 | 0.0042 | 0.0149 | 0.0385 | 0.0771 | 0.1248 | 0.1669 |
|   | 11 | 0.0000 | 0.0000 | 0.0000 | 0.0001 | 0.0010 | 0.0046 | 0.0151 | 0.0374 | 0.0742 | 0.1214 |
|   | 12 | 0.0000 | 0.0000 | 0.0000 | 0.0000 | 0.0002 | 0.0012 | 0.0047 | 0.0145 | 0.0354 | 0.0708 |
|   | 13 | 0.0000 | 0.0000 | 0.0000 | 0.0000 | 0.0000 | 0.0002 | 0.0012 | 0.0045 | 0.0134 | 0.0327 |
|   | 14 | 0.0000 | 0.0000 | 0.0000 | 0.0000 | 0.0000 | 0.0000 | 0.0002 | 0.0011 | 0.0039 | 0.0117 |
|   | 15 | 0.0000 | 0.0000 | 0.0000 | 0.0000 | 0.0000 | 0.0000 | 0.0000 | 0.0002 | 0.0009 | 0.0031 |
|   | 16 | 0.0000 | 0.0000 | 0.0000 | 0.0000 | 0.0000 | 0.0000 | 0.0000 | 0.0000 | 0.0001 | 0.0006 |
|   | 17 | 0.0000 | 0.0000 | 0.0000 | 0.0000 | 0.0000 | 0.0000 | 0.0000 | 0.0000 | 0.0000 | 0.0001 |
|   | 18 | 0.0000 | 0.0000 | 0.0000 | 0.0000 | 0.0000 | 0.0000 | 0.0000 | 0.0000 | 0.0000 | 0.0000 |
| 20 | 0  | 0.3585 | 0.1216 | 0.0388 | 0.0115 | 0.0032 | 0.0008 | 0.0002 | 0.0000 | 0.0000 | 0.0000 |
|   | 1  | 0.3774 | 0.2702 | 0.1368 | 0.0576 | 0.0211 | 0.0068 | 0.0020 | 0.0005 | 0.0001 | 0.0000 |
|   | 2  | 0.1887 | 0.2852 | 0.2293 | 0.1369 | 0.0669 | 0.0278 | 0.0100 | 0.0031 | 0.0008 | 0.0002 |
|   | 3  | 0.0596 | 0.1901 | 0.2428 | 0.2054 | 0.1339 | 0.0716 | 0.0323 | 0.0123 | 0.0040 | 0.0011 |
|   | 4  | 0.0133 | 0.0898 | 0.1821 | 0.2182 | 0.1897 | 0.1304 | 0.0738 | 0.0350 | 0.0139 | 0.0046 |
|   | 5  | 0.0022 | 0.0319 | 0.1028 | 0.1746 | 0.2023 | 0.1789 | 0.1272 | 0.0746 | 0.0365 | 0.0148 |
|   | 6  | 0.0003 | 0.0089 | 0.0454 | 0.1091 | 0.1686 | 0.1916 | 0.1712 | 0.1244 | 0.0746 | 0.0370 |
|   | 7  | 0.0000 | 0.0020 | 0.0160 | 0.0545 | 0.1124 | 0.1643 | 0.1844 | 0.1659 | 0.1221 | 0.0739 |
|   | 8  | 0.0000 | 0.0004 | 0.0046 | 0.0222 | 0.0609 | 0.1144 | 0.1614 | 0.1797 | 0.1623 | 0.1201 |
|   | 9  | 0.0000 | 0.0001 | 0.0011 | 0.0074 | 0.0271 | 0.0654 | 0.1158 | 0.1597 | 0.1771 | 0.1602 |
|   | 10 | 0.0000 | 0.0000 | 0.0002 | 0.0020 | 0.0099 | 0.0308 | 0.0686 | 0.1171 | 0.1593 | 0.1762 |
|   | 11 | 0.0000 | 0.0000 | 0.0000 | 0.0005 | 0.0030 | 0.0120 | 0.0336 | 0.0710 | 0.1185 | 0.1602 |
|   | 12 | 0.0000 | 0.0000 | 0.0000 | 0.0001 | 0.0008 | 0.0039 | 0.0136 | 0.0355 | 0.0727 | 0.1201 |
|   | 13 | 0.0000 | 0.0000 | 0.0000 | 0.0000 | 0.0002 | 0.0010 | 0.0045 | 0.0146 | 0.0366 | 0.0739 |
|   | 14 | 0.0000 | 0.0000 | 0.0000 | 0.0000 | 0.0000 | 0.0002 | 0.0012 | 0.0049 | 0.0150 | 0.0370 |

**Binomial Probabilities** (*Continued*)

| *n* | *x* | 0.05 | 0.10 | 0.15 | 0.20 | 0.25 | 0.30 | 0.35 | 0.40 | 0.45 | 0.50 |
|---|---|---|---|---|---|---|---|---|---|---|---|
| | | | | | | *p* | | | | | |
| | 15 | 0.0000 | 0.0000 | 0.0000 | 0.0000 | 0.0000 | 0.0000 | 0.0003 | 0.0013 | 0.0049 | 0.0148 |
| | 16 | 0.0000 | 0.0000 | 0.0000 | 0.0000 | 0.0000 | 0.0000 | 0.0000 | 0.0003 | 0.0013 | 0.0046 |
| | 17 | 0.0000 | 0.0000 | 0.0000 | 0.0000 | 0.0000 | 0.0000 | 0.0000 | 0.0000 | 0.0002 | 0.0011 |
| | 18 | 0.0000 | 0.0000 | 0.0000 | 0.0000 | 0.0000 | 0.0000 | 0.0000 | 0.0000 | 0.0000 | 0.0002 |
| | 19 | 0.0000 | 0.0000 | 0.0000 | 0.0000 | 0.0000 | 0.0000 | 0.0000 | 0.0000 | 0.0000 | 0.0000 |
| | 20 | 0.0000 | 0.0000 | 0.0000 | 0.0000 | 0.0000 | 0.0000 | 0.0000 | 0.0000 | 0.0000 | 0.0000 |

**Binomial Probabilities (*Continued*)**

| n | x | p 0.55 | 0.60 | 0.65 | 0.70 | 0.75 | 0.80 | 0.85 | 0.90 | 0.95 |
|---|---|--------|------|------|------|------|------|------|------|------|
| 2 | 0 | 0.2025 | 0.1600 | 0.1225 | 0.0900 | 0.0625 | 0.0400 | 0.0225 | 0.0100 | 0.0025 |
|   | 1 | 0.4950 | 0.4800 | 0.4550 | 0.4200 | 0.3750 | 0.3200 | 0.2550 | 0.1800 | 0.0950 |
|   | 2 | 0.3025 | 0.3600 | 0.4225 | 0.4900 | 0.5625 | 0.6400 | 0.7225 | 0.8100 | 0.9025 |
| 3 | 0 | 0.0911 | 0.0640 | 0.0429 | 0.0270 | 0.0156 | 0.0080 | 0.0034 | 0.0010 | 0.0001 |
|   | 1 | 0.3341 | 0.2880 | 0.2389 | 0.1890 | 0.1406 | 0.0960 | 0.0574 | 0.0270 | 0.0071 |
|   | 2 | 0.4084 | 0.4320 | 0.4436 | 0.4410 | 0.4219 | 0.3840 | 0.3251 | 0.2430 | 0.1354 |
|   | 3 | 0.1664 | 0.2160 | 0.2746 | 0.3430 | 0.4219 | 0.5120 | 0.6141 | 0.7290 | 0.8574 |
| 4 | 0 | 0.0410 | 0.0256 | 0.0150 | 0.0081 | 0.0039 | 0.0016 | 0.0005 | 0.0001 | 0.0000 |
|   | 1 | 0.2005 | 0.1536 | 0.1115 | 0.0756 | 0.0469 | 0.0256 | 0.0115 | 0.0036 | 0.0005 |
|   | 2 | 0.3675 | 0.3456 | 0.3105 | 0.2646 | 0.2109 | 0.1536 | 0.0975 | 0.0486 | 0.0135 |
|   | 3 | 0.2995 | 0.3456 | 0.3845 | 0.4116 | 0.4219 | 0.4096 | 0.3685 | 0.2916 | 0.1715 |
|   | 4 | 0.0915 | 0.1296 | 0.1785 | 0.2401 | 0.3164 | 0.4096 | 0.5220 | 0.6561 | 0.8145 |
| 5 | 0 | 0.0185 | 0.0102 | 0.0053 | 0.0024 | 0.0010 | 0.0003 | 0.0001 | 0.0000 | 0.0000 |
|   | 1 | 0.1128 | 0.0768 | 0.0488 | 0.0284 | 0.0146 | 0.0064 | 0.0022 | 0.0005 | 0.0000 |
|   | 2 | 0.2757 | 0.2304 | 0.1811 | 0.1323 | 0.0879 | 0.0512 | 0.0244 | 0.0081 | 0.0011 |
|   | 3 | 0.3369 | 0.3456 | 0.3364 | 0.3087 | 0.2637 | 0.2048 | 0.1382 | 0.0729 | 0.0214 |
|   | 4 | 0.2059 | 0.2592 | 0.3124 | 0.3601 | 0.3955 | 0.4096 | 0.3915 | 0.3281 | 0.2036 |
|   | 5 | 0.0503 | 0.0778 | 0.1160 | 0.1681 | 0.2373 | 0.3277 | 0.4437 | 0.5905 | 0.7738 |
| 6 | 0 | 0.0083 | 0.0041 | 0.0018 | 0.0007 | 0.0002 | 0.0001 | 0.0000 | 0.0000 | 0.0000 |
|   | 1 | 0.0609 | 0.0369 | 0.0205 | 0.0102 | 0.0044 | 0.0015 | 0.0004 | 0.0001 | 0.0000 |
|   | 2 | 0.1861 | 0.1382 | 0.0951 | 0.0595 | 0.0330 | 0.0154 | 0.0055 | 0.0012 | 0.0001 |
|   | 3 | 0.3032 | 0.2765 | 0.2355 | 0.1852 | 0.1318 | 0.0819 | 0.0415 | 0.0146 | 0.0021 |
|   | 4 | 0.2780 | 0.3110 | 0.3280 | 0.3241 | 0.2966 | 0.2458 | 0.1762 | 0.0984 | 0.0305 |
|   | 5 | 0.1359 | 0.1866 | 0.2437 | 0.3025 | 0.3560 | 0.3932 | 0.3993 | 0.3543 | 0.2321 |
|   | 6 | 0.0277 | 0.0467 | 0.0754 | 0.1176 | 0.1780 | 0.2621 | 0.3771 | 0.5314 | 0.7351 |
| 7 | 0 | 0.0037 | 0.0016 | 0.0006 | 0.0002 | 0.0001 | 0.0000 | 0.0000 | 0.0000 | 0.0000 |
|   | 1 | 0.0320 | 0.0172 | 0.0084 | 0.0036 | 0.0013 | 0.0004 | 0.0001 | 0.0000 | 0.0000 |
|   | 2 | 0.1172 | 0.0774 | 0.0466 | 0.0250 | 0.0115 | 0.0043 | 0.0012 | 0.0002 | 0.0000 |
|   | 3 | 0.2388 | 0.1935 | 0.1442 | 0.0972 | 0.0577 | 0.0287 | 0.0109 | 0.0026 | 0.0002 |
|   | 4 | 0.2918 | 0.2903 | 0.2679 | 0.2269 | 0.1730 | 0.1147 | 0.0617 | 0.0230 | 0.0036 |
|   | 5 | 0.2140 | 0.2613 | 0.2985 | 0.3177 | 0.3115 | 0.2753 | 0.2097 | 0.1240 | 0.0406 |
|   | 6 | 0.0872 | 0.1306 | 0.1848 | 0.2471 | 0.3115 | 0.3670 | 0.3960 | 0.3720 | 0.2573 |
|   | 7 | 0.0152 | 0.0280 | 0.0490 | 0.0824 | 0.1335 | 0.2097 | 0.3206 | 0.4783 | 0.6983 |
| 8 | 0 | 0.0017 | 0.0007 | 0.0002 | 0.0001 | 0.0000 | 0.0000 | 0.0000 | 0.0000 | 0.0000 |
|   | 1 | 0.0164 | 0.0079 | 0.0033 | 0.0012 | 0.0004 | 0.0001 | 0.0000 | 0.0000 | 0.0000 |
|   | 2 | 0.0703 | 0.0413 | 0.0217 | 0.0100 | 0.0038 | 0.0011 | 0.0002 | 0.0000 | 0.0000 |
|   | 3 | 0.1719 | 0.1239 | 0.0808 | 0.0467 | 0.0231 | 0.0092 | 0.0026 | 0.0004 | 0.0000 |
|   | 4 | 0.2627 | 0.2322 | 0.1875 | 0.1361 | 0.0865 | 0.0459 | 0.0185 | 0.0046 | 0.0004 |
|   | 5 | 0.2568 | 0.2787 | 0.2786 | 0.2541 | 0.2076 | 0.1468 | 0.0839 | 0.0331 | 0.0054 |
|   | 6 | 0.1569 | 0.2090 | 0.2587 | 0.2965 | 0.3115 | 0.2936 | 0.2376 | 0.1488 | 0.0515 |
|   | 7 | 0.0548 | 0.0896 | 0.1373 | 0.1977 | 0.2670 | 0.3355 | 0.3847 | 0.3826 | 0.2793 |
|   | 8 | 0.0084 | 0.0168 | 0.0319 | 0.0576 | 0.1001 | 0.1678 | 0.2725 | 0.4305 | 0.6634 |

**Binomial Probabilities** (*Continued*)

| | | | | | | *p* | | | | |
|---|---|---|---|---|---|---|---|---|---|---|
| *n* | *x* | 0.55 | 0.60 | 0.65 | 0.70 | 0.75 | 0.80 | 0.85 | 0.90 | 0.95 |
| 9 | 0 | 0.0008 | 0.0003 | 0.0001 | 0.0000 | 0.0000 | 0.0000 | 0.0000 | 0.0000 | 0.0000 |
| | 1 | 0.0083 | 0.0035 | 0.0013 | 0.0004 | 0.0001 | 0.0000 | 0.0000 | 0.0000 | 0.0000 |
| | 2 | 0.0407 | 0.0212 | 0.0098 | 0.0039 | 0.0012 | 0.0003 | 0.0000 | 0.0000 | 0.0000 |
| | 3 | 0.1160 | 0.0743 | 0.0424 | 0.0210 | 0.0087 | 0.0028 | 0.0006 | 0.0001 | 0.0000 |
| | 4 | 0.2128 | 0.1672 | 0.1181 | 0.0735 | 0.0389 | 0.0165 | 0.0050 | 0.0008 | 0.0000 |
| | 5 | 0.2600 | 0.2508 | 0.2194 | 0.1715 | 0.1168 | 0.0661 | 0.0283 | 0.0074 | 0.0006 |
| | 6 | 0.2119 | 0.2508 | 0.2716 | 0.2668 | 0.2336 | 0.1762 | 0.1069 | 0.0446 | 0.0077 |
| | 7 | 0.1110 | 0.1612 | 0.2162 | 0.2668 | 0.3003 | 0.3020 | 0.2597 | 0.1722 | 0.0629 |
| | 8 | 0.0339 | 0.0605 | 0.1004 | 0.1556 | 0.2253 | 0.3020 | 0.3679 | 0.3874 | 0.2985 |
| | 9 | 0.0046 | 0.0101 | 0.0207 | 0.0404 | 0.0751 | 0.1342 | 0.2316 | 0.3874 | 0.6302 |
| 10 | 0 | 0.0003 | 0.0001 | 0.0000 | 0.0000 | 0.0000 | 0.0000 | 0.0000 | 0.0000 | 0.0000 |
| | 1 | 0.0042 | 0.0016 | 0.0005 | 0.0001 | 0.0000 | 0.0000 | 0.0000 | 0.0000 | 0.0000 |
| | 2 | 0.0229 | 0.0106 | 0.0043 | 0.0014 | 0.0004 | 0.0001 | 0.0000 | 0.0000 | 0.0000 |
| | 3 | 0.0746 | 0.0425 | 0.0212 | 0.0090 | 0.0031 | 0.0008 | 0.0001 | 0.0000 | 0.0000 |
| | 4 | 0.1596 | 0.1115 | 0.0689 | 0.0368 | 0.0162 | 0.0055 | 0.0012 | 0.0001 | 0.0000 |
| | 5 | 0.2340 | 0.2007 | 0.1536 | 0.1029 | 0.0584 | 0.0264 | 0.0085 | 0.0015 | 0.0001 |
| | 6 | 0.2384 | 0.2508 | 0.2377 | 0.2001 | 0.1460 | 0.0881 | 0.0401 | 0.0112 | 0.0010 |
| | 7 | 0.1665 | 0.2150 | 0.2522 | 0.2668 | 0.2503 | 0.2013 | 0.1298 | 0.0574 | 0.0105 |
| | 8 | 0.0763 | 0.1209 | 0.1757 | 0.2335 | 0.2816 | 0.3020 | 0.2759 | 0.1937 | 0.0746 |
| | 9 | 0.0207 | 0.0403 | 0.0725 | 0.1211 | 0.1877 | 0.2684 | 0.3474 | 0.3874 | 0.3151 |
| | 10 | 0.0025 | 0.0060 | 0.0135 | 0.0282 | 0.0563 | 0.1074 | 0.1969 | 0.3487 | 0.5987 |
| 12 | 0 | 0.0001 | 0.0000 | 0.0000 | 0.0000 | 0.0000 | 0.0000 | 0.0000 | 0.0000 | 0.0000 |
| | 1 | 0.0010 | 0.0003 | 0.0001 | 0.0000 | 0.0000 | 0.0000 | 0.0000 | 0.0000 | 0.0000 |
| | 2 | 0.0068 | 0.0025 | 0.0008 | 0.0002 | 0.0000 | 0.0000 | 0.0000 | 0.0000 | 0.0000 |
| | 3 | 0.0277 | 0.0125 | 0.0048 | 0.0015 | 0.0004 | 0.0001 | 0.0000 | 0.0000 | 0.0000 |
| | 4 | 0.0762 | 0.0420 | 0.0199 | 0.0078 | 0.0024 | 0.0005 | 0.0001 | 0.0000 | 0.0000 |
| | 5 | 0.1489 | 0.1009 | 0.0591 | 0.0291 | 0.0115 | 0.0033 | 0.0006 | 0.0000 | 0.0000 |
| | 6 | 0.2124 | 0.1766 | 0.1281 | 0.0792 | 0.0401 | 0.0155 | 0.0040 | 0.0005 | 0.0000 |
| | 7 | 0.2225 | 0.2270 | 0.2039 | 0.1585 | 0.1032 | 0.0532 | 0.0193 | 0.0038 | 0.0002 |
| | 8 | 0.1700 | 0.2128 | 0.2367 | 0.2311 | 0.1936 | 0.1329 | 0.0683 | 0.0213 | 0.0021 |
| | 9 | 0.0923 | 0.1419 | 0.1954 | 0.2397 | 0.2581 | 0.2362 | 0.1720 | 0.0852 | 0.0173 |
| | 10 | 0.0339 | 0.0639 | 0.1088 | 0.1678 | 0.2323 | 0.2835 | 0.2924 | 0.2301 | 0.0988 |
| | 11 | 0.0075 | 0.0174 | 0.0368 | 0.0712 | 0.1267 | 0.2062 | 0.3012 | 0.3766 | 0.3413 |
| | 12 | 0.0008 | 0.0022 | 0.0057 | 0.0138 | 0.0317 | 0.0687 | 0.1422 | 0.2824 | 0.5404 |
| 15 | 0 | 0.0000 | 0.0000 | 0.0000 | 0.0000 | 0.0000 | 0.0000 | 0.0000 | 0.0000 | 0.0000 |
| | 1 | 0.0001 | 0.0000 | 0.0000 | 0.0000 | 0.0000 | 0.0000 | 0.0000 | 0.0000 | 0.0000 |
| | 2 | 0.0010 | 0.0003 | 0.0001 | 0.0000 | 0.0000 | 0.0000 | 0.0000 | 0.0000 | 0.0000 |
| | 3 | 0.0052 | 0.0016 | 0.0004 | 0.0001 | 0.0000 | 0.0000 | 0.0000 | 0.0000 | 0.0000 |
| | 4 | 0.0191 | 0.0074 | 0.0024 | 0.0006 | 0.0001 | 0.0000 | 0.0000 | 0.0000 | 0.0000 |
| | 5 | 0.0515 | 0.0245 | 0.0096 | 0.0030 | 0.0007 | 0.0001 | 0.0000 | 0.0000 | 0.0000 |
| | 6 | 0.1048 | 0.0612 | 0.0298 | 0.0116 | 0.0034 | 0.0007 | 0.0001 | 0.0000 | 0.0000 |
| | 7 | 0.1647 | 0.1181 | 0.0710 | 0.0348 | 0.0131 | 0.0035 | 0.0005 | 0.0000 | 0.0000 |
| | 8 | 0.2013 | 0.1771 | 0.1319 | 0.0811 | 0.0393 | 0.0138 | 0.0030 | 0.0003 | 0.0000 |
| | 9 | 0.1914 | 0.2066 | 0.1906 | 0.1472 | 0.0917 | 0.0430 | 0.0132 | 0.0019 | 0.0000 |
| | 10 | 0.1404 | 0.1859 | 0.2123 | 0.2061 | 0.1651 | 0.1032 | 0.0449 | 0.0105 | 0.0006 |
| | 11 | 0.0780 | 0.1268 | 0.1792 | 0.2186 | 0.2252 | 0.1876 | 0.1156 | 0.0428 | 0.0049 |

**Binomial Probabilities** (*Continued*)

| n | x | 0.55 | 0.60 | 0.65 | 0.70 | 0.75 | 0.80 | 0.85 | 0.90 | 0.95 |
|---|---|------|------|------|------|------|------|------|------|------|
| | | | | | | *p* | | | | |
| | 12 | 0.0318 | 0.0634 | 0.1110 | 0.1700 | 0.2252 | 0.2501 | 0.2184 | 0.1285 | 0.0307 |
| | 13 | 0.0090 | 0.0219 | 0.0476 | 0.0916 | 0.1559 | 0.2309 | 0.2856 | 0.2669 | 0.1348 |
| | 14 | 0.0016 | 0.0047 | 0.0126 | 0.0305 | 0.0668 | 0.1319 | 0.2312 | 0.3432 | 0.3658 |
| | 15 | 0.0001 | 0.0005 | 0.0016 | 0.0047 | 0.0134 | 0.0352 | 0.0874 | 0.2059 | 0.4633 |
| 18 | 0 | 0.0000 | 0.0000 | 0.0000 | 0.0000 | 0.0000 | 0.0000 | 0.0000 | 0.0000 | 0.0000 |
| | 1 | 0.0000 | 0.0000 | 0.0000 | 0.0000 | 0.0000 | 0.0000 | 0.0000 | 0.0000 | 0.0000 |
| | 2 | 0.0001 | 0.0000 | 0.0000 | 0.0000 | 0.0000 | 0.0000 | 0.0000 | 0.0000 | 0.0000 |
| | 3 | 0.0009 | 0.0002 | 0.0000 | 0.0000 | 0.0000 | 0.0000 | 0.0000 | 0.0000 | 0.0000 |
| | 4 | 0.0039 | 0.0011 | 0.0002 | 0.0000 | 0.0000 | 0.0000 | 0.0000 | 0.0000 | 0.0000 |
| | 5 | 0.0134 | 0.0045 | 0.0012 | 0.0002 | 0.0000 | 0.0000 | 0.0000 | 0.0000 | 0.0000 |
| | 6 | 0.0354 | 0.0145 | 0.0047 | 0.0012 | 0.0002 | 0.0000 | 0.0000 | 0.0000 | 0.0000 |
| | 7 | 0.0742 | 0.0374 | 0.0151 | 0.0046 | 0.0010 | 0.0001 | 0.0000 | 0.0000 | 0.0000 |
| | 8 | 0.1248 | 0.0771 | 0.0385 | 0.0149 | 0.0042 | 0.0008 | 0.0001 | 0.0000 | 0.0000 |
| | 9 | 0.1694 | 0.1284 | 0.0794 | 0.0386 | 0.0139 | 0.0033 | 0.0004 | 0.0000 | 0.0000 |
| | 10 | 0.1864 | 0.1734 | 0.1327 | 0.0811 | 0.0376 | 0.0120 | 0.0022 | 0.0002 | 0.0000 |
| | 11 | 0.1657 | 0.1892 | 0.1792 | 0.1376 | 0.0820 | 0.0350 | 0.0091 | 0.0010 | 0.0000 |
| | 12 | 0.1181 | 0.1655 | 0.1941 | 0.1873 | 0.1436 | 0.0816 | 0.0301 | 0.0052 | 0.0002 |
| | 13 | 0.0666 | 0.1146 | 0.1664 | 0.2017 | 0.1988 | 0.1507 | 0.0787 | 0.0218 | 0.0014 |
| | 14 | 0.0291 | 0.0614 | 0.1104 | 0.1681 | 0.2130 | 0.2153 | 0.1592 | 0.0700 | 0.0093 |
| | 15 | 0.0095 | 0.0246 | 0.0547 | 0.1046 | 0.1704 | 0.2297 | 0.2406 | 0.1680 | 0.0473 |
| | 16 | 0.0022 | 0.0069 | 0.0190 | 0.0458 | 0.0958 | 0.1723 | 0.2556 | 0.2835 | 0.1683 |
| | 17 | 0.0003 | 0.0012 | 0.0042 | 0.0126 | 0.0338 | 0.0811 | 0.1704 | 0.3002 | 0.3763 |
| | 18 | 0.0000 | 0.0001 | 0.0004 | 0.0016 | 0.0056 | 0.0180 | 0.0536 | 0.1501 | 0.3972 |
| 20 | 0 | 0.0000 | 0.0000 | 0.0000 | 0.0000 | 0.0000 | 0.0000 | 0.0000 | 0.0000 | 0.0000 |
| | 1 | 0.0000 | 0.0000 | 0.0000 | 0.0000 | 0.0000 | 0.0000 | 0.0000 | 0.0000 | 0.0000 |
| | 2 | 0.0000 | 0.0000 | 0.0000 | 0.0000 | 0.0000 | 0.0000 | 0.0000 | 0.0000 | 0.0000 |
| | 3 | 0.0002 | 0.0000 | 0.0000 | 0.0000 | 0.0000 | 0.0000 | 0.0000 | 0.0000 | 0.0000 |
| | 4 | 0.0013 | 0.0003 | 0.0000 | 0.0000 | 0.0000 | 0.0000 | 0.0000 | 0.0000 | 0.0000 |
| | 5 | 0.0049 | 0.0013 | 0.0003 | 0.0000 | 0.0000 | 0.0000 | 0.0000 | 0.0000 | 0.0000 |
| | 6 | 0.0150 | 0.0049 | 0.0012 | 0.0002 | 0.0000 | 0.0000 | 0.0000 | 0.0000 | 0.0000 |
| | 7 | 0.0366 | 0.0146 | 0.0045 | 0.0010 | 0.0002 | 0.0000 | 0.0000 | 0.0000 | 0.0000 |
| | 8 | 0.0727 | 0.0355 | 0.0136 | 0.0039 | 0.0008 | 0.0001 | 0.0000 | 0.0000 | 0.0000 |
| | 9 | 0.1185 | 0.0710 | 0.0336 | 0.0120 | 0.0030 | 0.0005 | 0.0000 | 0.0000 | 0.0000 |
| | 10 | 0.1593 | 0.1171 | 0.0686 | 0.0308 | 0.0099 | 0.0020 | 0.0002 | 0.0000 | 0.0000 |
| | 11 | 0.1771 | 0.1597 | 0.1158 | 0.0654 | 0.0271 | 0.0074 | 0.0011 | 0.0001 | 0.0000 |
| | 12 | 0.1623 | 0.1797 | 0.1614 | 0.1144 | 0.0609 | 0.0222 | 0.0046 | 0.0004 | 0.0000 |
| | 13 | 0.1221 | 0.1659 | 0.1844 | 0.1643 | 0.1124 | 0.0545 | 0.0160 | 0.0020 | 0.0000 |
| | 14 | 0.0746 | 0.1244 | 0.1712 | 0.1916 | 0.1686 | 0.1091 | 0.0454 | 0.0089 | 0.0003 |
| | 15 | 0.0365 | 0.0746 | 0.1272 | 0.1789 | 0.2023 | 0.1746 | 0.1028 | 0.0319 | 0.0022 |
| | 16 | 0.0139 | 0.0350 | 0.0738 | 0.1304 | 0.1897 | 0.2182 | 0.1821 | 0.0898 | 0.0133 |
| | 17 | 0.0040 | 0.0123 | 0.0323 | 0.0716 | 0.1339 | 0.2054 | 0.2428 | 0.1901 | 0.0596 |
| | 18 | 0.0008 | 0.0031 | 0.0100 | 0.0278 | 0.0669 | 0.1369 | 0.2293 | 0.2852 | 0.1887 |
| | 19 | 0.0001 | 0.0005 | 0.0020 | 0.0068 | 0.0211 | 0.0576 | 0.1368 | 0.2702 | 0.3774 |
| | 20 | 0.0000 | 0.0000 | 0.0002 | 0.0008 | 0.0032 | 0.0115 | 0.0388 | 0.1216 | 0.3585 |

# Appendix C    Poisson Probabilities

Entries in the following table give the probability of $x$ occurrences for a Poisson process with a mean $\lambda$. For example, when $\lambda = 2.5$, the probability of $x = 4$ occurrences is 0.1336.

| $x$ | $\lambda$ 0.1 | 0.2 | 0.3 | 0.4 | 0.5 | 0.6 | 0.7 | 0.8 | 0.9 | 1.0 |
|---|---|---|---|---|---|---|---|---|---|---|
| 0 | 0.9048 | 0.8187 | 0.7408 | 0.6703 | 0.6065 | 0.5488 | 0.4966 | 0.4493 | 0.4066 | 0.3679 |
| 1 | 0.0905 | 0.1637 | 0.2222 | 0.2681 | 0.3033 | 0.3293 | 0.3476 | 0.3595 | 0.3659 | 0.3679 |
| 2 | 0.0045 | 0.0164 | 0.0333 | 0.0536 | 0.0758 | 0.0988 | 0.1217 | 0.1438 | 0.1647 | 0.1839 |
| 3 | 0.0002 | 0.0011 | 0.0033 | 0.0072 | 0.0126 | 0.0198 | 0.0284 | 0.0383 | 0.0494 | 0.0613 |
| 4 | 0.0000 | 0.0001 | 0.0002 | 0.0007 | 0.0016 | 0.0030 | 0.0050 | 0.0077 | 0.0111 | 0.0153 |
| 5 | 0.0000 | 0.0000 | 0.0000 | 0.0001 | 0.0002 | 0.0004 | 0.0007 | 0.0012 | 0.0020 | 0.0031 |
| 6 | 0.0000 | 0.0000 | 0.0000 | 0.0000 | 0.0000 | 0.0000 | 0.0001 | 0.0002 | 0.0003 | 0.0005 |
| 7 | 0.0000 | 0.0000 | 0.0000 | 0.0000 | 0.0000 | 0.0000 | 0.0000 | 0.0000 | 0.0000 | 0.0001 |

| $x$ | $\lambda$ 1.1 | 1.2 | 1.3 | 1.4 | 1.5 | 1.6 | 1.7 | 1.8 | 1.9 | 2.0 |
|---|---|---|---|---|---|---|---|---|---|---|
| 0 | 0.3329 | 0.3012 | 0.2725 | 0.2466 | 0.2231 | 0.2019 | 0.1827 | 0.1653 | 0.1496 | 0.1353 |
| 1 | 0.3662 | 0.3614 | 0.3543 | 0.3452 | 0.3347 | 0.3230 | 0.3106 | 0.2975 | 0.2842 | 0.2707 |
| 2 | 0.2014 | 0.2169 | 0.2303 | 0.2417 | 0.2510 | 0.2584 | 0.2640 | 0.2678 | 0.2700 | 0.2707 |
| 3 | 0.0738 | 0.0867 | 0.0998 | 0.1128 | 0.1255 | 0.1378 | 0.1496 | 0.1607 | 0.1710 | 0.1804 |
| 4 | 0.0203 | 0.0260 | 0.0324 | 0.0395 | 0.0471 | 0.0551 | 0.0636 | 0.0723 | 0.0812 | 0.0902 |
| 5 | 0.0045 | 0.0062 | 0.0084 | 0.0111 | 0.0141 | 0.0176 | 0.0216 | 0.0260 | 0.0309 | 0.0361 |
| 6 | 0.0008 | 0.0012 | 0.0018 | 0.0026 | 0.0035 | 0.0047 | 0.0061 | 0.0078 | 0.0098 | 0.0120 |
| 7 | 0.0001 | 0.0002 | 0.0003 | 0.0005 | 0.0008 | 0.0011 | 0.0015 | 0.0020 | 0.0027 | 0.0034 |
| 8 | 0.0000 | 0.0000 | 0.0001 | 0.0001 | 0.0001 | 0.0002 | 0.0003 | 0.0005 | 0.0006 | 0.0009 |
| 9 | 0.0000 | 0.0000 | 0.0000 | 0.0000 | 0.0000 | 0.0000 | 0.0001 | 0.0001 | 0.0001 | 0.0002 |

| $x$ | $\lambda$ 2.1 | 2.2 | 2.3 | 2.4 | 2.5 | 2.6 | 2.7 | 2.8 | 2.9 | 3.0 |
|---|---|---|---|---|---|---|---|---|---|---|
| 0 | 0.1225 | 0.1108 | 0.1003 | 0.0907 | 0.0821 | 0.0743 | 0.0672 | 0.0608 | 0.0550 | 0.0498 |
| 1 | 0.2572 | 0.2438 | 0.2306 | 0.2177 | 0.2052 | 0.1931 | 0.1815 | 0.1703 | 0.1596 | 0.1494 |
| 2 | 0.2700 | 0.2681 | 0.2652 | 0.2613 | 0.2565 | 0.2510 | 0.2450 | 0.2384 | 0.2314 | 0.2240 |
| 3 | 0.1890 | 0.1966 | 0.2033 | 0.2090 | 0.2138 | 0.2176 | 0.2205 | 0.2225 | 0.2237 | 0.2240 |
| 4 | 0.0992 | 0.1082 | 0.1169 | 0.1254 | 0.1336 | 0.1414 | 0.1488 | 0.1557 | 0.1622 | 0.1680 |
| 5 | 0.0417 | 0.0476 | 0.0538 | 0.0602 | 0.0668 | 0.0735 | 0.0804 | 0.0872 | 0.0940 | 0.1008 |
| 6 | 0.0146 | 0.0174 | 0.0206 | 0.0241 | 0.0278 | 0.0319 | 0.0362 | 0.0407 | 0.0455 | 0.0540 |
| 7 | 0.0044 | 0.0055 | 0.0068 | 0.0083 | 0.0099 | 0.0118 | 0.0139 | 0.0163 | 0.0188 | 0.0216 |

**Poisson Probabilities** (*Continued*)

| x | 2.1 | 2.2 | 2.3 | 2.4 | 2.5 | 2.6 | 2.7 | 2.8 | 2.9 | 3.0 |
|---|---|---|---|---|---|---|---|---|---|---|
| | | | | | λ | | | | | |
| 8 | 0.0011 | 0.0015 | 0.0019 | 0.0025 | 0.0031 | 0.0038 | 0.0047 | 0.0057 | 0.0068 | 0.0081 |
| 9 | 0.0003 | 0.0004 | 0.0005 | 0.0007 | 0.0009 | 0.0011 | 0.0014 | 0.0018 | 0.0022 | 0.0027 |
| 10 | 0.0001 | 0.0001 | 0.0001 | 0.0002 | 0.0002 | 0.0003 | 0.0004 | 0.0005 | 0.0006 | 0.0008 |
| 11 | 0.0000 | 0.0000 | 0.0000 | 0.0000 | 0.0000 | 0.0001 | 0.0001 | 0.0001 | 0.0002 | 0.0002 |
| 12 | 0.0000 | 0.0000 | 0.0000 | 0.0000 | 0.0000 | 0.0000 | 0.0000 | 0.0000 | 0.0000 | 0.0001 |

| x | 3.1 | 3.2 | 3.3 | 3.4 | 3.5 | 3.6 | 3.7 | 3.8 | 3.9 | 4.0 |
|---|---|---|---|---|---|---|---|---|---|---|
| | | | | | λ | | | | | |
| 0 | 0.0450 | 0.0408 | 0.0369 | 0.0344 | 0.0302 | 0.0273 | 0.0247 | 0.0224 | 0.0202 | 0.0183 |
| 1 | 0.1397 | 0.1304 | 0.1217 | 0.1135 | 0.1057 | 0.0984 | 0.0915 | 0.0850 | 0.0789 | 0.0733 |
| 2 | 0.2165 | 0.2087 | 0.2008 | 0.1929 | 0.1850 | 0.1771 | 0.1692 | 0.1615 | 0.1539 | 0.1465 |
| 3 | 0.2237 | 0.2226 | 0.2209 | 0.2186 | 0.2158 | 0.2125 | 0.2087 | 0.2046 | 0.2001 | 0.1954 |
| 4 | 0.1734 | 0.1781 | 0.1823 | 0.1858 | 0.1888 | 0.1912 | 0.1931 | 0.1944 | 0.1951 | 0.1954 |
| 5 | 0.1075 | 0.1140 | 0.1203 | 0.1264 | 0.1322 | 0.1377 | 0.1429 | 0.1477 | 0.1522 | 0.1563 |
| 6 | 0.0555 | 0.0608 | 0.0662 | 0.0716 | 0.0771 | 0.0826 | 0.0881 | 0.0936 | 0.0989 | 0.1042 |
| 7 | 0.0246 | 0.0278 | 0.0312 | 0.0348 | 0.0385 | 0.0425 | 0.0466 | 0.0508 | 0.0551 | 0.0595 |
| 8 | 0.0095 | 0.0111 | 0.0129 | 0.0148 | 0.0169 | 0.0191 | 0.0215 | 0.0241 | 0.0269 | 0.0298 |
| 9 | 0.0033 | 0.0040 | 0.0047 | 0.0056 | 0.0066 | 0.0076 | 0.0089 | 0.0102 | 0.0116 | 0.0132 |
| 10 | 0.0010 | 0.0013 | 0.0016 | 0.0019 | 0.0023 | 0.0028 | 0.0033 | 0.0039 | 0.0045 | 0.0053 |
| 11 | 0.0003 | 0.0004 | 0.0005 | 0.0006 | 0.0007 | 0.0009 | 0.0011 | 0.0013 | 0.0016 | 0.0019 |
| 12 | 0.0001 | 0.0001 | 0.0001 | 0.0002 | 0.0002 | 0.0003 | 0.0003 | 0.0004 | 0.0005 | 0.0006 |
| 13 | 0.0000 | 0.0000 | 0.0000 | 0.0000 | 0.0001 | 0.0001 | 0.0001 | 0.0001 | 0.0002 | 0.0002 |
| 14 | 0.0000 | 0.0000 | 0.0000 | 0.0000 | 0.0000 | 0.0000 | 0.0000 | 0.0000 | 0.0000 | 0.0001 |

| x | 4.1 | 4.2 | 4.3 | 4.4 | 4.5 | 4.6 | 4.7 | 4.8 | 4.9 | 5.0 |
|---|---|---|---|---|---|---|---|---|---|---|
| | | | | | λ | | | | | |
| 0 | 0.0166 | 0.0150 | 0.0136 | 0.0123 | 0.0111 | 0.0101 | 0.0091 | 0.0082 | 0.0074 | 0.0067 |
| 1 | 0.0679 | 0.0630 | 0.0583 | 0.0540 | 0.0500 | 0.0462 | 0.0427 | 0.0395 | 0.0365 | 0.0337 |
| 2 | 0.1393 | 0.1323 | 0.1254 | 0.1188 | 0.1125 | 0.1063 | 0.1005 | 0.0948 | 0.0894 | 0.0842 |
| 3 | 0.1904 | 0.1852 | 0.1798 | 0.1743 | 0.1687 | 0.1631 | 0.1574 | 0.1517 | 0.1460 | 0.1404 |
| 4 | 0.1951 | 0.1944 | 0.1933 | 0.1917 | 0.1898 | 0.1875 | 0.1849 | 0.1820 | 0.1789 | 0.1755 |
| 5 | 0.1600 | 0.1633 | 0.1662 | 0.1687 | 0.1708 | 0.1725 | 0.1738 | 0.1747 | 0.1753 | 0.1755 |
| 6 | 0.1093 | 0.1143 | 0.1191 | 0.1237 | 0.1281 | 0.1323 | 0.1362 | 0.1398 | 0.1432 | 0.1462 |
| 7 | 0.0640 | 0.0686 | 0.0732 | 0.0778 | 0.0824 | 0.0869 | 0.0914 | 0.0959 | 0.1002 | 0.1044 |
| 8 | 0.0328 | 0.0360 | 0.0393 | 0.0428 | 0.0463 | 0.0500 | 0.0537 | 0.0575 | 0.0614 | 0.0653 |
| 9 | 0.0150 | 0.0168 | 0.0188 | 0.0209 | 0.0232 | 0.0255 | 0.0280 | 0.0307 | 0.0334 | 0.0363 |
| 10 | 0.0061 | 0.0071 | 0.0081 | 0.0092 | 0.0104 | 0.0118 | 0.0132 | 0.0147 | 0.0164 | 0.0181 |
| 11 | 0.0023 | 0.0027 | 0.0032 | 0.0037 | 0.0043 | 0.0049 | 0.0056 | 0.0064 | 0.0073 | 0.0082 |
| 12 | 0.0008 | 0.0009 | 0.0011 | 0.0014 | 0.0016 | 0.0019 | 0.0022 | 0.0026 | 0.0030 | 0.0034 |
| 13 | 0.0002 | 0.0003 | 0.0004 | 0.0005 | 0.0006 | 0.0007 | 0.0008 | 0.0009 | 0.0011 | 0.0013 |
| 14 | 0.0001 | 0.0001 | 0.0001 | 0.0001 | 0.0002 | 0.0002 | 0.0003 | 0.0003 | 0.0004 | 0.0005 |
| 15 | 0.0000 | 0.0000 | 0.0000 | 0.0000 | 0.0001 | 0.0001 | 0.0001 | 0.0001 | 0.0001 | 0.0002 |

**Poisson Probabilities** (*Continued*)

| | | | | | λ | | | | | |
|---|---|---|---|---|---|---|---|---|---|---|
| x | 5.1 | 5.2 | 5.3 | 5.4 | 5.5 | 5.6 | 5.7 | 5.8 | 5.9 | 6.0 |
| 0 | 0.0061 | 0.0055 | 0.0050 | 0.0045 | 0.0041 | 0.0037 | 0.0033 | 0.0030 | 0.0027 | 0.0025 |
| 1 | 0.0311 | 0.0287 | 0.0265 | 0.0244 | 0.0225 | 0.0207 | 0.0191 | 0.0176 | 0.0162 | 0.0149 |
| 2 | 0.0793 | 0.0746 | 0.0701 | 0.0659 | 0.0618 | 0.0580 | 0.0544 | 0.0509 | 0.0477 | 0.0446 |
| 3 | 0.1348 | 0.1293 | 0.1239 | 0.1185 | 0.1133 | 0.1082 | 0.1033 | 0.0985 | 0.0938 | 0.0892 |
| 4 | 0.1719 | 0.1681 | 0.1641 | 0.1600 | 0.1558 | 0.1515 | 0.1472 | 0.1428 | 0.1383 | 0.1339 |
| 5 | 0.1753 | 0.1748 | 0.1740 | 0.1728 | 0.1714 | 0.1697 | 0.1678 | 0.1656 | 0.1632 | 0.1606 |
| 6 | 0.1490 | 0.1515 | 0.1537 | 0.1555 | 0.1571 | 0.1587 | 0.1594 | 0.1601 | 0.1605 | 0.1606 |
| 7 | 0.1086 | 0.1125 | 0.1163 | 0.1200 | 0.1234 | 0.1267 | 0.1298 | 0.1326 | 0.1353 | 0.1377 |
| 8 | 0.0692 | 0.0731 | 0.0771 | 0.0810 | 0.0849 | 0.0887 | 0.0925 | 0.0962 | 0.0998 | 0.1033 |
| 9 | 0.0392 | 0.0423 | 0.0454 | 0.0486 | 0.0519 | 0.0552 | 0.0586 | 0.0620 | 0.0654 | 0.0688 |
| 10 | 0.0200 | 0.0220 | 0.0241 | 0.0262 | 0.0285 | 0.0309 | 0.0334 | 0.0359 | 0.0386 | 0.0413 |
| 11 | 0.0093 | 0.0104 | 0.0116 | 0.0129 | 0.0143 | 0.0157 | 0.0173 | 0.0190 | 0.0207 | 0.0225 |
| 12 | 0.0039 | 0.0045 | 0.0051 | 0.0058 | 0.0065 | 0.0073 | 0.0082 | 0.0092 | 0.0102 | 0.0113 |
| 13 | 0.0015 | 0.0018 | 0.0021 | 0.0024 | 0.0028 | 0.0032 | 0.0036 | 0.0041 | 0.0046 | 0.0052 |
| 14 | 0.0006 | 0.0007 | 0.0008 | 0.0009 | 0.0011 | 0.0013 | 0.0015 | 0.0017 | 0.0019 | 0.0022 |
| 15 | 0.0002 | 0.0002 | 0.0003 | 0.0003 | 0.0004 | 0.0005 | 0.0006 | 0.0007 | 0.0008 | 0.0009 |
| 16 | 0.0001 | 0.0001 | 0.0001 | 0.0001 | 0.0001 | 0.0002 | 0.0002 | 0.0002 | 0.0003 | 0.0003 |
| 17 | 0.0000 | 0.0000 | 0.0000 | 0.0000 | 0.0000 | 0.0001 | 0.0001 | 0.0001 | 0.0001 | 0.0001 |

| | | | | | λ | | | | | |
|---|---|---|---|---|---|---|---|---|---|---|
| x | 6.1 | 6.2 | 6.3 | 6.4 | 6.5 | 6.6 | 6.7 | 6.8 | 6.9 | 7.0 |
| 0 | 0.0022 | 0.0020 | 0.0018 | 0.0017 | 0.0015 | 0.0014 | 0.0012 | 0.0011 | 0.0010 | 0.0009 |
| 1 | 0.0137 | 0.0126 | 0.0116 | 0.0106 | 0.0098 | 0.0090 | 0.0082 | 0.0076 | 0.0070 | 0.0064 |
| 2 | 0.0417 | 0.0390 | 0.0364 | 0.0340 | 0.0318 | 0.0296 | 0.0276 | 0.0258 | 0.0240 | 0.0223 |
| 3 | 0.0848 | 0.0806 | 0.0765 | 0.0726 | 0.0688 | 0.0652 | 0.0617 | 0.0584 | 0.0552 | 0.0521 |
| 4 | 0.1294 | 0.1249 | 0.1205 | 0.1162 | 0.1118 | 0.1076 | 0.1034 | 0.0992 | 0.0952 | 0.0912 |
| 5 | 0.1579 | 0.1549 | 0.1519 | 0.1487 | 0.1454 | 0.1420 | 0.1385 | 0.1349 | 0.1314 | 0.1277 |
| 6 | 0.1605 | 0.1601 | 0.1595 | 0.1586 | 0.1575 | 0.1562 | 0.1546 | 0.1529 | 0.1511 | 0.1490 |
| 7 | 0.1399 | 0.1418 | 0.1435 | 0.1450 | 0.1462 | 0.1472 | 0.1480 | 0.1486 | 0.1489 | 0.1490 |
| 8 | 0.1066 | 0.1099 | 0.1130 | 0.1160 | 0.1188 | 0.1215 | 0.1240 | 0.1263 | 0.1284 | 0.1304 |
| 9 | 0.0723 | 0.0757 | 0.0791 | 0.0825 | 0.0858 | 0.0891 | 0.0923 | 0.0954 | 0.0985 | 0.1014 |
| 10 | 0.0441 | 0.0469 | 0.0498 | 0.0528 | 0.0558 | 0.0588 | 0.0618 | 0.0649 | 0.0679 | 0.0710 |
| 11 | 0.0245 | 0.0265 | 0.0285 | 0.0307 | 0.0330 | 0.0353 | 0.0377 | 0.0401 | 0.0426 | 0.0452 |
| 12 | 0.0124 | 0.0137 | 0.0150 | 0.0164 | 0.0179 | 0.0194 | 0.0210 | 0.0227 | 0.0245 | 0.0264 |
| 13 | 0.0058 | 0.0065 | 0.0073 | 0.0081 | 0.0089 | 0.0098 | 0.0108 | 0.0119 | 0.0130 | 0.0142 |
| 14 | 0.0025 | 0.0029 | 0.0033 | 0.0037 | 0.0041 | 0.0046 | 0.0052 | 0.0058 | 0.0064 | 0.0071 |
| 15 | 0.0010 | 0.0012 | 0.0014 | 0.0016 | 0.0018 | 0.0020 | 0.0023 | 0.0025 | 0.0029 | 0.0033 |
| 16 | 0.0004 | 0.0005 | 0.0005 | 0.0006 | 0.0007 | 0.0008 | 0.0010 | 0.0011 | 0.0013 | 0.0014 |
| 17 | 0.0001 | 0.0002 | 0.0002 | 0.0002 | 0.0003 | 0.0003 | 0.0004 | 0.0004 | 0.0005 | 0.0006 |
| 18 | 0.0000 | 0.0001 | 0.0001 | 0.0001 | 0.0001 | 0.0001 | 0.0001 | 0.0002 | 0.0002 | 0.0002 |
| 19 | 0.0000 | 0.0000 | 0.0000 | 0.0000 | 0.0000 | 0.0000 | 0.0000 | 0.0001 | 0.0001 | 0.0001 |

**Poisson Probabilities (*Continued*)**

| | | | | | | $\lambda$ | | | | | |
|---|---|---|---|---|---|---|---|---|---|---|---|
| $x$ | 7.1 | 7.2 | 7.3 | 7.4 | 7.5 | 7.6 | 7.7 | 7.8 | 7.9 | 8.0 |
| 0 | 0.0008 | 0.0007 | 0.0007 | 0.0006 | 0.0006 | 0.0005 | 0.0005 | 0.0004 | 0.0004 | 0.0003 |
| 1 | 0.0059 | 0.0054 | 0.0049 | 0.0045 | 0.0041 | 0.0038 | 0.0035 | 0.0032 | 0.0029 | 0.0027 |
| 2 | 0.0208 | 0.0194 | 0.0180 | 0.0167 | 0.0156 | 0.0145 | 0.0134 | 0.0125 | 0.0116 | 0.0107 |
| 3 | 0.0492 | 0.0464 | 0.0438 | 0.0413 | 0.0389 | 0.0366 | 0.0345 | 0.0324 | 0.0305 | 0.0286 |
| 4 | 0.0874 | 0.0836 | 0.0799 | 0.0764 | 0.0729 | 0.0696 | 0.0663 | 0.0632 | 0.0602 | 0.0573 |
| 5 | 0.1241 | 0.1204 | 0.1167 | 0.1130 | 0.1094 | 0.1057 | 0.1021 | 0.0986 | 0.0951 | 0.0916 |
| 6 | 0.1468 | 0.1445 | 0.1420 | 0.1394 | 0.1367 | 0.1339 | 0.1311 | 0.1282 | 0.1252 | 0.1221 |
| 7 | 0.1489 | 0.1486 | 0.1481 | 0.1474 | 0.1465 | 0.1454 | 0.1442 | 0.1428 | 0.1413 | 0.1396 |
| 8 | 0.1321 | 0.1337 | 0.1351 | 0.1363 | 0.1373 | 0.1382 | 0.1388 | 0.1392 | 0.1395 | 0.1396 |
| 9 | 0.1042 | 0.1070 | 0.1096 | 0.1121 | 0.1144 | 0.1167 | 0.1187 | 0.1207 | 0.1224 | 0.1241 |
| 10 | 0.0740 | 0.0770 | 0.0800 | 0.0829 | 0.0858 | 0.0887 | 0.0914 | 0.0941 | 0.0967 | 0.0993 |
| 11 | 0.0478 | 0.0504 | 0.0531 | 0.0558 | 0.0585 | 0.0613 | 0.0640 | 0.0667 | 0.0695 | 0.0722 |
| 12 | 0.0283 | 0.0303 | 0.0323 | 0.0344 | 0.0366 | 0.0388 | 0.0411 | 0.0434 | 0.0457 | 0.0481 |
| 13 | 0.0154 | 0.0168 | 0.0181 | 0.0196 | 0.0211 | 0.0227 | 0.0243 | 0.0260 | 0.0278 | 0.0296 |
| 14 | 0.0078 | 0.0086 | 0.0095 | 0.0104 | 0.0113 | 0.0123 | 0.0134 | 0.0145 | 0.0157 | 0.0169 |
| 15 | 0.0037 | 0.0041 | 0.0046 | 0.0051 | 0.0057 | 0.0062 | 0.0069 | 0.0075 | 0.0083 | 0.0090 |
| 16 | 0.0016 | 0.0019 | 0.0021 | 0.0024 | 0.0026 | 0.0030 | 0.0033 | 0.0037 | 0.0041 | 0.0045 |
| 17 | 0.0007 | 0.0008 | 0.0009 | 0.0010 | 0.0012 | 0.0013 | 0.0015 | 0.0017 | 0.0019 | 0.0021 |
| 18 | 0.0003 | 0.0003 | 0.0004 | 0.0004 | 0.0005 | 0.0006 | 0.0006 | 0.0007 | 0.0008 | 0.0009 |
| 19 | 0.0001 | 0.0001 | 0.0001 | 0.0002 | 0.0002 | 0.0002 | 0.0003 | 0.0003 | 0.0003 | 0.0004 |
| 20 | 0.0000 | 0.0000 | 0.0001 | 0.0001 | 0.0001 | 0.0001 | 0.0001 | 0.0001 | 0.0001 | 0.0002 |
| 21 | 0.0000 | 0.0000 | 0.0000 | 0.0000 | 0.0000 | 0.0000 | 0.0000 | 0.0000 | 0.0001 | 0.0001 |

| | | | | | | $\lambda$ | | | | | |
|---|---|---|---|---|---|---|---|---|---|---|---|
| $x$ | 8.1 | 8.2 | 8.3 | 8.4 | 8.5 | 8.6 | 8.7 | 8.8 | 8.9 | 9.0 |
| 0 | 0.0003 | 0.0003 | 0.0002 | 0.0002 | 0.0002 | 0.0002 | 0.0002 | 0.0002 | 0.0001 | 0.0001 |
| 1 | 0.0025 | 0.0023 | 0.0021 | 0.0019 | 0.0017 | 0.0016 | 0.0014 | 0.0013 | 0.0012 | 0.0011 |
| 2 | 0.0100 | 0.0092 | 0.0086 | 0.0079 | 0.0074 | 0.0068 | 0.0063 | 0.0058 | 0.0054 | 0.0050 |
| 3 | 0.0269 | 0.0252 | 0.0237 | 0.0222 | 0.0208 | 0.0195 | 0.0183 | 0.0171 | 0.0160 | 0.0150 |
| 4 | 0.0544 | 0.0517 | 0.0491 | 0.0466 | 0.0443 | 0.0420 | 0.0398 | 0.0377 | 0.0357 | 0.0337 |
| 5 | 0.0882 | 0.0849 | 0.0816 | 0.0784 | 0.0752 | 0.0722 | 0.0692 | 0.0663 | 0.0635 | 0.0607 |
| 6 | 0.1191 | 0.1160 | 0.1128 | 0.1097 | 0.1066 | 0.1034 | 0.1003 | 0.0972 | 0.0941 | 0.0911 |
| 7 | 0.1378 | 0.1358 | 0.1338 | 0.1317 | 0.1294 | 0.1271 | 0.1247 | 0.1222 | 0.1197 | 0.1171 |
| 8 | 0.1395 | 0.1392 | 0.1388 | 0.1382 | 0.1375 | 0.1366 | 0.1356 | 0.1344 | 0.1332 | 0.1318 |
| 9 | 0.1256 | 0.1269 | 0.1280 | 0.1290 | 0.1299 | 0.1306 | 0.1311 | 0.1315 | 0.1317 | 0.1318 |
| 10 | 0.1017 | 0.1040 | 0.1063 | 0.1084 | 0.1104 | 0.1123 | 0.1140 | 0.1157 | 0.1172 | 0.1186 |
| 11 | 0.0749 | 0.0776 | 0.0802 | 0.0828 | 0.0853 | 0.0878 | 0.0902 | 0.0925 | 0.0948 | 0.0970 |
| 12 | 0.0505 | 0.0530 | 0.0555 | 0.0579 | 0.0604 | 0.0629 | 0.0654 | 0.0679 | 0.0703 | 0.0728 |
| 13 | 0.0315 | 0.0334 | 0.0354 | 0.0374 | 0.0395 | 0.0416 | 0.0438 | 0.0459 | 0.0481 | 0.0504 |
| 14 | 0.0182 | 0.0196 | 0.0210 | 0.0225 | 0.0240 | 0.0256 | 0.0272 | 0.0289 | 0.0306 | 0.0324 |

**Poisson Probabilities** (*Continued*)

| | | | | | λ | | | | | |
|---|---|---|---|---|---|---|---|---|---|---|
| x | 8.1 | 8.2 | 8.3 | 8.4 | 8.5 | 8.6 | 8.7 | 8.8 | 8.9 | 9.0 |
| 15 | 0.0098 | 0.0107 | 0.0116 | 0.0126 | 0.0136 | 0.0147 | 0.0158 | 0.0169 | 0.0182 | 0.1094 |
| 16 | 0.0050 | 0.0055 | 0.0060 | 0.0066 | 0.0072 | 0.0079 | 0.0086 | 0.0093 | 0.0101 | 0.0109 |
| 17 | 0.0024 | 0.0026 | 0.0029 | 0.0033 | 0.0036 | 0.0040 | 0.0044 | 0.0048 | 0.0053 | 0.0058 |
| 18 | 0.0011 | 0.0012 | 0.0014 | 0.0015 | 0.0017 | 0.0019 | 0.0021 | 0.0024 | 0.0026 | 0.0029 |
| 19 | 0.0005 | 0.0005 | 0.0006 | 0.0007 | 0.0008 | 0.0009 | 0.0010 | 0.0011 | 0.0012 | 0.0014 |
| 20 | 0.0002 | 0.0002 | 0.0002 | 0.0003 | 0.0003 | 0.0004 | 0.0004 | 0.0005 | 0.0005 | 0.0006 |
| 21 | 0.0001 | 0.0001 | 0.0001 | 0.0001 | 0.0001 | 0.0002 | 0.0002 | 0.0002 | 0.0002 | 0.0003 |
| 22 | 0.0000 | 0.0000 | 0.0000 | 0.0000 | 0.0001 | 0.0001 | 0.0001 | 0.0001 | 0.0001 | 0.0001 |

| | | | | | λ | | | | | |
|---|---|---|---|---|---|---|---|---|---|---|
| x | 9.1 | 9.2 | 9.3 | 9.4 | 9.5 | 9.6 | 9.7 | 9.8 | 9.9 | 10 |
| 0 | 0.0001 | 0.0001 | 0.0001 | 0.0001 | 0.0001 | 0.0001 | 0.0001 | 0.0001 | 0.0001 | 0.0000 |
| 1 | 0.0010 | 0.0009 | 0.0009 | 0.0008 | 0.0007 | 0.0007 | 0.0006 | 0.0005 | 0.0005 | 0.0005 |
| 2 | 0.0046 | 0.0043 | 0.0040 | 0.0037 | 0.0034 | 0.0031 | 0.0029 | 0.0027 | 0.0025 | 0.0023 |
| 3 | 0.0140 | 0.0131 | 0.0123 | 0.0115 | 0.0107 | 0.0100 | 0.0093 | 0.0087 | 0.0081 | 0.0076 |
| 4 | 0.0319 | 0.0302 | 0.0285 | 0.0269 | 0.0254 | 0.0240 | 0.0226 | 0.0213 | 0.0201 | 0.0189 |
| 5 | 0.0581 | 0.0555 | 0.0530 | 0.0506 | 0.0483 | 0.0460 | 0.0439 | 0.0418 | 0.0398 | 0.0378 |
| 6 | 0.0881 | 0.0851 | 0.0822 | 0.0793 | 0.0764 | 0.0736 | 0.0709 | 0.0682 | 0.0656 | 0.0631 |
| 7 | 0.1145 | 0.1118 | 0.1091 | 0.1064 | 0.1037 | 0.1010 | 0.0982 | 0.0955 | 0.0928 | 0.0901 |
| 8 | 0.1302 | 0.1286 | 0.1269 | 0.1251 | 0.1232 | 0.1212 | 0.1191 | 0.1170 | 0.1148 | 0.1126 |
| 9 | 0.1317 | 0.1315 | 0.1311 | 0.1306 | 0.1300 | 0.1293 | 0.1284 | 0.1274 | 0.1263 | 0.1251 |
| 10 | 0.1198 | 0.1210 | 0.1219 | 0.1228 | 0.1235 | 0.1241 | 0.1245 | 0.1249 | 0.1250 | 0.1251 |
| 11 | 0.0991 | 0.1012 | 0.1031 | 0.1049 | 0.1067 | 0.1083 | 0.1098 | 0.1112 | 0.1125 | 0.1137 |
| 12 | 0.0752 | 0.0776 | 0.0799 | 0.0822 | 0.0844 | 0.0866 | 0.0888 | 0.0908 | 0.0928 | 0.0948 |
| 13 | 0.0526 | 0.0549 | 0.0572 | 0.0594 | 0.0617 | 0.0640 | 0.0662 | 0.0685 | 0.0707 | 0.0729 |
| 14 | 0.0342 | 0.0361 | 0.0380 | 0.0399 | 0.0419 | 0.0439 | 0.0459 | 0.0479 | 0.0500 | 0.0521 |
| 15 | 0.0208 | 0.0221 | 0.0235 | 0.0250 | 0.0265 | 0.0281 | 0.0297 | 0.0313 | 0.0330 | 0.0347 |
| 16 | 0.0118 | 0.0127 | 0.0137 | 0.0147 | 0.0157 | 0.0168 | 0.0180 | 0.0192 | 0.0204 | 0.0217 |
| 17 | 0.0063 | 0.0069 | 0.0075 | 0.0081 | 0.0088 | 0.0095 | 0.0103 | 0.0111 | 0.0119 | 0.0128 |
| 18 | 0.0032 | 0.0035 | 0.0039 | 0.0042 | 0.0046 | 0.0051 | 0.0055 | 0.0060 | 0.0065 | 0.0071 |
| 19 | 0.0015 | 0.0017 | 0.0019 | 0.0021 | 0.0023 | 0.0026 | 0.0028 | 0.0031 | 0.0034 | 0.0027 |
| 20 | 0.0007 | 0.0008 | 0.0009 | 0.0010 | 0.0011 | 0.0012 | 0.0014 | 0.0015 | 0.0017 | 0.0019 |
| 21 | 0.0003 | 0.0003 | 0.0004 | 0.0004 | 0.0005 | 0.0006 | 0.0006 | 0.0007 | 0.0008 | 0.0009 |
| 22 | 0.0001 | 0.0001 | 0.0002 | 0.0002 | 0.0002 | 0.0002 | 0.0003 | 0.0003 | 0.0004 | 0.0004 |
| 23 | 0.0000 | 0.0001 | 0.0001 | 0.0001 | 0.0001 | 0.0001 | 0.0001 | 0.0001 | 0.0002 | 0.0002 |
| 24 | 0.0000 | 0.0000 | 0.0000 | 0.0000 | 0.0000 | 0.0000 | 0.0000 | 0.0001 | 0.0001 | 0.0001 |

**Poisson Probabilities** (*Continued*)

| | | | | | $\lambda$ | | | | | |
|---|---|---|---|---|---|---|---|---|---|---|
| $x$ | 11 | 12 | 13 | 14 | 15 | 16 | 17 | 18 | 19 | 20 |
| 0 | 0.0000 | 0.0000 | 0.0000 | 0.0000 | 0.0000 | 0.0000 | 0.0000 | 0.0000 | 0.0000 | 0.0000 |
| 1 | 0.0002 | 0.0001 | 0.0000 | 0.0000 | 0.0000 | 0.0000 | 0.0000 | 0.0000 | 0.0000 | 0.0000 |
| 2 | 0.0010 | 0.0004 | 0.0002 | 0.0001 | 0.0000 | 0.0000 | 0.0000 | 0.0000 | 0.0000 | 0.0000 |
| 3 | 0.0037 | 0.0018 | 0.0008 | 0.0004 | 0.0002 | 0.0001 | 0.0000 | 0.0000 | 0.0000 | 0.0000 |
| 4 | 0.0102 | 0.0053 | 0.0027 | 0.0013 | 0.0006 | 0.0003 | 0.0001 | 0.0001 | 0.0000 | 0.0000 |
| 5 | 0.0224 | 0.0127 | 0.0070 | 0.0037 | 0.0019 | 0.0010 | 0.0005 | 0.0002 | 0.0001 | 0.0001 |
| 6 | 0.0411 | 0.0255 | 0.0152 | 0.0087 | 0.0048 | 0.0026 | 0.0014 | 0.0007 | 0.0004 | 0.0002 |
| 7 | 0.0646 | 0.0437 | 0.0281 | 0.0174 | 0.0104 | 0.0060 | 0.0034 | 0.0018 | 0.0010 | 0.0005 |
| 8 | 0.0888 | 0.0655 | 0.0457 | 0.0304 | 0.0194 | 0.0120 | 0.0072 | 0.0042 | 0.0024 | 0.0013 |
| 9 | 0.1085 | 0.0874 | 0.0661 | 0.0473 | 0.0324 | 0.0213 | 0.0135 | 0.0083 | 0.0050 | 0.0029 |
| 10 | 0.1194 | 0.1048 | 0.0859 | 0.0663 | 0.0486 | 0.0341 | 0.0230 | 0.0150 | 0.0095 | 0.0058 |
| 11 | 0.1194 | 0.1144 | 0.1015 | 0.0844 | 0.0663 | 0.0496 | 0.0355 | 0.0245 | 0.0164 | 0.0106 |
| 12 | 0.1094 | 0.1144 | 0.1099 | 0.0984 | 0.0829 | 0.0661 | 0.0504 | 0.0368 | 0.0259 | 0.0176 |
| 13 | 0.0926 | 0.1056 | 0.1099 | 0.1060 | 0.0956 | 0.0814 | 0.0658 | 0.0509 | 0.0378 | 0.0271 |
| 14 | 0.0728 | 0.0905 | 0.1021 | 0.1060 | 0.1024 | 0.0930 | 0.0800 | 0.0655 | 0.0514 | 0.0387 |
| 15 | 0.0534 | 0.0724 | 0.0885 | 0.0989 | 0.1024 | 0.0992 | 0.0906 | 0.0786 | 0.0650 | 0.0516 |
| 16 | 0.0367 | 0.0543 | 0.0719 | 0.0866 | 0.0960 | 0.0992 | 0.0963 | 0.0884 | 0.0772 | 0.0646 |
| 17 | 0.0237 | 0.0383 | 0.0550 | 0.0713 | 0.0847 | 0.0934 | 0.0963 | 0.0936 | 0.0863 | 0.0760 |
| 18 | 0.0145 | 0.0256 | 0.0397 | 0.0554 | 0.0706 | 0.0830 | 0.0909 | 0.0936 | 0.0911 | 0.0844 |
| 19 | 0.0084 | 0.0161 | 0.0272 | 0.0409 | 0.0557 | 0.0699 | 0.0814 | 0.0887 | 0.0911 | 0.0888 |
| 20 | 0.0046 | 0.0097 | 0.0177 | 0.0286 | 0.0418 | 0.0559 | 0.0692 | 0.0798 | 0.0866 | 0.0888 |
| 21 | 0.0024 | 0.0055 | 0.0109 | 0.0191 | 0.0299 | 0.0426 | 0.0560 | 0.0684 | 0.0783 | 0.0846 |
| 22 | 0.0012 | 0.0030 | 0.0065 | 0.0121 | 0.0204 | 0.0310 | 0.0433 | 0.0560 | 0.0676 | 0.0769 |
| 23 | 0.0006 | 0.0016 | 0.0037 | 0.0074 | 0.0133 | 0.0216 | 0.0320 | 0.0438 | 0.0559 | 0.0669 |
| 24 | 0.0003 | 0.0008 | 0.0020 | 0.0043 | 0.0083 | 0.0144 | 0.0226 | 0.0328 | 0.0442 | 0.0557 |
| 25 | 0.0001 | 0.0004 | 0.0010 | 0.0024 | 0.0050 | 0.0092 | 0.0154 | 0.0237 | 0.0336 | 0.0446 |
| 26 | 0.0000 | 0.0002 | 0.0005 | 0.0013 | 0.0029 | 0.0057 | 0.0101 | 0.0164 | 0.0246 | 0.0343 |
| 27 | 0.0000 | 0.0001 | 0.0002 | 0.0007 | 0.0016 | 0.0034 | 0.0063 | 0.0109 | 0.0173 | 0.0254 |
| 28 | 0.0000 | 0.0000 | 0.0001 | 0.0003 | 0.0009 | 0.0019 | 0.0038 | 0.0070 | 0.0117 | 0.0181 |
| 29 | 0.0000 | 0.0000 | 0.0001 | 0.0002 | 0.0004 | 0.0011 | 0.0023 | 0.0044 | 0.0077 | 0.0125 |
| 30 | 0.0000 | 0.0000 | 0.0000 | 0.0001 | 0.0002 | 0.0006 | 0.0013 | 0.0026 | 0.0049 | 0.0083 |
| 31 | 0.0000 | 0.0000 | 0.0000 | 0.0000 | 0.0001 | 0.0003 | 0.0007 | 0.0015 | 0.0030 | 0.0054 |
| 32 | 0.0000 | 0.0000 | 0.0000 | 0.0000 | 0.0001 | 0.0001 | 0.0004 | 0.0009 | 0.0018 | 0.0034 |
| 33 | 0.0000 | 0.0000 | 0.0000 | 0.0000 | 0.0000 | 0.0001 | 0.0002 | 0.0005 | 0.0010 | 0.0020 |
| 34 | 0.0000 | 0.0000 | 0.0000 | 0.0000 | 0.0000 | 0.0000 | 0.0001 | 0.0002 | 0.0006 | 0.0012 |
| 35 | 0.0000 | 0.0000 | 0.0000 | 0.0000 | 0.0000 | 0.0000 | 0.0000 | 0.0001 | 0.0003 | 0.0007 |
| 36 | 0.0000 | 0.0000 | 0.0000 | 0.0000 | 0.0000 | 0.0000 | 0.0000 | 0.0001 | 0.0002 | 0.0004 |
| 37 | 0.0000 | 0.0000 | 0.0000 | 0.0000 | 0.0000 | 0.0000 | 0.0000 | 0.0000 | 0.0001 | 0.0002 |
| 38 | 0.0000 | 0.0000 | 0.0000 | 0.0000 | 0.0000 | 0.0000 | 0.0000 | 0.0000 | 0.0000 | 0.0001 |
| 39 | 0.0000 | 0.0000 | 0.0000 | 0.0000 | 0.0000 | 0.0000 | 0.0000 | 0.0000 | 0.0000 | 0.0001 |

# Appendix D    Areas for the Standard Normal Distribution

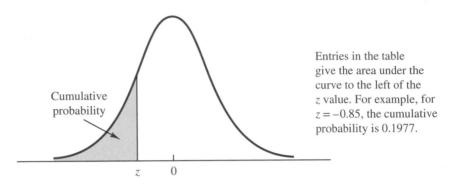

Cumulative probability

Entries in the table give the area under the curve to the left of the $z$ value. For example, for $z = -0.85$, the cumulative probability is 0.1977.

| z | 0.00 | 0.01 | 0.02 | 0.03 | 0.04 | 0.05 | 0.06 | 0.07 | 0.08 | 0.09 |
|------|--------|--------|--------|--------|--------|--------|--------|--------|--------|--------|
| −3.0 | 0.0013 | 0.0013 | 0.0013 | 0.0012 | 0.0012 | 0.0011 | 0.0011 | 0.0011 | 0.0010 | 0.0010 |
| −2.9 | 0.0019 | 0.0018 | 0.0018 | 0.0017 | 0.0016 | 0.0016 | 0.0015 | 0.0015 | 0.0014 | 0.0014 |
| −2.8 | 0.0026 | 0.0025 | 0.0024 | 0.0023 | 0.0023 | 0.0022 | 0.0021 | 0.0021 | 0.0020 | 0.0019 |
| −2.7 | 0.0035 | 0.0034 | 0.0033 | 0.0032 | 0.0031 | 0.0030 | 0.0029 | 0.0028 | 0.0027 | 0.0026 |
| −2.6 | 0.0047 | 0.0045 | 0.0044 | 0.0043 | 0.0041 | 0.0040 | 0.0039 | 0.0038 | 0.0037 | 0.0036 |
| −2.5 | 0.0062 | 0.0060 | 0.0059 | 0.0057 | 0.0055 | 0.0054 | 0.0052 | 0.0051 | 0.0049 | 0.0048 |
| −2.4 | 0.0082 | 0.0080 | 0.0078 | 0.0075 | 0.0073 | 0.0071 | 0.0069 | 0.0068 | 0.0066 | 0.0064 |
| −2.3 | 0.0107 | 0.0104 | 0.0102 | 0.0099 | 0.0096 | 0.0094 | 0.0091 | 0.0089 | 0.0087 | 0.0084 |
| −2.2 | 0.0139 | 0.0136 | 0.0132 | 0.0129 | 0.0125 | 0.0122 | 0.0119 | 0.0116 | 0.0113 | 0.0110 |
| −2.1 | 0.0179 | 0.0174 | 0.0170 | 0.0166 | 0.0162 | 0.0158 | 0.0154 | 0.0150 | 0.0146 | 0.0143 |
| −2.0 | 0.0228 | 0.0222 | 0.0217 | 0.0212 | 0.0207 | 0.0202 | 0.0197 | 0.0192 | 0.0188 | 0.0183 |
| −1.9 | 0.0287 | 0.0281 | 0.0274 | 0.0268 | 0.0262 | 0.0256 | 0.0250 | 0.0244 | 0.0239 | 0.0233 |
| −1.8 | 0.0359 | 0.0351 | 0.0344 | 0.0336 | 0.0329 | 0.0322 | 0.0314 | 0.0307 | 0.0301 | 0.0294 |
| −1.7 | 0.0446 | 0.0436 | 0.0427 | 0.0418 | 0.0409 | 0.0401 | 0.0392 | 0.0384 | 0.0375 | 0.0367 |
| −1.6 | 0.0548 | 0.0537 | 0.0526 | 0.0516 | 0.0505 | 0.0495 | 0.0485 | 0.0475 | 0.0465 | 0.0455 |
| −1.5 | 0.0668 | 0.0655 | 0.0643 | 0.0630 | 0.0618 | 0.0606 | 0.0594 | 0.0582 | 0.0571 | 0.0559 |
| −1.4 | 0.0808 | 0.0793 | 0.0778 | 0.0764 | 0.0749 | 0.0735 | 0.0721 | 0.0708 | 0.0694 | 0.0681 |
| −1.3 | 0.0968 | 0.0951 | 0.0934 | 0.0918 | 0.0901 | 0.0885 | 0.0869 | 0.0853 | 0.0838 | 0.0823 |
| −1.2 | 0.1151 | 0.1131 | 0.1112 | 0.1093 | 0.1075 | 0.1056 | 0.1038 | 0.1020 | 0.1003 | 0.0985 |
| −1.1 | 0.1357 | 0.1335 | 0.1314 | 0.1292 | 0.1271 | 0.1251 | 0.1230 | 0.1210 | 0.1190 | 0.1170 |
| −1.0 | 0.1587 | 0.1562 | 0.1539 | 0.1515 | 0.1492 | 0.1469 | 0.1446 | 0.1423 | 0.1401 | 0.1379 |
| −0.9 | 0.1841 | 0.1814 | 0.1788 | 0.1762 | 0.1736 | 0.1711 | 0.1685 | 0.1660 | 0.1635 | 0.1611 |
| −0.8 | 0.2119 | 0.2090 | 0.2061 | 0.2033 | 0.2005 | 0.1977 | 0.1949 | 0.1922 | 0.1894 | 0.1867 |
| −0.7 | 0.2420 | 0.2389 | 0.2358 | 0.2327 | 0.2296 | 0.2266 | 0.2236 | 0.2206 | 0.2177 | 0.2148 |
| −0.6 | 0.2743 | 0.2709 | 0.2676 | 0.2643 | 0.2611 | 0.2578 | 0.2546 | 0.2514 | 0.2483 | 0.2451 |
| −0.5 | 0.3085 | 0.3050 | 0.3015 | 0.2981 | 0.2946 | 0.2912 | 0.2877 | 0.2843 | 0.2810 | 0.2776 |
| −0.4 | 0.3446 | 0.3409 | 0.3372 | 0.3336 | 0.3300 | 0.3264 | 0.3228 | 0.3192 | 0.3156 | 0.3121 |
| −0.3 | 0.3821 | 0.3783 | 0.3745 | 0.3707 | 0.3669 | 0.3632 | 0.3594 | 0.3557 | 0.3520 | 0.3483 |
| −0.2 | 0.4207 | 0.4168 | 0.4129 | 0.4090 | 0.4052 | 0.4013 | 0.3974 | 0.3936 | 0.3897 | 0.3859 |
| −0.1 | 0.4602 | 0.4562 | 0.4522 | 0.4483 | 0.4443 | 0.4404 | 0.4364 | 0.4325 | 0.4286 | 0.4247 |
| −0.0 | 0.5000 | 0.4960 | 0.4920 | 0.4880 | 0.4840 | 0.4801 | 0.4761 | 0.4721 | 0.4681 | 0.4641 |

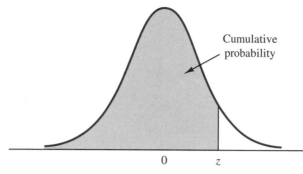

Cumulative probability

Entries in the table give the area under the curve to the left of the z value. For example, for z = 1.25, the cumulative probability is 0.8944.

0                    z

| z | 0.00 | 0.01 | 0.02 | 0.03 | 0.04 | 0.05 | 0.06 | 0.07 | 0.08 | 0.09 |
|---|------|------|------|------|------|------|------|------|------|------|
| 0.0 | 0.5000 | 0.5040 | 0.5080 | 0.5120 | 0.5160 | 0.5199 | 0.5239 | 0.5279 | 0.5319 | 0.5359 |
| 0.1 | 0.5398 | 0.5438 | 0.5478 | 0.5517 | 0.5557 | 0.5596 | 0.5636 | 0.5675 | 0.5714 | 0.5753 |
| 0.2 | 0.5793 | 0.5832 | 0.5871 | 0.5910 | 0.5948 | 0.5987 | 0.6026 | 0.6064 | 0.6103 | 0.6141 |
| 0.3 | 0.6179 | 0.6217 | 0.6255 | 0.6293 | 0.6331 | 0.6368 | 0.6406 | 0.6443 | 0.6480 | 0.6517 |
| 0.4 | 0.6554 | 0.6591 | 0.6628 | 0.6664 | 0.6700 | 0.6736 | 0.6772 | 0.6808 | 0.6844 | 0.6879 |
| 0.5 | 0.6915 | 0.6950 | 0.6985 | 0.7019 | 0.7054 | 0.7088 | 0.7123 | 0.7157 | 0.7190 | 0.7224 |
| 0.6 | 0.7257 | 0.7291 | 0.7324 | 0.7357 | 0.7389 | 0.7422 | 0.7454 | 0.7486 | 0.7517 | 0.7549 |
| 0.7 | 0.7580 | 0.7611 | 0.7642 | 0.7673 | 0.7704 | 0.7734 | 0.7764 | 0.7794 | 0.7823 | 0.7852 |
| 0.8 | 0.7881 | 0.7910 | 0.7939 | 0.7967 | 0.7995 | 0.8023 | 0.8051 | 0.8078 | 0.8106 | 0.8133 |
| 0.9 | 0.8159 | 0.8186 | 0.8212 | 0.8238 | 0.8264 | 0.8289 | 0.8315 | 0.8340 | 0.8365 | 0.8389 |
| 1.0 | 0.8413 | 0.8438 | 0.8461 | 0.8485 | 0.8508 | 0.8531 | 0.8554 | 0.8577 | 0.8599 | 0.8621 |
| 1.1 | 0.8643 | 0.8665 | 0.8686 | 0.8708 | 0.8729 | 0.8749 | 0.8770 | 0.8790 | 0.8810 | 0.8830 |
| 1.2 | 0.8849 | 0.8869 | 0.8888 | 0.8907 | 0.8925 | 0.8944 | 0.8962 | 0.8980 | 0.8997 | 0.9015 |
| 1.3 | 0.9032 | 0.9049 | 0.9066 | 0.9082 | 0.9099 | 0.9115 | 0.9131 | 0.9147 | 0.9162 | 0.9177 |
| 1.4 | 0.9192 | 0.9207 | 0.9222 | 0.9236 | 0.9251 | 0.9265 | 0.9279 | 0.9292 | 0.9306 | 0.9319 |
| 1.5 | 0.9332 | 0.9345 | 0.9357 | 0.9370 | 0.9382 | 0.9394 | 0.9406 | 0.9418 | 0.9429 | 0.9441 |
| 1.6 | 0.9452 | 0.9463 | 0.9474 | 0.9484 | 0.9495 | 0.9505 | 0.9515 | 0.9525 | 0.9535 | 0.9545 |
| 1.7 | 0.9554 | 0.9564 | 0.9573 | 0.9582 | 0.9591 | 0.9599 | 0.9608 | 0.9616 | 0.9625 | 0.9633 |
| 1.8 | 0.9641 | 0.9649 | 0.9656 | 0.9664 | 0.9671 | 0.9678 | 0.9686 | 0.9693 | 0.9699 | 0.9706 |
| 1.9 | 0.9713 | 0.9719 | 0.9726 | 0.9732 | 0.9738 | 0.9744 | 0.9750 | 0.9756 | 0.9761 | 0.9767 |
| 2.0 | 0.9772 | 0.9778 | 0.9783 | 0.9788 | 0.9793 | 0.9798 | 0.9803 | 0.9808 | 0.9812 | 0.9817 |
| 2.1 | 0.9821 | 0.9826 | 0.9830 | 0.9834 | 0.9838 | 0.9842 | 0.9846 | 0.9850 | 0.9854 | 0.9857 |
| 2.2 | 0.9861 | 0.9864 | 0.9868 | 0.9871 | 0.9875 | 0.9878 | 0.9881 | 0.9884 | 0.9887 | 0.9890 |
| 2.3 | 0.9893 | 0.9896 | 0.9898 | 0.9901 | 0.9904 | 0.9906 | 0.9909 | 0.9911 | 0.9913 | 0.9916 |
| 2.4 | 0.9918 | 0.9920 | 0.9922 | 0.9925 | 0.9927 | 0.9929 | 0.9931 | 0.9932 | 0.9934 | 0.9936 |
| 2.5 | 0.9938 | 0.9940 | 0.9941 | 0.9943 | 0.9945 | 0.9946 | 0.9948 | 0.9949 | 0.9951 | 0.9952 |
| 2.6 | 0.9953 | 0.9955 | 0.9956 | 0.9957 | 0.9959 | 0.9960 | 0.9961 | 0.9962 | 0.9963 | 0.9964 |
| 2.7 | 0.9965 | 0.9966 | 0.9967 | 0.9968 | 0.9969 | 0.9970 | 0.9971 | 0.9972 | 0.9973 | 0.9974 |
| 2.8 | 0.9974 | 0.9975 | 0.9976 | 0.9977 | 0.9977 | 0.9978 | 0.9979 | 0.9979 | 0.9980 | 0.9981 |
| 2.9 | 0.9981 | 0.9982 | 0.9982 | 0.9983 | 0.9984 | 0.9984 | 0.9985 | 0.9985 | 0.9986 | 0.9986 |
| 3.0 | 0.9987 | 0.9987 | 0.9987 | 0.9988 | 0.9988 | 0.9989 | 0.9989 | 0.9989 | 0.9990 | 0.9990 |

# Appendix E    Values of $e^{-\lambda}$

| $\lambda$ | $e^{-\lambda}$ | $\lambda$ | $e^{-\lambda}$ | $\lambda$ | $e^{-\lambda}$ |
|---|---|---|---|---|---|
| 0.05 | 0.9512 | 2.05 | 0.1287 | 4.05 | 0.0174 |
| 0.10 | 0.9048 | 2.10 | 0.1225 | 4.10 | 0.0166 |
| 0.15 | 0.8607 | 2.15 | 0.1165 | 4.15 | 0.0158 |
| 0.20 | 0.8187 | 2.20 | 0.1108 | 4.20 | 0.0150 |
| 0.25 | 0.7788 | 2.25 | 0.1054 | 4.25 | 0.0143 |
| 0.30 | 0.7408 | 2.30 | 0.1003 | 4.30 | 0.0136 |
| 0.35 | 0.7047 | 2.35 | 0.0954 | 4.35 | 0.0129 |
| 0.40 | 0.6703 | 2.40 | 0.0907 | 4.40 | 0.0123 |
| 0.45 | 0.6376 | 2.45 | 0.0863 | 4.45 | 0.0117 |
| 0.50 | 0.6065 | 2.50 | 0.0821 | 4.50 | 0.0111 |
| 0.55 | 0.5769 | 2.55 | 0.0781 | 4.55 | 0.0106 |
| 0.60 | 0.5488 | 2.60 | 0.0743 | 4.60 | 0.0101 |
| 0.65 | 0.5220 | 2.65 | 0.0707 | 4.65 | 0.0096 |
| 0.70 | 0.4966 | 2.70 | 0.0672 | 4.70 | 0.0091 |
| 0.75 | 0.4724 | 2.75 | 0.0639 | 4.75 | 0.0087 |
| 0.80 | 0.4493 | 2.80 | 0.0608 | 4.80 | 0.0082 |
| 0.85 | 0.4274 | 2.85 | 0.0578 | 4.85 | 0.0078 |
| 0.90 | 0.4066 | 2.90 | 0.0550 | 4.90 | 0.0074 |
| 0.95 | 0.3867 | 2.95 | 0.0523 | 4.95 | 0.0071 |
| 1.00 | 0.3679 | 3.00 | 0.0498 | 5.00 | 0.0067 |
| 1.05 | 0.3499 | 3.05 | 0.0474 | 5.05 | 0.0064 |
| 1.10 | 0.3329 | 3.10 | 0.0450 | 5.10 | 0.0061 |
| 1.15 | 0.3166 | 3.15 | 0.0429 | 5.15 | 0.0058 |
| 1.20 | 0.3012 | 3.20 | 0.0408 | 5.20 | 0.0055 |
| 1.25 | 0.2865 | 3.25 | 0.0388 | 5.25 | 0.0052 |
| 1.30 | 0.2725 | 3.30 | 0.0369 | 5.30 | 0.0050 |
| 1.35 | 0.2592 | 3.35 | 0.0351 | 5.35 | 0.0047 |
| 1.40 | 0.2466 | 3.40 | 0.0334 | 5.40 | 0.0045 |
| 1.45 | 0.2346 | 3.45 | 0.0317 | 5.45 | 0.0043 |
| 1.50 | 0.2231 | 3.50 | 0.0302 | 5.50 | 0.0041 |
| 1.55 | 0.2122 | 3.55 | 0.0287 | 5.55 | 0.0039 |
| 1.60 | 0.2019 | 3.60 | 0.0273 | 5.60 | 0.0037 |
| 1.65 | 0.1920 | 3.65 | 0.0260 | 5.65 | 0.0035 |
| 1.70 | 0.1827 | 3.70 | 0.0247 | 5.70 | 0.0033 |
| 1.75 | 0.1738 | 3.75 | 0.0235 | 5.75 | 0.0032 |
| 1.80 | 0.1653 | 3.80 | 0.0224 | 5.80 | 0.0030 |
| 1.85 | 0.1572 | 3.85 | 0.0213 | 5.85 | 0.0029 |
| 1.90 | 0.1496 | 3.90 | 0.0202 | 5.90 | 0.0027 |
| 1.95 | 0.1423 | 3.95 | 0.0193 | 5.95 | 0.0026 |
| 2.00 | 0.1353 | 4.00 | 0.0183 | 6.00 | 0.0025 |
| | | | | 7.00 | 0.0009 |
| | | | | 8.00 | 0.000335 |
| | | | | 9.00 | 0.000123 |
| | | | | 10.00 | 0.000045 |

## Chapter 1 Introduction

Churchman, C. W., R. L. Ackoff, and E. L. Arnoff. *Introduction to Operations Research.* Wiley, 1957.

Horner, P. "The Sabre Story." *OR/MS Today* (June 2000).

Leon, L., Z. Przasnyski, and K. C. Seal. "Spreadsheets and OR/MS Models: An End-User Perspective." *Interfaces* (March/April 1996).

Powell, S. G. "Innovative Approaches to Management Science." *OR/MS Today* (October 1996).

Savage, S. "Weighing the Pros and Cons of Decision Technology and Spreadsheets." *OR/MS Today* (February 1997).

Winston, W. L. "The Teachers' Forum: Management Science with Spreadsheets for MBAs at Indiana University." *Interfaces* (March/April 1996).

## Chapters 2 and 3 Probability

Anderson, D. R., D. J. Sweeney, and T. A. Williams. *Statistics for Business and Economics,* 10th ed. South-Western, 2008.

Hogg, R. V., and E. A. Tanis. *Probability and Statistical Inference,* 6th ed. Prentice Hall, 2001.

Ross, S. M. *Introduction to Probability Models,* 7th ed. Academic Press, 1993.

Wackerly, D. D., W. Mendenhall, and R. L. Scheaffer. *Mathematical Statistics with Applications,* 6th ed. Duxbury Press, 2002.

## Chapters 4 and 5 Decision Analysis and Game Theory

Clemen, R. T., and T. Reilly. *Making Hard Decisions with Decision Tools.* Duxbury Press, 2001.

Davis, M. D. *Game Theory: A Nontechnical Introduction.* Dover, 1997.

Goodwin, P., and G. Wright. *Decision Analysis for Management Judgment,* 2nd ed. Wiley, 1999.

McMillian, J. *Games, Strategies, and Managers.* Oxford University Press, 1992.

Myerson, R. B. *Game Theory: Analysis of Conflict.* Harvard University Press, 1997.

Osborne, M. J. *An Introduction to Game Theory.* Oxford University Press, 2004.

Pratt, J. W., H. Raiffa, and R. Schlaiter. *Introduction to Statistical Decision Theory.* MIT Press, 1995.

Raiffa, H. *Decision Analysis.* McGraw-Hill, 1997.

Schlaiter, R. *Analysis of Decisions Under Uncertainty.* Krieger, 1978.

## Chapter 6 Forecasting

Bowerman, B. L., and R. T. O'Connell. *Forecasting and Time Series: An Applied Approach,* 3rd ed. Duxbury Press, 1993.

Box, G. E. P., G. M. Jenkins, and G. C. Reinsel. *Time Series Analysis: Forecasting and Control,* 3rd ed. Prentice Hall, 1994.

Hanke, J. E., and A. G. Reitsch. *Business Forecasting,* 6th ed. Prentice Hall, 1998.

Makridakis, S. G., S. C. Wheelwright, and R. J. Hyndman. *Forecasting: Methods and Applications,* 3rd ed. Wiley, 1997.

Wilson, J. H., and B. Keating. *Business Forecasting,* 3rd ed. Irwin, 1998.

## Chapters 7 to 11 Linear Programming, Distribution and Network Models, Integer Programming Problems

Ahuja, R. K., T. L. Magnanti, and J. B. Orlin. *Network Flows, Theory, Algorithms, and Applications.* Prentice-Hall 1993.

Bazarra, M. S., J. J. Jarvis, and H. D. Sherali. *Linear Programming and Network Flows,* 2nd ed. Wiley, 1990.

Dantzig, G. B. *Linear Programming and Extensions.* Princeton University Press, 1963.

Greenberg, H. J. "How to Analyze the Results of Linear Programs—Part 1: Preliminaries." *Interfaces* 23, no. 4 (July/August 1993): 56–67.

Greenberg, H. J. "How to Analyze the Results of Linear Programs—Part 2: Price Interpretation." *Interfaces* 23, no. 5 (September/October 1993): 97–114.

Greenberg, H. J. "How to Analyze the Results of Linear Programs—Part 3: Infeasibility Diagnosis." *Interfaces* 23, no. 6 (November/December 1993): 120–139.

Lillien, G., and A. Rangaswamy. *Marketing Engineering: Computer-Assisted Marketing Analysis and Planning.* Addison-Wesley, 1998.

Nemhauser, G. L., and L. A. Wolsey. *Integer and Combinatorial Optimization.* Wiley, 1988.

Schrage, L. *Optimization Modeling with LINGO,* 4th ed. LINDO Systems Inc., 2000.

Winston, W. L., and S. C. Albright. *Practical Management Science,* 2nd ed. Duxbury Press, 2001.

## Chapter 12 Advanced Optimization Applications

Bazarra, M. S., H. D. Sherali, and C. M. Shetty. *Nonlinear Programming Theory and Applications*. Wiley, 1993.

Benninga, S. *Financial Modeling*. The MIT Press, 2000.

Luenberger, D. *Linear and Nonlinear Programming*, 2nd ed. Addison-Wesley Publishing Company, 1984.

Rardin, R. L. *Optimization in Operations Research*. Prentice-Hall, 1998.

## Chapter 13 Project Scheduling: PERT/CPM

Moder, J. J., C. R. Phillips, and E. W. Davis. *Project Management with CPM, PERT and Precedence Diagramming*, 3rd ed. Blitz, 1995.

Wiest, J., and F. Levy. *Management Guide to PERT-CPM*, 2nd ed. Prentice Hall, 1977.

## Chapter 14 Inventory Models

Fogarty, D. W., J. H. Blackstone, and T. R. Hoffman. *Production and Inventory Management*, 2nd ed. South-Western, 1990.

Hillier, F., and G. J. Lieberman. *Introduction to Operations Research*, 7th ed. McGraw-Hill, 2000.

Narasimhan, S. L., D. W. McLeavey, and P. B. Lington. *Production Planning and Inventory Control*, 2nd ed. Prentice Hall, 1995.

Orlicky, J., and G. W. Plossi. *Orlicky's Material Requirements Planning*. McGraw-Hill, 1994.

Vollmann, T. E., W. L. Berry, and D. C. Whybark. *Manufacturing Planning and Control Systems*, 4th ed. McGraw-Hill, 1997.

Zipkin, P. H. *Foundations of Inventory Management*. McGraw-Hill/Irwin, 2000.

## Chapter 15 Waiting Line Models

Bunday, B. D. *An Introduction to Queueing Theory*. Wiley, 1996.

Gross, D., and C. M. Harris. *Fundamentals of Queueing Theory*, 3rd ed. Wiley, 1997.

Hall, R. W. *Queueing Methods: For Service and Manufacturing*. Prentice Hall, 1991.

Hillier, F., and G. J. Lieberman. *Introduction to Operations Research*, 7th ed. McGraw-Hill, 2000.

Kao, E. P. C. *An Introduction to Stochastic Processes*. Duxbury Press, 1996.

## Chapter 16 Simulation

Banks, J., J. S. Carson, and B. L. Nelson. *Discrete-Event System Simulation*, 2nd ed. Prentice Hall, 1995.

Fishwick, P. A. *Simulation Model Design and Execution: Building Digital Worlds*. Prentice Hall, 1995.

Harrell, C. R., and K. Tumau. *Simulation Made Easy: A Manager's Guide*. Institute of Industrial Engineers, 1996.

Kelton, W. D., R. P. Sadowski, and D. T. Sturrock. *Simulation with Arena*, 4th ed. McGraw-Hill, 2007.

Law, A. M., and W. D. Kelton. *Simulation Modeling and Analysis*, 3rd ed. McGraw-Hill, 1999.

Pidd, M. *Computer Simulation in Management Science*, 4th ed. Wiley, 1998.

Thesen, A., and L. E. Travis. *Simulation for Decision Making*. Wadsworth, 1992.

## Chapter 17 Markov Processes

Bharucha-Reid, A. T. *Elements of the Theory of Markov Processes and Their Applications*. Dover, 1997.

Filar, J. A., and K. Vrieze. *Competitive Markov Decision Processes*. Springer-Verlag, 1996.

Norris, J. *Markov Chains*. Cambridge, 1997.

## Chapter 1

**2.** Define the problem; identify the alternatives; determine the criteria; evaluate the alternatives; choose an alternative.

**4.** A quantitative approach should be considered because the problem is large, complex, important, new, and repetitive.

**6.** Quicker to formulate, easier to solve, and/or more easily understood

**8. a.** Max  $10x + 5y$
s.t.
$$5x + 2y \leq 40$$
$$x \geq 0, y \geq 0$$

  **b.** Controllable inputs: $x$ and $y$
  Uncontrollable inputs: profit $(10, 5)$, labor-hours $(5, 2)$, and labor-hour availability $(40)$

  **c.** See Figure G1.8c.

  **d.** $x = 0, y = 20$; Profit $= \$100$ (solution by trial and error)

  **e.** Deterministic

**10. a.** Total units received $= x + y$
  **b.** Total cost $= 0.20x + 0.25y$
  **c.** $x + y = 5000$
  **d.** $x \leq 4000$ Kansas City
  $y \leq 3000$ Minneapolis
  **e.** Min  $0.20x + 0.25y$
  s.t.
$$x + \quad y = 5000$$
$$x \qquad \leq 4000$$
$$y \leq 3000$$
$$x, y \geq 0$$

**FIGURE G1.8c   SOLUTION**

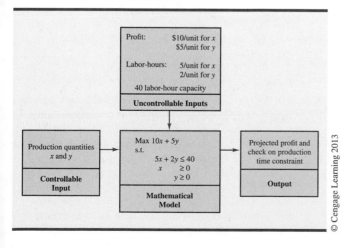

Profit:    $10/unit for $x$
           $5/unit for $y$

Labor-hours:  5/unit for $x$
              2/unit for $y$

40 labor-hour capacity

**Uncontrollable Inputs**

Production quantities
$x$ and $y$

**Controllable Input**

Max $10x + 5y$
s.t.
$5x + 2y \leq 40$
$x \qquad \geq 0$
$y \geq 0$

**Mathematical Model**

Projected profit and check on production time constraint

**Output**

© Cengage Learning 2013

**12. a.** If $x$ represents the number of pairs of shoes produced, a mathematical model for the total cost of producing $x$ pairs of shoes is $TC = 2000 + 60x$. The two components of total cost in this model are fixed cost ($\$2,000$) and variable cost ($60x$).

  **b.** If $P$ represents the total profit, the total revenue (TR) is $80x$ and a mathematical model for the total profit realized from an order for $x$ pairs of shoes is $P = TR - TC = 80x - (2000 + 60x) = 20x - 2000$.

  **c.** The breakeven point is the number of shoes produced $(x)$ at the point of no profit $(P = 0)$.
  Thus the breakeven point is the value of $x$ when $P = 20x - 2000 = 0$. This occurs when $20x = 2000$ or $x = 100$ (i.e., the breakeven point is 100 pairs of shoes).

**14. a.** If $x$ represents the number of copies of the book that are sold, total revenue (TR) $= 46x$ and total cost (TC) $= 160,000 + 6x$, so Profit $= TR - TC = 46x - (160,000 + 6x) = 40x - 160,000$. The breakeven point is the number of books produced $(x)$ at the point of no profit $(P = 0)$. Thus the breakeven point is the value of $x$ when $P = 40x - 160,000 = 0$. This occurs when $40x = 160,00$ or $x = 4000$ (i.e., the breakeven point is 4000 copies of the book).

  **b.** At a demand of 3800 copies, the publisher can expect a profit of $40(3800) - 160,000 = 152,000 - 160,000 = -8000$ (i.e., a loss of $\$8,000$).

  **c.** Here we know demand $(d = 3800)$ and want to determine the price $p$ at which we will breakeven (the point at which profit is 0). The minimum price per copy that the publisher must charge to break even is Profit $= p(3800) - (160,000 + 6(3800)) = 3800p - 182,800$. This occurs where $3800p = 182,800$ or $p = 48.10526316$ or a price of approximately $\$48$.

  **d.** If the publisher believes demand will remain at 4000 copies if the price per copy is increased to $\$50.95$, then the publisher could anticipate a profit of $TR - TC = 50.95(4000) - (160,000 + 6(4000)) = 203,800 - 184,000 = 19,800$ or a profit of $\$19,800$. This is a return of $p/TC = 10.8\%$ on the total cost of $\$184,000$, and the publisher should proceed if this return is sufficient.

**16. a.** The annual return per share of Oil Alaska is $\$6.00$ and the annual return per share of Southwest Petroleum is $\$4.00$, so the objective function that maximizes the total annual return is Max $6x + 4y$.

  **b.** The price per share of Oil Alaska is $\$50.00$ and the price per share of Southwest Petroleum is $\$30.00$, so

(1) the mathematical expression for the constraint that limits total investment funds to \$800,000 is $50x + 30y \leq 800000$,

(2) the mathematical expression for the constraint that limits investment in Oil Alaska to \$500,000 is $50x \leq 500000$, and

(3) the mathematical expression for the constraint that limits investment in Southwest Petroleum to \$450,000 is $30x \leq 450000$.

# Chapter 2

**1. a.** Record the number of persons waiting at the X-ray department at 9:00 A.M.

**b.** The experimental outcomes (sample points) are the number of people waiting: 0, 1, 2, 3, and 4. (*Note:* Although it is theoretically possible for more than four people to be waiting, we use what has actually been observed to define the experimental outcomes.)

**c.**

| Number Waiting | Probability |
|---|---|
| 0 | 0.10 |
| 1 | 0.25 |
| 2 | 0.30 |
| 3 | 0.20 |
| 4 | 0.15 |
| **Total** | **1.00** |

**d.** The relative frequency method

**2. a.** Choose a person at random, and have him/her taste the four blends of coffee and state a preference.

**b.** Assign a probability of $^1/_4$ to each blend, using the classical method of equally likely outcomes.

**c.**

| Blend | Probability |
|---|---|
| 1 | 0.20 |
| 2 | 0.30 |
| 3 | 0.35 |
| 4 | 0.15 |
| **Total** | **1.00** |

The relative frequency method was used.

**4. a.** Of the 132,275,830 individual tax returns received by the IRS in 2006, 31,675,935 were in the 1040A, Income Under \$25,000 category. Using the relative frequency approach, the probability a return from the 1040A, Income Under \$25,000 category would be chosen at random is $31675935/132275830 = 0.239$.

**b.** Of the 132,275,830 individual tax returns received by the IRS in 2006, 3,376,943 were in the Schedule C, Receipts Under \$25,000 category; 3,867,743 were in the Schedule C, Receipts \$25,000–\$100,000 category; and were 2,288,550 in the Schedule C, Receipts \$100,000

& Over category. Therefore, 9,533,236 Schedule Cs were filed in 2006, and the remaining $132,275,830 - 9,533,236 = 122,742,594$ individual returns did not use Schedule C. By the relative frequency approach, the probability that the chosen return did not use Schedule C is $122742594/132275830 = 0.928$.

**c.** Of the 132,275,830 individual tax returns received by the IRS in 2006, 12,893,802 were in the Non 1040A, Income \$100,000 & Over category; 2,288,550 were in the Schedule C, Receipts \$100,000 & Over category; and 265,612 were in the Schedule F, Receipts \$100,000 & Over category. By the relative frequency approach, the probability that the chosen return reported income/receipts of \$100,000 and over is $(12893802 + 2288550 + 265612)/132275830 = 15447964/132275830 = 0.117$.

**d.** 26,463,973 Non 1040A, Income \$50,000–\$100,000 returns were filed in 2006, so assuming examined returns were evenly distributed across the 10 categories (i.e., the IRS examined 1% of individual returns in each category), the number of returns from the Non 1040A, Income \$50,000–\$100,000 category that were examined is $0.01(26463973) = 264,639.73$ (or 264,640).

**e.** The proportion of total 2006 returns in the Schedule C, receipts \$100,000 & Over is $2,288,550/132,275,830 = 0.0173$. Therefore, if we assume the recommended additional taxes are evenly distributed across the ten categories, the amount of recommended additional taxes for the Schedule C, Receipts \$100,000 & Over category is $0.0173(\$13,045,221,000.00) = \$225,699,891.81$.

**6. a.** $P(A) = P(150 - 199) + P(200 \text{ and over})$

$$= \frac{26}{100} + \frac{5}{100}$$

$$= 0.31$$

**b.** $P(B) = P(\text{less than } 50) + P(50 - 99) + P(100 - 149)$
$$= 0.13 + 0.22 + 0.34$$
$$= 0.69$$

**7. a.** $P(A) = 0.40, P(B) = 0.40, P(C) = 0.60$

**b.** $P(A < B) = P(E_1, E_2, E_3, E_4) = 0.80$.
Yes, $P(A < B) = P(A) + P(B)$

**c.** $A^c = \{E_3, E_4, E_5\}$; $C^c = \{E_1, E_4\}$; $P(A^c) = 0.60$; $P(C^c) = 0.40$

**d.** $A < B^c = \{E_1, E_2, E_5\}$; $P(A < B^c) = 0.60$

**e.** $P(B < C) = P(E_2, E_3, E_4, E_5) = 0.80$

**8. a.** Let $P(A)$ be the probability a hospital had a daily inpatient volume of at least 200 and $P(B)$ be the probability a hospital had a nurse to patient ratio of at least 3.0. From the list of 30 hospitals, 16 had a daily inpatient volume of at least 200, so by the relative frequency approach the probability one of these hospitals had a daily inpatient volume of at least 200 is $P(A) = 16/30 = 0.533$, Similarly, since 10 (one-third) of the hospitals had a nurse-to-patient ratio of at least 3.0, the probability of a hospital having a nurse-to-patient ratio of at least

3.0 is $P(B) = 10/30 = 0.333$. Finally, since seven of the hospitals had both a daily inpatient volume of at least 200 and a nurse-to-patient ratio of at least 3.0, the probability of a hospital having both a daily inpatient volume of at least 200 and a nurse-to-patient ratio of at least 3.0 is $P(A \cap B) = 7/30 = 0.233$.

**b.** The probability that a hospital had a daily inpatient volume of at least 200 or a nurse-to-patient ratio of at least 3.0 or both is $P(A \cup B) = P(A) + P(B) - P(A \cap B) = 16/30 + 10/30 - 7/30 = (16 + 10 - 7)/30 = 19/30 = 0.633$.

**c.** The probability that a hospital had neither a daily inpatient volume of at least 200 nor a nurse-to-patient ratio of at least 3.0 is $1 - P(A \cup B) = 1 - 19/30 = 11/30 = 0.367$.

**10.** $P(\text{Defective and Minor}) = 4/25$
$P(\text{Defective and Major}) = 2/25$
$P(\text{Defective}) = (4/25) + (2/25) = 6/25$
$P(\text{Major Defect} \mid \text{Defective}) = P(\text{Defective and Major})/P(\text{Defective}) = (2/25)/(6/25) = 2/6 = 1/3$.

**12. a.** $P(A \mid B) = \dfrac{P(A \cap B)}{P(B)} = \dfrac{0.40}{0.60} = 0.6667$

**b.** $P(B \mid A) = \dfrac{P(A \cap B)}{P(A)} = \dfrac{0.40}{0.50} = 0.80$

**c.** No, because $P(A \mid B) \neq P(A)$

**13. a.**

**Reason for Applying**

|  | **Quality** | Cost/ **Convenience** | **Other** | **Total** |
|---|---|---|---|---|
| Full Time | 0.218 | 0.204 | 0.039 | 0.461 |
| Part Time | 0.208 | 0.307 | 0.024 | 0.539 |
| **Total** | 0.426 | 0.511 | 0.063 | 1.000 |

**b.** A student will most likely cite cost or convenience as the first reason: probability = 0.511; school quality is the first reason cited by the second largest number of students: probability = 0.426.

**c.** $P(\text{Quality} \mid \text{Full Time}) = 0.218/0.461 = 0.473$

**d.** $P(\text{Quality} \mid \text{Part Time}) = 0.208/0.539 = 0.386$

**e.** $P(B) = 0.426$ and $P(B \mid A) = 0.473$
Because $P(B) \neq P(B \mid A)$, the events are dependent.

**14.**

|  | **$0–$499** | **$500–$999** | **$\geq$1000** |  |
|---|---|---|---|---|
| <2 yrs | 120 | 240 | 90 | 450 |
| $\geq$2 yrs | 75 | 275 | 200 | 550 |
|  | 195 | 515 | 290 | 1000 |

|  | **$0–$499** | **$500–$999** | **$\geq$1000** |  |
|---|---|---|---|---|
| <2 yrs | 0.12 | 0.24 | 0.09 | 0.45 |
| $\geq$2 yrs | 0.075 | 0.275 | 0.2 | 0.55 |
|  | 0.195 | 0.515 | 0.29 | 1.00 |

**a.** $P(< 2 \text{ yrs}) = 0.45$
**b.** $P(\geq \$1000) = 0.29$
**c.** $P(2 \text{ accounts have} \geq \$1000) = (0.29)(0.29) = 0.0841$
**d.** $P(\$500 - \$999 \mid \geq 2 \text{ yrs}) = P(\$500 - \$999 \text{ and} \geq 2 \text{ yrs})/P(\geq 2\text{yrs}) = 0.275/0.55 = 0.5$
**e.** $P(< 2 \text{ yrs and} \geq \$1000) = 0.09$
**f.** $P(\geq 2 \text{ yrs} \mid \$500 - \$999) = 0.275/0.515 = 0.533981$

**16. a.** 0.19
**b.** 0.71
**c.** 0.29

**18. a.** 0.25, 0.40, 0.10
**b.** 0.25
**c.** Independent; program does not help

**20. a.** $P(B \cap A_1) = P(A_1)P(B \mid A_1) = (0.20)(0.50) = 0.10$
$P(B \cap A_2) = P(A_2)P(B \mid A_2) = (0.50)(0.40) = 0.20$
$P(B \cap A_3) = P(A_3)P(B \mid A_3) = (0.30)(0.30) = 0.09$

**b.** $P(A_2 \mid B) = \dfrac{0.20}{0.10 + 0.20 + 0.09} = 0.51$

**c.**

| Events | $P(A_i)$ | $P(B \mid A_i)$ | $P(A_i \cap B)$ | $P(A_i \mid B)$ |
|---|---|---|---|---|
| $A_1$ | 0.20 | 0.50 | 0.10 | 0.26 |
| $A_2$ | 0.50 | 0.40 | 0.20 | 0.51 |
| $A_3$ | 0.30 | 0.30 | 0.09 | 0.23 |
|  | 1.00 |  | 0.39 | 1.00 |

**22. a.** 0.40
**b.** 0.67

**24.** Let $S$ = speeding is reported
$S^C$ = speeding is not reported
$F$ = Accident results in fatality for vehicle occupant
We have $P(S) = 0.129$, so $P(S^C) = 0.871$. Also $P(F \mid S) = 0.196$ and $P(F \mid S^C) = 0.05$. Using the tabular form of Bayes' theorem provides:

| Events | Prior Proba-bilities | Conditional Proba-bilities | Joint Proba-bilities | Posterior Proba-bilities |
|---|---|---|---|---|
| $S$ | 0.129 | 0.196 | 0.0384 | 0.939 |
| $S^C$ | 0.871 | 0.050 | 0.0025 | 0.061 |
|  | 1.000 |  | 0.0409 | 1.000 |

**25. a.** $P$(defective part) = 0.0065 (see below)

| Events | $P(A_i)$ | $P(D\,|\,A_i)$ | $P(A_i \cap D)$ | $P(A_i \cap D)$ |
|---|---|---|---|---|
| Supplier A | 0.60 | 0.0025 | 0.0015 | 0.23 |
| Supplier B | 0.30 | 0.0100 | 0.0030 | 0.46 |
| Supplier C | 0.10 | 0.020 | 0.0020 | 0.31 |
|  | 1.00 |  | $P(D)$ = 0.0065 | 1.00 |

**b.** Supplier B (prob. = 0.46) is the most likely source.

**26. a.** $P(D_1\,|\,S_1)$ = 0.2195, $P(D_2\,|\,S_1)$ = 0.7805
   **b.** $P(D_1\,|\,S_2)$ = 0.5000, $P(D_2\,|\,S_2)$ = 0.5000
   **c.** $P(D_1\,|\,S_3)$ = 0.8824, $P(D_2\,|\,S_3)$ = 0.1176
   **d.** 0.1582 and 0.8418

**28. a.**

|  | Male Applicants | Female Applicants |
|---|---|---|
| Accept | 70 | 40 |
| Deny | 90 | 80 |

After combining these two crosstabulations into a single crosstabulation with Accept and Deny as the row labels and Male and Female as the column labels, we see that the rate of acceptance for males across the university is 70/(70 + 90) = 0.4375 or approximately 44%, while the rate of acceptance for females across the university is 40/(40 + 80) = 0.33 or 33%.

**b.** If we focus solely on the overall data, we would conclude that the university's admission process is biased in favor of male applicant. However, this occurs because most females apply to the College of Business (which has a far lower rate of acceptance that the College of Engineering). When we look at each college's acceptance rate by gender, we see that the acceptance rate of males and females are equal in the College of Engineering (75%) and the acceptance rate of males and females are equal in the College of Business (33%). The data do not support the accusation that the university favors male applicants in its admissions process.

# Chapter 3

**1. a.** Values: 0, 1, 2, . . . , 20 discrete
   **b.** Values: 0, 1, 2, . . . discrete
   **c.** Values: 0, 1, 2, . . . , 50 discrete
   **d.** Values: $0 \le x \le 8$ continuous
   **e.** Values: $x \ge 0$ continuous

**2. a.** 0.05; probability of a $200,000 profit
   **b.** 0.70
   **c.** 0.40

**3. a.**

| $x$ | $f(x)$ |
|---|---|
| 1 | 3/20 = 0.15 |
| 2 | 5/20 = 0.25 |
| 3 | 8/20 = 0.40 |
| 4 | 4/20 = 0.20 |
|  | Total   1.00 |

**b.**

**c.** $f(x) \ge 0$ for $x = 1, 2, 3, 4$
   $\Sigma f(x) = 1$

**4. a.**

| $x$ | $f(x)$ | $xf(x)$ |
|---|---|---|
| 3 | 0.25 | 0.75 |
| 6 | 0.50 | 3.00 |
| 9 | 0.25 | 2.25 |
| Totals | 1.00 | 6.00 |

$E(x) = \mu = 6.00$

**b.**

| $x$ | $x - \mu$ | $(x - \mu)^2$ | $f(x)$ | $(x - \mu)^2 f(x)$ |
|---|---|---|---|---|
| 3 | $-3$ | 9 | 0.25 | 2.25 |
| 6 | 0 | 0 | 0.50 | 0.00 |
| 9 | 3 | 9 | 0.25 | 2.25 |
|  |  |  |  | 4.50 |

$\mathrm{Var}(x) = \sigma^2 = 4.50$

**c.** $\sigma = \sqrt{4.50} = 2.12$

**6. a.**

| $x$ | $f(x)$ |
|---|---|
| 1 | 0.97176 |
| 2 | 0.026675 |
| 3 | 0.00140 |
| 4 | 0.00014 |
| 5 | 0.00002 |

If we let $x = 5$ represent quintuplets or more, the probability distribution of the number children born per pregnancy in 1996 is provided in the first two columns of the preceding table.

**b.**

| x | f(x) | xf(x) | x − μ | (x − μ)² | (x − μ)²f(x) |
|---|------|-------|-------|----------|--------------|
| 1 | 0.97176 | 0.97176 | −0.03000 | 0.00090 | 0.00087 |
| 2 | 0.026675 | 0.05333 | 0.97000 | 0.94090 | 0.02509 |
| 3 | 0.00140 | 0.004218 | 1.97000 | 3.88090 | 0.00544 |
| 4 | 0.00014 | 0.00059 | 2.97000 | 8.82090 | 0.00131 |
| 5 | 0.00002 | 0.00011 | 3.97000 | 15.76089 | 0.00034 |
| | | 1.0300 | | | 0.03305 |

The expected value of the number children born per pregnancy in 1996 is E[x] = 1.030 and the variance of the number children born per pregnancy in 1996 is Var[x] = $\sigma^2$ = 0.03305.

**c.**

| y | f(y) |
|---|------|
| 1 | 0.965964 |
| 2 | 0.0333143 |
| 3 | 0.0014868 |
| 4 | 0.0000863 |
| 5 | 0.0000163 |

If we let y = 5 represent quintuplets or more, the probability distribution of the number children born per pregnancy in 2006 is provided in the first two columns of the preceding table.

**d.**

| y | f(y) | yf(y) | y − μ | (y − μ)² | (y − μ)²f(y) |
|---|------|-------|-------|----------|--------------|
| 1 | 0.965964 | 0.9650964 | −0.0366118 | 0.0013404 | 0.001293639 |
| 2 | 0.0333143 | 0.0666286 | 0.9633882 | 0.9281168 | 0.030919551 |
| 3 | 0.0014868 | 0.0044604 | 1.9633882 | 3.8548932 | 0.005731423 |
| 4 | 0.0000863 | 0.0003451 | 2.9633882 | 8.7816695 | 0.000757611 |
| 5 | 0.0000163 | 0.0000814 | 3.9633882 | 15.7084459 | 0.000255769 |
| | 1.0000000 | 1.0366118 | | | 0.038957993 |

The expected value of the number children born per pregnancy in 2006 is E[y] = 1.030 and the variance of the number children born per pregnancy in 2006 (after rounding) is Var[y] = $\sigma^2$ = 0.0390.

**e.** The number of children born per pregnancy is greater in 2006 than in 1996, and the variation in the number of children born per pregnancy is also greater in 2006 than in 1996. However, these data provide no information on which we could base a determination of causes of this upward trend.

**8. a.** Medium 145; large 140; prefer medium
**b.** Medium 2725; large 12,400; prefer medium

**9. a.** $f(1) = \binom{2}{1}(0.4)^1(0.6)^1 = \frac{2!}{1!1!}(0.4)(0.6) = 0.48$

**b.** $f(0) = \binom{2}{0}(0.4)^0(0.6)^2 = \frac{2!}{0!2!}(1)(0.36) = 0.36$

**c.** $f(2) = \binom{2}{2}(0.4)^2(0.6)^0 = \frac{2!}{2!0!}(0.16)(1) = 0.16$

**d.** $P(x \geq 1) = f(1) + f(2) = 0.48 + 0.16 = 0.64$

**e.** $E(x) = np = 2(0.4) = 0.8$
$Var(x) = np(1 - p) = 2(0.4)(0.6) = 0.48$
$\sigma = \sqrt{0.48} = 0.6928$

**10. a.** $f(0) = 0.3487$
**b.** $f(2) = 0.1937$
**c.** 0.9298
**d.** 0.6513
**e.** 1
**f.** $\sigma_2 = 0.9000$, $\sigma = 0.9487$

**12. a.** Probability of a defective part being produced must be 0.03 for each trial; trials must be independent.
**b.** Two outcomes result in exactly one defect.
**c.** P(no defects) = (0.97)(0.97) = 0.9409
P(1 defect) = 2(0.03)(0.97) = 0.0582
P(2 defects) = (0.03)(0.03) = 0.0009

**14. a.** $f(x) = \frac{2^x e^{-2}}{x!}$
**b.** $\mu = 6$ for 3 time periods
**c.** $f(x) = \frac{6^x e^{-6}}{x!}$
**d.** $f(2) = \frac{2^2 e^{-2}}{2!} = \frac{4(0.1353)}{2} = 0.2706$
**e.** $f(6) = \frac{6^6 e^{-6}}{6!} = 0.1606$
**f.** $f(5) = \frac{4^5 e^{-4}}{5!} = 0.1563$

**16. a.** 0.0009
**b.** 0.9927
**c.** 0.0302
**d.** 0.8271

**18. a.**

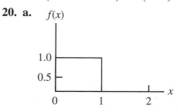

**b.** P(x = 1.25) = 0; the probability of any single point is zero because the area under the curve above any single point is zero.
**c.** P(1.0 ≤ x ≤ 1.25) = 2(0.25) = 0.50
**d.** P(1.2 < x < 1.5) = 2(0.30) = 0.60

**20. a.**

**b.** 0.50

**c.** 0.30

**d.** 0.40

**21. a.** $P(0 \le z \le 0.83) = 0.7967 - 0.5000 = 0.2967$

    **b.** $P(-1.57 \le z \le 0) = 0.5000 - 0.0582 = 0.4418$

    **c.** $P(z > 0.44) = 1.0000 - 0.6700 = 0.2300$

    **d.** $P(z \ge -0.23) = 1.0000 - 0.4090 = 0.5910$

    **e.** $P(z < 1.20) = 0.8849$

    **f.** $P(z < -0.71) = 0.2389$

**22. a.** 1.96

    **b.** 1.96

    **c.** 0.61

    **d.** 1.12

    **e.** 0.44

    **f.** 0.44

**23. a.** Area $= 0.2119$    $z = -0.80$

    **b.** Area outside the interval 0.0970 must be split between the two tails.
Cumulative probability $= 0.5(0.0970) + 0.9030 = 0.9515$    $z = 1.66$

    **c.** Area outside the interval 0.7948 must be split between the two tails.
Cumulative probability $= 0.5(0.7948) + 0.2052 = 0.6026$    $z = 0.26$

    **d.** Area $= 0.9948$    $z = 2.56$

    **e.** Area $= 1.0000 - 0.6915 = 0.3085$    $z = -0.50$

**24. a.** 0.3830

    **b.** 0.1056

    **c.** 0.0062

    **d.** 0.1603

**26. a.** 0.7745

    **b.** 36.32 days

    **c.** 19%

**28.** $\mu = 19.23$

**29. a.** $P(x \le x_0) = 1 - e^{-x_0/3}$

    **b.** $P(x \le 2) = 1 - e^{-2/3} = 1 - 0.5134 = 0.4866$

    **c.** $P(x \ge 3) = 1 - P(x \le 3) = 1 - (1 - e^{-3/3}) = e^{-1} = 0.3679$

    **d.** $P(x \le 5) = 1 - e^{-5/3} = 1 - 0.1889 = 0.8111$

    **e.** $P(2 \le x \le 5) = P(x \le 5) - P(x \le 2) = 0.8111 - 0.4866 = 0.3245$

**30. a.** 0.3935

    **b.** 0.2231

    **c.** 0.3834

**31. a.**

f(x)

.09
.08
.07
.06
.05
.04
.03
.02
.01

6    12    18    24    x

**b.** $P(x \le 12) = 1 - e^{-12/12} = 0.6321$

**c.** $P(x \le 6) = 1 - e^{-6/12} = 0.3935$

**d.** $P(x \ge 30) = 1 - P(x < 30) = 1 - (1 - e^{-30/12}) = 0.0821$

**32. a.** 50 hours

    **b.** 0.3935

    **c.** 0.1353

**34. a.** 0.5130

    **b.** 0.1655

    **c.** 0.3679

# Chapter 4

**1. a.**

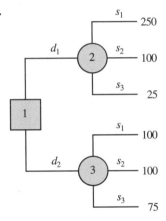

**b.**

| Decision | Maximum Profit | Minimum Profit |
|---|---|---|
| $d_1$ | 250 | 25 |
| $d_2$ | 100 | 75 |

Optimistic approach: Select $d_1$
Conservative approach: Select $d_2$
Regret or opportunity loss table:

| Decision | $s_1$ | $s_2$ | $s_3$ |
|---|---|---|---|
| $d_1$ | 0 | 0 | 50 |
| $d_2$ | 150 | 0 | 0 |

Maximum regret: 50 for $d_1$ and 150 for $d_2$; select $d_1$

**2. a.** Optimistic: $d_1$
Conservative: $d_3$
Minimax regret: $d_3$

    **c.** Optimistic: $d_1$
Conservative: $d_2$ or $d_3$
Minimax regret: $d_2$

**3. a.** Decision: Choose the best plant size from the two alternatives—a small plant and a large plant.

Chance event: Market demand for the new product line with three possible outcomes (states of nature): low, medium, and high

**b.** Influence Diagram:

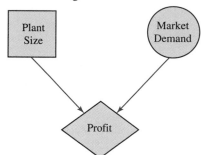

**c.**

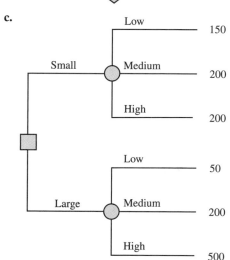

**d.**

| Decision | Maximum Profit | Minimum Profit | Maximum Regret |
|----------|----------------|----------------|----------------|
| Small | 200 | 150 | 300 |
| Large | 500 | 50 | 100 |

Optimistic Approach: Large plant
Conservative Approach: Small plant
Minimax Regret: Large plant

**4. a.** The decision faced by Amy is to select the best lease option from three alternatives (Hepburn Honda, Midtown Motors, and Hopkins Automotive). The chance event is the number of miles Amy will drive.

**b.** The payoff for any combination of alternative and chance event is the sum of the total monthly charges and total additional mileage cost; that is,

For the Hepburn Honda lease option:

36000 miles (12000 miles for 3 years):
  36($299) + $0.15(36000 − 36000) = $10,764

45000 miles (15000 miles for 3 years):
  36($299) + $0.15(45000 − 36000) = $12,114
54000 miles (18000 miles for 3 years):
  36($299) + $0.15(54000 − 36000) = $13,464

For the Midtown Motors lease option:

36000 miles (12000 miles for 3 years):
  36($310) + $0.20*max(36000 − 45000,0) = $11,160.00
45000 miles (15000 miles for 3 years):
  36($310) + $0.20*max(45000 − 45000,0) = $11,160.00
54000 miles (18000 miles for 3 years):
  36($310) + $0.20*max(54000 − 45000,0) = $12,960.00

For the Hopkins Automotive lease option:

36000 miles (12000 miles for 3 years):
  36($325) + $0.15*max(36000 − 54000,0) = $11,700
45000 miles (15000 miles for 3 years):
  36($325) + $0.15*max(45000 − 54000,0) = $11,700
54000 miles (18000 miles for 3 years):
  36($325) + $0.15*max(54000 − 54000,0) = $11,700

So the payoff table for Amy's problem is:

| Dealer | Actual Miles Driven Annually | | |
|--------|---------|---------|---------|
| | **12,000** | **15,000** | **18,000** |
| Hepburn Honda | $10,764 | $12,114 | $13,464 |
| Midtown Motors | $11,160 | $11,160 | $12,960 |
| Hopkins Automotive | $11,700 | $11,700 | $11,700 |

**c.** The minimum and maximum payoffs for each of Amy's three alternatives are:

| Dealer | Minimum Cost | Maximum Cost |
|--------|--------------|--------------|
| Hepburn Honda | $10,764 | $13,464 |
| Midtown Motors | $11,160 | $12,960 |
| Hopkins Automotive | $11,700 | $11,700 |

Thus:
The optimistic approach results in selection of the Hepburn Automotive lease option (which has the smallest minimum cost of the three alternatives—$10,764).

The conservative approach results in selection of the Hopkins Automotive lease option (which has the smallest maximum cost of the three alternatives—$11,700).

To find the lease option to select under the minimax regret approach, we must first construct an opportunity loss (or regret) table. For each of the three chance events (driving 12,000 miles, driving 15,000 miles, driving 18,000 miles), subtract the minimum payoff from the payoff for each decision alternative.

**Regret Table**

**State of Nature**
**(Actual Miles Driven Annually)**
**Maximum Regret**

| Decision Alternative | 12,000 | 15,000 | 18,000 |
|---|---|---|---|
| Hepburn Honda | $0 | $954 | $1,764 |
| Midtown Motors | $396 | $0 | $1,260 |
| Hopkins Automotive | $936 | $540 | $0 |

The maximum regret associated with each of the three decision alternatives is as follows:

| Decision Alternative | Maximum Regret |
|---|---|
| Hepburn Honda | $1764 |
| Midtown Motors | $1260 |
| Hopkins Automotive | $ 936 |

The minimax regret approach results in selection of the Hopkins Automotive lease option (which has the smallest regret of the three alternatives: $936).

**d.** We first find the expected value for the payoffs associated with each of Amy's three alternatives:

$$EV(\text{Hepburn Honda}) = 0.5(\$10,764) + 0.4(\$12,114) + 0.1(\$13,464) = \$11,574$$
$$EV(\text{Midtown Motors}) = 0.5(\$11,160) + 0.4(\$11,160) + 0.1(\$12,960) = \$11,340$$
$$EV(\text{Hopkins Automotive}) = 0.5(\$11,700) + 0.4(\$11,700) + 0.1(\$11,700) = \$11,700$$

The expected value approach results in selection of the Midtown Motors lease option (which has the minimum expected value of the three alternatives—$11,340).

**e.** The risk profile for the decision to lease from Midtown Motors is as follows:

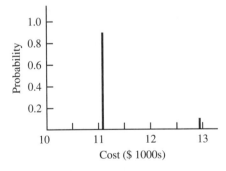

Note that although we have three chance outcomes (drive 12,000 miles annually, drive 15,000 miles annually, and drive 18,000 miles annually), we only have two unique costs on this graph. This is because for this decision alternative (lease from Midtown Motors) there are only two unique payoffs associated with the three chance outcomes—the payoff (cost) associated with the Midtown Motors lease is the same for two of

the chance outcomes (whether Amy drives 12,000 miles or 15,000 miles annually, her payoff is $11,160).

**f.** We first find the expected value for the payoffs associated with each of Amy's three alternatives:

$$EV(\text{Hepburn Honda}) = 0.3(\$10,764) + 0.4(\$12,114) + 0.3(\$13,464) = \$12,114$$
$$EV(\text{Midtown Motors}) = 0.3(\$11,160) + 0.4(\$11,160) + 0.3(\$12,960) = \$11,700$$
$$EV(\text{Hopkins Automotive}) = 0.3(\$11,700) + 0.4(\$11,700) + 0.3(\$11,700) = \$11,700$$

The expected value approach results in selection of either the Midtown Motors lease option or the Hopkins Automotive lease option (both of which have the minimum expected value of the three alternatives—$11,700).

**5. a.** $EV(d_1) = 0.65(250) + 0.15(100) + 0.20(25) = 182.5$
$EV(d_2) = 0.65(100) + 0.15(100) + 0.20(75) = 95$
The optimal decision is $d_1$.

**6. a.** Pharmaceuticals; 3.4%
  **b.** Financial; 4.6%

**7. a.** $EV(\text{own staff}) = 0.2(650) + 0.5(650) + 0.3(600) = 635$
$EV(\text{outside vendor}) = 0.2(900) + 0.5(600) + 0.3(300) = 570$
$EV(\text{combination}) = 0.2(800) + 0.5(650) + 0.3(500) = 635$

Optimal decision: Hire an outside vendor with an expected cost of $570,000

  **b.**

| | Cost | Probability |
|---|---|---|
| Own staff | 300 | 0.3 |
| Outside vendor | 600 | 0.5 |
| Combination | 900 | 0.2 |
| | | 1.0 |

**8. a.** $EV(d_1) = p(10) + (1 - p)(1) = 9p + 1$
$EV(d_2) = p(4) + (1 - p)(3) = 1p + 3$

$9p + 1 = 1p + 3$ and hence $p = 0.25$
$d_2$ is optimal for $p \geq 0.25$, $d_1$ is optimal for $p \geq 0.25$

**b.** $d_2$

**c.** As long as the payoff for $s_1 \geq 2$, then $d_2$ is optimal.

**10. b.** Space Pirates

EV = \$724,000

\$84,000 better than Battle Pacific

**c.** $200   0.18

$400   0.32

$800   0.30

$1600   0.20

**d.** $P(\text{Competition}) > 0.7273$

**12. a.** Decision: Whether to lengthen the runway

Chance event: The location decisions of Air Express and DRI

Consequence: Annual revenue

**b.** $255,000

**c.** $270,000

**d.** No

**e.** Lengthen the runway.

**14. a.** If $s_1$, then $d_1$; if $s_2$, then $d_1$ or $d_2$; if $s_3$, then $d_2$

**b.** EvwPI = $0.65(250) + 0.15(100) + 0.20(75) = 192.5$

**c.** From the solution to Problem 5, we know that $EV(d_1) = 182.5$ and $EV(d_2) = 95$; thus, recommended decision is $d_1$; hence, EvwoPI = 182.5.

**d.** EVPI = EvwPI − EvwoPI = $192.5 − 182.5 = 10$

**16. a.**

**b.** EV (node 6)  $= 0.57(100) + 0.43(300) = 186$

EV (node 7)  $= 0.57(400) + 0.43(200) = 314$

EV (node 8)  $= 0.18(100) + 0.82(300) = 264$

EV (node 9)  $= 0.18(400) + 0.82(200) = 236$

EV (node 10) $= 0.40(100) + 0.60(300) = 220$

EV (node 11) $= 0.40(400) + 0.60(200) = 280$

EV (node 3)  $= \text{Max}(186,314) = 314 d_2$

EV (node 4)  $= \text{Max}(264,236) = 264 d_1$

EV (node 5)  $= \text{Max}(220,280) = 280 d_2$

EV (node 2)  $= 0.56(314) + 0.44(264) = 292$

EV (node 1)  $= \text{Max}(292,280) = 292$

∴ Market Research

If favorable, decision $d_2$

If unfavorable, decision $d_1$

**18. a.** $5000 − 200 − 2000 − 150 = 2650$

$3000 − 200 − 2000 − 150 = 650$

**b.** Expected values at nodes:

8: 2350    5: 2350    9: 1100

6: 1150    10: 2000   7: 2000

4: 1870    3: 2000    2: 1560

1: 1560

**c.** Cost would have to decrease by at least $130,000.

**d.**

| Payoff (in millions) | Probability |
|---|---|
| −$200 | 0.20 |
| 800 | 0.32 |
| 2800 | 0.48 |
| | 1.00 |

**20. b.** If Do Not Review, Accept

If Review and $F$, Accept

If Review and $U$, Accept

Always Accept

**c.** Do not review; EVSI = $0

**d.** $87,500; better method of predicting success

**22. a.** Order two lots; $60,000

**b.** If $E$, order two lots

If $V$, order one lot

EV = $60,500

**c.** EVPI = $14,000

EVSI = $500

Efficiency = 3.6%

Yes, use consultant.

**23.**

| State of Nature | $P(s_j)$ | $P(I\|s_j)$ | $P(I \cap s_j)$ | $P(s_j\|I)$ |
|---|---|---|---|---|
| $s_1$ | 0.2 | 0.10 | 0.020 | 0.1905 |
| $s_2$ | 0.5 | 0.05 | 0.025 | 0.2381 |
| $s_3$ | 0.3 | 0.20 | 0.060 | 0.5714 |
| | 1.0 | | $P(I) = 0.105$ | 1.0000 |

**24. a.** 0.695, 0.215, 0.090

0.98, 0.02

0.79, 0.21

0.00, 1.00

**c.** If $C$, Expressway
If $O$, Expressway
If $R$, Queen City
26.6 minutes

## Chapter 5

**1. a.** $EV(d_1) = 0.40(100) + 0.30(25) + 0.30(0) = 47.5$
$EV(d_2) = 0.40(75) + 0.30(50) + 0.30(25) = 52.5$
$EV(d_3) = 0.40(50) + 0.30(50) + 0.30(50) = 50.0$
The optimal solution is $d_2$.

**b.** Using utilities

| Decision Maker A | Decision Maker B |
|---|---|
| $EU(d_1) = 4.9$ | $EU(d_1) = 4.45$ Best |
| $EU(d_2) = 5.9$ | $EU(d_2) = 3.75$ |
| $EU(d_1) = 6.0$ Best | $EU(d_1) = 3.00$ |

**c.** Difference in attitude toward risk; decision maker A tends to avoid risk, whereas decision maker B tends to take a risk for the opportunity of a large payoff.

**2. a.** $d_2$; $EV(d_2) = \$5000$
**b.** $p$ = probability of a $0 cost
$1 - p$ = probability of a $200,000 cost
**c.** $d_1$; $EV(d_1) = 9.9$
**d.** Expected utility approach; it avoids risk of large loss.

**4. a.** Route B; $EV = 58.5$
**b.** $p$ = probability of a 45-minute travel time
$1 - p$ = probability of a 90-minute travel time
**c.** Route A; $EV = 7.6$; risk avoider

**5. a.**

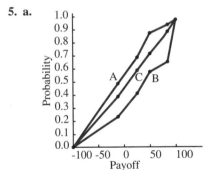

**b.** A—risk avoider
B—risk taker
C—risk neutral
**c.** Risk avoider A, at $20 payoff $p = 0.70$
$EV(\text{Lottery}) = 0.70(100) + 0.30(-100) = \$40$
Therefore, will pay $40 - 20 = \$20$
Risk taker B, at $20 payoff $p = 0.45$
$EV(\text{Lottery}) = 0.45(100) + 0.55(-100) = -\$10$
Therefore, will pay $20 - (-10) = \$30$

**6.** A: $d_1$; B: $d_2$; C: $d_2$

**8. a.**

|  | Win | Lose |
|---|---|---|
| Bet | 350 | −10 |
| Do not bet | 0 | 0 |

**b.** $d_2$
**c.** Risk takers
**d.** Between 0 and 0.26

**10. a.** $EV(\text{Comedy}) = 0.30(30\%) + 0.60(25\%)$
$+ 0.10(20\%) = 26.0\%$
and
$EV(\text{Reality Show}) = 0.30(40\%) + 0.40(20\%)$
$+ 0.30(15\%) = 24.5\%$
Using the expected value approach, the manager should choose the Comedy.

**b.** $p$ = probability of a 40% percentage of viewing audience
$1 - p$ = probability of a 15% percentage of viewing audience

**c.** Arbitrarily using a utility of 10 for the best payoff and a utility of 0 for the worst payoff, the utility table is as follows:

| Percentage of Viewing Audience | Indifference Value of $p$ | Utility Value |
|---|---|---|
| 40% | Does not apply | 10 |
| 30% | 0.40 | 4 |
| 25% | 0.30 | 3 |
| 20% | 0.10 | 1 |
| 15% | Does not apply | 0 |

and so the expected payoffs in terms of utilities are as follows:

$EV(\text{Comedy}) = 0.30(4) + 0.60(3) + 0.10(1) = 3.1$
and
$EV(\text{Reality Show}) = 0.30(10) + 0.40(1)$
$+ 0.30(0) = 3.4$

Using the expected utility approach, the manager should choose the Reality Show.
Although the Comedy has the higher expected payoff in terms of percentage of viewing audience, the Reality Show has the higher expected utility. This suggests the manager is a risk taker.

**11.**

|  |  | Player B | | | |
|---|---|---|---|---|---|
|  |  | $b_1$ | $b_2$ | $b_3$ | Minimum |
| Player A | $a_1$ | 8 | 5 | 7 | ⑤ |
|  | $a_2$ | 2 | 4 | 10 | 2 |
|  | Maximum | 8 | ⑤ | 10 | |

The maximum of the row minimums is 5 and the minimum of the column maximums is 5. The game has a pure strategy. Player A should take strategy $a_1$ and Player B should take strategy $b_2$. The value of the game is 5.

**12. a.** The payoff table is as follows:

|  |  | Blue Army | | |
|---|---|---|---|---|
|  |  | Attack | Defend | Minimum |
|  | **Attack** | 30 | 50 | 30 |
| **Red Army** | **Defend** | 40 | 0 | 0 |
|  | **Maximum** | 40 | 50 |  |

The maximum of the row minimums is 30 and the minimum of the column maximums is 40. Because these values are not equal, a mixed strategy is optimal. Therefore, we must determine the best probability, $p$, for which the Red Army should choose the Attack strategy. Assume the Red Army chooses Attack with probability $p$ and Defend with probability $1 - p$. If the Blue Army chooses Attack, the expected payoff is $30p + 40(1 - p)$. If the Blue Army chooses Defend, the expected payoff is $50p + 0(1 - p)$.

Setting these equations equal to each other and solving for $p$, we get $p = 2/3$.

Red Army should choose to Attack with probability $2/3$ and Defend with probability $1/3$.

**b.** Assume the Blue Army chooses Attack with probability $q$ and Defend with probability $1 - q$. If the Red Army chooses Attack, the expected payoff for the Blue Army is $30q + 50(1 - q)$. If the Red Army chooses Defend, the expected payoff for the Blue Army is $40q + 0(1 - q)$. Setting these equations equal to each other and solving for $q$, we get $q = 0.833$. Therefore, the Blue Army should choose to Attack with probability $0.833$ and Defend with probability $1 - 0.833 = 0.167$.

**14. a.** Strategy $a_3$ dominated by $a_2$
Strategy $b_1$ dominated by $b_2$

|  |  | Player B | |
|---|---|---|---|
|  |  | $b_2$ | $b_3$ |
| **Player A** | $a_1$ | $-1$ | $2$ |
|  | $a_2$ | $4$ | $-3$ |

**b.** Let $p$ = probability of $a_1$ and $(1 - p)$ = probability of $a_2$
If $b_1$, EV = $-1p + 4(1 - p)$
If $b_2$, EV = $2p - 3(1 - p)$
$$-1p + 4(1 - p) = 2p - 3(1 - p)$$
$$-1p + 4 - 4p = 2p - 3 + 3p$$
$$10p = 7$$
$$p = 0.70$$
$p(a_1) = p = 0.70$
$p(a_2) = 1 - 0.70 = 0.30$
Let $q$ = probability of $b_2$ and $(1 - q)$ = probability of $b_3$
If $a_1$, EV = $-1q + 2(1 - q)$

If $a_2$, EV = $4q - 3(1 - q)$
$$-1q + 2(1 - q) = 4q - 3(1 - q)$$
$$-1q + 2 - 2q = 4q - 3 + 3q$$
$$10q = 5$$
$$q = 0.50$$
$P(b_2) = q = 0.50$
$P(b_3) = 1 - 0.50 = 0.50$

**c.** $-1p + 4(1 - p) = -(0.70) + 4(0.30) = +0.50$

**16.** A: $P(a_3) = 0.80$, $P(a_4) = 0.20$
B: $P(b_1) = 0.40$, $P(b_2) = 0.60$
Value = 2.8

# Chapter 6

**1.** The following table shows the calculations for parts (a), (b), and (c).

| Week | Time Series Value | Forecast | Forecast Error | Absolute Value of Forecast Error | Squared Forecast Error | Percentage Error | Absolute Value of Percentage Error |
|---|---|---|---|---|---|---|---|
| 1 | 18 |  |  |  |  |  |  |
| 2 | 13 | 18 | $-5$ | 5 | 25 | $-38.46$ | 38.46 |
| 3 | 16 | 13 | 3 | 3 | 9 | 18.75 | 18.75 |
| 4 | 11 | 16 | $-5$ | 5 | 25 | $-45.45$ | 45.45 |
| 5 | 17 | 11 | 6 | 6 | 36 | 35.29 | 35.29 |
| 6 | 14 | 17 | $-3$ | 3 | 9 | $-21.43$ | 21.43 |
|  |  | Totals |  | 22 | 104 | $-51.30$ | 159.38 |

**a.** MAE = $22/5 = 4.4$
**b.** MSE = $104/5 = 20.8$
**c.** MAPE = $159.38/5 = 31.88$
**d.** The forecast for week 7 is $F_7 = Y_7 = 14$.

**2.** The following table shows the calculations for parts (a), (b), and (c).

| Week | Time Series Value | Forecast | Forecast Error | Absolute Value of Forecast Error | Squared Forecast Error | Percentage Error | Absolute Value of Percentage Error |
|---|---|---|---|---|---|---|---|
| 1 | 18 |  |  |  |  |  |  |
| 2 | 13 | 18.00 | $-5.00$ | 5.00 | 25.00 | $-38.46$ | 38.46 |
| 3 | 16 | 15.50 | 0.50 | 0.50 | 0.25 | 3.13 | 3.13 |
| 4 | 11 | 15.67 | $-4.67$ | 4.67 | 21.81 | $-42.45$ | 42.45 |
| 5 | 17 | 14.50 | 2.50 | 2.50 | 6.25 | 14.71 | 14.71 |
| 6 | 14 | 15.00 | $-1.00$ | 1.00 | 1.00 | $-7.14$ | 7.14 |
|  |  | Totals |  | 13.67 | 54.31 | $-70.21$ | 105.86 |

**a.** MAE = $13.67/5 = 2.73$
**b.** MSE = $54.31/5 = 10.86$
**c.** MAPE = $105.89/5 = 21.18$

**d.** The forecast for week 7 is $F_7 = (Y_1 + Y_2 + Y_3 + Y_4 + Y_5 + Y_6)/6 = (18 + 13 + 16 + 11 + 17 + 14)/6 = 14.83$.

**3.** The following table shows the measures of forecast error for both methods.

|  | **Exercise 1** | **Exercise 2** |
|---|---|---|
| MAE | 4.40 | 2.73 |
| MSE | 20.80 | 10.86 |
| MAPE | 31.88 | 21.18 |

For each measure of forecast accuracy, the average of all the historical data provided more accurate forecasts than simply using the most recent value.

**4. a.**

| Month | Time Series Value | Forecast | Forecast Error | Squared Forecast Error |
|---|---|---|---|---|
| 1 | 24 | | | |
| 2 | 13 | 24 | −11 | 121 |
| 3 | 20 | 13 | 7 | 49 |
| 4 | 12 | 20 | −8 | 64 |
| 5 | 19 | 12 | 7 | 49 |
| 6 | 23 | 19 | 4 | 16 |
| 7 | 15 | 23 | −8 | 64 |
| | | | Total | 363 |

$MSE = 363/6 = 60.5$

The forecast for month 8 is $F_8 = Y_8 = 15$.

**b.**

| Week | Time Series Value | Forecast | Forecast Error | Squared Forecast Error |
|---|---|---|---|---|
| 1 | 24 | | | |
| 2 | 13 | 24.00 | −11.00 | 121.00 |
| 3 | 20 | 18.50 | 1.50 | 2.25 |
| 4 | 12 | 19.00 | −7.00 | 49.00 |
| 5 | 19 | 17.25 | 1.75 | 3.06 |
| 6 | 23 | 17.60 | 5.40 | 29.16 |
| 7 | 15 | 18.50 | −3.50 | 12.25 |
| | | | Total | 216.72 |

$MSE = 216.72/6 = 36.12$

Forecast for month 8 is $F_8 = (Y_1 + Y_2 + Y_3 + Y_4 + Y_5 + Y_6 + Y_7)/7 = (24 + 13 + 20 + 12 + 19 + 23 + 15)/7 = 18$.

**c.** The average of all the previous values is better because MSE is smaller.

**5. a.**

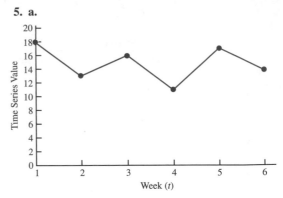

The data appear to follow a horizontal pattern.

**b.** Three-week moving average

| Week | Time Series Value | Forecast | Forecast Error | Squared Forecast Error |
|---|---|---|---|---|
| 1 | 18 | | | |
| 2 | 13 | | | |
| 3 | 16 | | | |
| 4 | 11 | 15.67 | −4.67 | 21.78 |
| 5 | 17 | 13.33 | 3.67 | 13.44 |
| 6 | 14 | 14.67 | −0.67 | 0.44 |
| | | | Total | 35.67 |

$MSE = 35.67/3 = 11.89$.

The forecast for week 7 is $F_7 = (Y_4 + Y_5 + Y_6)/3 = (11 + 17 + 14)/3 = 14$.

**c.** Smoothing constant $\alpha = 0.2$

| Week | Time Series Value | Forecast | Forecast Error | Squared Forecast Error |
|---|---|---|---|---|
| 1 | 18 | | | |
| 2 | 13 | 18.00 | −5.00 | 25.00 |
| 3 | 16 | 17.00 | −1.00 | 1.00 |
| 4 | 11 | 16.80 | −5.80 | 33.64 |
| 5 | 17 | 15.64 | 1.36 | 1.85 |
| 6 | 14 | 15.91 | −1.91 | 3.66 |
| | | | Total | 65.15 |

$MSE = 65.15/5 = 13.03$

The forecast for week 7 is $F_7 = \alpha Y_6 + (1 - \alpha)F_6 = 0.2(14) + (1 - 0.2)15.91 = 15.53$.

**d.** The three-week moving average provides a better forecast since it has a smaller MSE.

**e.** Several values of $\alpha$ will yield an MSE smaller than the MSE associated with $\alpha = 0.2$. The value of $\alpha$ that yields the minimum MSE is $\alpha = 0.367694922$, which yields an MSE of 12.060999.

$$\alpha = 0.367694922$$

| Week | Time Series Value | Forecast | Forecast Error | Squared Forecast Error |
|---|---|---|---|---|
| 1 | 18 | | | |
| 2 | 13 | 18 | −5.00 | 25.00 |
| 3 | 16 | 16.16 | −0.16 | 0.03 |
| 4 | 11 | 16.10 | −5.10 | 26.03 |
| 5 | 17 | 14.23 | 2.77 | 7.69 |
| 6 | 14 | 15.25 | −1.25 | 1.55 |
| | | | Total | 60.30 |

$$\text{MSE} = 60.30/5 = 12.060999$$

**6. a.**

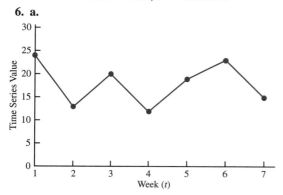

The data appear to follow a horizontal pattern.

**b.** Three-week moving average

| Week | Time Series Value | Forecast | Forecast Error | Squared Forecast Error |
|---|---|---|---|---|
| 1 | 24 | | | |
| 2 | 13 | | | |
| 3 | 20 | | | |
| 4 | 12 | 19.00 | −7.00 | 49.00 |
| 5 | 19 | 15.00 | 4.00 | 16.00 |
| 6 | 23 | 17.00 | 6.00 | 36.00 |
| 7 | 15 | 18.00 | −3.00 | 9.00 |
| | | | Total | 110.00 |

$\text{MSE} = 110/4 = 27.5.$

The forecast for week 8 is $F_8 = (Y_5 + Y_6 + Y_7)/3 = (19 + 23 + 15)/3 = 19.$

**c.** Smoothing constant $\alpha = 0.2$

| Week | Time Series Value | Forecast | Forecast Error | Squared Forecast Error |
|---|---|---|---|---|
| 1 | 24 | | | |
| 2 | 13 | 24.00 | −11.00 | 121.00 |
| 3 | 20 | 21.80 | −1.80 | 3.24 |
| 4 | 12 | 21.44 | −9.44 | 89.11 |
| 5 | 19 | 19.55 | −0.55 | 0.30 |
| 6 | 23 | 19.44 | 3.56 | 12.66 |
| 7 | 15 | 20.15 | −5.15 | 26.56 |
| | | | Total | 252.87 |

$\text{MSE} = 252.87/6 = 42.15$

The forecast for week 8 is $F_8 = \alpha Y_7 + (1 - \alpha)F_7 = 0.2(15) + (1 - 0.2)20.15 = 19.12.$

**d.** The three-week moving average provides a better forecast since it has a smaller MSE.

**e.** Several values of $\alpha$ will yield an MSE smaller than the MSE associated with $\alpha = 0.2$. The value of $\alpha$ that yields the minimum MSE is $\alpha = 0.351404848$, which yields an MSE of 39.61428577.

$$\alpha = 0.351404848$$

| Week | Time Series Value | Forecast | Forecast Error | Squared Forecast Error |
|---|---|---|---|---|
| 1 | 24 | | | |
| 2 | 13 | 24.00 | −11.00 | 121.00 |
| 3 | 20 | 20.13 | −0.13 | 0.02 |
| 4 | 12 | 20.09 | −8.09 | 65.40 |
| 5 | 19 | 17.25 | 1.75 | 3.08 |
| 6 | 23 | 17.86 | 5.14 | 26.40 |
| 7 | 15 | 19.67 | −4.67 | 21.79 |
| | | | Total | 237.69 |

$$\text{MSE} = 237.69/6 = 39.61428577$$

**8. a.**

| Week | Time Series Value | Weighted Moving Average Forecast | Forecast Error | Squared Forecast Error |
|---|---|---|---|---|
| 1 | 17 | | | |
| 2 | 21 | | | |
| 3 | 19 | | | |
| 4 | 23 | 19.33 | 3.67 | 13.47 |
| 5 | 18 | 21.33 | −3.33 | 11.09 |
| 6 | 16 | 19.83 | −3.83 | 14.67 |
| 7 | 20 | 17.83 | 2.17 | 4.71 |
| 8 | 18 | 18.33 | −0.33 | 0.11 |
| 9 | 22 | 18.33 | 3.67 | 13.47 |
| 10 | 20 | 20.33 | −0.33 | 0.11 |
| 11 | 15 | 20.33 | −5.33 | 28.41 |
| 12 | 22 | 17.83 | 4.17 | 17.39 |
| | | | Total | 103.43 |

**b.** $\text{MSE} = 103.43/9 = 11.49$

Prefer the unweighted moving average here; it has a smaller MSE.

**c.** You could always find a weighted moving average at least as good as the unweighted moving average. Actually, the unweighted moving average is a special case of the weighted average for which the weights are equal.

**10. a.** $F_{13} = 0.2Y_{12} + 0.16Y_{11} + 0.64(0.2Y_{10} + 0.8F_{10}) = 0.2Y_{12} + 0.16Y_{11} + 0.128Y_{10} + 0.512F_{10}$

$F_{13} = 0.2Y_{12} + 0.16Y_{11} + 0.128Y_{10} + 0.512(0.2Y_9 + 0.8F_9) = 0.2Y_{12} + 0.16Y_{11} + 0.128Y_{10} + 0.1024Y_9 + 0.4096F_9$

$F_{13} = 0.2Y_{12} + 0.16Y_{11} + 0.128Y_{10} + 0.1024Y_9 + 0.4096(0.2Y_8 + 0.8F_8) = 0.2Y_{12} + 0.16Y_{11} + 0.128Y_{10} + 0.1024Y_9 + 0.08192Y_8 + 0.32768F_8$

**b.** The more recent data receive the greater weight or importance in determining the forecast. The moving averages method weights the last $n$ data values equally in determining the forecast.

**12. a.**

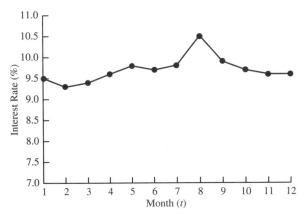

The data appear to follow a horizontal pattern.

**b.**

| Month | Time Series Value | 3-Month Moving Average Forecast | (Error)$^2$ | 4-Month Moving Average Forecast | (Error)$^2$ |
|---|---|---|---|---|---|
| 1 | 9.5 | | | | |
| 2 | 9.3 | | | | |
| 3 | 9.4 | | | | |
| 4 | 9.6 | 9.40 | 0.04 | | |
| 5 | 9.8 | 9.43 | 0.14 | 9.45 | 0.12 |
| 6 | 9.7 | 9.60 | 0.01 | 9.53 | 0.03 |
| 7 | 9.8 | 9.70 | 0.01 | 9.63 | 0.03 |
| 8 | 10.5 | 9.77 | 0.53 | 9.73 | 0.59 |
| 9 | 9.9 | 10.00 | 0.01 | 9.95 | 0.00 |
| 10 | 9.7 | 10.07 | 0.14 | 9.98 | 0.08 |
| 11 | 9.6 | 10.03 | 0.18 | 9.97 | 0.14 |
| 12 | 9.6 | 9.73 | 0.02 | 9.92 | 0.10 |
| | | | 1.08 | | 1.09 |

MSE(3-Month) = 1.08/9 = 0.12

MSE(4-Month) = 1.09/8 = 0.14

The MSE for the 3-month moving average is smaller, so use the 3-month moving average.

**c.** The forecast for month 13 is $F_{13} = (Y_{10} + Y_{11} + Y_{12})/3 = (9.7 + 9.6 + 9.6)/3 = 9.63$.

**13. a.**

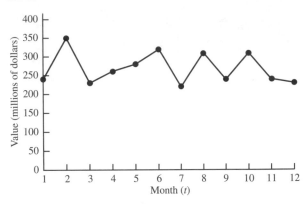

The data appear to follow a horizontal pattern.

**b.**

$$\alpha = 0.2$$

| Month | Time Series Value | 3-Month Moving Average Forecast | (Error)$^2$ | Average Forecast | (Error)$^2$ |
|---|---|---|---|---|---|
| 1 | 240 | | | | |
| 2 | 350 | | | 240.00 | 12100.00 |
| 3 | 230 | | | 262.00 | 1024.00 |
| 4 | 260 | 273.33 | 177.69 | 255.60 | 19.36 |
| 5 | 280 | 280.00 | 0.00 | 256.48 | 553.19 |
| 6 | 320 | 256.67 | 4010.69 | 261.18 | 3459.79 |
| 7 | 220 | 286.67 | 4444.89 | 272.95 | 2803.70 |
| 8 | 310 | 273.33 | 1344.69 | 262.36 | 2269.57 |
| 9 | 240 | 283.33 | 1877.49 | 271.89 | 1016.97 |
| 10 | 310 | 256.67 | 2844.09 | 265.51 | 1979.36 |
| 11 | 240 | 286.67 | 2178.09 | 274.41 | 1184.05 |
| 12 | 230 | 263.33 | 1110.89 | 267.53 | 1408.50 |
| | | | 17,988.52 | | 27,818.49 |

MSE(3-Month) = 17,988.52/9 = 1998.72

MSE($\alpha = 0.2$) = 27,818.49/11 = 2528.95

Based on the above MSE values, the 3-month moving average appears better. However, exponential smoothing was penalized by including month 2, which was difficult for any method to forecast. Using only the errors for months 4 to 12, the MSE for exponential smoothing is as follows:

MSE($\alpha = 0.2$) = 14,694.49/9 = 1632.72

Thus, exponential smoothing was better considering months 4 to 12.

**c.** Using exponential smoothing,

$$F_{13} = \alpha Y_{12} + (1 - \alpha)F_{12} = 0.20(230) + 0.80(267.53) = 260.$$

**14. a.**

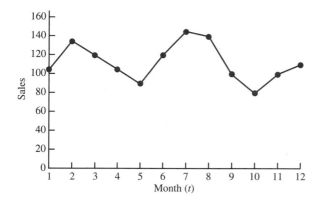

Month (t)

The data appear to follow a horizontal pattern.

**b.** Smoothing constant $\alpha = 0.3$.

| Month $t$ | Time Series Value $Y_t$ | Forecast $F_t$ | Forecast Error $Y_t - F_t$ | Squared Error $(Y_t - F_t)^2$ |
|---|---|---|---|---|
| 1 | 105 | | | |
| 2 | 135 | 105.00 | 30.00 | 900.00 |
| 3 | 120 | 114.00 | 6.00 | 36.00 |
| 4 | 105 | 115.80 | −10.80 | 116.64 |
| 5 | 90 | 112.56 | −22.56 | 508.95 |
| 6 | 120 | 105.79 | 14.21 | 201.92 |
| 7 | 145 | 110.05 | 34.95 | 1221.50 |
| 8 | 140 | 120.54 | 19.46 | 378.69 |
| 9 | 100 | 126.38 | −26.38 | 695.90 |
| 10 | 80 | 118.46 | −38.46 | 1479.17 |
| 11 | 100 | 106.92 | −6.92 | 47.89 |
| 12 | 110 | 104.85 | 5.15 | 26.52 |
| | | | Total | 5613.18 |

MSE = 5613.18/11 = 510.29

The forecast for month 13 is $F_{13} = \alpha Y_{12} + (1 - \alpha)F_{12} = 0.3(110) + 0.7(104.85) = 106.4$.

**c.** The value of $\alpha$ that yields the smallest possible MSE is $\alpha = 0.032564518$, which yields an MSE of 459.6929489.

$$\alpha = 0.032564518$$

| Month | Time Series Value | Forecast | Forecast Error | Squared Error |
|---|---|---|---|---|
| 1 | 105 | | | |
| 2 | 135 | 105 | 30.00 | 900.00 |
| 3 | 120 | 105.98 | 14.02 | 196.65 |
| 4 | 105 | 106.43 | −1.43 | 2.06 |
| 5 | 90 | 106.39 | −16.39 | 268.53 |
| 6 | 120 | 105.85 | 14.15 | 200.13 |
| 7 | 145 | 106.31 | 38.69 | 1496.61 |
| 8 | 140 | 107.57 | 32.43 | 1051.46 |
| 9 | 100 | 108.63 | −8.63 | 74.47 |
| 10 | 80 | 108.35 | −28.35 | 803.65 |
| 11 | 100 | 107.43 | −7.43 | 55.14 |
| 12 | 110 | 107.18 | 2.82 | 7.93 |
| | | | Total | 5056.62 |

MSE = 5056.62/11 = 459.6929489

**16. a.**

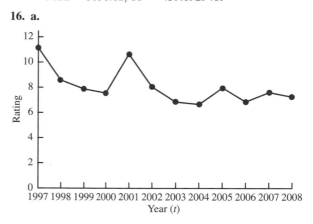

Year (t)

The time series plot indicates a possible linear trend in the data. This could be due to decreasing viewer interest in watching the Masters. But closer inspection of the data indicates that the two highest ratings correspond to years 1997 and 2001, years in which Tiger Woods won the tournament. In fact, four of the five highest ratings occurred when Tiger Woods won the tournament. So, instead of an underlying linear trend in the time series, the pattern observed may be simply due to the effect Tiger Woods has on ratings and not necessarily on any long-term decrease in viewer interest.

**b.** The methods discussed in this section are only applicable for a time series that has a horizontal pattern. So, if there is really a long-term linear trend in the data, the methods discussed in this section are not appropriate.

**c.** The following time series plot shows the ratings for years 2002–2008.

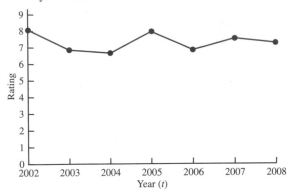

The time series plot for the data for years 2002–2008 exhibits a horizontal pattern. It seems reasonable to conclude that the extreme values observed in 1997 and 2001 are more attributable to viewer interest in the performance of Tiger Woods. Basing the forecast on years 2002–2008 does seem reasonable. But because of the injury that Tiger Woods experienced in the 2008 season, if he is able to play in the 2009 Masters then the rating for 2009 may be significantly higher than suggested by the data for years 2002–2008. These types of issues are what make forecasting in practice so difficult. For the methods to work, we have to be able to assume that the pattern in the past is appropriate for the future. But, because of the great influence Tiger Woods has on viewer interest, making this assumption for this time series may not be appropriate.

**17. a.**

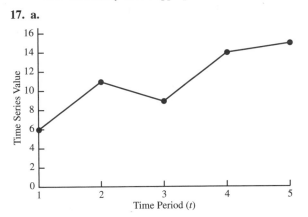

The time series plot shows a linear trend.

**b.** The regression estimates for the slope and $y$-intercept are as follows:

$$b_1 = \frac{\sum_{t=1}^{n} tY_t - \sum_{t=1}^{n} t \sum_{t=1}^{n} Y_t \big/ n}{\sum_{t=1}^{n} t^2 - \left(\sum_{t=1}^{n} t\right)^2 \big/ n} = \frac{186 - (15)(55)/5}{55 - (15)^2/5} = 2.10$$

$$b_0 = \bar{Y} - b_1 \bar{t} = \frac{55}{5} - 2.10\left(\frac{15}{3}\right) = 4.70$$

which results in the following forecasts, errors, and MSE:

| Year | Sales | Forecast | Forecast Error | Squared Forecast Error |
|---|---|---|---|---|
| 1 | 6.00 | 6.80 | −0.80 | 0.64 |
| 2 | 11.00 | 8.90 | 2.10 | 4.41 |
| 3 | 9.00 | 11.00 | −2.00 | 4.00 |
| 4 | 14.00 | 13.10 | 0.90 | 0.81 |
| 5 | 15.00 | 15.20 | −0.20 | 0.04 |
| 6 | | 17.30 | Total | 9.9 |

$$\text{MSE} = 9.9/5 = 1.982.475$$

**c.** $F_6 = b_0 + b_1 t = 4.7 + 2.1(6) = 17.3$

**18. a.**

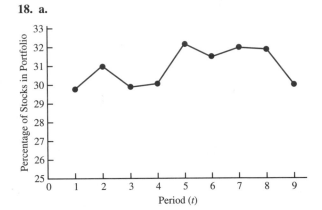

**b.** The value of the MSE will vary depending on the ultimate value of $\alpha$ that you select. The value of $\alpha$ that yields the smallest possible MSE is $\alpha = 0.467307293$, which yields an MSE of 1.222838367.

$$\alpha = 0.467307293$$

| Period | Stock% | Forecast | Forecast Error | Squared Forecast Error |
|---|---|---|---|---|
| 1st-2007 | 29.8 | | | |
| 2nd-2007 | 31.0 | 29.80 | 1.20 | 1.44 |
| 3rd-2007 | 29.9 | 30.36 | −0.46 | 0.21 |
| 4th-2007 | 30.1 | 30.15 | −0.05 | 0.00 |
| 1st-2008 | 32.2 | 30.12 | 2.08 | 4.31 |
| 2nd-2008 | 31.5 | 31.09 | 0.41 | 0.16 |
| 3rd-2008 | 32.0 | 31.28 | 0.72 | 0.51 |
| 4th-2008 | 31.9 | 31.62 | 0.28 | 0.08 |
| 1st-2009 | 30.0 | 31.75 | −1.75 | 3.06 |
| 2nd-2009 | | 30.93 | Total | 9.78 |

$$\text{MSE} = 1.222838367$$

**c.** The forecast for second quarter 2009 will vary depending on the ultimate value of $\alpha$ that you selected in part (b). Using an exponential smoothing model with $\alpha = 0.467307293$, the forecast for second quarter 2009 = 30.93.

**20. a.**

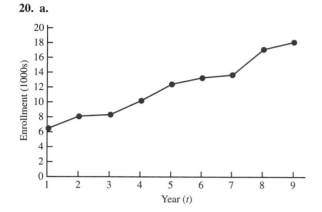

The time series plot shows a linear trend.

**b.** The regression estimates for the slope and y-intercept are as follows:

$$b_1 = \frac{\sum\limits_{t=1}^{n} tY_t - \sum\limits_{t=1}^{n} t \sum\limits_{t=1}^{n} Y_t \big/ n}{\sum\limits_{t=1}^{n} t^2 - \left(\sum\limits_{t=1}^{n} t\right)^2 \big/ n} = \frac{627.4 - (45)(108)/9}{285 - (45)^2/9} = 4.7167$$

$$b_0 = \bar{Y} - b_1 \bar{t} = \frac{108}{9} - 4.7167\left(\frac{45}{9}\right) = 1.4567$$

which results in the following forecasts, errors, and MSE:

| Period | Year | Enroll-ment | Forecast | Forecast Error | Squared Forecast Error |
|---|---|---|---|---|---|
| 1 | 2001 | 6.50 | 6.17 | 0.33 | 0.11 |
| 2 | 2002 | 8.10 | 7.63 | 0.47 | 0.22 |
| 3 | 2003 | 8.40 | 9.09 | -0.69 | 0.47 |
| 4 | 2004 | 10.20 | 10.54 | -0.34 | 0.12 |
| 5 | 2005 | 12.50 | 12.00 | 0.50 | 0.25 |
| 6 | 2006 | 13.30 | 13.46 | -0.16 | 0.02 |
| 7 | 2007 | 13.70 | 14.91 | -1.21 | 1.47 |
| 8 | 2008 | 17.20 | 16.37 | 0.83 | 0.69 |
| 9 | 2009 | 18.10 | 17.83 | 0.27 | 0.07 |
| 10 | 2010 | | 19.28 | | Total 3.427 |

MSE = 0.3808

**c.** $F_{10} = b_0 + b_1 t = 4.7167 + 1.4567(10) = 19.28$

**22. a.**

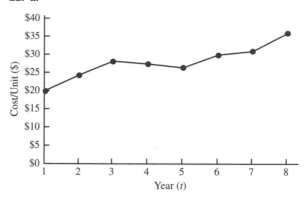

The time series plot shows an upward linear trend.

**b.** The regression estimates for the slope and y-intercept are as follows:

$$b_1 = \frac{\sum\limits_{t=1}^{n} tY_t - \sum\limits_{t=1}^{n} t \sum\limits_{t=1}^{n} Y_t \big/ n}{\sum\limits_{t=1}^{n} t^2 - \left(\sum\limits_{t=1}^{n} t\right)^2 \big/ n} = \frac{1081.6 - (36)(223.8)/8}{204 - (36)^2/8} = 1.7738$$

$$b_0 = \bar{Y} - b_1 \bar{t} = \frac{223.8}{8} - 1.774\left(\frac{36}{8}\right) = 19.9928$$

which results in the following forecasts, errors, and MSE:

| Year | Cost/Unit($) | Forecast | Forecast Error | Squared Forecast Error |
|---|---|---|---|---|
| 1 | 20.00 | 21.77 | -1.77 | 3.12 |
| 2 | 24.50 | 23.54 | 0.96 | 0.92 |
| 3 | 28.20 | 25.31 | 2.89 | 8.33 |
| 4 | 27.50 | 27.09 | 0.41 | 0.17 |
| 5 | 26.60 | 28.86 | -2.26 | 5.12 |
| 6 | 30.00 | 30.64 | -0.64 | 0.40 |
| 7 | 31.00 | 32.41 | -1.41 | 1.99 |
| 8 | 36.00 | 34.18 | 1.82 | 3.30 |
| 9 | | 35.96 | Total | 23.34619 |

MSE = 2.9183

**c.** The average cost/unit has been increasing by approximately $1.77 per year.

**d.** $F_9 = b_0 + b_1 t = 19.9928 + 1.7738(9) = 35.96$

**24. a.**

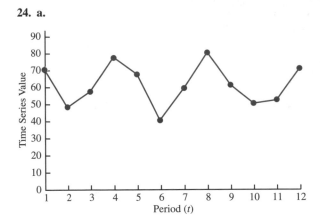

The time series plot shows a horizontal pattern. But there is a seasonal pattern in the data. For instance, in each year the lowest value occurs in quarter 2 and the highest value occurs in quarter 4.

**b.** After putting the data into the following format:

| | | Dummy Variables | | | |
|---|---|---|---|---|---|
| Year | Quarter | Quarter 1 | Quarter 2 | Quarter 3 | $Y_t$ |
| 1 | 1 | 1 | 0 | 0 | 71 |
| 1 | 2 | 0 | 1 | 0 | 48 |
| 1 | 3 | 0 | 0 | 1 | 58 |
| 1 | 4 | 0 | 0 | 0 | 78 |
| 2 | 1 | 1 | 0 | 0 | 68 |
| 2 | 2 | 0 | 1 | 0 | 41 |
| 2 | 3 | 0 | 0 | 1 | 60 |
| 2 | 4 | 0 | 0 | 0 | 81 |
| 3 | 1 | 1 | 0 | 0 | 62 |
| 3 | 2 | 0 | 1 | 0 | 51 |
| 3 | 3 | 0 | 0 | 1 | 53 |
| 3 | 4 | 0 | 0 | 0 | 72 |

we can use the LINEST function to find the regression model:

Value = 77.00 − 10.00 Qtr1 − 30.33 Qtr2 − 20.00 Qtr3

**c.** The quarterly forecasts for next year are as follows:

Quarter 1 forecast = 77.0 − 10.0(1) − 30.33(0) − 20.0(0)
= 67.00

Quarter 2 forecast = 77.0 − 10.0(0) − 30.33(1) − 20.0(0)
= 46.67

Quarter 3 forecast = 77.0 − 10.0(0) − 30.33(0) − 20.0(1)
= 57.00

Quarter 4 forecast = 77.0 − 10.0(0) − 30.33(0) − 20.0(0)
= 77.00

**26. a.**

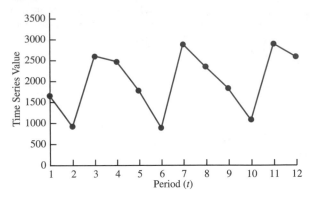

There appears to be a seasonal pattern in the data and perhaps a moderate upward linear trend.

**b.** After putting the data into the following format:

| | | Dummy Variables | | | |
|---|---|---|---|---|---|
| Year | Quarter | Quarter 1 | Quarter 2 | Quarter 3 | $Y_t$ |
| 1 | 1 | 1 | 0 | 0 | 1690 |
| 1 | 2 | 0 | 1 | 0 | 940 |
| 1 | 3 | 0 | 0 | 1 | 2625 |
| 1 | 4 | 0 | 0 | 0 | 2500 |
| 2 | 1 | 1 | 0 | 0 | 1800 |
| 2 | 2 | 0 | 1 | 0 | 900 |
| 2 | 3 | 0 | 0 | 1 | 2900 |
| 2 | 4 | 0 | 0 | 0 | 2360 |
| 3 | 1 | 1 | 0 | 0 | 1850 |
| 3 | 2 | 0 | 1 | 0 | 1100 |
| 3 | 3 | 0 | 0 | 1 | 2930 |
| 3 | 4 | 0 | 0 | 0 | 2615 |

we can use the LINEST function to find the regression model:

Value = 2491.67 − 711.67 Qtr1 − 1511.67 Qtr2
+ 326.67 Qtr3

**c.** The quarterly forecasts for next year are as follows:

Quarter 1 forecast = 2491.67 − 711.67(1) − 1511.67(0)
+ 326.67(0) = 1780.00

Quarter 2 forecast = 2491.67 − 711.67(0) − 1511.67(1)
+ 326.67(0) = 980.00

Quarter 3 forecast = 2491.67 − 711.67(0) − 1511.67(0)
+ 326.67(1) = 2818.33

Quarter 4 forecast = 2491.67 − 711.67(0) − 1511.67(0)
+ 326.67(0) = 2491.67

**d.** After putting the data into the following format:

| | | **Dummy Variables** | | | | |
|---|---|---|---|---|---|---|
| Year | Quarter | Quarter 1 | Quarter 2 | Quarter 3 | $t$ | $Y_t$ |
| 1 | 1 | 1 | 0 | 0 | 1 | 1690 |
| 1 | 2 | 0 | 1 | 0 | 2 | 940 |
| 1 | 3 | 0 | 0 | 1 | 3 | 2625 |
| 1 | 4 | 0 | 0 | 0 | 4 | 2500 |
| 2 | 1 | 1 | 0 | 0 | 5 | 1800 |
| 2 | 2 | 0 | 1 | 0 | 6 | 900 |
| 2 | 3 | 0 | 0 | 1 | 7 | 2900 |
| 2 | 4 | 0 | 0 | 0 | 8 | 2360 |
| 3 | 1 | 1 | 0 | 0 | 9 | 1850 |
| 3 | 2 | 0 | 1 | 0 | 10 | 1100 |
| 3 | 3 | 0 | 0 | 1 | 11 | 2930 |
| 3 | 4 | 0 | 0 | 0 | 12 | 2615 |

we can use the LINEST function to find the regression model:

Value = 2306.67 − 642.29 Qtr1 − 1465.42 Qtr2 + 349.79 Qtr3 + 23.13$t$

The quarterly forecasts for next year are as follows:

Quarter 1 forecast = 2306.67 − 642.29(1) − 1465.42(0) + 349.79(0) + 23.13(13) = 1965.00
Quarter 2 forecast = 2306.67 − 642.29(0) − 1465.42(1) + 349.79(0) + 23.13(14) = 1165.00
Quarter 3 forecast = 2306.67 − 642.29(0) − 1465.42(0) + 349.79(1) + 23.13(15) = 2011.33
Quarter 4 forecast = 2306.67 − 642.29(0) − 1465.42(0) + 349.79(0) + 23.13(16) = 2676.67

**28. a.**

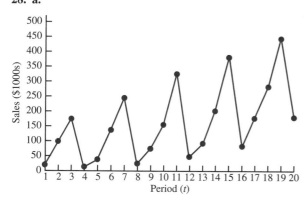

The time series plot shows both a linear trend and seasonal effects.

**b.** After putting the data into the following format:

| | | **Dummy Variables** | | | |
|---|---|---|---|---|---|
| Year | Quarter | Quarter 1 | Quarter 2 | Quarter 3 | $Y_t$ |
| 1 | 1 | 1 | 0 | 0 | 20 |
| 1 | 2 | 0 | 1 | 0 | 100 |
| 1 | 3 | 0 | 0 | 1 | 175 |
| 1 | 4 | 0 | 0 | 0 | 13 |
| 2 | 1 | 1 | 0 | 0 | 37 |
| 2 | 2 | 0 | 1 | 0 | 136 |
| 2 | 3 | 0 | 0 | 1 | 245 |
| 2 | 4 | 0 | 0 | 0 | 26 |
| 3 | 1 | 1 | 0 | 0 | 75 |
| 3 | 2 | 0 | 1 | 0 | 155 |
| 3 | 3 | 0 | 0 | 1 | 326 |
| 3 | 4 | 0 | 0 | 0 | 48 |
| 4 | 1 | 1 | 0 | 0 | 92 |
| 4 | 2 | 0 | 1 | 0 | 202 |
| 4 | 3 | 0 | 0 | 1 | 384 |
| 4 | 4 | 0 | 0 | 0 | 82 |
| 5 | 1 | 1 | 0 | 0 | 176 |
| 5 | 2 | 0 | 1 | 0 | 282 |
| 5 | 3 | 0 | 0 | 1 | 445 |
| 5 | 4 | 0 | 0 | 0 | 181 |

we can use the LINEST function to find the regression model:

Revenue = 70.0 + 10.0 Qtr1 + 105 Qtr2 + 245 Qtr3

Quarter 1 forecast = 70.0 + 10.0(1) + 105(0) + 245(0) = 80
Quarter 2 forecast = 70.0 + 10.0(0) + 105(1) + 245(0) = 175
Quarter 3 forecast = 70.0 + 10.0(0) + 105(0) + 245(1) = 315
Quarter 4 forecast = 70.0 + 10.0(0) + 105(0) + 245(0) = 70

**c.** After putting the data into the following format:

| | | **Dummy Variables** | | | | |
|---|---|---|---|---|---|---|
| Year | Quarter | Quarter 1 | Quarter 2 | Quarter 3 | $t$ | $Y_t$ |
| 1 | 1 | 1 | 0 | 0 | 1 | 20 |
| 1 | 2 | 0 | 1 | 0 | 2 | 100 |
| 1 | 3 | 0 | 0 | 1 | 3 | 175 |
| 1 | 4 | 0 | 0 | 0 | 4 | 13 |
| 2 | 1 | 1 | 0 | 0 | 5 | 37 |
| 2 | 2 | 0 | 1 | 0 | 6 | 136 |
| 2 | 3 | 0 | 0 | 1 | 7 | 245 |
| 2 | 4 | 0 | 0 | 0 | 8 | 26 |
| 3 | 1 | 1 | 0 | 0 | 9 | 75 |
| 3 | 2 | 0 | 1 | 0 | 10 | 155 |
| 3 | 3 | 0 | 0 | 1 | 11 | 326 |
| 3 | 4 | 0 | 0 | 0 | 12 | 48 |
| 4 | 1 | 1 | 0 | 0 | 13 | 92 |
| 4 | 2 | 0 | 1 | 0 | 14 | 202 |
| 4 | 3 | 0 | 0 | 1 | 15 | 384 |
| 4 | 4 | 0 | 0 | 0 | 16 | 82 |
| 5 | 1 | 1 | 0 | 0 | 17 | 176 |
| 5 | 2 | 0 | 1 | 0 | 18 | 282 |
| 5 | 3 | 0 | 0 | 1 | 19 | 445 |
| 5 | 4 | 0 | 0 | 0 | 20 | 181 |

we can use the LINEST function to find the regression model:

Revenue = $-70.10 + 45.03$ Qtr1 $+ 128.35$ Qtr2
$+ 256.68$ Qtr3 $+ 11.68t$

Quarter 1 forecast = $-70.10 + 45.03(1) + 128.35(0)$
$+ 256.68(0) + 11.68(21) = 221$

Quarter 2 forecast = $-70.10 + 45.03(0) + 128.35(1)$
$+ 256.68(0) + 11.68(22) = 315$

Quarter 3 forecast = $-70.10 + 45.03(0) + 128.35(0)$
$+ 256.68(1) + 11.68(23) = 456$

Quarter 4 forecast = $-70.10 + 45.03(0) + 128.35(0)$
$+ 256.68(0) + 11.68(24) = 211$

# Chapter 7

**1.** Parts (a), (b), and (e) are acceptable linear programming relationships.

Part (c) is not acceptable because of $-2x_2^2$.

Part (d) is not acceptable because of $3\sqrt{x_1}$.

Part (f) is not acceptable because of $1x_1x_2$.

Parts (c), (d), and (f) could not be found in a linear programming model because they contain nonlinear terms.

**2. a.**

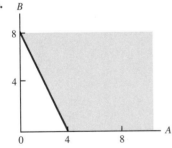

**b.**

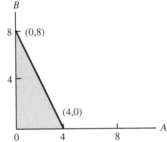

**c.**

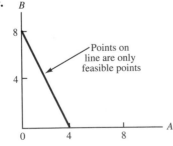

**6.** $7A + 10B = 420$
$6A + \phantom{0}4B = 420$
$4A + \phantom{0}7B = 420$

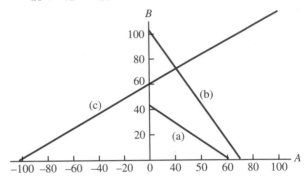

**7.**

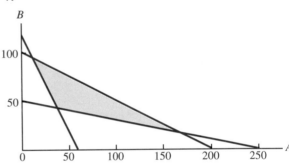

**10.**

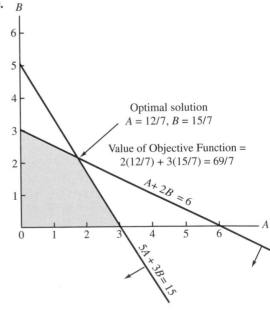

$$
\begin{array}{llrll}
& & A + 2B = & 6 & (1)\\
& & 5A + 3B = & 15 & (2)
\end{array}
$$

Equation (1) times 5:      $5A + 10B = 30$  (3)

Equation (2) minus equation (3):    $-7B = -15$

$$B = 15/7$$

From equation (1):      $A = 6 - 2(15/7)$

$$= 6 - 30/7 = 12/7$$

**12. a.** $A = 3, B = 1.5$; Value of optimal solution = 13.5

  **b.** $A = 0, B = 3$; Value of optimal solution = 18

  **c.** Four: (0, 0), (4, 0), (3, 1.5), and (0.3)

**13. a.**

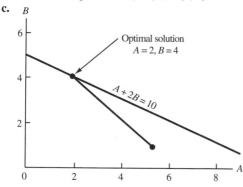

  **b.** The extreme points are (5, 1) and (2, 4).

  **c.**

B
6

Optimal solution
A = 2, B = 4

4

$A + 2B = 10$

2

0   2   4   6   8   A

**14. a.** 540 standard bags, 252 deluxe bags

  **b.** 7668

  **c.** 630, 480, 708, 117

  **d.** 0, 120, 0, 18

**16. a.** $3S + 9D$

  **b.** (0,540)

  **c.** 90, 150, 348, 0

**17.** Max    $5A + 2B + 0s_1 + 0s_2 + 0s_3$

s.t.

$$
\begin{array}{rrrl}
1A - 2B + 1s_1 & & & = 420\\
2A + 3B - & + 1s_2 & & = 610\\
6A - 1B + & & + 1s_3 & = 125\\
\end{array}
$$

$$A, B, s_1, s_2, s_3 \geq 0$$

**18. b.** $A = 18/7, B = 15/7$

  **c.** 0, 0, 4/7

**20. b.** $A = 3.43, B = 3.43$

  **c.** 2.86, 0, 1.43, 0

**22. b.**

| Extreme Point | Coordinates | Profit ($) |
|---|---|---|
| 1 | (0, 0) | 0 |
| 2 | (1700, 0) | 8500 |
| 3 | (1400, 600) | 9400 |
| 4 | (800, 1200) | 8800 |
| 5 | (0, 1680) | 6720 |

Extreme point 3 generates the highest profit.

  **c.** $A = 1400, C = 600$

  **d.** Cutting and dyeing constraint and the packaging constraint

  **e.** $A = 800, C = 1200$; profit = $9200

**24. a.** Let   $R$ = number of units of regular model

           $C$ = number of units of catcher's model

Max   $5R + 8C$

$$
\begin{array}{lll}
1R + C + \tfrac{3}{2}C \leq 900 & \text{Cutting and sewing}\\
\tfrac{1}{2}R + \tfrac{1}{3}C \leq 300 & \text{Finishing}\\
\tfrac{1}{8}R + \tfrac{1}{4}C \leq 100 & \text{Packaging and}\\
& \text{shipping}
\end{array}
$$

$$R, C \geq 0$$

  **b.**

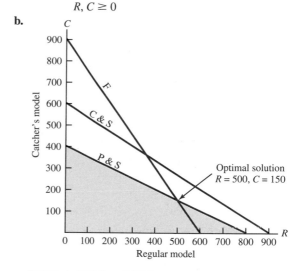

  **c.** $5(500) + 8(150) = \$3700$

  **d.** C & S      $1(500) + \tfrac{3}{2}(150) = 725$

     F          $\tfrac{1}{2}(500) + \tfrac{1}{3}(150) = 300$

     P & S     $\tfrac{1}{8}(500) + \tfrac{1}{4}(150) = 100$

  **e.**

| Department | Capacity | Usage | Slack |
|---|---|---|---|
| Cutting and sewing | 900 | 725 | 175 hours |
| Finishing | 300 | 300 | 0 hours |
| Packaging and shipping | 100 | 100 | 0 hours |

**26. a.** Max $\quad 50N + 80R$

    s.t.

$$
\begin{aligned}
N + R &= 1000 \\
N &\geq 250 \\
R &\geq 250 \\
N - 2R &\geq 0 \\
N, R &\geq 0
\end{aligned}
$$

  **b.** $N = 666.67, R = 333.33$; Audience exposure $= 60{,}000$

**28. a.** Max $\quad 1W + 1.25M$

    s.t.

$$
\begin{aligned}
5W + 7M &\leq 4480 \\
3W + 1M &\leq 2080 \\
2W + 2M &\leq 1600 \\
W, M &\geq 0
\end{aligned}
$$

  **b.** $W = 560, M = 240$; Profit $= 860$

**30. a.** Max $\quad 15E + 18C$

    s.t.

$$
\begin{aligned}
40E + 25C &\leq 50{,}000 \\
40E &\geq 15{,}000 \\
25C &\geq 10{,}000 \\
25C &\leq 25{,}000 \\
E, C &\geq 0
\end{aligned}
$$

  **c.** (375, 400); (1000, 400); (625, 1000); (375, 1000)

  **d.** $E = 625, C = 1000$

    Total return $= \$27{,}375$

**31.**

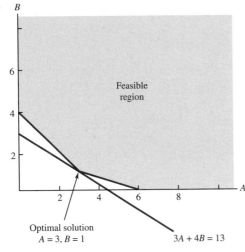

Optimal solution
$A = 3, B = 1$

$3A + 4B = 13$

Objective function value $= 13$

**32.**

| Objective Extreme Points | Function Value | Surplus Demand | Stock Total Production | Processing Time |
|---|---|---|---|---|
| (250, 100) | 800 | 125 | — | — |
| (125, 225) | 925 | — | — | 125 |
| (125, 350) | 1300 | — | 125 | — |

**34. a.**

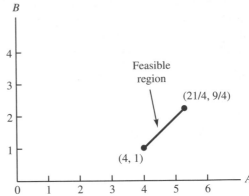

Feasible region

(21/4, 9/4)

(4, 1)

  **b.** There are two extreme points:

    $(A = 4, B = 1)$ and $(A = 21/4, B = 9/4)$

  **c.** The optimal solution [see part (a)] is $A = 4, B = 1$.

**35. a.** Min $\quad 6A + 4B + 0s_1 + 0s_2 + 0s_3$

    s.t.

$$
\begin{aligned}
2A + 1B - s_1 &= 12 \\
1A + 1B - s_2 &= 10 \\
1B + s_3 &= 4 \\
A, B, s_1, s_2, s_3 &\geq 0
\end{aligned}
$$

  **b.** The optimal solution is $A = 6, B = 4$

  **c.** $s_1 = 4, s_2 = 0, s_3 = 0$

**36. a.** Min $\quad 10{,}000T + 8000P$

    s.t.

$$
\begin{aligned}
T &\geq 8 \\
P &\geq 10 \\
T + P &\geq 25 \\
3T + 2P &\leq 84
\end{aligned}
$$

  **c.** (15, 10); (21.33, 10); (8, 30); (8, 17)

  **d.** $T = 8, P = 17$

    Total cost $= \$216{,}000$

**38. a.** Min $\quad 7.50S + 9.00P$

    s.t.

$$
\begin{aligned}
0.10S + 0.30P &\geq 6 \\
0.06S + 0.12P &\leq 3 \\
S + P &= 30 \\
S, P &\geq 0
\end{aligned}
$$

  **c.** The optimal solution is $S = 15, P = 15$.

  **d.** No

  **e.** Yes

**40.** $P_1 = 30, P_2 = 25$, Cost $= \$55$

**42.**

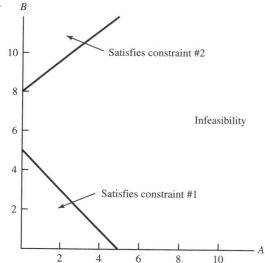

Satisfies constraint #2

Infeasibility

Satisfies constraint #1

**43.**

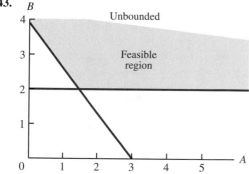

Unbounded

Feasible region

**44. a.** $A = 30/16, B = 30/16$; Value of optimal solution $= {}^{60}/_{16}$
**b.** $A = 0, B = 3$; Value of optimal solution $= 6$

**46. a.** 180, 20
**b.** Alternative optimal solutions
**c.** 120, 80

**48.** No feasible solution

**50.** $M = 65.45, R = 261.82$; Profit $= \$45,818$

**52.** $S = 384, O = 80$

**54. a.** Max    $160M_1 + 345M_2$
s.t.
$$
\begin{aligned}
M_1 &\leq 15 \\
M_2 &\leq 10 \\
M_1 &\geq 5 \\
M_2 &\geq 5 \\
40M_1 + 50M_2 &\leq 1000 \\
M_1, M_2 &\geq 0
\end{aligned}
$$
**b.** $M_1 = 12.5, M_2 = 10$

# Chapter 8

**1. a.**

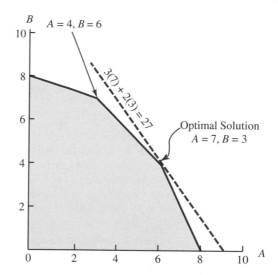

$A = 4, B = 6$

$3(7) + 2(3) = 27$

Optimal Solution
$A = 7, B = 3$

**b.** The same extreme point, $A = 7$ and $B = 3$, remains optimal; Value of the objective function becomes $5(7) + 2(3) = 41$.
**c.** A new extreme point, $A = 4$ and $B = 6$, becomes optimal; Value of the objective function becomes $3(4) + 4(6) = 36$.
**d.** The objective coefficient range for variable $A$ is 2 to 6; the optimal solution, $A = 7$ and $B = 3$, does not change. The objective coefficient range for variable $B$ is 1 to 3; resolve the problem to find the new optimal solution.

**2. a.** The feasible region becomes larger with the new optimal solution of $A = 6.5$ and $B = 4.5$.
**b.** Value of the optimal solution to the revised problem is $3(6.5) + 2(4.5) = 28.5$; the one-unit increase in the right-hand side of constraint 1 increases the value of the optimal solution by $28.5 - 27 = 1.5$; therefore, the shadow price for constraint 1 is 1.5.
**c.** The right-hand-side range for constraint 1 is 8 to 11.2; as long as the right-hand side stays within this range, the shadow price of 1.5 is applicable.
**d.** The value of the optimal solution will increase by 0.5 for every unit increase in the right-hand side of constraint 2 as long as the right-hand side is between 18 and 30.

**4. a.** $X = 2.5, Y = 2.5$
**b.** $-2$
**c.** 5 to 11
**d.** The value of the optimal solution will increase by 3 for every unit increase in the right-hand side of constraint 2 as long as the right-hand side is between 9 and 18.

**5. a.** Regular glove = 500; Catcher's mitt = 150;
   Value = 3700

   **b.** The finishing, packaging, and shipping constraints are binding; there is no slack

   **c.** Cutting and sewing = 0
   Finishing = 3
   Packaging and shipping = 28
   Additional finishing time is worth $3 per unit, and additional packaging and shipping time is worth $28 per unit.

   **d.** In the packaging and shipping department, each additional hour is worth $28.

**6. a.** The optimal value for the Regular Glove variable is 5, the Allowable Decrease is 1, and the Allowable Increase is 7. The optimal value for the Catcher's Mitt variable is 8, the Allowable Decrease is 4.667, and the Allowable Increase is 2. Therefore, we can express the Objective Coefficient Ranges as follows:

| Variable | Objective Coefficient Range |
|---|---|
| Regular Glove | 5 − 1 = 4 to 5 + 7 = 12 |
| Catcher's Mitt | 8 − 4.667 = 3.333 to 8 + 2 = 10 |

   **b.** As long as the profit contribution for the regular glove is between $4.00 and $12.00, the current solution is optimal; as long as the profit contribution for the catcher's mitt stays between $3.33 and $10.00, the current solution is optimal; the optimal solution is not sensitive to small changes in the profit contributions for the gloves.

   **c.** The shadow prices for the resources are applicable over the following ranges:

| Constraint | Right-Hand-Side Range |
|---|---|
| Cutting and sewing | 900 − 175 = 725 to No Upper Limit |
| Finishing | 300 − 166.667 = 133.333 to 300 + 100 = 400 |
| Packaging | 100 − 25 = 75 to 100 + 35 = 135 |

   **d.** The shadow price of packaging and shipping constraint is 28, so the amount of increase = (28) (20) = $560.

**8. a.** More than $7.00
   **b.** More than $3.50
   **c.** None

**10. a.** $S = 4000$
   $M = 10,000$
   Total risk = 8(4000) + 3(10,000) = 62,000

   **b.**

| Variable | Objective Coefficient Range |
|---|---|
| S | 8.000 − 4.250 = 3.750 to No Upper Limit |
| M | No Upper Limit to 3.000 + 3.400 = 6.400 |

   **c.** 5(4000) + 4(10,000) = $60,000
   **d.** 60,000/1,200,000 = 0.05 or 5%
   **e.** 0.057 risk units
   **f.** 0.057(100) = 5.7%

**12. a.** $E = 80$, $S = 120$, $D = 0$
   Profit = 63(80) + 95(120) + 135(0) = $16,440

   **b.** Fan motors and cooling coils

   **c.** The manufacturing time constraint has slack; 2400 − 2080 = 320 hours are available.

   **d.** This represents an increase in the objective function coefficient for $D$ of $150 − $135 = $15. Because this is less than the allowable increase of $24 for the objective function coefficient for $D$, there is no change in the optimal solution.

**13. a.** The range of optimality for each objective function coefficient is as follows:

   $E$  63.000 − 15.5000 = 47.500 to 63.000 + 12.000 = 75
   $S$  95.000 − 8.000 = 87.000 to 95.000 + 31.000 = 126
   $D$  No lower limit to 135.000 + 24.000 = 159.000

   **b.** Because more than one objective function coefficient value is changing at the same time here, we must re-solve the problem to answer this question. Re-solving the problem with the new profit values shows that the optimal solution will not change. However, the change in total profit will be 69(80) + 93(120) + 135(0) = $16,680.

   **c.** The range of feasibility for the right-hand side values for each constraint is as follows:

| Fan motors constraint | 200.000 − 40.000 = 160.000 to 200.000 + 80.000 = 280.000 |
|---|---|
| Cooling coils constraint | 320.000 − 120.000 = 200.000 to 320.000 + 80.000 = 400.000 |
| Manufacturing time constraint | 2400.000 − 320.000 = 2080.000 to No Upper Limit |

   **d.** Yes, 100 is greater than the allowable increase for the fan motors constraint (80.000).

   The shadow price will change.

**14. a.** The optimal solution is to manufacture 100 cases of model A and 60 cases of model B and purchase 90 cases of model B.

   Total Cost = 10(100) + 6(60) + 14(0) + 9(90) = $2170

   **b.** Demand for A, demand for B, assembly time

   **c.**

| Constraint | Shadow Price |
|---|---|
| 1 | 12.25 |
| 2 | 9.0 |
| 3 | 0 |
| 4 | −0.375 |

If demand for model A increases by 1 unit, total cost will increase by $12.25.

If demand for model B increases by 1 unit, total cost will increase by $9.00.

If an additional minute of assembly time is available, total cost will decrease by $.375.

   **d.** Assembly time constraint

**16. a.** 100 suits, 150 sport coats

Profit = $40,900

40 hours of cutting overtime

   **b.** Optimal solution will not change.

   **c.** Consider ordering additional material.

$34.50 is the maximum price.

   **d.** Profit will improve by $875.

**18. a.** The linear programming model is as follows:

$$\text{Min} \quad 30AN + 50AO + 25BN + 40BO$$

$$
\begin{aligned}
AN + \quad AO && \geq 50{,}000 \\
BN + \quad BO && \geq 70{,}000 \\
AN \quad\quad + \quad BN && \leq 80{,}000 \\
AO \quad\quad + \quad BO && \leq 60{,}000 \\
AN, AO, BN, BO \geq 0
\end{aligned}
$$

   **b.** Optimal solution

| | New Line | Old Line |
|---|---|---|
| Model A | 50,000 | 0 |
| Model B | 30,000 | 40,000 |
| Total cost: $3,850,000 | | |

   **c.** The first three constraints are binding.

   **d.** The shadow price for the new production line capacity constraint is $-15$. Because the shadow price is negative, increasing the right-hand side of constraint 3 will cause the objective function to decrease. Thus, every 1-unit increase in the right hand side of this constraint will actually reduce the total production cost by $15. In other words, an increase in capacity for the new production line is desirable.

   **e.** Because constraint 4 is not a binding constraint, any increase in the production line capacity of the old production line will have no effect on the optimal solution; thus, increasing the capacity of the old production line results in no benefit.

   **f.** The reduced cost for model A made on the old production line is 5; thus, the cost would have to decrease by at least $5 before any units of model A would be produced on the old production line.

   **g.** The right-hand-side range for constraint 2 shows an allowable decrease of 40,000. Thus, if the minimum production requirement is reduced 10,000 units to 60,000, the shadow price of 40 is applicable. Thus, total cost would decrease by 10,000(40) = $400,000.

**20. a.** $\text{Max} \quad 0.07H + 0.12P + 0.09A$

$$
\begin{aligned}
H + \quad P + \quad A &= 1{,}000{,}000 \\
0.6H - \quad 0.4P - \quad 0.4A &\geq 0 \\
P - \quad 0.6A &\leq 0 \\
H, P, A &\geq 0
\end{aligned}
$$

   **b.** $H = \$400{,}000$, $P = \$225{,}000$, $A = \$375{,}000$

Total annual return = $88,750

Annual percentage return = 8.875%

   **c.** No change

   **d.** Increase of $890

   **e.** Increase of $312.50, or 0.031%

**22. a.** $\text{Min} \quad 30L + \quad 25D + \quad 18S$

$$
\begin{aligned}
L + \quad D + \quad S &= 100 \\
0.6L - \quad 0.4D &\geq 0 \\
-0.15L - 0.15D + 0.85S &\geq 0 \\
-0.25L - 0.25D + \quad S &\leq 0 \\
L &\leq 50 \\
L, D, S &\geq 0
\end{aligned}
$$

   **b.** $L = 48$, $D = 72$, $S = 30$

Total cost = $3780

   **c.** No change

   **d.** No change

**24. a.** 333.3, 0, 833.3; Risk = 14,666.7; Return = 18,000, or 9%

   **b.** 1000, 0, 0, 2500; Risk = 18,000; Return = 22,000, or 11%

   **c.** $4000

**26. a.** Let $M_1$ = units of component 1 manufactured

$M_2$ = units of component 2 manufactured

$M_3$ = units of component 3 manufactured

$P_1$ = units of component 1 purchased

$P_2$ = units of component 2 purchased

$P_3$ = units of component 3 purchased

$$\text{Min} \quad 4.50M_1 + 5.00M_2 + 2.75M_3 + 6.50P_1 + 8.80P_2 + 7.00P_3$$

$$
\begin{aligned}
2M_1 + \quad 3M_2 + 4M_3 && \leq 21{,}600 \quad &\text{Production} \\
1M_1 + 1.5M_2 + 3M_3 && \leq 15{,}000 \quad &\text{Assembly} \\
1.5M_1 + \quad 2M_2 + 5M_3 && \leq 18{,}000 \quad &\text{Testing/Packaging} \\
1M_1 \quad\quad\quad\quad + 1P_1 && = 6{,}000 \quad &\text{Component 1} \\
1M_2 \quad\quad\quad\quad + 1P_2 && = 4{,}000 \quad &\text{Component 2} \\
1M_3 \quad\quad\quad\quad + 1P_3 && = 3{,}500 \quad &\text{Component 3} \\
M_1, M_2, M_3, P_1, P_2, P_3 \geq 0
\end{aligned}
$$

   **b.**

| Source | Component 1 | Component 2 | Component 3 |
|---|---|---|---|
| Manufacture | 2000 | 4000 | 1400 |
| Purchase | 4000 | | 2100 |
| Total Cost $73,550 | | | |

   **c.** Production: $54.36 per hour

Testing & Packaging: $7.50 per hour

   **d.** Shadow prices = $7.969; it would cost Benson $7.969 to add a unit of component 2.

**28. a.** Let　$G$ = amount invested in growth stock fund
　　　　　$S$ = amount invested in income stock fund
　　　　　$M$ = amount invested in money market fund

Max $0.20G + 0.10S + 0.06M$

s.t.
$$0.10G + 0.05S + 0.01M \leq (0.05)(300,000)$$
$$G \qquad\qquad\qquad \geq (0.10)(300,000)$$
$$S \qquad\qquad \geq (0.10)(300,000)$$
$$M \geq (0.20)(300,000)$$
$$G + \quad S + \quad M \leq 300,000$$
$$G, S, M \geq 0$$

**b.** $G = 120,000; S = 30,000; M = 150,000$
**c.** 0.15 to 0.60; No Lower Limit to 0.122; 0.02 to 0.20
**d.** 4668
**e.** $G = 48,000; S = 192,000; M = 60,000$
**f.** The client's risk index and the amount of funds available

**30. a.** $L = 3, N = 7, W = 5, S = 5$
**b.** Each additional minute of broadcast time increases cost by $100.
**c.** If local coverage is increased by 1 minute, total cost will increase by $100.
**d.** If the time devoted to local and national news is increased by 1 minute, total cost will increase by $100.
**e.** Increasing the sports by 1 minute will have no effect because the shadow price is 0.

**32. a.** Let　$P_1$ = number of PT-100 battery packs produced at the Philippines plant
　　　　$P_2$ = number of PT-200 battery packs produced at the Philippines plant
　　　　$P_3$ = number of PT-300 battery packs produced at the Philippines plant
　　　　$M_1$ = number of PT-100 battery packs produced at the Mexico plant
　　　　$M_2$ = number of PT-200 battery packs produced at the Mexico plant
　　　　$M_3$ = number of PT-300 battery packs produced at the Mexico plant

Min $1.13P_1 + 1.16P_2 + 1.52P_3 + 1.08M_1 + 1.16M_2 + 1.25M_3$
$$P_1 + \qquad\qquad M_1 \qquad\qquad = 200,000$$
$$P_2 + \qquad\qquad M_2 \qquad = 100,000$$
$$P_3 + \qquad\qquad M_3 = 150,000$$
$$P_1 + \quad P_2 \qquad\qquad\qquad \leq 175,000$$
$$M_1 + \quad M_2 \qquad \leq 160,000$$
$$P_3 \qquad\qquad \leq 75,000$$
$$M_3 \leq 100,000$$

$P_1, P_2, P_3, M_1, M_2, M_3 \geq 0$

**b.** The optimal solution is as follows:

|  | Philippines | Mexico |
|---|---|---|
| PT-100 | 40,000 | 160,000 |
| PT-200 | 100,000 | 0 |
| PT-300 | 50,000 | 100,000 |

Total production and transportation cost is $535,000.

**c.** The range of optimality for the objective function coefficient for $P_1$ shows a lower limit of $1.08; thus, the production and/or shipping cost would have to decrease by at least 5 cents per unit.
**d.** The range of optimality for the objective function coefficient for $M_1$ shows a lower limit of $1.11; thus, the production and/or shipping cost would have to decrease by at least 5 cents per unit.

# Chapter 9

**1. a.** Let　$T$ = number of television spot advertisements
　　　　$R$ = number of radio advertisements
　　　　$N$ = number of newspaper advertisements

Max $100,000T + 18,000R + 40,000N$

s.t.
$$2,000T + 300R + 600N \leq 18,200 \text{ Budget}$$
$$T \qquad\qquad\qquad \leq \quad 10 \text{ Max TV}$$
$$R \qquad\qquad \leq \quad 20 \text{ Max Radio}$$
$$N \leq \quad 10 \text{ Max News}$$
$$-0.5T + 0.5R - 0.5N \leq \quad 0 \text{ Max 50\% Radio}$$
$$0.9T - 0.1R - 0.1N \geq \quad 0 \text{ Min 10\% TV}$$
$$T, R, N, \geq 0$$

**Budget $**

Solution: $T = 4$ 　　$ 8000
　　　　　$R = 14$ 　　4200
　　　　　$N = 10$ 　　6000
　　　　　　　　　　$18,200

Audience = 1,052,000

**b.** The shadow price for the budget constraint is 51.30. Thus, a $100 increase in budget should provide an increase in audience coverage of approximately 5130. The right-hand-side range for the budget constraint will show this interpretation is correct.

**2. a.** Let　$x_1$ = units of product 1 produced
　　　　$x_2$ = units of product 2 produced

Max　$30x_1 + 15x_2$

s.t.
$$x_1 + 0.35x_2 \leq 100 \quad \text{Dept. A}$$
$$0.30x_1 + 0.20x_2 \leq \quad 36 \quad \text{Dept. B}$$
$$0.20x_1 + 0.50x_2 \leq \quad 50 \quad \text{Dept. C}$$
$$x_1, x_2 \leq 0$$

Solution: $x_1 = 77.89, x_2 = 63.16$; Profit = $3284.21

**b.** The shadow price for Department A is $15.79; for Department B it is $47.37; and for Department C it is $0.00. Therefore, we would attempt to schedule overtime in Departments A and B. Assuming the current labor available is a sunk cost, we should be willing to pay up to $15.79 per hour in Department A and up to $47.37 in Department B.

**c.** Let　$x_A$ = hours of overtime in Department A
　　　　$x_B$ = hours of overtime in Department B
　　　　$x_C$ = hours of overtime in Department C

Max $\quad 30x_1 + 15x_2 - 18x_A - 22.5x_B - 12x_C$

s.t.

$$
\begin{aligned}
x_1 + 0.35x_2 - x_A & \leq 100 \\
0.30x_1 + 0.20x_2 \qquad - x_B & \leq 36 \\
0.20x_1 + 0.50x_2 \qquad - x_C & \leq 50 \\
x_A & \leq 10 \\
x_B & \leq 6 \\
x_C & \leq 8
\end{aligned}
$$

$$x_1, x_2, x_A, x_B, x_C \leq 0$$

$$x_1 = 87.21$$
$$x_2 = 65.12$$
Profit = $3341.34

### Overtime

| | |
|---|---|
| Department A | 10 hours |
| Department B | 3.186 hours |
| Department C | 0 hours |

Increase in profit from overtime = $3341.34 − 3284.21 = $57.13

4. Let $X_1$ = the number of pounds of Party Nuts to produce
   $X_2$ = the number of pounds of Mixed Nuts to produce
   $X_3$ = the number of pounds of Premium Nuts to produce

Max $2(1.00)X_1 + 2(2.10)X_2 + 2(3.63)X_3 - 1.5(X_1 + 0.55X_2) - 5.35(0.25X_2 + 0.40X_3) - 6.25(0.1X_2 + 0.2X_3)$

s.t.

$$
\begin{aligned}
X_1 + 0.55X_2 & \leq 500 \quad \text{(Peanuts)} \\
0.25X_2 + 0.40X_2 & \leq 180 \quad \text{(Cashews)} \\
0.1X_2 + 0.2X_2 & \leq 100 \quad \text{(Brazil Nuts)} \\
0.1X_2 + 0.4X_2 & \leq 80 \quad \text{(Hazelnuts)} \\
X_1, X_2, X_2 & \geq 0
\end{aligned}
$$

The optimal solution is as follows:
$133\,1/3$ pounds of Party Nuts (or $266\,2/3$ bags)
$666\,2/3$ pounds of Mixed Nuts (or $1333\,1/3$ bags)
$33\,1/3$ pounds of Premium Nuts (or $66\,2/3$ bags)
Profit of $537.33
The binding constraints are Peanuts, Cashews, and Hazelnuts.
Brazil Nuts are not binding (only $73\,1/3$ pounds are used resulting in slack of $26\,2/3$ pounds).

6. Let $\quad x_1$ = units of product 1
   $x_2$ = units of product 2
   $b_1$ = labor-hours Department A
   $b_2$ = labor-hours Department B

Max $\quad 25x_1 + 20x_2 + 0b_1 + 0b_2$

s.t.

$$
\begin{aligned}
6x_1 + 8x_2 - 1b_1 & = 0 \\
12x_1 + 10x_2 - 1b_2 & = 0 \\
1b_1 + 1b_2 & \leq 900 \\
x_1, x_2, b_1, b_2 & \geq 0
\end{aligned}
$$

Solution: $x_1 = 50, x_2 = 0, b_1 = 300, b_2 = 600$; Profit: $1250

8. Let $x_1$ = the number of officers scheduled to begin at 8:00 A.M.
   $x_2$ = the number of officers scheduled to begin at noon

$x_3$ = the number of officers scheduled to begin at 4:00 P.M.
$x_4$ = the number of officers scheduled to begin at 8:00 P.M.
$x_5$ = the number of officers scheduled to begin at midnight
$x_6$ = the number of officers scheduled to begin at 4:00 A.M.

The objective function to minimize the number of officers required is as follows:

Min $\quad x_1 + x_2 + x_3 + x_4 + x_5 + x_6$

The constraints require the total number of officers on duty each of the six 4-hour periods to be at least equal to the minimum officer requirements. The constraints for the six 4-hour periods are as follows:

### Time of Day

$$
\begin{aligned}
\text{8:00 A.M.–Noon} & & x_1 & & + x_6 & \geq 5 \\
\text{Noon–4:00 P.M.} & & x_1 + x_2 & & & \geq 6 \\
\text{4:00 P.M.–8:00 P.M.} & & x_2 + x_3 & & & \geq 10 \\
\text{8:00 P.M.–Midnight} & & x_3 + x_4 & & & \geq 7 \\
\text{Midnight–4:00 A.M.} & & x_4 + x_5 & & & \geq 4 \\
\text{4:00 A.M.–8:00 A.M.} & & x_5 + x_6 & & & \geq 6
\end{aligned}
$$

$$x_1, x_2, x_3, x_4, x_5, x_6 \geq 0$$

Schedule 19 officers as follows:
$x_1 = 3$ begin at 8:00 A.M.
$x_2 = 3$ begin at noon
$x_3 = 7$ begin at 4:00 P.M.
$x_4 = 0$ begin at 8:00 P.M.
$x_5 = 4$ begin at midnight
$x_6 = 2$ begin at 4:00 A.M.

9. **a.** Let each decision variable, $A$, $P$, $M$, $H$, and $G$, represent the fraction or proportion of the total investment placed in each investment alternative.

Max $\quad 0.073A + 0.103P + 0.064M + 0.075H + 0.045G$

s.t.

$$
\begin{aligned}
A + P + M + H + G & = 1 \\
0.5A + 0.5P - 0.5M - 0.5H & \leq 0 \\
-0.5A - 0.5P + 0.5M + 0.5H & \leq 0 \\
- 0.25M - 0.25H + G & \geq 0 \\
-0.6A + 0.4P & \leq 0 \\
A, P, M, H, G & \geq 0
\end{aligned}
$$

Solution: Objective function = 0.079 with
Atlantic Oil = 0.178
Pacific Oil = 0.267
Midwest Oil = 0.000
Huber Steel = 0.444
Government Bonds = 0.111

**b.** For a total investment of $100,000, we show

| | |
|---|---:|
| Atlantic Oil = | $ 17,800 |
| Pacific Oil = | 26,700 |
| Midwest Oil = | 0 |
| Huber Steel = | 44,400 |
| Government Bonds = | 11,100 |
| Total | $100,000 |

**c.** Total earnings = $100,000 (0.079) = $7,900

**d.** Marginal rate of return = 0.079

**10. a.** Let    $S$ = the proportion of funds invested in stocks
$B$ = the proportion of funds invested in bonds
$M$ = the proportion of funds invested in mutual funds
$C$ = the proportion of funds invested in cash

The linear program and optimal solution are as follows:

Max    $0.1S + 0.03B + 0.04M + 0.01C$

s.t.

(1)    $1S + 1B + 1M + 1C = 1$
(2)    $0.8S + 0.2B + 0.3M < 0.4$
(3)    $1S < (0.75$
(4)    $-1B + 1M > 0$
(5)    $1C > 0.1$
(6)    $1C < 0.3$

The optimal allocation among the four investment alternatives:

| | |
|---|---|
| Stocks | 40.9% |
| Bonds | 14.5% |
| Mutual Funds | 14.5% |
| Cash | 30.0% |

The annual return associated with the optimal portfolio is 5.4%.

Total risk = $0.409(0.8) + 0.145(0.2) + 0.145(0.3) + 0.300(0.0) = 0.4$

**b.** Changing the right-hand-side value for constraint 2 to 0.18 and re-solving, we obtain the following optimal solution:

| | |
|---|---|
| Stocks | 0.0% |
| Bonds | 36.0% |
| Mutual Funds | 36.0% |
| Cash | 28.0% |

The annual return associated with the optimal portfolio is 2.52%.

Total risk = $0.0(0.8) + 0.36(0.2) + 0.36(0.3) + 0.28(0.0) = 0.18$

**c.** Changing the right-hand-side value for constraint 2 to 0.7 and re-solving, we obtain the following optimal allocation among the four investment alternatives:

| | |
|---|---|
| Stocks | 75.0% |
| Bonds | 0.0% |
| Mutual Funds | 15.0% |
| Cash | 10.0% |

The annual return associated with the optimal portfolio is 8.2%.

Total risk = $0.75(0.8) + 0.0(0.2) + 0.15(0.3) + 0.10(0.0) = 0.65$

**d.** Note that a maximum risk of 0.7 was specified for this aggressive investor, but that the risk index for the

portfolio is only 0.65. Thus, this investor is willing to take more risk than the solution shown above provides. There are only two ways the investor can become even more aggressive: by increasing the proportion invested in stocks to more than 75% or reducing the cash requirement of at least 10% so that additional cash could be put into stocks. For the data given here, the investor should ask the investment advisor to relax either or both of these constraints.

**e.** Defining the decision variables as proportions means the investment advisor can use the linear programming model for any investor, regardless of the amount of the investment. All the investor advisor must do is to establish the maximum total risk for the investor and resolve the problem using the new value for maximum total risk.

**12.** Let $B_i$ = pounds of shrimp bought in week $i$, $i = 1, 2, 3, 4$
$S_i$ = pounds of shrimp sold in week $i$, $i = 1, 2, 3, 4$
$I_i$ = pounds of shrimp held in storage (inventory) in week $i$

Total purchase cost = $6.00B_1 + 6.20B_2 + 6.65B_3 + 5.55B_4$
Total sales revenue = $6.00S_1 + 6.20S_2 + 6.65S_3 + 5.55S_4$
Total storage cost = $0.15I_1 + 0.15I_2 + 0.15I_3 + 0.15I_4$
Total profit contribution = (total sales revenue) − (total purchase cost) − (total storage cost)

Objective: Maximize total profit contribution subject to balance equations for each week, storage capacity for each week, and ending inventory requirement for week 4.

Max  $6.00S_1 + 6.20S_2 + 6.65S_3 + 5.55S_4 - 6.00B_1 - 6.20B_2 - 6.65B_3 - 5.55B_4 - 0.15I_1 - 0.15I_2 - 0.15I_3 - 0.15I_4$

s.t.

$$20,000 + B_1 - S_1 = I_1 \quad \text{Balance equation—week 1}$$
$$I_1 + B_2 - S_2 = I_2 \quad \text{Balance equation—week 2}$$
$$I_2 + B_3 - S_3 = I_3 \quad \text{Balance equation—week 3}$$
$$I_3 + B_4 - S_4 = I_4 \quad \text{Balance equation—week 4}$$
$$I_1 \leq 100,000 \quad \text{Storage capacity—week 1}$$
$$I_2 \leq 100,000 \quad \text{Storage capacity—week 2}$$
$$I_3 \leq 100,000 \quad \text{Storage capacity—week 3}$$
$$I_4 \leq 100,000 \quad \text{Storage capacity—week 4}$$
$$I_4 \leq 25,000 \quad \text{Required inventory—week 4}$$

all variables $\geq 0$

Note that the first four constraints can be written as follows:

$$I_1 - B_1 + S_1 = 20,000$$
$$I_1 - I_2 + B_2 - S_2 = 0$$
$$I_2 - I_3 + B_3 - S_3 = 0$$
$$I_3 - I_4 + B_4 - S_4 = 0$$

The optimal solution follows:

| Week ($i$) | $B_i$ | $S_i$ | $I_i$ |
|---|---|---|---|
| 1 | 80,000 | 0 | 100,000 |
| 2 | 0 | 0 | 100,000 |
| 3 | 0 | 100,000 | 0 |
| 4 | 25,000 | 0 | 25,000 |

Total profit contribution = $12,500

Note, however, that ASC started week 1 with 20,000 pounds of shrimp and ended week 4 with 25,000 pounds of shrimp. During the 4-week period, ASC has taken profits to reinvest and build inventory by 5000 pounds in anticipation of future higher prices. The amount of profit reinvested in inventory is ($5.55 + $0.15)(5000) = $28,500. Thus, total profit for the 4-week period including reinvested profit is $12,500 + $28,500 = $41,000.

**14. a.** Let    $x_i$ = number of Classic 21 boats produced in Quarter $i$; $i = 1, 2, 3, 4$

$s_i$ = ending inventory of Classic 21 boats in Quarter $i$; $i = 1, 2, 3, 4$

Min  $10,000x_1 + 11,000x_2 + 12,100x_3 + 13,310x_4 + 250s_1 + 250s_2 + 300s_3 + 300s_4$

s.t.

| | |
|---|---|
| $x_1 - s_1 = 1900$ | Quarter 1 demand |
| $s_1 + x_2 - s_2 = 4000$ | Quarter 2 demand |
| $s_2 + x_3 - s_3 = 3000$ | Quarter 3 demand |
| $s_3 + x_4 - s_4 = 1500$ | Quarter 4 demand |
| $s_4 \geq 500$ | Ending Inventory |
| $x_1 \leq 4000$ | Quarter 1 capacity |
| $x_2 \leq 3000$ | Quarter 2 capacity |
| $x_3 \leq 2000$ | Quarter 3 capacity |
| $x_4 \leq 4000$ | Quarter 4 capacity |

**b.**

| Quarter | Production | Ending Inventory | Cost ($) |
|---|---|---|---|
| 1 | 4000 | 2100 | 40,525,000 |
| 2 | 3000 | 1100 | 33,275,000 |
| 3 | 2000 | 100 | 24,230,000 |
| 4 | 1900 | 500 | 25,439,000 |
| | | | $123,469,000 |

**c.** The shadow prices tell us how much it would cost if demand were to increase by one additional unit. For example, in Quarter 2 the shadow price is $12,760; thus, demand for one more boat in Quarter 2 will increase costs by $12,760.

**d.** The shadow price of 0 for Quarter 4 tells us we have excess capacity in Quarter 4. The negative shadow prices in Quarters 1–3 tell us how much increasing the production capacity will decrease costs. For example, the shadow price of −$2510 for Quarter 1 tells us that if capacity were increased by 1 unit for this quarter, costs would go down $2510.

**15.** Let    $R_i$ = the number of barrels of input $i$ to use to produce Regular, $i = 1, 2, 3$

$S_i$ = the number of barrels of input $i$ to use to produce Super, $i = 1, 2, 3$

Max  $\{18.5\,(R_i1 + R_i2 + R_i3) + 20(R_i1 + R_i2 + R_i3) - 16.5(R_i1 + S_i1) - 14(R_i2 - S_i2) - 17.5(R_i3 + S_i3)\}$

s.t.

| | | |
|---|---|---|
| $R_1 + S_1$ | $\leq 110,000$ | Input 1 Capacity |
| $R_2 + S_2$ | $\leq 350,000$ | Input 2 Capaicty |
| $R_3 + S_3$ | $\leq 300,000$ | Input 3 Capacity |
| $R_1 + R_2 + R_3 \leq 350,000$ | | Max Demand for Regular |
| $S_1 + S_2 + S_3 \leq 500,000$ | | Max Demand for Super |
| $100R_1 + 87R_2 + 110R_2 \geq 90 \,(R_1 + R_2 + R_3)$ | | Required Octane Level Regular |
| $100S_1 + 87S_2 + 110S_2 \geq 100 \,(S_1 + S_2 + S_3)$ | | Required Octane Level Super |

$R_1, R_2, R_3, S_1, S_2, SS_3 \geq 0$

Maximum Profit = $2,845,000 by making 260,000 barrels of Regular and 500,000 barrels of Super. The 260,000 barrels of Regular are produced by mixing 110,000 barrels of Input 1, 132,608.7 barrels of Input 2, and 17,391.3 barrels of Input 3. The 500,000 barrels of Super are produced by mixing 217,391.3 barrels of Input 2, and 282,608.7 barrels of Input 3.

All available inputs are used, so each input capacity constraint is binding. The limit on maximum amount of Super we can sell is binding, as is the minimum octane requirement for Super.

**16.** Let    $x_i$ = number of 10-inch rolls of paper processed by cutting alternative $i$; $i = 1, 2, \ldots, 7$

Min    $x_1 + x_2 + x_3 + x_4 + x_5 + x_6 + x_7$

s.t.

| | | |
|---|---|---|
| $6x_1 \qquad + 2x_3 \qquad + x_5 + x_6 + 4x_7 \geq 1000$ | | $1\frac{1}{2}$" production |
| $4x_2 \qquad + x_4 + 3x_5 + 2x_6 \qquad \geq 2000$ | | $2\frac{1}{2}$" production |
| $2x_3 + 2x_4 \qquad + x_6 + x_7 \geq 4000$ | | $3\frac{1}{2}$" production |

$x_1, x_2, x_3, x_4, x_5, x_6, x_7 \geq 0$

$x_1 = 0$
$x_2 = 125$
$x_3 = 500$
$x_4 = 1500$
$x_5 = 0$
$x_6 = 0$
$x_7 = 0$

Total Rolls = 125 + 500 + 1500 = 2125 Rolls

Production:

$1\frac{1}{2}$"  1000
$2\frac{1}{2}$"  2000
$3\frac{1}{2}$"  4000

Waste: Cut alternative 4 ($\frac{1}{2}$" per roll)

Therefore, waste = $\frac{1}{2}(1500) = 750$ inches

**b.** Only the objective function needs to be changed. An objective function minimizing waste production and the new optimal solution are given.

Min  $x_1 + 0x_2 + 0x_3 + 0.5x_4 + x_5 + 0x_6 + 0.5x_7$

$x_1 = 0$
$x_2 = 500$
$x_3 = 2000$
$x_4 = 0$

$x_5 = 0$

$x_6 = 0$

$x_7 = 0$

Total Rolls = 2500 Rolls

    Production:

    $1^1/_2"$   4000

    $2^1/_2"$   2000

    $3^1/_2"$   4000

Waste is 0; however, we have overproduced the $1^1/_2"$ size by 3000 units. Perhaps these can be inventoried for future use.

c. Minimizing waste may cause you to overproduce. In this case, we used 375 more rolls to generate a 3000 surplus of the $1^1/_2"$ product. Alternative b might be preferred on the basis that the 3000 surplus could be held in inventory for later demand. However, in some trim problems, excess production cannot be used and must be scrapped. If this were the case, the 3000 unit $1^1/_2"$ size would result in 4500 inches of waste, and thus alternative 1 would be the preferred solution.

18. a. Let $x_1$ = number of Super Tankers purchased

        $x_2$ = number of Regular Line Tankers purchased

        $x_3$ = number of Econo-Tankers purchased

Min     $550x_1 + 425x_2 + 350x_3$

s.t.

     $6700x_1 + 55000x_2 + 4600x_3 \leq 600,000$   Budget

    $15(5000)x_1 + 20(2500)x_2 + 25(1000)x_3 \geq 550,000$

or

     $75000x_1 + 50000x_2 + 25000x_3 \geq 550,000$   Meet Demand

        $x_1 + x_2 + x_3 \leq 15$   Max. Total Vehicles

                     $x_3 \geq 3$   Min. Econo-Tankers

     $x_1 \leq \frac{1}{2}(x_1 + x_2 + x_3)$

or

     $\frac{1}{2}x_1 - \frac{1}{2}x_2 - \frac{1}{2}x_3 \leq 0$   No more than 50% Super Tankers

         $x_1, x_2, x_3 \geq 0$

Solution: 5 Super Tankers, 2 Regular Tankers, 3 Econo-Tankers

Total Cost: $583,000

Monthly Operating Cost: $4650

b. The last two constraints in the preceding formulation must be deleted and the problem re-solved.

The optimal solution calls for $7^1/_3$ Super Tankers at an annual operating cost of $4033. However, because a partial Super Tanker can't be purchased, we must round up to find a feasible solution of 8 Super Tankers with a monthly operating cost of $4400.

Actually, this is an integer programming problem, because partial tankers can't be purchased. We were fortunate in part (a) that the optimal solution turned out integer.

The true optimal integer solution to part (b) is $x_1 = 6$ and $x_2 = 2$, with a monthly operating cost of $4150. This is 6 Super Tankers and 2 Regular Line Tankers.

19. a. Let $x_{11}$ = amount of men's model in month 1

        $x_{21}$ = amount of women's model in month 1

        $x_{12}$ = amount of men's model in month 2

        $x_{22}$ = amount of women's model in month 2

        $s_{11}$ = inventory of men's model at end of month 1

        $s_{21}$ = inventory of women's model at end of month 1

        $s_{12}$ = inventory of men's model at end of month 2

        $s_{22}$ = inventory of women's model at end of month 2

The model formulation for part (a) is given.

Min   $120x_{11} + 90x_{21} + 120x_{12} + 90x_{22} + 2.4s_{11} + 1.8s_{21} + 2.4s_{12} + 1.8s_{22}$

s.t.

     $20 + x_{11} - s_{11} = 150$

or

     $x_{11} - s_{11} = 130$           Satisfy Demand    (1)

     $30 + x_{21} - s_{21} = 125$

or

     $x_{21} - s_{21} = 95$            Satisfy Demand    (2)

     $s_{11} + x_{12} - s_{12} = 200$     Satisfy Demand    (3)

     $s_{21} + x_{22} - s_{22} = 150$     Satisfy Demand    (4)

            $s_{12} \geq 25$          Ending Inventory    (5)

            $s_{22} \geq 25$          Ending Inventory    (6)

Labor-hours: Men's   = 2.0 + 1.5 = 3.5

             Women's = 1.6 + 1.0 = 2.6

     $3.5x_{11} + 2.6x_{21} \geq 900$      Labor Smoothing for   (7)

     $3.5x_{11} + 2.6x_{21} \leq 1100$     Month 1               (8)

     $3.5x_{11} + 2.6x_{21} - 3.5x_{12} - 2.6x_{22} \leq 100$   Labor Smoothing for   (9)

     $3.5x_{11} + 2.6x_{21} + 3.5x_{12} + 2.6x_{22} \leq 100$   Month 2       (10)

     $x_{11}, x_{12}, x_{21}, x_{22}, s_{11}, s_{12}, s_{21}, s_{22} \geq 0$

The optimal solution is to produce 193 of the men's model in month 1, 162 of the men's model in month 2, 95 units of the women's model in month 1, and 175 of the women's model in month 2. Total Cost = $67,156.

**Inventory Schedule**

| | | |
|---|---|---|
| Month 1 | 63 Men's | 0 Women's |
| Month 2 | 25 Men's | 25 Women's |

**Labor Levels**

| | |
|---|---|
| Previous month | 1000.00 hours |
| Month 1 | 922.25 hours |
| Month 2 | 1022.25 hours |

b. To accommodate this new policy, the right-hand sides of constraints 7–10 must be changed to 950, 1050, 50, and 50, respectively. The revised optimal solution is given.

$$x_{11} = 201$$
$$x_{21} = 95$$
$$x_{12} = 154$$
$$x_{22} = 175 \quad \text{Total Cost} = \$67,175$$

We produce more men's models in the first month and carry a larger men's model inventory; the added cost, however, is only $19. This seems to be a small expense to have less drastic labor force fluctuations. The new labor levels are 1000, 950, and 994.5 hours each month. Because the added cost is only $19, management might want to experiment with the labor force smoothing restrictions to enforce even less fluctuations. You may want to experiment yourself to see what happens.

**20.** Let   $x_m$ = number of units produced in month $m$
$I_m$ = increase in the total production level in month $m$
$D_m$ = decrease in the total production level in month $m$
$s_m$ = inventory level at the end of month $m$

where

$m = 1$ refers to March
$m = 2$ refers to April
$m = 3$ refers to May

Min $1.25\,I_1 + 1.25\,I_2 + 1.25\,I_3 + 1.00\,D_1 + 1.00\,D_2 + 1.00\,D_3$
s.t.

Change in production level in March:

$$x_1 - 10,000 = I_1 - D_1$$

or

$$x_1 - I_1 + D_1 = 10,000$$

Change in production level in April:

$$x_2 - x_1 = I_2 - D_2$$

or

$$x_2 - x_1 - I_2 + D_2 = 0$$

Change in production level in May:

$$x_3 - x_2 = I_3 - D_3$$

or

$$x_3 - x_2 - I_3 + D_3 = 0$$

Demand in March:

$$2500 + x_1 - s_1 = 12,000$$

or

$$x_1 - s_1 = 9500$$

Demand in April:

$$s_1 + x_2 - s_2 = 8000$$

Demand in May:

$$s_2 + x_3 = 15,000$$

Inventory capacity in March:

$$s_1 \le 3000$$

Inventory capacity in April:

$$s_2 \le 3000$$

Optimal Solution:

Total cost of monthly production increases and decreases
= $2500

| | | |
|---|---|---|
| $x_1 = 10,250$ | $I_1 = 250$ | $D_1 = 0$ |
| $x_2 = 10,250$ | $I_2 = 0$ | $D_2 = 0$ |
| $x_3 = 12,000$ | $I_3 = 1750$ | $D_3 = 0$ |
| $s_1 = 750$ | | |
| $s_2 = 3000$ | | |

**22.** Let   $SM_1$ = No. of small on machine $M_1$
$SM_2$ = No. of small on machine $M_2$
$SM_3$ = No. of small on machine $M_3$

$LM_1$ = No. of large on machine $M_1$
$LM_2$ = No. of large on machine $M_2$
$LM_3$ = No. of large on machine $M_3$
$MM_2$ = No. of meal on machine $M_2$
$MM_3$ = No. of meal on machine $M_3$

The formulation and solution follows. Note that constraints 1–3 guarantee that next week's schedule will be met and constraints 4–6 enforce machine capacities.

```
MIN
20SM1+24SM2+32SM3+15LM1+28LM2+35LM3+18MM2+36MM3

    S.T.

    1)   1SM1+1SM2+1SM3≤80000
    2)   +1LM1+1LM2+1LM3≥80000
    3)   +1MM2+1MM3≥65000
    4)   0.03333SM1+0.04LM1≤2100
    5)   +0.02222SM2+0.025LM2+0.03333MM2≤2100
    6)   +0.01667SM3+0.01923LM3+0.02273MM3≤2400


Optimal Solution

Objective Function Value =      5515886.58866

    Variable          Value
    ----------     -----------      SM1    0.00000
      SM2           0.00000
      SM3           80000.00000
      LM1           52500.00000
      LM2           0.00000
      LM3           27500.00000
      MM2           63006.30063
      MM3           1993.69937


    Constraint            Slack/Surplus
    ----------            -------------
        1                    0.00000
        2                    0.00000
        3                    0.00000
        4                    0.00000
        5                    0.00000
        6                  492.25821
```

Note that 5,515,887 square inches of waste are generated. Machine 3 has 492 minutes of idle capacity.

**24.** Let   $x_1$ = proportion of investment A undertaken
$x_2$ = proportion of investment B undertaken
$s_1$ = funds placed in savings for period 1
$s_2$ = funds placed in savings for period 2
$s_3$ = funds placed in savings for period 3
$s_4$ = funds placed in savings for period 4
$L_1$ = funds received from loan in period 1
$L_2$ = funds received from loan in period 2
$L_3$ = funds received from loan in period 3
$L_4$ = funds received from loan in period 4

Objective Function:

In order to maximize the cash value at the end of the four periods, we must consider the value of investment A, the value of investment B, savings income from period 4, and loan expenses for period 4.

$$\text{Max} \quad 3200x_1 + 2500x_2 + 1.1s_4 - 1.18L_4$$

Constraints require the *use* of funds to equal the *source* of funds for each period.

Period 1:

$$1000x_1 + 800x_2 + s_1 = 1500 + L_1$$

or

$$1000x_1 + 800x_2 + s_1 - L_1 = 1500$$

Period 2:

$$800x_1 + 500x_2 + s_2 + 1.18L_1 = 400 + 1.1s_1 + L_2$$

or

$$800x_1 + 500x_2 - 1.1s_1 + s_2 + 1.18L_1 - L_2 = 400$$

Period 3:

$$200x_1 + 300x_2 + s_3 + 1.18L_2 = 500 + 1.1s_2 + L_3$$

or

$$200x_1 + 300x_2 - 1.1s_2 + s_3 + 1.18L_2 - L_3 = 500$$

Period 4:

$$s_4 + 1.18L_3 = 100 + 200x_1 + 300x_2 + 1.1s_3 + L_4$$

or

$$-200x_1 - 300x_2 - 1.1s_3 + s_4 + 1.18L_3 - L_4 = 100$$

Limits on Loan Funds Available:

$$L_1 \le 200$$
$$L_2 \le 200$$
$$L_3 \le 200$$
$$L_4 \le 200$$

Proportion of Investment Undertaken:

$$x_1 \le 1$$
$$x_2 \le 1$$

Optimal Solution: $4340.40

| | | | |
|---|---|---|---|
| Investment A | $x_1 = 0.458$ | or | 45.8% |
| Investment B | $x_2 = 1.0$ | or | 100.0% |

Savings/Loan Schedule:

| | Period 1 | Period 2 | Period 3 | Period 4 |
|---|---|---|---|---|
| Savings | 242.11 | — | — | 341.04 |
| Loan | — | 200.00 | 127.58 | — |

# Chapter 10

**1.** The network model is shown:

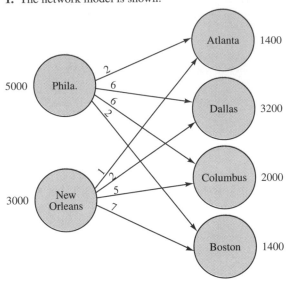

**2. a.** Let $x_{11}$ = amount shipped from Jefferson City to Des Moines

$x_{12}$ = amount shipped from Jefferson City to Kansas City

⋮

$$\text{Min} \quad 14x_{11} + 9x_{12} + 7x_{13} + 8x_{21} + 10x_{22} + 5x_{23}$$

s.t.

$$
\begin{aligned}
x_{11} + x_{12} + x_{13} & & & \le 30 \\
& x_{21} + x_{22} + x_{23} & & \le 20 \\
x_{11} & + x_{21} & & = 25 \\
x_{12} & + x_{22} & & = 15 \\
x_{13} & + x_{23} & & = 10 \\
\end{aligned}
$$

$$x_{11}, x_{12}, x_{13}, x_{21}, x_{22}, x_{23} \ge 0$$

**b.** Optimal Solution:

| | Amount | Cost |
|---|---|---|
| Jefferson City–Des Moines | 5 | 70 |
| Jefferson City–Kansas City | 15 | 135 |
| Jefferson City–St. Louis | 10 | 70 |
| Omaha–Des Moines | 20 | 160 |
| | Total | 435 |

**4.** The optimization model can be written as

$x_{ij}$ = Red GloFish shipped from $i$ to $j$ $i = M$ for Michigan, $T$ for Texas; $j = 1, 2, 3$.

$y_{ij}$ = Blue GloFish shipped from $i$ to $j$, $i = M$ for Michigan, $T$ for Texas; $j = 1, 2, 3$.

$\text{Min } x_{M1} + 2.50x_{M2} + 0.50x_{M3} + y_{M1} + 2.50y_{M2} + 0.50y_{M3} + 2.00y_{T1} + 1.50y_{T2} + 2.80y_{T3}$

subject to

| | | | | | | | | |
|---|---|---|---|---|---|---|---|---|
| $x_{M1} +$ | $x_{M2} +$ | $x_{M3}$ | | | | | $\leq$ | 1,000,000 |
| | $y_{M1} +$ | $y_{M2} +$ | $y_{M3}$ | | | | $\leq$ | 1,000,000 |
| | | | | $y_{T1} +$ | $y_{T2} +$ | $y_{T3}$ | $\leq$ | 600,000 |
| $x_{M1}$ | | | | | | | $\geq$ | 320,000 |
| | $x_{M2}$ | | | | | | $\geq$ | 300,000 |
| | | $x_{M3}$ | | | | | $\geq$ | 160,000 |
| | $y_{M1} +$ | | | $y_{T1}$ | | | $\geq$ | 380,000 |
| | | $y_{M2} +$ | | | $y_{T2}$ | | $\geq$ | 450,000 |
| | | | $y_{M3} +$ | | | $y_{T3}$ | $\geq$ | 290,000 |

$xij \geq 0$

Solving this linear program using Solver, we find that we should produce 780,000 red GloFish in Michigan, 670,000 blue GloFish in Michigan, and 450,000 blue GloFish in Texas.

Using the notation in the model, the number of GloFish shipped from each farm to each retailer can be expressed as follows:

$x_{M1} = 320,000$
$x_{M2} = 300,000$
$x_{M3} = 160,000$
$y_{M1} = 380,000$
$y_{M2} = 0$
$y_{M3} = 290,000$
$y_{T1} = 0$
$y_{T2} = 450,000$
$y_{T3} = 0$

**a.** From Solver, the minimum transportation cost is $2.35 million.

**b.** We have to add variables $x_{T1}$, $x_{T2}$, and $x_{T3}$ for Red GloFish shipped between Texas and Retailers 1, 2 and 3. The revised objective function is

Minimize $x_{M1} + 2.50x_{M2} + 0.50x_{M3} + y_{M1} + 2.50y_{M2} + 0.50y_{M3} + 2.00y_{T1} + 1.50y_{T2} + 2.80y_{T3} + x_{T1} + 2.50x_{T2} + 0.50x_{T3}$

We replace the third constraint above with

$x_{T1} + x_{T2} + x_{T3} + y_{T1} + y_{T2} + y_{T3} \leq 600,000$

And we change the constraints

$\quad x_{M1} \quad \geq 320,000$
$\quad x_{M2} \quad \geq 300,000$
$\quad x_{M3} \quad \geq 160,000$

to

$\quad x_{M1} + x_{T1} \geq 320,000$
$\quad x_{M2} + x_{T2} \geq 300,000$
$\quad x_{M3} | x_{T3} \geq 160,000$

Using this new objective function and constraint the optimal solution is $2.2 million, so the savings are $150,000.

**6.** The network model, the linear programming formulation, and the optimal solution are shown. Note that the third constraint corresponds to the dummy origin. The variables $x_{31}$, $x_{32}$, $x_{33}$, and $x_{34}$ are the amounts shipped out of the

dummy origin; they do not appear in the objective function because they are given a coefficient of zero.

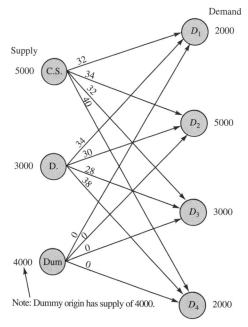

Note: Dummy origin has supply of 4000.

$\text{Max } 32x_{11} + 34x_{12} + 32x_{13} + 40x_{14} + 34x_{21} + 30x_{22} + 28x_{23} + 38x_{24}$

s.t.

| | | | | |
|---|---|---|---|---|
| $x_{11} + x_{12} + x_{13} + x_{14}$ | | | $\leq 5000$ | |
| $x_{21} + x_{22} + x_{23} + x_{24}$ | | | $\leq 3000$ | |
| $x_{31} + x_{32} + x_{33} + x_{34}$ | | | $\leq 4000$ | Dummy |
| $x_{11} + x_{21} + x_{31}$ | | | $= 2000$ | |
| $x_{12} + x_{22} + x_{32}$ | | | $= 5000$ | |
| $x_{13} + x_{23} + x_{33}$ | | | $= 3000$ | |
| $x_{14} + x_{24} + x_{34}$ | | | $= 2000$ | |

$x_{ij} \geq 0 \quad \text{for all } i, j$

| Optimal Solution | Units | Cost |
|---|---|---|
| Clifton Springs–$D_2$ | 4000 | $136,000 |
| Clifton Springs–$D_4$ | 1000 | 40,000 |
| Danville–$D_1$ | 2000 | 68,000 |
| Danville–$D_4$ | 1000 | 38,000 |
| Total Cost | | $282,000 |

Customer 2 demand has a shortfall of 1000.

Customer 3 demand of 3000 is not satisfied.

**8. a.**

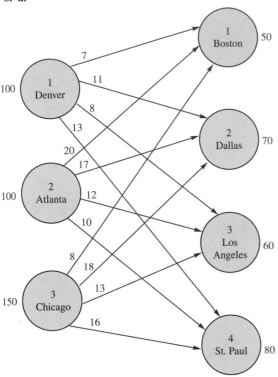

**b.** There are alternative optimal solutions.

| Solution 1 | | Solution 2 | |
|---|---|---|---|
| Denver to St. Paul: | 10 | Denver to St. Paul: | 10 |
| Atlanta to Boston: | 50 | Atlanta to Boston: | 50 |
| Atlanta to Dallas: | 50 | Atlanta to Los Angeles: | 50 |
| Chicago to Dallas: | 20 | Chicago to Dallas: | 70 |
| Chicago to Los Angeles: | 60 | Chicago to Los Angeles: | 10 |
| Chicago to St. Paul: | 70 | Chicago to St. Paul: | 70 |
| Total Profit: | $4240 | | |

If solution 1 is used, Forbelt should produce 10 motors at Denver, 100 motors at Atlanta, and 150 motors at Chicago. There will be idle capacity for 90 motors at Denver.

If solution 2 is used, Forbelt should adopt the same production schedule but a modified shipping schedule.

**10. a.** The total cost is the sum of the purchase cost and the transportation cost. We show the calculation for Division 1–Supplier 1 and present the result for the other Division-Supplier combinations.

**Division 1–Supplier 1**

| | |
|---|---|
| Purchase cost (40,000 × $12.60) | $504,000 |
| Transportation Cost (40,000 × $2.75) | 110,000 |
| Total Cost: | $614,000 |

**Cost Matrix ($1000s)**

| | Supplier | | | | | |
|---|---|---|---|---|---|---|
| **Division** | **1** | **2** | **3** | **4** | **5** | **6** |
| 1 | 614 | 660 | 534 | 680 | 590 | 630 |
| 2 | 603 | 639 | 702 | 693 | 693 | 630 |
| 3 | 865 | 830 | 775 | 850 | 900 | 930 |
| 4 | 532 | 553 | 511 | 581 | 595 | 553 |
| 5 | 720 | 648 | 684 | 693 | 657 | 747 |

**b.** Optimal Solution:

| | |
|---|---|
| Supplier 1–Division 2 | $ 603 |
| Supplier 2–Division 5 | 648 |
| Supplier 3–Division 3 | 775 |
| Supplier 5–Division 1 | 590 |
| Supplier 6–Division 4 | 553 |
| Total | $3169 |

**11. a.** Network Model

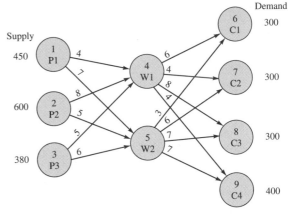

**b. & c.** The linear programming formulation and solution is shown below:

```
LINEAR PROGRAMMING PROBLEM

MIN 4X14 + 7X15 + 8X24 + 5X25 + 5X34 + 6X35
+ 6X46 + 4X47 + 8X48 + 4X49 + 3X56 + 6X57
+ 7X58 + 7X59

S.T.

(1) X14 + X15 < 450
(2) X24 + X25 < 600
(3) X34 + X35 < 380
(4) X46 + X47 + X48 + X49 - X14 - X24
    - X34 = 0
(5) X56 + X57 + X58 + X59 - X15 - X25
    - X35 = 0
(6) X46 + X56 = 300
(7) X47 + X57 = 300
(8) X48 + X58 = 300
(9) X49 + X59 = 400
```

OPTIMAL SOLUTION

Objective Function Value =    11850.000

| Variable | Value | Reduced Costs |
| --- | --- | --- |
| X14 | 450.000 | 0.000 |
| X15 | 0.000 | 3.000 |
| X24 | 0.000 | 3.000 |
| X25 | 600.000 | 0.000 |
| X34 | 250.000 | 0.000 |
| X35 | 0.000 | 1.000 |
| X46 | 0.000 | 3.000 |
| X47 | 300.000 | 0.000 |
| X48 | 0.000 | 1.000 |
| X49 | 400.000 | 0.000 |
| X56 | 300.000 | 0.000 |
| X57 | 0.000 | 2.000 |
| X58 | 300.000 | 0.000 |
| X59 | 0.000 | 3.000 |

There is an excess capacity of 130 units at plant 3.

**12. a.** Three arcs must be added to the network model in Problem 11a. The new network is shown:

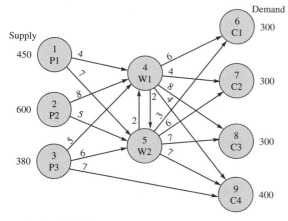

**b. & c.** The linear programming formulation and optimal solution is shown below:

LINEAR PROGRAMMING PROBLEM

MIN 4X14 + 7X15 + 8X24 + 5X25 + 5X34 I
6X35 + 6X46 + 4X47 + 8X48 + 4X49 + 3X56 +
6X57 + 7X58 + 7X59 + 7X39 + 2X45 + 2X54

S.T.

(1) X14 + X15 < 450
(2) X24 + X25 < 600
(3) X34 + X35 + X39 < 380
(4) X45 + X46 + X47 + X48 + X49 − X14 − X24
    − X34 − X54 = 0
(5) X54 + X56 + X57 + X58 + X59 − X15 − X25
    − X35 − X45 = 0
(6) X46 + X56 = 300
(7) X47 + X57 = 300
(8) X48 + X58 = 300
(9) X39 + X49 + X59 = 400

OPTIMAL SOLUTION

Objective Function Value = 11220.000

| Variable | Value | Reduced Costs |
| --- | --- | --- |
| X14 | 320.000 | 0.000 |
| X15 | 0.000 | 2.000 |
| X24 | 0.000 | 4.000 |
| X25 | 600.000 | 0.000 |
| X34 | 0.000 | 2.000 |
| X35 | 0.000 | 2.000 |
| X46 | 0.000 | 2.000 |
| X47 | 300.000 | 0.000 |
| X48 | 0.000 | 0.000 |
| X49 | 20.000 | 0.000 |
| X56 | 300.000 | 0.000 |
| X57 | 0.000 | 3.000 |
| X58 | 300.000 | 0.000 |
| X59 | 0.000 | 4.000 |
| X39 | 380.000 | 0.000 |
| X45 | 0.000 | 1.000 |
| X54 | 0.000 | 3.000 |

The value of the solution here is $630 less than the value of the solution for Problem 23. The new shipping route from plant 3 to customer 4 has helped ($x_{39} = 380$). There is now excess capacity of 130 units at plant 1.

**14.**

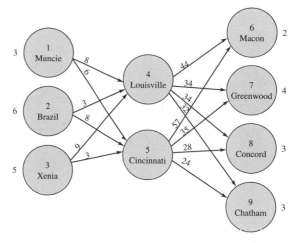

A linear programming model is

Min $8x_{14}+6x_{15}+3x_{24}+8x_{25}+9x_{34}+3x_{35}+44x_{46}+34x_{47}+34x_{48}+32x_{49}+57x_{56}+35x_{57}+28x_{58}+24x_{59}$
s.t.

$$
\begin{array}{l}
x_{14}+x_{15} \leq 3\\
x_{24}+x_{25} \leq 6\\
x_{34}+x_{35} \leq 5\\
-x_{14}\quad -x_{24}\quad -x_{34}\quad +x_{46}+x_{47}+x_{48}+x_{49} = 0\\
-x_{15}\quad -x_{25}\quad -x_{35}\quad +x_{56}+x_{57}+x_{58}+x_{59}= 0\\
x_{46}\quad +x_{56} = 2\\
x_{47}\quad +x_{57} = 4\\
x_{48}\quad +x_{58} = 3\\
x_{49}\quad +x_{59}= 3
\end{array}
$$

$x_{ij} \geq 0$   for all $i, j$

| Optimal Solution | Units Shipped | Cost |
|---|---|---|
| Muncie–Cincinnati | 1 | 6 |
| Cincinnati–Concord | 3 | 84 |
| Brazil–Louisville | 6 | 18 |
| Louisville–Macon | 2 | 88 |
| Louisville–Greenwood | 4 | 136 |
| Xenia–Cincinnati | 5 | 15 |
| Cincinnati–Chatham | 3 | 72 |
| | | 419 |

Two rail cars must be held at Muncie until a buyer is found.

**16. a.**

$$\text{Min } 20x_{12} + 25x_{15} + 30x_{25} + 45x_{27} + 20x_{31} + 35x_{36}$$
$$+ 30x_{42} + 25x_{53} + 15x_{54} + 28x_{56} + 12x_{67} + 27x_{74}$$

s.t.

$$x_{31} - x_{12} - x_{15} = 8$$
$$x_{25} + x_{27} - x_{12} - x_{42} = 5$$
$$x_{31} + x_{36} - x_{53} = 3$$
$$x_{54} + x_{74} - x_{42} = 3$$
$$x_{53} + x_{54} + x_{56} - x_{15} - x_{25} = 2$$
$$x_{36} + x_{56} - x_{67} = 5$$
$$x_{74} - x_{27} - x_{67} = 6$$
$$x_{ij} \geq 0 \text{ for all } i, j$$

**b.**

| | |
|---|---|
| $x_{12} = 0$ | $x_{53} = 5$ |
| $x_{15} = 0$ | $x_{54} = 0$ |
| $x_{25} = 8$ | $x_{56} = 5$ |
| $x_{27} = 0$ | $x_{67} = 0$ |
| $x_{31} = 8$ | $x_{74} = 6$ |
| $x_{36} = 0$ | $x_{56} = 5$ |
| $x_{42} = 3$ | |

Total cost of redistributing cars = \$917

**17. a.**

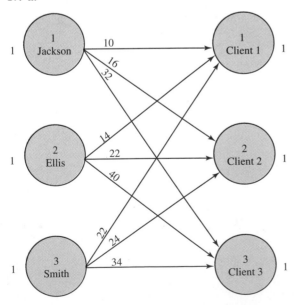

**b.**

$$\text{Min } 10x_{11} + 16x_{12} + 32x_{13} + 14x_{21} + 22x_{22} + 40x_{23} + 22x_{31} + 24x_{32} + 34x_{33}$$

s.t.

$$x_{11} + x_{12} + x_{13} \leq 1$$
$$x_{21} + x_{22} + x_{23} \leq 1$$
$$x_{31} + x_{32} + x_{33} \leq 1$$
$$x_{11} + x_{21} + x_{31} = 1$$
$$x_{12} + x_{22} + x_{32} = 1$$
$$x_{13} + x_{23} + x_{33} = 1$$
$$x_{ij} \geq 0 \text{ for all } i, j$$

Solution: $x_{12} = 1$, $x_{21} = 1$, $x_{33} = 1$
Total completion time = 64

**18. a.**

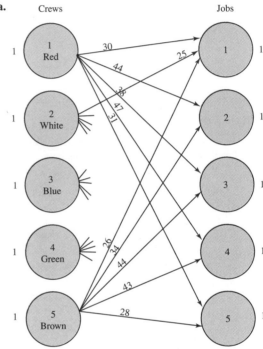

**b.**

$$\text{Min } 30x_{11} + 44x_{12} + 38x_{13} + 47x_{14} + 31x_{15} + 25x_{21} + \cdots + 28x_{55}$$

s.t.

$$x_{11} + x_{12} + x_{13} + x_{14} + x_{15} \leq 1$$
$$x_{21} + x_{22} + x_{23} + x_{24} + x_{25} \leq 1$$
$$x_{31} + x_{32} + x_{33} + x_{34} + x_{35} \leq 1$$
$$x_{41} + x_{42} + x_{43} + x_{44} + x_{45} \leq 1$$
$$x_{51} + x_{52} + x_{53} + x_{54} + x_{55} \leq 1$$
$$x_{11} + x_{21} + x_{31} + x_{41} + x_{51} = 1$$
$$x_{12} + x_{22} + x_{32} + x_{42} + x_{52} = 1$$
$$x_{13} + x_{23} + x_{33} + x_{43} + x_{53} = 1$$
$$x_{14} + x_{24} + x_{34} + x_{44} + x_{54} = 1$$
$$x_{15} + x_{25} + x_{35} + x_{45} + x_{55} = 1$$
$$x_{ij} \geq 0, \ i = 1, 2, \ldots, 5; \ j = 1, 2, \ldots, 5$$

Optimal Solution:

| | |
|---|---|
| Green to Job 1 | \$ 26 |
| Brown to Job 2 | 34 |
| Red to Job 3 | 38 |
| Blue to Job 4 | 39 |
| White to Job 5 | 25 |
| | \$162 |

Because the data are in hundreds of dollars, the total installation cost for the five contracts is $16,200.

**20. a.** This is the variation of the assignment problem in which multiple assignments are possible. Each distribution center may be assigned up to three customer zones.

The linear programming model of this problem has 40 variables (one for each combination of distribution center and customer zone). It has 13 constraints. There are five supply ($\leq 3$) constraints and eight demand ($=1$) constraints.

The optimal solution is as follows:

| Assignments | | Cost ($1000s) |
|---|---|---|
| Plano | Kansas City, Dallas | 34 |
| Flagstaff | Los Angeles | 15 |
| Springfield | Chicago, Columbus, Atlanta | 70 |
| Boulder | Newark, Denver | 97 |
| | Total Cost | $216 |

**b.** The Nashville distribution center is not used.

**c.** All the distribution centers are used. Columbus is switched from Springfield to Nashville. Total cost increases by $11,000 to $227,000.

**22.** A linear programming formulation of this problem can be developed as follows. Let the first letter of each variable name represent the professor and the second two the course. Note that a $DPH$ variable is not created because the assignment is unacceptable.

Max $2.8AUG + 2.2AMB + 3.3AMS + 3.0APH + 3.2BUG + \cdots + 2.5DMS$

s.t.

$$
\begin{aligned}
AUG + AMB + AMS + APH &\leq 1 \\
BUG + BMB + BMS + BPH &\leq 1 \\
CUG + CMB + CMS + CPH &\leq 1 \\
DUG + DMB + DMS &\leq 1 \\
AUG + BUG + CUG + DUG &= 1 \\
AMB + BMB + CMB + DMB &= 1 \\
AMS + BMS + CMS + DMS &= 1 \\
APH + BPH + CPH &= 1
\end{aligned}
$$

All Variables $\geq 0$

| Optimal Solution | Rating |
|---|---|
| A to MS course | 3.3 |
| B to Ph.D. course | 3.6 |
| C to MBA course | 3.2 |
| D to Undergraduate course | 3.2 |
| Max Total Rating | 13.3 |

**23.** Origin—Node 1
Transshipment—Nodes 2–5
Destination—Node 7

The linear program will have 14 variables for the arcs and 7 constraints for the nodes.

Let

$$
x_{ij} = \begin{cases} 1 & \text{if the arc from node } i \text{ to node } j \text{ is on the shortest route} \\ 0 & \text{otherwise} \end{cases}
$$

Min $7x_{12} + 9x_{13} + 18x_{14} + 3x_{23} + 5x_{25} + 3x_{32} + 4x_{35} + 3x_{46} + 5x_{52} + 4x_{53} + 2x_{56} + 6x_{57} + 2x_{65} + 3x_{67}$

s.t.

| | Flow Out | Flow In | |
|---|---|---|---|
| Node 1 | $x_{12} + x_{13} + x_{14}$ | | $= 1$ |
| Node 2 | $x_{23} + x_{25}$ | $-x_{12} - x_{32} - x_{52}$ | $= 0$ |
| Node 3 | $x_{32} + x_{35}$ | $-x_{13} - x_{23} - x_{53}$ | $= 0$ |
| Node 4 | $x_{46}$ | $-x_{14}$ | $= 0$ |
| Node 5 | $x_{52} + x_{53} + x_{56} + x_{57}$ | $-x_{25} - x_{35} - x_{65}$ | $= 0$ |
| Node 6 | $x_{65} + x_{67}$ | $-x_{46} - x_{56}$ | $= 0$ |
| Node 7 | | $+x_{57} + x_{67}$ | $= 1$ |

$x_{ij} \geq 0$ for all $i$ and $j$

Optimal Solution: $x_{12} = 1$, $x_{25} = 1$, $x_{56} = 1$, and $x_{67} = 1$

Shortest Route: 1–2–5–6–7

Length $= 17$

**24.** The linear program has 13 variables for the arcs and 6 constraints for the nodes. Use the same 6 constraints for the Gorman shortest route problem, as shown in the text. The objective function changes to travel time as follows:

Min $40x_{12} + 36x_{13} + 6x_{23} + 6x_{32} + 12x_{24} + 12x_{42} + 25x_{26} + 15x_{35} + 15x_{53} + 8x_{45} + 8x_{54} + 11x_{46} + 23x_{56}$

Optimal Solution: $x_{12} = 1$, $x_{24} = 1$, and $x_{46} = 1$

Shortest Route: 1–2–4–6

Total Time $= 63$ minutes

**26.** Origin—Node 1
Transshipment—Nodes 2–5 and node 7
Destination—Node 6

The linear program will have 18 variables for the arcs and 7 constraints for the nodes.

Let

$$
x_{ij} = \begin{cases} 1 & \text{if the arc from node } i \text{ to node } j \text{ is on the shortest route} \\ 0 & \text{otherwise} \end{cases}
$$

Min $35x_{12} + 30x_{13} + 20x_{14} + 8x_{23} + 12x_{25} + 8x_{32} + 9x_{34} + 10x_{35} + 20x_{36} + 9x_{43} + 15x_{47} + 12x_{52} + 10x_{53} + 5x_{56} + 20x_{57} + 15x_{74} + 20x_{75} + 5x_{76}$

s.t.

| | Flow Out | Flow In | |
|---|---|---|---|
| Node 1 | $x_{12} + x_{13} + x_{14}$ | | $= 1$ |
| Node 2 | $x_{23} + x_{25}$ | $-x_{12} - x_{32} - x_{52}$ | $= 0$ |
| Node 3 | $x_{32} + x_{34} + x_{35} + x_{36}$ | $-x_{13} - x_{23} - x_{43} - x_{53}$ | $= 0$ |
| Node 4 | $x_{43} + x_{47}$ | $-x_{14} - x_{34} - x_{74}$ | $= 0$ |
| Node 5 | $x_{52} + x_{53} + x_{56} + x_{57}$ | $-x_{25} - x_{35} - x_{75}$ | $= 0$ |
| Node 6 | | $+x_{36} + x_{56} + x_{76}$ | $= 1$ |
| Node 7 | $x_{74} + x_{75} + x_{76}$ | $-x_{47} - x_{57}$ | $= 0$ |

$x_{ij} \geq 0$    for all $i$ and $j$

Optimal Solution: $x_{14} = 1$, $x_{47} = 1$, and $x_{76} = 1$

Shortest Route: 1–4–7–6

Total Distance $= 40$ miles

**28.** Origin—Node 0

Transshipment—Nodes 1 to 3

Destination—Node 4

The linear program will have 10 variables for the arcs and 5 constraints for the nodes.

Let

$$x_{ij} = \begin{cases} 1 & \text{if the arc from node } i \text{ to node } j \text{ is on the minimum cost route} \\ 0 & \text{otherwise} \end{cases}$$

Min $600x_{01} + 1000x_{02} + 2000x_{03} + 2800x_{04} + 500x_{12} + 1400x_{13} + 2100x_{14} + 800x_{23} + 1600x_{24} + 700x_{34}$

s.t.

|  | Flow Out | Flow In |  |
|---|---|---|---|
| Node 0 | $x_{01} + x_{02} + x_{03} + x_{04}$ |  | $= 1$ |
| Node 1 | $x_{12} + x_{13} + x_{14}$ | $-x_{01}$ | $= 0$ |
| Node 2 | $x_{23} + x_{24}$ | $-x_{02} - x_{12}$ | $= 0$ |
| Node 3 | $x_{34}$ | $-x_{03} - x_{13} - x_{23}$ | $= 0$ |
| Node 4 |  | $-x_{04} - x_{14} - x_{24} - x_{34}$ | $= 1$ |

$$x_{ij} \geq 0 \quad \text{for all } i \text{ and } j$$

Optimal Solution: $x_{02} = 1$, $x_{23} = 1$, and $x_{34} = 1$

Shortest Route: 0–2–3–4

Total Cost $= \$2500$

**29.** The capacitated transshipment problem to solve is given:

Max $x_{61}$

s.t.

$$\begin{aligned}
x_{12} + x_{13} + x_{14} - x_{61} &= 0 \\
x_{24} + x_{25} - x_{12} - x_{42} &= 0 \\
x_{34} + x_{36} - x_{13} - x_{43} &= 0 \\
x_{42} + x_{43} + x_{45} + x_{46} - x_{14} - x_{24} - x_{34} - x_{54} &= 0 \\
x_{54} + x_{56} - x_{25} - x_{45} &= 0 \\
x_{61} - x_{36} + x_{46} - x_{56} &= 0
\end{aligned}$$

$$\begin{array}{lll}
x_{12} \leq 2 & x_{13} \leq 6 & x_{14} \leq 3 \\
x_{24} \leq 1 & x_{25} \leq 4 \\
x_{34} \leq 3 & x_{36} \leq 2 \\
x_{42} \leq 1 & x_{43} \leq 3 & x_{45} \leq 1 \quad x_{46} \leq 3 \\
x_{54} \leq 1 & x_{56} \leq 6
\end{array}$$

$$x_{ij} \geq 0 \text{ for all } i, j$$

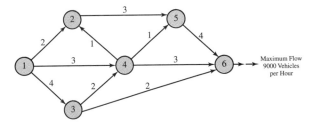

The system cannot accommodate a flow of 10,000 vehicles per hour.

**30.**

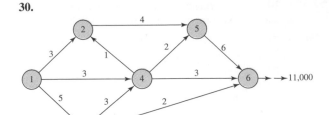

**32. a.** 10,000 gallons per hour or 10 hours

**b.** Flow reduced to 9000 gallons per hour; 11.1 hours.

**34.** Maximal Flow $= 23$ gallons/minute. Five gallons will flow from node 3 to node 5.

**36. a.** Let $R_1, R_2, R_3$ represent regular time production in months 1, 2, 3

$O_1, O_2, O_3$ represent overtime production in months 1, 2, 3

$D_1, D_2, D_3$ represent demand in months 1, 2, 3

Using these nine nodes, a network model is shown:

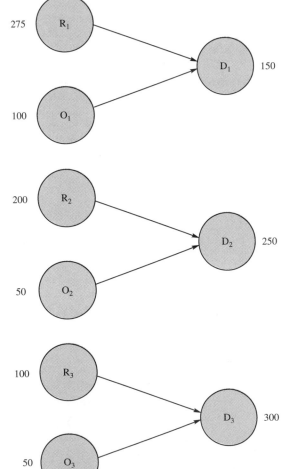

**b.** Use the following notation to define the variables: The first two characters designate the "from node" and the second two characters designate the "to node" of the arc. For instance, $R_1D_1$ is amount of regular time production available to satisfy demand in month 1; $O_1D_1$ is amount of overtime production in month 1 available to satisfy demand in month 1; $D_1D_2$ is the amount of inventory carried over from month 1 to month 2; and so on.

$$\text{Min } 50R_1D_1 + 80O_1D_1 + 20D_1D_2 + 50R_2D_2 + 80O_2D_2 \\ + 20D_2D_3 + 60R_3D_3 + 100O_3D_3$$

S.T.

$$
\begin{array}{ll}
(1) & R_1D_1 \le 275 \\
(2) & O_1D_1 \le 100 \\
(3) & R_2D_2 \le 200 \\
(4) & O_2D_2 \le 50 \\
(5) & R_3D_3 \le 100 \\
(6) & O_3D_3 \le 50 \\
(7) & R_1D_1 + O_1D_1 - D_1D_2 = 150 \\
(8) & R_2D_2 + O_2D_2 + D_1D_2 - D_2D_3 = 250 \\
(9) & R_3D_3 + O_3D_3 + D_2D_3 = 300
\end{array}
$$

**c.** Optimal Solution:

| Variable | Value |
| --- | --- |
| $R_1D_1$ | 275.000 |
| $O_1D_1$ | 25.000 |
| $D_1D_2$ | 150.000 |
| $R_2D_2$ | 200.000 |
| $O_2D_2$ | 50.000 |
| $D_2D_3$ | 150.000 |
| $R_3D_3$ | 100.000 |
| $O_3D_3$ | 50.000 |

Value = \$46,750

*Note:* Slack variable for constraint 2 = 75

**d.** The values of the slack variables for constraints 1 through 6 represent unused capacity. The only nonzero slack variable is for constraint 2; its value is 75. Thus, there are 75 units of unused overtime capacity in month 1.

# Chapter 11

**2. a.**

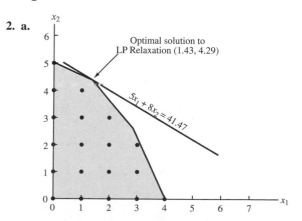

**b.** The optimal solution to the LP Relaxation is given by $x_1 = 1.43$, $x_2 = 4.29$ with an objective function value of 41.47. Rounding down gives the feasible integer solution $x_1 = 1$, $x_2 = 4$; its value is 37.

**c.**

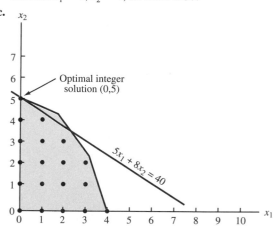

The optimal solution is given by $x_1 = 0$, $x_2 = 5$; its value is 40. It is not the same solution as found by rounding down; it provides a 3-unit increase in the value of the objective function.

**4. a.** $x_1 = 3.67$, $x_2 = 0$; Value = 36.7
Rounded: $x_1 = 3$, $x_2 = 0$; Value = 30
Lower bound = 30; Upper bound = 36.7
**b.** $x_1 = 3$, $x_2 = 2$; Value = 36
**c.** Alternative optimal solutions: $-x_1 = 0$, $x_2 = 5$
$x_1 = 2$, $x_2 = 4$

**5. a.** The feasible mixed-integer solutions are indicated by the boldface vertical lines in the graph.

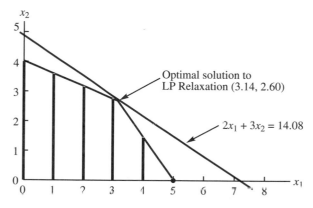

**b.** The optimal solution to the LP Relaxation is given by $x_1 = 3.14$, $x_2 = 2.60$; its value is 14.08.
Rounding down the value of $x_1$ to find a feasible mixed-integer solution yields $x_1 = 3$, $x_2 = 2.60$ with a value of 13.8; this solution is clearly not optimal; with $x_1 = 3$, $x_2$ can be made larger without violating the constraints.

**c.** The optimal solution to the MILP is given by $x_1 = 3$, $x_2 = 2.67$; its value is 14, as shown in the following figure:

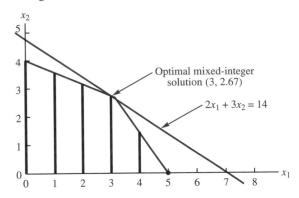

**6. b.** $x_1 = 1.96$, $x_2 = 5.48$; Value = 7.44
Rounded: $x_1 = 1.96$, $x_2 = 5$; Value = 6.96
Lower bound = 6.96; Upper bound = 7.44
**c.** $x_1 = 1.29$, $x_2 = 6$; Value = 7.29

**7. a.** $x_1 + x_3 + x_5 + x_6 = 2$
**b.** $x_3 - x_5 = 0$
**c.** $x_1 + x_4 = 1$
**d.** $x_4 \leq x_1$
$x_4 \leq x_3$
**e.** $x_4 \leq x_1$
$x_4 \leq x_3$
$x_4 \leq x_1 + x_3 - 1$

**8. a.** $x_3 = 1$, $x_4 = 1$, $x_6 = 1$; Value = 17,500
**b.** Add $x_1 + x_2 \leq 1$.
**c.** Add $x_3 - x_4 = 0$.

**10. b.** Choose locations B and E.

**12. a.** We use the following data:

$b_{ij}$ = the bid for city $i$ from carrier $j$,
$i = 1, 2, \ldots 20$   $j = 1, 2, \ldots 7$
$dem_i$ = the demand in truckload for city $i$
$i = 1, 2, \ldots 20$
$c_{ij}$ = the cost of assigning city $i$ to carrier $j$
$i = 1, 2, \ldots 20$   $j = 1, 2, \ldots 7$

Note: $c_{ij} = (dem_i)(b_{ij})$ used in the objective function.

Let $y[j] = 1$ if carrier $j$ is selected, 0 if not $j = 1, 2, \ldots 7$

$x[i,j] = 1$ if city $i$ is assigned to carrier $j$, 0 if not $i = 1, 2, \ldots 20$   $j = 1, 2, \ldots 7$

Minimize the cost of city-carrier assignments (note: for brevity, zeros are not shown).

Minimize

65640\*x[1, 5] + 49980\*x[1, 6] + 53700\*x[1, 7] + 14530\*x[2, 2] + 26020\*x[2, 5] + 17670\*x[2, 6] + 30680\*x[3, 2] + 45660\*x[3, 5] + 37140\*x[3, 6] + 37400\*x[3, 7] + 67480\*x[4, 2] + 104680\*x[4, 5] + 69520\*x[4, 6] + 15230\*x[5, 2] + 22390\*x[5, 5] + 17710\*x[5, 6] +

18550\*x[5, 7] + 15210\*x[6, 2] + 15710\*x[6, 5] + 15450\*x[6, 7] + 25200\*x[7, 2] + 23064\*x[7, 4] + 23256\*x[7, 5] + 24600\*x[7, 7] + 45000\*x[8, 2] + 35800\*x[8, 4] + 35400\*x[8, 5] + 43475\*x[8, 7] + 28350\*x[9, 2] + 30825\*x[9, 4] + 29525\*x[9, 5] + 28750\*x[9, 7] + 22176\*x[10, 2] + 20130\*x[10, 4] + 22077\*x[10, 5] + 22374\*x[10, 7] + 7964\*x[11, 1] + 7953\*x[11, 3] + 6897\*x[11, 4] + 7227\*x[11, 5] + 7766\*x[11, 7] + 22214\*x[12, 1] + 22214\*x[12, 3] + 20909\*x[12, 4] + 19778\*x[12, 5] + 21257\*x[12, 7] + 8892\*x[13, 1] + 8940\*x[13, 3] + 8184\*x[13, 5] + 8796\*x[13, 7] + 19560\*x[14, 1] + 19200\*x[14, 2] + 19872\*x[14, 3] + 17880\*x[14, 5] + 19968\*x[14, 7] + 9040\*x[15, 1] + 8800\*x[15, 3] + 8910\*x[15, 5] + 9140\*x[15, 7] + 9580\*x[16, 1] + 9330\*x[16, 3] + 8910\*x[16, 5] + 9140\*x[16, 7] + 21275\*x[17, 1] + 21367\*x[17, 3] + 21551\*x[17, 5] + 22632\*x[17, 7] + 22300\*x[18, 1] + 21725\*x[18, 3] + 20550\*x[18, 4] + 20725\*x[18, 5] + 21600\*x[18, 7] + 11124\*x[19, 1] + 11628\*x[19, 3] + 11604\*x[19, 5] + 12096\*x[19, 7] + 9630\*x[20, 1] + 9380\*x[20, 3] + 9550\*x[20, 5] + 9950\*x[20, 7]

subject to

Every city is assigned to exactly one carrier:

x[1, 1] + x[1, 2] + x[1, 3] + x[1, 4] + x[1, 5] + x[1, 6] + x[1, 7] = 1
x[2, 1] + x[2, 2] + x[2, 3] + x[2, 4] + x[2, 5] + x[2, 6] + x[2, 7] = 1
x[3, 1] + x[3, 2] + x[3, 3] + x[3, 4] + x[3, 5] + x[3, 6] + x[3, 7] = 1
x[4, 1] + x[4, 2] + x[4, 3] + x[4, 4] + x[4, 5] + x[4, 6] + x[4, 7] = 1
x[5, 1] + x[5, 2] + x[5, 3] + x[5, 4] + x[5, 5] + x[5, 6] + x[5, 7] = 1
x[6, 1] + x[6, 2] + x[6, 3] + x[6, 4] + x[6, 5] + x[6, 6] + x[6, 7] = 1
x[7, 1] + x[7, 2] + x[7, 3] + x[7, 4] + x[7, 5] + x[7, 6] + x[7, 7] = 1
x[8, 1] + x[8, 2] + x[8, 3] + x[8, 4] + x[8, 5] + x[8, 6] + x[8, 7] = 1
x[9, 1] + x[9, 2] + x[9, 3] + x[9, 4] + x[9, 5] + x[9, 6] + x[9, 7] = 1
x[10, 1] + x[10, 2] + x[10, 3] + x[10, 4] + x[10, 5] + x[10, 6] + x[10, 7] = 1
x[11, 1] + x[11, 2] + x[11, 3] + x[11, 4] + x[11, 5] + x[11, 6] + x[11, 7] = 1
x[12, 1] + x[12, 2] + x[12, 3] + x[12, 4] + x[12, 5] + x[12, 6] + x[12, 7] = 1
x[13, 1] + x[13, 2] + x[13, 3] + x[13, 4] + x[13, 5] + x[13, 6] + x[13, 7] = 1
x[14, 1] + x[14, 2] + x[14, 3] + x[14, 4] + x[14, 5] + x[14, 6] + x[14, 7] = 1
x[15, 1] + x[15, 2] + x[15, 3] + x[15, 4] + x[15, 5] + x[15, 6] + x[15, 7] = 1
x[16, 1] + x[16, 2] + x[16, 3] + x[16, 4] + x[16, 5] + x[16, 6] + x[16, 7] = 1
x[17, 1] + x[17, 2] + x[17, 3] + x[17, 4] + x[17, 5] + x[17, 6] + x[17, 7] = 1
x[18, 1] + x[18, 2] + x[18, 3] + x[18, 4] + x[18, 5] + x[18, 6] + x[18, 7] = 1
x[19, 1] + x[19, 2] + x[19, 3] + x[19, 4] + x[19, 5] + x[19, 6] + x[19, 7] = 1
x[20, 1] + x[20, 2] + x[20, 3] + x[20, 4] + x[20, 5] + x[20, 6] + x[20, 7] = 1

If a carrier is selected, it can be assigned only the number of bids made:

Note:

The idea here is that if carrier $j$ is not chosen, then no cities can be assigned to that carrier. Hence if $y[j] = 0$, the sum must be less than or equal to zero and hence all the associated $x$'s must be zero. If $y[j] = 1$, then the constraint becomes redundant. It could also be modeled as $x[i,j] <= y[j]$, but this would generate more constraints:

x[1, 1] + x[2, 1] + x[3, 1] + x[4, 1] + x[5, 1] + x[6, 1] + x[7, 1]+ x[8, 1] + x[9, 1] + x[10, 1] + x[11, 1] + x[12, 1] + x[13, 1] + x[14, 1] + x[15, 1] + x[16, 1] + x[17, 1] + x[18, 1] + x[19, 1] + x[20, 1] <= 10\*y[1]

x[1, 2] + x[2, 2] + x[3, 2] + x[4, 2] + x[5, 2] + x[6, 2] + x[7, 2] + x[8, 2] + x[9, 2] + x[10, 2] + x[11, 2] + x[12, 2] + x[13, 2] + x[14, 2] + x[15, 2] + x[16, 2] + x[17, 2] + x[18, 2] + x[19, 2] + x[20, 2] <= 10\*y[2]

$x[1, 3] + x[2, 3] + x[3, 3] + x[4, 3] + x[5, 3] + x[6, 3] + x[7, 3] +$
$x[8, 3] + x[9, 3] + x[10, 3] + x[11, 3] + x[12, 3] + x[13, 3] +$
$x[14, 3] + x[15, 3] + x[16, 3] + x[17, 3] + x[18, 3] + x[19, 3] +$
$x[20, 3] <= 10*y[3]$

$x[1, 4] + x[2, 4] + x[3, 4] + x[4, 4] + x[5, 4] + x[6, 4] + x[7, 4]+$
$x[8, 4] + x[9, 4] + x[10, 4] + x[11, 4] + x[12, 4] + x[13, 4] +$
$x[14, 4] + x[15, 4] + x[16, 4] + x[17, 4] + x[18, 4] + x[19, 4] +$
$x[20, 4] <= 7*y[4]$

$x[1, 5] + x[2, 5] + x[3, 5] + x[4, 5] + x[5, 5] + x[6, 5] + x[7, 5] +$
$x[8, 5] + x[9, 5] + x[10, 5] + x[11, 5] + x[12, 5] + x[13, 5] +$
$x[14, 5] + x[15, 5] + x[16, 5] + x[17, 5] + x[18, 5] + x[19, 5] +$
$x[20, 5] <= 20*y[5]$

$x[1, 6] + x[2, 6] + x[3, 6] + x[4, 6] + x[5, 6] + x[6, 6] + x[7, 6]+$
$x[8, 6] + x[9, 6] + x[10, 6] + x[11, 6] + x[12, 6] + x[13, 6] +$
$x[14, 6] + x[15, 6] + x[16, 6] + x[17, 6] + x[18, 6] + x[19, 6] +$
$x[20, 6] <= 5*y[6]$

$x[1, 7] + x[2, 7] + x[3, 7] + x[4, 7] + x[5, 7] + x[6, 7] + x[7, 7] +$
$x[8, 7] + x[9, 7] + x[10, 7] + x[11, 7] + x[12, 7] + x[13, 7] +$
$x[14, 7] + x[15, 7] + x[16, 7] + x[17, 7] + x[18, 7] + x[19, 7] +$
$x[20, 7] <= 18*y[7]$

Nonbids must be set to 0:

$x[1, 1] + x[2, 1] + x[3, 1] + x[4, 1] + x[5, 1] + x[6, 1] + x[7, 1] +$
$x[8, 1] + x[9, 1] + x[10, 1] = 0$

$x[1, 2] + x[11, 2] + x[12, 2] + x[13, 2] + x[15, 2] + x[16, 2] +$
$x[17, 2] + x[18, 2] + x[19, 2] + x[20, 2] = 0$

$x[1, 3] + x[2, 3] + x[3, 3] + x[4, 3] + x[5, 3] + x[6, 3] + x[7, 3] +$
$x[8, 3] + x[9, 3] + x[10, 3] = 0$

$x[1, 4] + x[2, 4] + x[3, 4] + x[4, 4] + x[5, 4] + x[6, 4] + x[13, 4] +$
$x[14, 4] + x[15, 4] + x[16, 4] + x[17, 4] + x[19, 4] + x[20, 4] = 0$

$x[6, 6] + x[7, 6] + x[8, 6] + x[9, 6] + x[10, 6] + x[11, 6] +$
$|x[12, 6] + x[13, 6] + x[14, 6] + x[15, 6] + x[16, 6] + x[17, 6] +$
$x[18, 6] + x[19, 6] + x[20, 6] = 0$

$x[2, 7] + x[4, 7] = 0$

No more than three carriers

$y[1] + y[2] + y[3] + y[4] + y[5] + y[6] + y[7] <= 3$

Solution:          Total Cost = \$436,512
Carrier 2:         assigned cities 2, 3, 4, 5, 6, and 9
Carrier 5:         assigned cities 7, 8, and 10–20
Carrier 6:         assigned city 1

**b.**

| # Carriers | Cost | Carriers Chosen |
|---|---|---|
| 1 | \$524,677 | 5 |
| 2 | \$452,172 | 2,5 |
| 3 | \$436,512 | 2,5,6 |
| 4 | \$433,868 | 2,4,5,6 |
| 5 | \$433,112 | 1,2,4,5,6 |
| 6 | \$432,832 | 1,2,3,4,5,6 |
| 7 | \$432,832 | 1,2,3,4,5,6,7 |

Given the incremental drop in cost, three seems like the correct number of carriers (the curve flattens considerably after three carriers). Notice that when seven carriers are allowed, only six carriers are actually assigned a city. That is, allowing a seventh carrier provides no benefit.

**13. a.** Add the following multiple-choice constraint to the problem:

$y_1 + y_2 - 1$

New optimal solution: $y_1 = 1, y_3 = 1, x_{12} = 10, x_{31} = 30,$
$x_{52} = 10, x_{53} = 20$
Value = 940

**b.** Because one plant is already located in St. Louis, it is only necessary to add the following constraint to the model:

$y_3 + y_4 \le 1$

New optimal solution: $y_4 = 1, x_{42} = 20, x_{43} = 20,$
$x_{51} = 30$
Value = 860

**14. a.** Let   1 denote the Michigan plant
         2 denote the first New York plant
         3 denote the second New York plant
         4 denote the Ohio plant
         5 denote the California plant

It is not possible to meet needs by modernizing only one plant.

The following table shows the options which involve modernizing two plants.

| | Plant | | | | Transmission | Engine Block | | |
|---|---|---|---|---|---|---|---|---|
| 1 | 2 | 3 | 4 | 5 | Capacity | Capacity | Feasible? | Cost |
| √ | √ | | | | 700 | 1300 | No | |
| √ | | √ | | | 1100 | 900 | Yes | 60 |
| √ | | | √ | | 900 | 1400 | Yes | 65 |
| √ | | | | √ | 600 | 700 | No | |
| | √ | √ | | | 1200 | 1200 | Yes | 70 |
| | √ | | √ | | 1000 | 1700 | Yes | 75 |
| | √ | | | √ | 700 | 1000 | No | |
| | | √ | √ | | 1400 | 1300 | Yes | 75 |
| | | √ | | √ | 1100 | 600 | No | |
| | | | √ | √ | 900 | 1100 | Yes | 60 |

**b.** Modernize plants 1 and 3 or plants 4 and 5.

**c.** Let $x_i = \begin{cases} 1 & \text{if plant } i \text{ is modernized} \\ 0 & \text{if plant } i \text{ is not modernized} \end{cases}$

Min  $25x_1 + 35x_2 + 35x_3 + 40x_4 + 25x_5$

s.t.

$300x_1 + 400x_2 + 800x_3 + 600x_4 + 300x_5 \geq 900$ Transmissions
$500x_1 + 800x_2 + 400x_3 + 900x_4 + 200x_5 \geq 900$ Engine Blocks

$$x_1, x_2, x_3, x_4, x_5 \geq 0$$

**d.** Modernize plants 1 and 3.

**16. a.**

Min  $105x_9 + 105x_{10} + 105x_{11} + 32y_9 + 32y_{10} + 32y_{11} + 32y_{12} + 32y_1 + 32y_2 + 32y_3$

$$
\begin{array}{llr}
x_9 & + y_9 & \geq 6 \\
x_9 + x_{10} & + y_9 + y_{10} & \geq 4 \\
x_9 + x_{10} + x_{11} + y_9 + y_{10} + y_{11} & & \geq 8 \\
x_9 + x_{10} + x_{11} + y_9 + y_{10} + y_{11} + y_{12} & & \geq 10 \\
x_{10} + x_{11} & + y_{10} + y_{11} + y_{12} + y_1 & \geq 9 \\
x_9 & + x_{11} & + y_{11} + y_{12} + y_1 + y_2 & \geq 6 \\
x_9 + x_{10} & + y_{12} + y_1 + y_2 + y_3 & \geq 4 \\
x_9 + x_{10} + x_{11} & + y_1 + y_2 + y_3 & \geq 7 \\
x_{10} + x_{11} & + y_2 + y_3 & \geq 6 \\
x_{11} & + y_3 & \geq 6 \\
\end{array}
$$

$x_i, y_j \geq 0$ and integer for $i = 9, 10, 11$ and $j = 9, 10, 11, 12, 1, 2, 3$

**b.** Use all part-time employees.
Bring on as follows: 9:00 A.M.–6, 11:00 A.M.–2, 12:00 noon–6, 1:00 P.M.–1, 3:00 P.M.–6
Cost = $672

**c.** Same as in part (b)

**d.** New solution is to bring on one full-time employee at 9:00 A.M., four more at 11:00 A.M., and part-time employees as follows:
9:00 A.M.–5, 12:00 noon–5, and 3:00 P.M.–2

**18. a.** 52, 49, 36, 83, 39, 70, 79, 59

**b.** Thick crust, cheese blend, chunky sauce, medium sausage. Six of eight consumers will prefer this pizza (75%).

**20. a.** New objective function: Min $25x_1 + 40x_2 + 40x_3 + 40x_4 + 25x_5$

**b.** $x_4 = x_5 = 1$; modernize the Ohio and California plants

**c.** Add the constraint $x_2 + x_3 = 1$.

**d.** $x_1 = x_3 = 1$

**22.** $x_1 + x_2 + x_3 = 3y_1 + 5y_2 + 7y_3$
$y_1 + y_2 + y_3 = 1$

**24. a.** $x_{111}, x_{112}, x_{121}$

**b.** $x_{111} + x_{112} + x_{121} \leq 1$

**c.** $x_{531} + x_{532} + x_{533} + x_{541} + x_{542} + x_{543} + x_{551} + x_{552} + x_{561} \leq 1$

**d.** Only two screens are available.

**e.** $x_{222} + x_{231} + x_{422} + x_{431} + x_{531} + x_{532} + x_{533} + x_{631} + x_{632} + x_{633} \leq 2$

**26.** Let  $X_i$ = the amount (dollars) to invest in alternative $i$
$i = 1, 2, \ldots 10$
$Y_i = 1$ if Dave invests in alternative $i$, 0 if not
$i = 1, 2 \ldots 10$

Max  $0.067X_1 + 0.0765X_2 + 0.0755X_3 + 0.0745X_4 + 0.075X_5 + 0.0645X_6 + 0.0705X_7 + 0.069X_8 + 0.052X_9 + 0.059X_{10}$

Subject to

$X_1 + X_2 + X_3 + X_4 + X_5 + X_6 + X_7 + X_8 + X_9 + X_{10} = 100{,}000$
Invest $100,000

$X_i \leq 25{,}000Y_i$   $i = 1, 2, \ldots 10$
Invest no more than $25,000 in any one fund

$X_i \geq 10{,}000Y_i$   $i = 1, 2, \ldots 10$
If invest in a fund, invest at least $10,000 in a fund

$Y_1 + Y_2 + Y_3 + Y_4 \leq 2$
No more than 2 pure growth funds

$Y_9 + Y_{10} \geq 1$
At least 1 must be a pure bond fund

$X_9 + X_{10} \geq X_1 + X_2 + X_3 + X_4$

Amount in pure bonds must be at least that invested in pure growth funds

$X_i \geq 0$       $i = 1, 2, \ldots 10$

The optimal solution:

| Fund | Amount Invested | Exp Return |
|---|---|---|
| 1 | $       0 | $       0.00 |
| 2 | $  12,500 | $    956.25 |
| 3 | $       0 | $       0.00 |
| 4 | $       0 | $       0.00 |
| 5 | $  25,000 | $  1,875.00 |
| 6 | $       0 | $       0.00 |
| 7 | $  25,000 | $  1,762.50 |
| 8 | $  25,000 | $  1,725.50 |
| 9 | $0 | $0.00 |
| 10 | $  12,500 | $    737.50 |
| | $100,000 | $7,056.25 |

# Chapter 12

**2. a.**

Min $E$

s.t.

$$wa + wb + wc + wd + we + wf + wg = 1$$
$$55.31wa + 37.64wb + 32.91wc + 33.53wd + 32.48we + 48.78wf + 58.41wg \geq 33.53$$
$$49.52wa + 55.63wb + 25.77wc + 41.99wd + 55.30we + 81.92wf + 119.70wg \geq 41.99$$
$$281wa + 156wb + 141wc + 160wd + 157we + 285wf + 111wg \geq 160$$
$$47wa + 3wb + 26wc + 21wd + 82we + 92wf + 89wg \geq 21$$

$$-250E + 310wa + 278.5wb + 165.6wc + 250wd + 206.4we + 384wf + 530.1wg \leq 0$$
$$-316E + 134.6wa + 114.3wb + 131.3wc + 316wd + 151.2we + 217wf + 770.8wg \leq 0$$
$$-94.4E + 116wa + 106.8wb + 65.52wc + 94.4wd + 102.1we + 153.7wf + 215wg \leq 0$$
$$wa, wb, wc, wd, we, wf, wg \geq 0$$

**b.**   $E = 0.924$
$wa = 0.074$
$wc = 0.436$
$we = 0.489$

All other weights are zero.

**c.**   $D$ is relatively inefficient.
Composite requires 92.4 of $D$'s resources.

**d.**   34.37 patient days (65 or older)
41.99 patient days (under 65)

**e.**   Hospitals A, C, and E

**4. a.**

Min $E$

s.t.

$$wb + wc + wj + wn + ws = 1$$
$$3800wb + 4600wc + 4400wj + 6500wn + 6000ws \geq 4600$$
$$25wb + 32wc + 35wj + 30wn + 28ws \geq 32$$
$$8wb + 8.5wc + 8wj + 10wn + 9ws \geq 8.5$$
$$-110E + 96wb + 110wc + 100wj + 125wn + 120ws \leq 0$$
$$-22E + 16wb + 22wc + 18wj + 25wn + 24ws \leq 0$$
$$-1400E + 850wb + 1400wc + 1200wj + 1500wn + 1600ws \leq 0$$

$$wb, wc, wj, wn, ws \geq 0$$

**b.**

```
OPTIMAL SOLUTION

Objective Function Value = 0.960

   Variable        Value        Reduced Costs
 ------------   ------------    ----------------
      E           0.960            0.000
      wb          0.175            0.000
      wc          0.000            0.040
      wj          0.575            0.000
      wn          0.250            0.000
      ws          0.000            0.085
```

**c.**   Yes; $E = 0.960$ indicates a composite restaurant can produce Clarksville's output with 96% of Clarksville's available resources.

**d.**   More Output (Constraint 2 Surplus) $220 more profit per week.

Less Input

Hours of Operation $110E = 105.6$ hours
FTE Staff $22 - 1.71$ (Constraint 6 Slack) $= 19.41$
Supply Expense $1400E - 129.614$ (Constraint 7 Slack) $= \$1214.39$

The composite restaurant uses 4.4 hours less operation time, 2.6 less employees, and $185.61 less supplies expense when compared to the Clarksville restaurant.

**e.**   $wb = 0.175$, $wj = 0.575$, and $wn = 0.250$. Consider the Bardstown, Jeffersonville, and New Albany restaurants.

**6. a.**   Flight Leg 1: $8 + 0 + 4 + 4 + 1 + 2 = 19$
Flight Leg 2: $6 + 3 + 2 + 4 + 2 + 1 = 18$
Flight Leg 3: $0 + 1 + 3 + 2 + 4 + 2 = 12$
Flight Leg 4: $4 + 2 + 2 + 1 + 6 + 3 = 18$

**b.**   The calculation of the remaining demand for each ODIF is as follows:

| ODIF | ODIF Code | Original Allocation | Seats Sold | Seats Available |
|------|-----------|---------------------|------------|-----------------|
| 1 | PCQ | 33 | 25 | 8 |
| 2 | PMQ | 44 | 44 | 0 |
| 3 | POQ | 45 | 18 | 27 |
| 4 | PCY | 16 | 12 | 4 |
| 5 | PMY | 6 | 5 | 1 |
| 6 | POY | 11 | 9 | 2 |
| 7 | NCQ | 26 | 20 | 6 |
| 8 | NMQ | 56 | 33 | 23 |
| 9 | NOQ | 39 | 37 | 2 |
| 10 | NCY | 15 | 11 | 4 |
| 11 | NMY | 7 | 5 | 2 |
| 12 | NOY | 9 | 8 | 1 |
| 13 | CMQ | 64 | 27 | 37 |
| 14 | CMY | 8 | 6 | 2 |
| 15 | COQ | 46 | 35 | 11 |
| 16 | COY | 10 | 7 | 3 |

**c.**

```
OPTIMAL SOLUTION

Objective Function Value = 15730.000

   Variable        Value        Reduced Costs
 ------------   ------------    ----------------
     PCQ          8.000            0.000
     PMQ          1.000            0.000
     POQ          3.000            0.000
     PCY          4.000            0.000
     PMY          1.000            0.000
     POY          2.000            0.000
     NCQ          6.000            0.000
     NMQ          3.000            0.000
     NOQ          2.000            0.000
     NCY          4.000            0.000
     NMY          2.000            0.000
     NOY          1.000            0.000
     CMQ          3.000            0.000
     CMY          2.000            0.000
     COQ          7.000            0.000
     COY          3.000            0.000
```

**8. b.** 65.7% small-cap growth fund
34.3% of the portfolio in a small-cap value
Expected return = 18.5%

**c.** 10% foreign stock
50.8% small-cap fund
39.2% of the portfolio in small-cap value
Expected return = 17.178%

**10.** Using LINGO or Excel Solver, the optimal solution is $X = 2, Y = -4$, for an optimal solution value of 0.

**12. a.** With \$1000 being spent on radio and \$1000 being spent on direct mail, we substitute those values into the sales function:

$$S = -2R^2 - 10M^2 - 8RM + 18R + 43M$$
$$= -2(2^2) - 10(1^2) - 8(2)(1) + 18(2) + 43(1)$$
$$= 18$$

Sales of \$18,000 will be realized with this allocation of the media budget.

**b.** Add a budget constraint to the sales function that is to be maximized.

$$\text{Max} \ -2R^2 - 10M^2 - 8RM + 18R + 34M$$

s.t.

$$R + M \le 3$$

**c.** The optimal solution is to invest \$2500 in radio advertising and \$500 in direct mail advertising. The total sales generated is \$37,000.

**14. a.** The optimization model is

$$\text{Max} \ 5L^{.25}C^{.75}$$

s.t.

$$25L + 75C \le 75000$$
$$L, C \ge 0$$

**b.** The optimal solution to this is $L = 750$ and $C = 750$ for an optimal objective function value of 3750. If Excel Solver is used for this problem, we recommend starting with an initial solution that has $L > 0$ and $C > 0$.

**16. a.** Let $OT$ be the number of overtime hours scheduled. Then the optimization model is

$$\text{Max} \ -3x_1^2 + 42x_1 - 3x_2^2 + 48x_2 + 700 - 5OT$$

s.t.

$$4x_1 + 6x_2 \le 24 + OT$$
$$x_1, x_2, OT \ge 0$$

**b.** The optimal solution is to schedule $OT = 8.66667$ overtime hours and produce $x_1 = 3.66667$ units of product 1 and $x_2 = 3.00000$ units of product 2 for a profit of 887.3333.

**17. a.** If $X$ is the weekly production volume in thousands of units at the Dayton plant and $Y$ is the weekly production

volume in thousands of units at the Hamilton plant, then the optimization model is

$$\text{Min} \ X^2 - X + 5 + Y^2 + 2Y + 3$$

s.t.

$$X + Y = 8$$
$$X, Y \ge 0$$

**b.** Using LINGO or Excel Solver, the optimal solution is $X = 4.75$ and $Y = 3.25$ for an optimal objective value of 42.875.

**18.** Define the variables to be the dollars invested in the mutual fund. For example, IB = 500 means that \$500 is invested in the Intermediate-Term bond fund. The LINGO formulation is

```
MIN = (1/5)*((R1 - RBAR)^2 + (R2 - RBAR)^2 +
     (R3 - RBAR)^2 + (R4 - RBAR)^2 + (R5 -
     RBAR)^2);

0.1006*FS + 0.1764*IB + 0.3241*LG
+ 0.3236*LV + 0.3344*SG + 0.2456*SV = R1;
0.1312*FS + 0.0325*IB + 0.1871*LG
+ 0.2061*LV + 0.1940*SG + 0.2532*SV = R2;
0.1347*FS + 0.0751*IB + 0.3328*LG
+ 0.1293*LV + 0.0385*SG - 0.0670*SV = R3;
0.4542*FS - 0.0133*IB + 0.4146*LG
+ 0.0706*LV + 0.5868*SG + 0.0543*SV = R4;
-0.2193*FS + 0.0736*IB - 0.2326*LG
- 0.0537*LV - 0.0902*SG + 0.1731*SV = R5;
FS + IB + LG + LV + SG + SV = 50000;
(1/5)*(R1 + R2 + R3 + R4 + R5) = RBAR;
RBAR > RMIN;
RMIN = 5000;

@FREE(R1);
@FREE(R2);
@FREE(R3);
@FREE(R4);
@FREE(R5);
```

The optimal solution to this model using LINGO is

```
Local optimal solution found.
    Objective value:              6,784,038
    Total solver iterations:             19

    Model Title: MARKOWITZ

    Variable        Value        Reduced Cost
    ----------    ----------    --------------
       R1         9478.492        0.000000
      RBAR        5000.000        0.000000
       R2         5756.023        0.000000
       R3         2821.951        0.000000
       R4         4864.037        0.000000
       R5         2079.496        0.000000
       FS         7920.372        0.000000
       IB        26273.98         0.000000
       LG         2103.251        0.000000
       LV         0.000000        208.2068
       SG         0.000000         78.04764
       SV        13702.40         0.000000
      RMIN        5000.000        0.000000
```

Excel Solver will also produce the same optimal solution.

**19.** The optimal value of $\alpha$ is 0.1743882, and the resulting sum of squared errors is 98.56.

**20.** The returns appear in Figure 12.17.

**22.**

| Model Title: MATCHING S&P INFO TECH RETURNS | | |
|---|---|---|
| Variable | Value | Reduced Cost |
| R1 | -0.1526620 | 0.000000 |
| R2 | 0.7916129 | 0.000000 |
| R3 | 0.9403282 | 0.000000 |
| R4 | 0.1694353 | 0.000000 |
| R5 | -0.5132641 | 0.000000 |
| R6 | -0.4379140 | 0.000000 |
| R7 | 0.2329556 | 0.000000 |
| R8 | 0.3760108E-03 | 0.000000 |
| R9 | 0.1671686E-01 | 0.000000 |
| AAPL | 0.000000 | 1.624161 |
| AMD | 0.1014161 | 0.000000 |
| ORCL | 0.8985839 | 0.000000 |

**24. a.** The optimal value is 2.118493.

**b.** No, minimizing risk is not the same thing as minimizing VaR. Minimizing $\sigma$ is not the same thing as maximizing Value at Risk. If we maximize Value at Risk, the objective function is

Max $\mu - 2.33\sigma$ = Min $2.33\sigma - \mu$

and the objective has two variables, $\sigma$ and $\mu$.

**c.** If we fix mean return, then it is a constant and

Max $\mu - 2.33\sigma$ = Min $2.33\sigma - \mu = -\mu +$ Min $2.33\sigma$
$= -\mu + 2.33$ Min $\sigma$

Finally, observe that minimizing $\sigma$ is the same as minimizing $\sigma^2$ because the standard deviation is always nonnegative.

**26.** This is a nonlinear 0-1 integer programming problem. Let $X_{ij} = 1$ if tanker 1 is assigned loading dock $j$ and 0 if not. The optimal solution to this model is 10000.00. Tanker 1 should be assigned to dock 2, tanker 2 to dock 1, and tanker 3 to dock 3. Depending on the starting point, Excel Solver will likely get stuck at a local optimum and not find the optimal solution that LINGO finds.

**28. a.**

Let    $X$ = the $x$ coordinate of the tool bin
    $Y$ = the $y$ coordinate of the tool bin

Minimize $-(X - 1)^2 + (Y - 4)^2$
$+ \sqrt{(X - 1)^2 + (Y - 2)^2} + \sqrt{(X - 2.5)^2 + (Y - 2)^2}$
$+ \sqrt{(X - 3)^2 + (Y - 5)^2} + \sqrt{(X - 4)^2 + (Y - 4)^2}$

Solution: $X = 2.23$, $Y = 3.35$

**b.**

Minimize $12\sqrt{(X - 1)^2 + (Y - 4)^2}$
$+ 24\sqrt{(X - 1)^2 + (Y - 2)^2} + 13\sqrt{(X - 2.5)^2 + (Y - 2)^2}$
$+ 7\sqrt{(X - 3)^2 + (Y - 5)^2} + 17\sqrt{(X - 4)^2 + (Y - 4)^2}$

Solution: $X = 1.91$, $Y = 2.72$

**c.**

Distance:

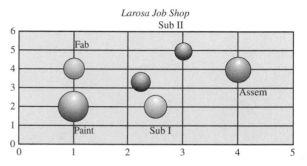

Demand-Weighted Distance

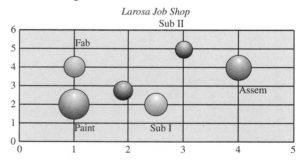

Using demand shifts the optimal location toward the paint cell (it has heavy demand).

# Chapter 13

**2.**

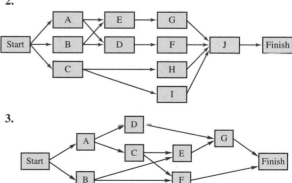

**3.**

**4. a.** A–D–G
**b.** No; Time = 15 months

**6. a.** Critical path: A–D–F–H
  **b.** 22 weeks
  **c.** No, it is a critical activity.
  **d.** Yes, 2 weeks
  **e.** Schedule for activity E:

| | |
|---|---|
| Earliest start | 3 |
| Latest start | 4 |
| Earliest finish | 10 |
| Latest finish | 11 |

**8. a.**

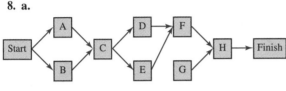

  **b.** B–C–E–F–H
  **c.**

| Activity | Earliest Start | Latest Start | Earliest Finish | Latest Finish | Slack | Critical Activity |
|---|---|---|---|---|---|---|
| A | 0 | 2 | 6 | 8 | 2 | |
| B | 0 | 0 | 8 | 8 | 0 | Yes |
| C | 8 | 8 | 20 | 20 | 0 | Yes |
| D | 20 | 22 | 24 | 26 | 2 | |
| E | 20 | 20 | 26 | 26 | 0 | Yes |
| F | 26 | 26 | 41 | 41 | 0 | Yes |
| G | 26 | 29 | 38 | 41 | 3 | |
| H | 41 | 41 | 49 | 49 | 0 | Yes |

  **d.** Yes, time = 49 weeks

**10. a.**

| Activity | Optimistic | Most Probable | Pessimistic | Expected Times | Variance |
|---|---|---|---|---|---|
| A | 4 | 5.0 | 6 | 5.00 | 0.11 |
| B | 8 | 9.0 | 10 | 9.00 | 0.11 |
| C | 7 | 7.5 | 11 | 8.00 | 0.44 |
| D | 7 | 9.0 | 10 | 8.83 | 0.25 |
| E | 6 | 7.0 | 9 | 7.17 | 0.25 |
| F | 5 | 6.0 | 7 | 6.00 | 0.11 |

  **b.** Critical activities: B–D–F
    Expected project completion time: $9.00 + 8.83 + 6.00 = 23.83$
    Variance of projection completion time: $0.11 + 0.25 + 0.11 = 0.47$

**12. a.** A–D–H–I
  **b.** 25.66 days
  **c.** 0.2578

**13.**

| Activity | Expected Time | Variance |
|---|---|---|
| A | 5 | 0.11 |
| B | 3 | 0.03 |
| C | 7 | 0.11 |
| D | 6 | 0.44 |
| E | 7 | 0.44 |
| F | 3 | 0.11 |
| G | 10 | 0.44 |
| H | 8 | 1.78 |

From Problem 6, A–D–F–H is the critical path, so $E(T) = 5 + 6 + 3 + 8 = 22$.
$\sigma^2 = 0.11 + 0.44 + 0.11 + 1.78 = 2.44$.

$$z = \frac{\text{Time} - E(T)}{\sigma} = \frac{\text{Time} - 22}{\sqrt{2.44}}$$

  **a.** Time = 21:          $z = -0.64$
    Cumulative Probability = 0.2611
        $P(21 \text{ weeks}) = 0.2611$
  **b.** Time = 22:          $z = 0.00$
    Cumulative Probability = 0.5000
        $P(22 \text{ weeks}) = 0.5000$
  **c.** Time = 25:          $z = +1.92$
    Cumulative Probability = 0.9726
        $P(25 \text{ weeks}) = 0.9726$

**14. a.** A–C–E–G–H
  **b.** 52 weeks (1 year)
  **c.** 0.0174
  **d.** 0.0934
  **e.** 10 months—doubtful
    13 months—very likely
    Estimate 12 months (1 year)

**16. a.**

| $E(T)$ | Variance |
|---|---|
| 16 | 3.92 |
| 13 | 2.03 |
| 10 | 1.27 |

  **b.** 0.9783, approximately 1.00, approximately 1.00
  **c.** Critical path is the longest path and generally will have the lowest probability of being completed by the desired time. The noncritical paths should have a higher probability of being completed on time.
    It may be desirable to consider the probability calculation for a noncritical path if the path activities have little slack, if the path completion time is almost equal to the critical path completion time, or if the path activity times have relatively high variances. When all of these situations occur, the noncritical path may have a probability of completion on time that is less than the critical path.

**18. a.**

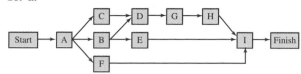

**b.**

| Activity | Expected Time | Variance |
|---|---|---|
| A | 1.17 | 0.03 |
| B | 6.00 | 0.44 |
| C | 4.00 | 0.44 |
| D | 2.00 | 0.11 |
| E | 3.00 | 0.11 |
| F | 2.00 | 0.11 |
| G | 2.00 | 0.11 |
| H | 2.00 | 0.11 |
| I | 1.00 | 0.00 |

| Activity | Earliest Start | Latest Start | Earliest Finish | Latest Finish | Slack | Critical Activity |
|---|---|---|---|---|---|---|
| A | 0.00 | 0.00 | 1.17 | 1.17 | 0.00 | Yes |
| B | 1.17 | 1.17 | 7.17 | 7.17 | 0.00 | Yes |
| C | 1.17 | 3.17 | 5.17 | 7.17 | 2.00 | |
| D | 7.17 | 7.17 | 9.17 | 9.17 | 0.00 | Yes |
| E | 7.17 | 10.17 | 10.17 | 13.17 | 3.00 | |
| F | 1.17 | 11.17 | 3.17 | 13.17 | 10.00 | |
| G | 9.17 | 9.17 | 11.17 | 11.17 | 0.00 | Yes |
| H | 11.17 | 11.17 | 13.17 | 13.17 | 0.00 | Yes |
| I | 13.17 | 13.17 | 14.17 | 14.17 | 0.00 | Yes |

**c.** A–B–D–G–H–I, 14.17 weeks
**d.** 0.0951, yes

**20. a.**

| Activity | Maximum Crash | Crash Cost/Week |
|---|---|---|
| A | 2 | 400 |
| B | 3 | 667 |
| C | 1 | 500 |
| D | 2 | 300 |
| E | 1 | 350 |
| F | 2 | 450 |
| G | 5 | 360 |
| H | 1 | 1000 |

Min  $400Y_A + 667Y_B + 500Y_C + 300Y_D + 350Y_E + 450Y_F$
$+ 360Y_G + 1000Y_H$
s.t.

$$x_A + y_A \geq 3 \quad x_E + y_E - x_D \geq 4 \quad x_H + y_H - x_G \geq 3$$
$$x_B + y_B \geq 6 \quad x_F + y_F - x_E \geq 3 \quad x_H \leq 16$$
$$x_C + y_C - x_A \geq 2 \quad x_G + y_G - x_C \geq 9$$
$$x_D + y_D - x_C \geq 5 \quad x_G + y_G - x_B \geq 9$$
$$x_D + y_D - x_B \geq 5 \quad x_H + y_H - x_F \geq 3$$

Maximum Crashing:

$$y_A \leq 2$$
$$y_B \leq 3$$
$$y_C \leq 1$$
$$y_D \leq 2$$
$$y_E \leq 1$$
$$y_F \leq 2$$
$$y_G \leq 5$$
$$y_H \leq 1$$
$$\text{All } x, y \geq 0$$

**b.** Crash B(1 week), D(2 weeks), E(1 week), F(1 week),
G(1 week)
Total cost = $2427
**c.** All activities are critical

**21. a.**

| Activity | Earliest Start | Latest Start | Earliest Finish | Latest Finish | Slack | Critical Activity |
|---|---|---|---|---|---|---|
| A | 0 | 0 | 3 | 3 | 0 | Yes |
| B | 0 | 1 | 2 | 3 | 1 | |
| C | 3 | 3 | 8 | 8 | 0 | Yes |
| D | 2 | 3 | 7 | 8 | 1 | |
| E | 8 | 8 | 14 | 14 | 0 | Yes |
| F | 8 | 10 | 10 | 12 | 2 | |
| G | 10 | 12 | 12 | 14 | 2 | |

Critical Path: A-C-E
Project completion time = $t_A + t_C + t_E = 3 + 5 + 6 = 14$ days
**b.** Total cost = $8400

**22. a.**

| Activity | Max. Crash Days | Crash Cost/Day |
|---|---|---|
| A | 1 | 600 |
| B | 1 | 700 |
| C | 2 | 400 |
| D | 2 | 400 |
| E | 2 | 500 |
| F | 1 | 400 |
| G | 1 | 500 |

Min  $600Y_A + 700Y_B + 400Y_C + 400Y_D + 500Y_E + 400Y_F + 400Y_G$
s.t.

$$X_A + Y_A \geq 3$$
$$X_B + Y_B \geq 2$$
$$X_A + X_C + Y_C \geq 5$$
$$-X_B + X_D + Y_D \geq 5$$
$$-X_C + X_E + Y_E \geq 6$$
$$-X_D + X_E + Y_E \geq 6$$
$$-X_C + X_F + Y_F \geq 2$$
$$-X_D + X_F + Y_F \geq 2$$

$$-X_F + X_G + Y_G \geq 2$$
$$-X_E + X_{FIN} \geq 0$$
$$-X_G + X_{FIN} \geq 0$$
$$X_{FIN} \leq 12$$
$$Y_A \leq 1$$
$$Y_B \leq 1$$
$$Y_C \leq 2$$
$$Y_D \leq 2$$
$$Y_E \leq 2$$
$$Y_F \leq 1$$
$$Y_G \leq 1$$
All $X, Y \geq 0$

**b.** Solution of the linear programming model in part (a) shows the following:

| Activity | Crash | Crashing Cost |
|---|---|---|
| C | 1 day | $400 |
| E | 1 day | 500 |
| | Total | $900 |

**c.** Total cost = Normal cost + Crashing cost
= $8400 + $900 = $9300

**24. a.**

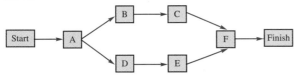

**b.**

| Activity | Earliest Start | Latest Start | Earliest Finish | Latest Finish | Slack |
|---|---|---|---|---|---|
| A | 0 | 0 | 10 | 10 | 0 |
| B | 10 | 10 | 18 | 18 | 0 |
| C | 18 | 18 | 28 | 28 | 0 |
| D | 10 | 11 | 17 | 18 | 1 |
| E | 17 | 18 | 27 | 28 | 1 |
| F | 28 | 28 | 31 | 31 | 0 |

**c.** A–B–C–F, 31 weeks
**d.** Crash A(2 weeks), B(2 weeks), C(1 week), D(1 week), E(1 week)
**e.** All activities are critical.
**f.** $112,500

# Chapter 14

**1. a.** $Q^* = \sqrt{\dfrac{2DC_0}{C_h}} = \sqrt{\dfrac{2(3600)(20)}{0.25(3)}} = 438.18$

**b.** $r = dm = \dfrac{3600}{250}(5) = 72$

**c.** $T = \dfrac{250Q^*}{D} = \dfrac{250(438.18)}{3600} = 30.43$ days

**d.** $TC = \dfrac{1}{2}QC_h + \dfrac{D}{Q}C_0$

$= \dfrac{1}{2}(438.18)(0.25)(3) + \dfrac{3600}{438.18}(20) = \$328.63$

**2.** $164.32 for each; Total cost = $328.64

**4. a.** 1095.45
**b.** 240
**c.** 22.82 days
**d.** $273.86 for each; Total cost = $547.72

**6. a.** 15.95
**b.** $2106
**c.** 15.04
**d.** 16.62 days

**8.** $Q^* = 11.73$, use 12
5 classes per year
$225,200

**10.** $Q^* = 1414.21$
$T = 28.28$ days
Production runs of 7.07 days

**12. a.** 1500
**b.** 4; 3-month cycle time
**c.** Change to $Q^* = 1500$
**d.** Savings = $12,510

**13. a.** $Q^* = \sqrt{\dfrac{2DC_0}{(1 - D/P)C_h}}$

$= \sqrt{\dfrac{2(7200)(150)}{(1 - 7200/25,000)(0.18)(14.50)}} = 1078.12$

**b.** Number of production runs $= \dfrac{D}{Q^*} = \dfrac{7200}{1078.12} = 6.68$

**c.** $T = \dfrac{250Q}{D} = \dfrac{250(1078.12)}{7200} = 37.43$ days

**d.** Production run length $= \dfrac{Q}{P/250}$

$= \dfrac{1078.12}{25,000/250} = 10.78$ days

**e.** Maximum inventory $= \left(1 - \dfrac{D}{P}\right)Q$

$= \left(1 - \dfrac{7200}{25,000}\right)(1078.12)$

$= 767.62$

**f.** Holding cost $= \dfrac{1}{2}\left(1 - \dfrac{D}{P}\right)QC_h$

$= \dfrac{1}{2}\left(1 - \dfrac{7200}{25,000}\right)(1078.12)(0.18)(14.50)$

$= \$1001.74$

Ordering cost $= \dfrac{D}{Q}C_0 = \dfrac{7200}{1078.12}(150) = \$1001.74$

Total cost $= \$2003.48$

**g.** $r = dm = \left(\dfrac{D}{250}\right)m = \dfrac{7200}{250}(15) = 432$

**14.** New $Q^* = 4509$

**15. a.** $Q^* = \sqrt{\dfrac{2DC_0}{C_h}\left(\dfrac{C_h + C_b}{C_b}\right)}$

$= \sqrt{\dfrac{2(12,000)(25)}{0.50}\left(\dfrac{0.50 + 5}{0.50}\right)} = 1148.91$

**b.** $S^* = Q^*\left(\dfrac{C_h}{C_h + C_b}\right) = 1148.91\left(\dfrac{0.50}{0.50 + 5}\right) = 104.45$

**c.** Max inventory $= Q^* - S^* = 1044.46$

**d.** $T = \dfrac{250Q^*}{D} = \dfrac{250(1148.91)}{12,000} = 23.94$ days

**e.** Holding $= \dfrac{(Q - S)^2}{2Q}C_h = \$237.38$

Ordering $= \dfrac{D}{Q}C_0 = \$261.12$

Backorder $= \dfrac{S^2}{2Q}C_b = \$23.74$

Total cost $= \$522.24$
The total cost for the EOQ model in Problem 4 was
$547.72; allowing backorders reduces the total cost.

**16.** 135.55; $r = dm - S$; less than

**18.** 64, 24.44

**20.** $Q^* = 100$; Total cost $= \$3,601.50$

**21.** $Q = \sqrt{\dfrac{2DC_0}{C_h}}$

$Q_1 = \sqrt{\dfrac{2(500)(40)}{0.20(10)}} = 141.42$

$Q_2 = \sqrt{\dfrac{2(500)(40)}{0.20(9.7)}} = 143.59$

Because $Q_1$ is over its limit of 99 units, $Q_1$ cannot be
optimal (see Problem 23); use $Q_2 = 143.59$ as the optimal
order quantity.

Total cost $= \dfrac{1}{2}QC_h + \dfrac{D}{Q}C_0 + DC$

$= 139.28 + 139.28 + 4850.00 = \$5128.56$

**22.** $Q^* = 300$; Savings $= \$480$

**24. a.** 500
  **b.** 580.4

**25. a.** $c_0 = 80 - 50 = 30$
  $c_u = 125 - 80 = 45$

  $P(D \le Q^*) = \dfrac{c_u}{c_u + c_0} = \dfrac{45}{45 + 30} = 0.60$

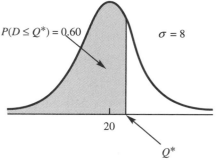

For the cumulative standard normal probability 0.60,
$z = 0.25$;
  $Q^* = 20 + 0.25(8) = 22$.

  **b.** $P(\text{Sell all}) = P(D \ge Q^*) = 1 - 0.60 = 0.40$

**26. a.** $150
  **b.** $240 - \$150 = \$90$
  **c.** 47
  **d.** 0.625

**28. a.** 440
  **b.** 0.60
  **c.** 710
  **d.** $c_u = \$17$

**29. a.** $r = dm = (200/250)15 = 12$
  **b.** $\dfrac{D}{Q} = \dfrac{200}{25} = 8$ orders/year

The limit of 1 stock-out per year means that $P(\text{Stock-out/cycle}) = 1/8 = 0.125$.

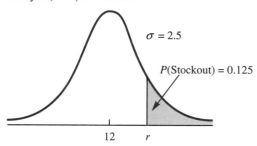

$P(\text{No Stockout/cycle}) = 1 - 0.125 = 0.875$
For cumulative probability 0.875, $z = 1.15$

Thus, $z = \dfrac{r - 12}{2.5} = 1.15$

$r = 12 + 1.15(2.5) = 14.875$   Use 15.
  **c.** Safety stock $= 3$ units
  Added cost $= 3(\$5) = \$15$/year

**30. a.** 13.68 (14)
  **b.** 17.83 (18)
  **c.** 2, $10; 6, $30

**32. a.** 31.62
  **b.** 19.8 (20); 0.2108
  **c.** 5, $15

**33. a.** $1/52 = 0.0192$

**b.** $P(\text{No Stockout}) = 1 - 0.0192 = 0.9808$

For cumulative probability 0.9808, $z = 2.07$.

Thus, $z = \dfrac{M - 60}{12} = 2.07$

$M = \mu + z\sigma = 60 + 2.07(12) = 85$

**c.** $M = 35 + (0.9808)(85 - 35) = 84$

**34. a.** 243

**b.** 93, \$54.87

**c.** 613

**d.** 163, \$96.17

**e.** Yes, added cost would be only \$41.30 per year.

**f.** Yes, added cost would be \$4130 per year.

**36. a.** 40

**b.** 62.25; 7.9

**c.** 54

**d.** 36

# Chapter 15

**2. a.** 0.4512

**b.** 0.6988

**c.** 0.3012

**4.** 0.3333, 0.2222, 0.1481, 0.0988; 0.1976

**5. a.** $P_0 = 1 - \dfrac{\lambda}{\mu} = 1 - \dfrac{10}{12} = 0.1667$

**b.** $L_q = \dfrac{\lambda^2}{\mu(\mu - \lambda)} = \dfrac{10^2}{12(12 - 10)} = 4.1667$

**c.** $W_q = \dfrac{L_q}{\lambda} = 0.4167$ hour (25 minutes)

**d.** $W = W_q + \dfrac{1}{\mu} = 0.5$ hour (30 minutes)

**e.** $P_w = \dfrac{\lambda}{\mu} = \dfrac{10}{12} = 0.8333$

**6. a.** 0.3750

**b.** 1.0417

**c.** 0.8333 minutes (50 seconds)

**d.** 0.6250

**e.** Yes

**8.** 0.20, 3.2, 4, 3.2, 4, 0.80

Slightly poorer service

**10. a.** New: 0.3333, 1.3333, 2, 0.6667, 1, 0.6667

Experienced: 0.50, 0.50, 1, 0.25, 0.50, 0.50

**b.** New \$74; experienced \$50; hire experienced

**11. a.** $\lambda = 2.5$;   $\mu = \dfrac{60}{10} = 6$ customers per hour

$L_q = \dfrac{\lambda^2}{\mu(\mu - \lambda)} = \dfrac{(2.5)^2}{6(6 - 2.5)} = 0.2976$

$L = L_q + \dfrac{\lambda}{\mu} = 0.7143$

$W_q = \dfrac{L_q}{\lambda} = 0.1190$ hours (7.14 minutes)

$W = W_q + \dfrac{1}{\mu} = 0.2857$ hours

$P_w = \dfrac{\lambda}{\mu} = \dfrac{2.5}{6} = 0.4167$

**b.** No; $W_q = 7.14$ minutes; firm should increase the service rate ($\mu$) for the consultant or hire a second consultant.

**c.**   $\mu = \dfrac{60}{8} = 7.5$ customers per hour

$L_q = \dfrac{\lambda^2}{\mu(\mu - \lambda)} = \dfrac{(2.5)^2}{7.5(7.5 - 2.5)} = 0.1667$

$W_q = \dfrac{L_q}{\lambda} = 0.0667$ hour (4 minutes)

The service goal is being met.

**12. a.** 0.25, 2.25, 3, 0.15 hours, 0.20 hours, 0.75

**b.** The service needs improvement.

**14. a.** 8

**b.** 0.3750

**c.** 1.0417

**d.** 12.5 minutes

**e.** 0.6250

**f.** Add a second consultant.

**16. a.** 0.50

**b.** 0.50

**c.** 0.10 hours (6 minutes)

**d.** 0.20 hours (12 minutes)

**e.** Yes, $W_q = 6$ minutes is most likely acceptable for a marina.

**18. a.** $k = 2; \lambda/\mu = 5.4/3 = 1.8; P_0 = 0.0526$

$L_q = \dfrac{(\lambda/\mu)^2 \lambda\mu}{(k - 1)!(2\mu - \lambda)^2} P_0$

$= \dfrac{(1.8)^2(5.4)(3)}{(2 - 1)!(6 - 5.4)^2}(0.0526) = 7.67$

$L = L_q + \lambda/\mu = 7.67 + 1.8 = 9.47$

$W_q = \dfrac{L_q}{\lambda} = \dfrac{7.67}{5.4} = 1.42$ minutes

$W = W_q + 1/\mu = 1.42 + 0.33 = 1.75$ minutes

$P_w = \dfrac{1}{k!}\left(\dfrac{\lambda}{\mu}\right)^k \left(\dfrac{k\mu}{k\mu - \lambda}\right) P_0$

$= \dfrac{1}{2!}(1.8)^2\left(\dfrac{6}{6 - 5.4}\right)0.0526 = 0.8526$

**b.** $L_q = 7.67$; Yes

**c.** $W = 1.75$ minutes

**20. a.** Use $k = 2$.

$W = 3.7037$ minutes

$L = 4.4444$

$P_w = 0.7111$

**b.** For $k = 3$

$W = 7.1778$ minutes

$L = 15.0735$ customers

$P_N = 0.8767$

Expand post office.

**21.** From Problem 11, a service time of 8 minutes has $\mu = 60/8 = 7.5$.

$$L_q = \frac{\lambda^2}{\mu(\mu - \lambda)} = \frac{(2.5)^2}{7.5(7.5 - 2.5)} = 0.1667$$

$$L = L_q + \frac{\lambda}{\mu} = 0.50$$

Total cost $= \$25L + \$16$
$$= 25(0.50) + 16 = \$28.50$$

Two channels: $\lambda = 2.5$; $\mu = 60/10 = 6$
With $P_0 = 0.6552$,

$$L_q = \frac{(\lambda/\mu)^2 \lambda \mu}{1!(2\mu - \lambda)^2} P_0 = 0.0189$$

$$L = L_q + \frac{\lambda}{\mu} = 0.4356$$

Total cost $= 25(0.4356) + 2(16) = \$42.89$
Use one consultant with an 8-minute service time.

**22.**

| Characteristic | A | B | C |
|---|---|---|---|
| **a.** $P_0$ | 0.2000 | 0.5000 | 0.4286 |
| **b.** $L_q$ | 3.2000 | 0.5000 | 0.1524 |
| **c.** $L$ | 4.0000 | 1.0000 | 0.9524 |
| **d.** $W_q$ | 0.1333 | 0.0208 | 0.0063 |
| **e.** $W$ | 0.1667 | 0.0417 | 0.0397 |
| **f.** $P_w$ | 0.8000 | 0.5000 | 0.2286 |

The two-channel System C provides the best service.

**24.** $\lambda = 4$, $W = 10$ minutes
  **a.** $\mu = \frac{1}{2} = 0.5$
  **b.** $W_q = W - 1/\mu = 10 - 1/0.5 = 8$ minutes
  **c.** $L = \lambda W = 4(10) = 40$

**26. a.** 0.2668, 10 minutes, 0.6667
  **b.** 0.0667, 7 minutes, 0.4669
  **c.** \$25.33; \$33.34; one-channel

**27. a.** $\frac{2}{8}$ hours $= 0.25$ per hour
  **b.** $1/3.2$ hours $= 0.3125$ per hour

  **c.** $L_q = \dfrac{\lambda^2 \sigma^2 + (\lambda/\mu)^2}{2(1 - \lambda/\mu)}$

  $= \dfrac{(0.25)^2(2)^2 + (0.25/0.3125)^2}{2(1 - 0.25/0.3125)} = 2.225$

  **d.** $W_q = \dfrac{L_q}{\lambda} = \dfrac{2.225}{0.25} = 8.9$ hours

  **e.** $W = W_q + \dfrac{1}{\mu} = 8.9 + \dfrac{1}{0.3125} = 12.1$ hours

  **f.** Same as $P_w = \dfrac{\lambda}{\mu} = \dfrac{0.25}{0.3125} = 0.80$

  80% of the time the welder is busy.

**28. a.** 10, 9.6
  **b.** Design A with $\mu = 10$
  **c.** 0.05, 0.01
  **d.** A: 0.5, 0.3125, 0.8125, 0.0625, 0.1625, 0.5
  B: 0.4792, 0.2857, 0.8065, 0.0571, 0.1613, 0.5208
  **e.** Design B has slightly less waiting time.

**30. a.** $\lambda = 42$; $\mu = 20$

| $i$ | $(\lambda/\mu)^i/i!$ |
|---|---|
| 0 | 1.0000 |
| 1 | 2.1000 |
| 2 | 2.2050 |
| 3 | 1.5435 |
| Total | 6.8485 |

| $j$ | | $P_j$ |
|---|---|---|
| 0 | 1/6.8485 | $= -0.1460$ |
| 1 | 2.1/6.8485 | $= -0.3066$ |
| 2 | 2.2050/6.8485 | $= -0.3220$ |
| 3 | 1.5435/6.8485 | $= -0.2254$ |
| | | 1.0000 |

  **b.** 0.2254
  **c.** $L = \lambda/\mu(1 - P_k) = 42/20(1 - 0.2254) = 1.6267$
  **d.** Four lines will be necessary; the probability of denied access is 0.1499.

**32. a.** 31.03%
  **b.** 27.59%
  **c.** 0.2759, 0.1092, 0.0351
  **d.** 3, 10.92%

**34.** $N = 5$; $\lambda = 0.025$; $\mu = 0.20$; $\lambda/\mu = 0.125$
  **a.**

| $n$ | $\dfrac{N!}{(N-n)!}\left(\dfrac{\lambda}{\mu}\right)^n$ |
|---|---|
| 0 | 1.0000 |
| 1 | 0.6250 |
| 2 | 0.3125 |
| 3 | 0.1172 |
| 4 | 0.0293 |
| 5 | 0.0037 |
| Total | 2.0877 |

  $P_0 = 1/2.0877 = 0.4790$

  **b.** $L_q = N - \left(\dfrac{\lambda + \mu}{\lambda}\right)(1 - P_0)$

  $= 5 - \left(\dfrac{0.225}{0.025}\right)(1 - 0.4790) = 0.3110$

  **c.** $L = L_q + (1 - P_0) = 0.3110 + (1 - 0.4790) = 0.8321$

  **d.** $W_q = \dfrac{L_q}{(N - L)\lambda} = \dfrac{0.3110}{(5 - 0.8321)(0.025)}$

  $= 2.9854$ minutes

  **e.** $W = W_q + \dfrac{1}{\mu} = 2.9854 + \dfrac{1}{0.20} = 7.9854$ minutes

  **f.** Trips/day = (8 hours)(60 minutes/hour)($\lambda$)
  $= (8)(60)(0.025) = 12$ trips
  Time at copier: $12 \times 7.9854 = 95.8$ minutes/day
  Wait time at copier: $12 \times 2.9854 = 35.8$ minutes/day

**g.** Yes, five assistants $\times$ 35.8 = 179 minutes (3 hours/day), so 3 hours per day are lost to waiting.
(35.8/480)(100) = 7.5% of each assistant's day is spent waiting for the copier.

# Chapter 16

**2. a.** $c$ = variable cost per unit
$x$ = demand
Profit = $(50 - c)x - 30,000$

**b.** Base: Profit = $(50 - 20)1200 - 30,000 = 6000$
Worst: Profit = $(50 - 24)300 - 30,000 = -22,200$
Best: Profit = $(50 - 16)2100 - 30,000 = 41,400$

**c.** Simulation will be helpful in estimating the probability of a loss.

**4. a.**

| Number of New Accounts | Interval |
|---|---|
| 0 | 0.00 but less than 0.01 |
| 1 | 0.01 but less than 0.05 |
| 2 | 0.05 but less than 0.15 |
| 3 | 0.15 but less than 0.40 |
| 4 | 0.40 but less than 0.80 |
| 5 | 0.80 but less than 0.95 |
| 6 | 0.95 but less than 1.00 |

**b.** 4, 3, 3, 5, 2, 6, 4, 4, 4, 2
37 new accounts

**c.** First-year commission = $185,000
Cost of 10 seminars = $35,000
Yes

**5. a.**

| Stock Price Change | Interval |
|---|---|
| $-2$ | 0.00 but less than 0.05 |
| $-1$ | 0.05 but less than 0.15 |
| 0 | 0.15 but less than 0.40 |

| Stock Price Change | Interval |
|---|---|
| $+1$ | 0.40 but less than 0.60 |
| $+2$ | 0.60 but less than 0.80 |
| $+3$ | 0.80 but less than 0.90 |
| $+4$ | 0.90 but less than 1.00 |

**b.** Beginning price $39
0.1091 indicates $-1$ change; $38
0.9407 indicates $+4$ change; $42
0.1941 indicates 0 change; $42
0.8083 indicates $+3$ change; $45 (ending price)

**6. a.** 0.00–0.83, 0.83–0.89, 0.89–0.94, 0.94–0.96, 0.96–0.98, 0.98–0.99, 0.99–1.00

**b.** 4 claims paid; Total = $22,000

**8. a.** Atlanta wins each game if random number is in interval 0.00–0.60, 0.00–0.55, 0.00–0.48, 0.00–0.45, 0.00–0.48, 0.00–0.55, 0.00–0.50.

**b.** Atlanta wins games 1, 2, 4, and 6.
Atlanta wins series, 4 to 2.

**c.** Repeat many times; record % of Atlanta wins.

**9. a.** Base case based on most likely;
Time = 6 + 5 + 14 + 8 = 33 weeks

Worst: Time = 8 + 7 + 18 + 10 = 43 weeks
Best: Time = 5 + 3 + 10 + 8 = 26 weeks

**b.** 0.1778 for A: 5 weeks
0.9617 for B: 7 weeks
0.6849 for C: 14 weeks
0.4503 for D: 8 weeks; Total = 34 weeks

**c.** Simulation will provide an estimate of the probability of 35 weeks or less.

**10. a.**

| Hand Value | Interval |
|---|---|
| 17 | 0.0000 but less than 0.1654 |
| 18 | 0.1654 but less than 0.2717 |
| 19 | 0.2717 but less than 0.3780 |
| 20 | 0.3780 but less than 0.4797 |
| 21 | 0.4797 but less than 0.5769 |
| Broke | 0.5769 but less than 1.0000 |

**b, c, & d.** Dealer wins 13 hands, player wins 5, 2 pushes.

**e.** Player wins 7, dealer wins 13.

**12. a.** $7, $3, $12

**b.** Purchase: 0.00–0.25, 0.25–0.70, 0.70–1.00
Labor: 0.00–0.10, 0.10–0.35, 0.35–0.70, 0.70–1.00
Transportation: 0.00–0.75, 0.75–1.00

**c.** $5

**d.** $7

**e.** Provide probability profit less than $5/unit

**14.** Selected cell formulas for the worksheet shown in Figure G16.14 are as follows:

| Cell | Formula |
|---|---|
| B13 | =$C$7+RAND()*($C$8−$C$7) |
| C13 | =NORMINV(RAND(),$G$7,$G$8) |
| D13 | =($C$3−B13)*C13−$C$4 |

**a.** The mean profit should be approximately $6000; simulation results will vary with most simulations having a mean profit between $5500 and $6500.

**b.** 120 to 150 of the 500 simulation trials should show a loss; thus, the probability of a loss should be between 0.24 and 0.30.

**c.** This project appears too risky.

**16. a.** About 36% of simulation runs will show $130,000 as the winning bid.

**b.** $150,000; $10,000

**c.** Recommended $140,000

**18.** Selected cell formulas for the worksheet shown in Figure G16.18 are as follows:

| Cell | Formula |
|---|---|
| B11 | =$C$4+RAND()*($C$5−$C$4) |
| C11 | =NORMINV(RAND(),$H$4,$H$5) |
| D11 | =MAX(B11:C11) |
| G11 | =COUNTIF(D11:D1010,"<750") |
| H11 | =G11/COUNT(D11:D1010) |

**FIGURE G16.14**   WORKSHEET FOR THE MADEIRA MANUFACTURING COMPANY

| | A | B | C | D | E | F |
|---|---|---|---|---|---|---|
| 1 | **Madeira Manufacturing Company** | | | | | |
| 2 | | | | | | |
| 3 | Unit Selling Price | $50 | | | | |
| 4 | Fixed Cost | $30,000 | | | | |
| 5 | | | | | | |
| 6 | **Variable Cost (Uniform Distribution)** | | | **Demand (Normal Distribution)** | | |
| 7 | Smallest Value | $16 | | Mean | 1,200 | |
| 8 | Largest Value | $24 | | Standard Deviation | 300 | |
| 9 | | | | | | |
| 10 | **Simulation** | | | | | |
| 11 | Trial | Unit Variable Cost | Demand | Profit | | |
| 12 | 1 | $20.82 | 1,130 | $2,984.92 | | |
| 13 | 2 | $21.60 | 1,006 | -$1,429.17 | | |
| 510 | 499 | $23.32 | 1,754 | $16,802.47 | | |
| 511 | 500 | $23.95 | 1,704 | $14,382.10 | | |
| 512 | | | | | | |
| 513 | | **Summary Statistics** | | | | |
| 514 | | Mean Profit | $6,472 | | | |
| 515 | | Standard Deviation | $9,443 | | | |
| 516 | | Minimum Profit | -$20,854 | | | |
| 517 | | Maximum Profit | $35,850 | | | |
| 518 | | Number of Losses | 133 | | | |
| 519 | | Probability of Loss | 0.266 | | | |
| 520 | | | | | | |

© Cengage Learning 2013

**FIGURE G16.18**   WORKSHEET FOR THE CONTRACTOR BIDDING

| | A | B | C | D | E | F |
|---|---|---|---|---|---|---|
| 1 | **Contractor Bidding** | | | | | |
| 2 | | | | | | |
| 3 | **Contractor A (Uniform Distribution)** | | | **Contractor A (Normal Distribution)** | | |
| 4 | Smallest Value | $600,000 | | Mean | $700,000 | |
| 5 | Largest Value | $800,000 | | Standard Deviation | $50,000 | |
| 6 | | | | | | |
| 7 | | | | | | |
| 8 | **Simulation** | | | | | |
| 9 | Trial | Contractor A's Bid | Contractor B's Bid | Highest Bid | | |
| 10 | 1 | $785,020 | $630,729 | $785,020.16 | | |
| 11 | 2 | $698,925 | $742,675 | $742,675.28 | | |
| 1008 | 999 | $795,023 | $822,027 | $822,027.17 | | |
| 1009 | 1000 | $672,159 | $708,791 | $708,791.25 | | |
| 1010 | | | | | | |
| 1011 | | **Results** | | | | |
| 1012 | | Contractor's Bid | Number of Wins | Probability of Winning | | |
| 1013 | | $750,000 | 641 | 0.641 | | |
| 1014 | | $775,000 | 826 | 0.826 | | |
| 1015 | | $785,000 | 894 | 0.894 | | |
| 1016 | | | | | | |

© Cengage Learning 2013

**a.** $750,000 should win roughly 600 to 650 of the 1000 times; the probability of winning the bid should be between 0.60 and 0.65.

**b.** The probability of $775,000 winning should be roughly 0.82, and the probability of $785,000 winning should be roughly 0.88; a contractor's bid of $775,000 is recommended.

**20. a.** Results vary with each simulation run.
Approximate results:  50,000 provided $230,000
60,000 provided $190,000
70,000 less than $100,000

**b.** Recommend 50,000 units

**c.** Roughly 0.75

**22.** Very poor operation; some customers wait 30 minutes or more.

**24. b.** Waiting time approximately 0.8 minutes

**c.** 30% to 35% of customers have to wait.

# Chapter 17

**2. a.** 0.82

**b.** $\pi_1 = 0.5, \pi_2 = 0.5$

**c.** $\pi_1 = 0.6, \pi_2 = 0.4$

**3. a.** 0.10 as given by the transition probability

**b.**
$$\pi_1 = 0.90\pi_1 + 0.30\pi_2 \quad (1)$$
$$\pi_2 = 0.10\pi_1 + 0.70\pi_2 \quad (2)$$
$$\pi_1 + \pi_2 = 1 \quad (3)$$
Using (1) and (3),
$$0.10\pi_1 - 0.30\pi_2 = 0$$
$$0.10\pi_1 - 0.30(1 - \pi_1) = 0$$
$$0.10\pi_1 - 0.30 + 0.30\pi_1 = 0$$
$$0.40\pi_1 = 0.30$$
$$\pi_1 = 0.75$$
$$\pi_2 = (1 - \pi_1) = 0.25$$

**4. a.** $\pi_1 = 0.92, \pi_2 = 0.08$

**b.** $85

**6. a.** Given the opposing player last chose Rock, the transition matrix shows that she is most likely to choose Paper next (with probability 0.42). Therefore, you should choose Scissors (because Scissors beats Paper).

**b.**

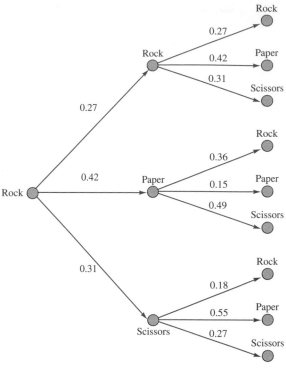

**c.** The one step probability matrix is

$$P = \begin{bmatrix} 0.27 & 0.42 & 0.31 \\ 0.36 & 0.15 & 0.49 \\ 0.18 & 0.55 & 0.27 \end{bmatrix}$$

The probability your opponent will choose Paper in the second round is given by $\pi_2(2)$. This can be found from $\Pi(2)$ by first finding $\Pi(1)$ as follows:

$$\Pi(1) = \begin{bmatrix} 0 & 1 & 0 \end{bmatrix} \begin{bmatrix} 0.27 & 0.42 & 0.31 \\ 0.36 & 0.15 & 0.49 \\ 0.18 & 0.55 & 0.27 \end{bmatrix}$$
$$= \begin{bmatrix} 0.36 & 0.15 & 0.49 \end{bmatrix}$$

$$\Pi(2) = \begin{bmatrix} 0.36 & 0.15 & 0.49 \end{bmatrix} \begin{bmatrix} 0.27 & 0.42 & 0.31 \\ 0.36 & 0.15 & 0.49 \\ 0.18 & 0.55 & 0.27 \end{bmatrix}$$
$$= \begin{bmatrix} 0.24 & 0.44 & 0.32 \end{bmatrix}$$

So, $\pi_2(2)$ is 0.44.

**8. a.**
$$\pi_1 = 0.85\pi_1 + 0.20\pi_2 + 0.15\pi_3 \qquad (1)$$
$$\pi_2 = 0.10\pi_1 + 0.75\pi_2 + 0.10\pi_3 \qquad (2)$$
$$\pi_3 = 0.05\pi_1 + 0.05\pi_2 + 0.75\pi_3 \qquad (3)$$
$$\pi_1 + \pi_2 + \pi_3 = 1 \qquad (4)$$

Using (1), (2), and (4) provides three equations with three unknowns; solving provides $\pi_1 = 0.548$, $\pi_2 = 0.286$, and $\pi_3 = 0.166$.

**b.** 16.6% as given by $\pi_3$

**c.** Quick Stop should take

$667 - 0.548(1000) = 119$ Murphy's customers
and $333 - 0.286(1000) = \underline{\ 47}$ Ashley's customers

Total    166 Quick Stop customers

It will take customers from Murphy's and Ashley's.

**10.**
$$\pi_1 = 0.80\pi_1 + 0.05\pi_2 + 0.40\pi_3 \qquad (1)$$
$$\pi_2 = 0.10\pi_1 + 0.75\pi_2 + 0.30\pi_3 \qquad (2)$$
$$\pi_3 = 0.10\pi_1 + 0.20\pi_2 + 0.30\pi_3 \qquad (3)$$
also
$$\pi_1 + \pi_2 + \pi_3 = 1 \qquad (4)$$

Using equations 1, 2, and 4, we have $\pi_1 = 0.442$, $\pi_2 = 0.385$, and $\pi_3 = 0.173$.

The Markov analysis shows that Special B now has the largest market share. In fact, its market share has increased by almost 11%. The MDA brand will be hurt most by the introduction of the new brand, T-White. People who switch from MDA to T-White are more likely to make a second switch back to MDA.

**12.** $(I - Q) = \begin{bmatrix} 1 & 0 \\ 0 & 1 \end{bmatrix} - \begin{bmatrix} 0.4 & 0.3 \\ 0.1 & 0.5 \end{bmatrix} = \begin{bmatrix} 0.6 & -0.3 \\ -0.1 & 0.5 \end{bmatrix}$

$N = (I - Q)^{-1} = \begin{bmatrix} 1.85 & 1.11 \\ 0.37 & 2.22 \end{bmatrix}$

$NR = \begin{bmatrix} 1.85 & 1.11 \\ 0.37 & 2.22 \end{bmatrix}\begin{bmatrix} 0.2 & 0.1 \\ 0.2 & 0.2 \end{bmatrix} = \begin{bmatrix} 0.59 & 0.41 \\ 0.52 & 0.48 \end{bmatrix}$

0.59 probability state 3 units end up in state 1;
0.52 probability state 4 units end up in state 1.

**13.** $I = \begin{bmatrix} 1 & 0 \\ 0 & 1 \end{bmatrix}$    $Q = \begin{bmatrix} 0.25 & 0.25 \\ 0.05 & 0.25 \end{bmatrix}$

$(I - Q) = \begin{bmatrix} 0.75 & -0.25 \\ -0.05 & 0.75 \end{bmatrix}$

$N = (I - Q)^{-1} = \begin{bmatrix} 1.3636 & 0.4545 \\ 0.0909 & 1.3636 \end{bmatrix}$

$NR = \begin{bmatrix} 1.3636 & 0.4545 \\ 0.0909 & 1.3636 \end{bmatrix}\begin{bmatrix} 0.5 & 0.01 \\ 0.5 & 0.5 \end{bmatrix} = \begin{bmatrix} 0.909 & 0.091 \\ 0.727 & 0.273 \end{bmatrix}$

$BNR = \begin{bmatrix} 4000 & 5000 \end{bmatrix}\begin{bmatrix} 0.909 & 0.091 \\ 0.727 & 0.273 \end{bmatrix} = \begin{bmatrix} 7271 & 1729 \end{bmatrix}$

Estimate $1729 in bad debts.

**14.** 3580 will be sold eventually; 1420 will be lost.

**16. a.** The Injured and Retired states are absorbing states.

**b.** Rearrange the transition probability matrix to the following:

| | Injured | Retired | Backup | Starter |
|---|---|---|---|---|
| **Injured** | 1 | 0 | 0 | 0 |
| **Retired** | 0 | 1 | 0 | 0 |
| **Backup** | 0.1 | 0.1 | 0.4 | 0.4 |
| **Starter** | 0.15 | 0.25 | 0.1 | 0.5 |

$(I - Q) = \begin{bmatrix} 0.6 & -0.4 \\ -0.1 & 0.5 \end{bmatrix}$

$N = (I - Q)^{-1} = \begin{bmatrix} 1.923 & 1.538 \\ 0.385 & 2.308 \end{bmatrix}$

$NR = \begin{bmatrix} 0.423 & 0.577 \\ 0.385 & 0.615 \end{bmatrix}$

38.5% of Starters will eventually be Injured and 61.5% will be Retired.

**c.** $BNR = \begin{bmatrix} 8 & 5 \end{bmatrix}\begin{bmatrix} 0.426 & 0.577 \\ 0.385 & 0.615 \end{bmatrix}$

$= \begin{bmatrix} 5.308 & 7.691 \end{bmatrix}$

We expect that 5.308 players will end up injured and 7.691 will retire.

# Appendix A

**2.** =F6*$F$3

**4.**

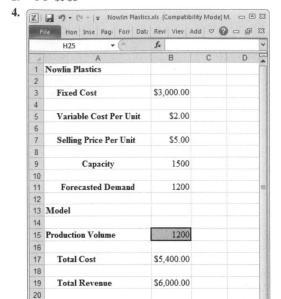

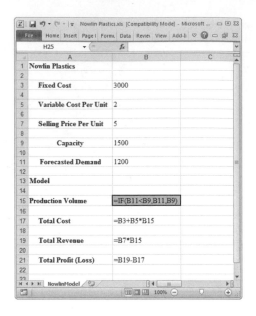

**6.**

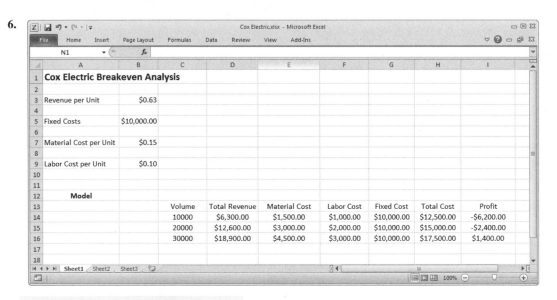

| Cell | Formula |
|------|---------|
| D14 | =C14*$B$3 |
| E14 | =C14*$B$7 |
| F14 | =C14*$B$9 |
| G14 | =$B$5 |
| H14 | =SUM(E14:G14) |
| I14 | =D14-H14 |

**8.**

| Grade | Count |
|-------|-------|
| F | 1 |
| D | 2 |
| C− | 1 |
| C− | 1 |
| C+ | 0 |
| B− | 2 |
| B | 1 |
| B+ | 0 |
| A− | 1 |
| A | 3 |

**10.** Error #1:  The formula in cell C17 is:
=SUMPRODUCT(C8:G11,B22:F25)
but should be
=SUMPRODUCT(C8:F11,B22:F25)

Error #2:  The formula in cell G22 is:
=SUM(B22:E22)
but should be
=SUM(B22:F22)

**12.** Discounted savings net of out-of-pocket expense = $17,791.44. Screen shots for this solution are included below.

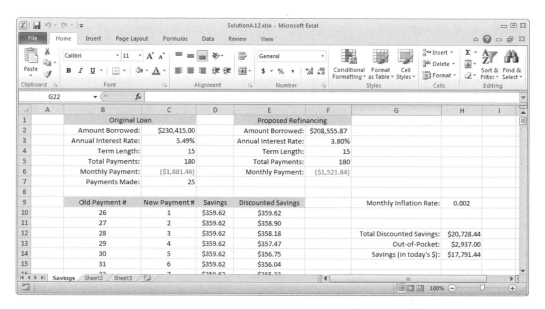

Formulas:

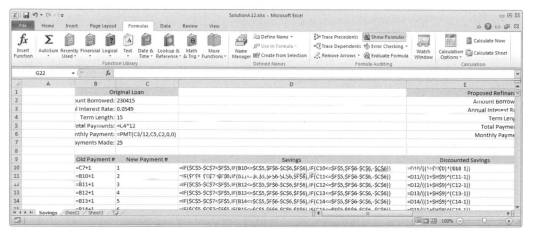

These formulas hold until the row after new payment 155. Payments 156–180 are after the old loan would have been repaid and hence are negative savings (that is, costs) of $1,521.84 per month from months 156 to180.

# Index